Academic Systems®

Elementary Algebra

Elementary Algebra Personal Academic Notebook Contributors

Writers:

D. Patrick Kinney, Ph.D.
Douglas F. Robertson, Ph.D.

Pat Kinney and Doug Robertson earned doctorates in mathematics education at the University of Minnesota, where they taught developmental mathematics for many years. In 1999 they implemented Interactive Mathematics (the predecessor to Academic Systems Algebra) with the support of a National Science Foundation grant (DUE 9972445) and studied developmental students' learning of mathematics through computer-mediated instruction.

Thank you to the following people for their input:

Kurt Norlin, Ph.D.
LaurelTech Integrated Publishing Services

Kathleen Peak
Rochester Community and Technical College (RCTC)

Janet Stottlemyer, Ph.D.
University of Minnesota—General College

Academic Systems—Elementary Algebra
Copyright © 1994–2007 PLATO Learning, Inc. All rights reserved. PLATO® and Academic Systems® are registered trademarks of PLATO Learning, Inc. Straight Curve and PLATO Learning are trademarks of PLATO Learning, Inc. PLATO, Inc. is a PLATO Learning, Inc. company.

PLATO Learning
10801 Nesbitt Avenue South
Bloomington, MN 55437

800.44.PLATO
www.plato.com

ISBN 978-0-7419-1364-7

03/07

Table of Contents

TOPIC EI ESSENTIALS — PREPARING FOR ALGEBRA

Much of what you have learned in arithmetic will be useful in your study of algebra. In particular, you will use what you know about fractions and about signed numbers.

This topic begins with a brief review of the basic operations on fractions — multiplication, division, addition, and subtraction. The topic continues with the arithmetic of positive and negative numbers, which we refer to as signed numbers.

Lesson EI.A Fractions

Concept 1: Multiplying and Dividing
Introduction to Fractions
Equivalent Fractions
Prime Factorization
Greatest Common Factor (GCF)
Reducing to Lowest Terms
Multiplying Fractions
Dividing Fractions

Concept 2: Adding and Subtracting
Adding and Subtracting Fractions With the Same Denominator
Least Common Multiple (LCM)
Least Common Denominator (LCD)
Adding and Subtracting Fractions With Different Denominators

Lesson EI.B Signed Numbers

Concept 1: Adding and Subtracting
Number Line
Adding Numbers That Have the Same Sign
Adding Numbers That Have Different Signs
Subtracting Signed Numbers

Concept 2: Multiplying And Dividing
Multiplying and Dividing Signed Numbers
Exponential Notation
Properties of Real Numbers
Distributive Property
Order of Operations

LESSON EI.A
FRACTIONS

 Overview

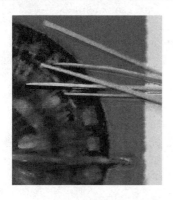

This lesson provides a review of fractions — how to change their form and how to combine them by adding, subtracting, multiplying, and dividing.

You may already understand some of the concepts in this lesson. In many of the examples, you may be able to find the answer in a way that differs from the given solution.

If you have a method that works well for you, keep using it. But, also try to understand the notation and the procedures you see here. It will help you as you study algebra.

 Explain

Concept 1 has sections on

- **Introduction to Fractions**
- **Equivalent Fractions**
- **Prime Factorization**
- **Greatest Common Factor (GCF)**
- **Reducing to Lowest Terms**
- **Multiplying Fractions**
- **Dividing Fractions**

CONCEPT 1: MULTIPLYING AND DIVIDING

Introduction to Fractions

A **fraction** is the quotient of two numbers written one over the other and separated by a horizontal bar, called a **fraction bar**.

For example, we write the fraction two-eighths as follows: $\frac{2}{8}$.

To save space, we sometimes write a fraction using a slanted bar, /.

Using this notation, we write two-eighths as 2/8.

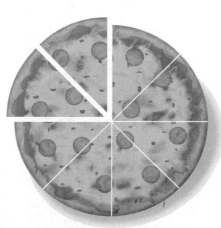

We often use a fraction to represent the number of parts selected from a total number of equal-size parts. For example, we can use the fraction $\frac{2}{8}$ to represent 2 slices of a pizza cut into 8 equal slices.

The number in the bottom of the fraction is called the **denominator**; it can indicate the number of equal parts into which a whole has been divided.

In the pizza example, the 8 in $\frac{2}{8}$ indicates there are 8 equal-size slices.

The number in the top of the fraction is called the **numerator**; it can indicate the number of parts selected.

In the pizza example, the 2 in $\frac{2}{8}$ indicates 2 of the 8 pizza slices.

We can write a whole number as a fraction by writing the number over 1.

For example: $6 = \frac{6}{1}; 9 = \frac{9}{1}$

Equivalent Fractions

Equivalent fractions are fractions that represent the same number.

For example, $\frac{1}{4}, \frac{2}{8}, \frac{6}{24}$, and $\frac{17}{68}$ are equivalent fractions.
To verify this, divide each numerator by its denominator.

$$1 \div 4 = 0.25 \qquad 2 \div 8 = 0.25 \qquad 6 \div 24 = 0.25 \qquad 17 \div 68 = 0.25$$

In each case, the result is the decimal 0.25.

To picture why $\frac{1}{4}$ and $\frac{2}{8}$ represent the same number, look at the pizza.

You can see that 2 pieces out of 8 represents $\frac{1}{4}$ of the pizza.

To add or subtract fractions, we will often need to convert a given fraction to an equivalent fraction that has a larger denominator.

Here is a procedure for finding equivalent fractions.

For example, before we add $\frac{1}{4}$ and $\frac{1}{8}$, we find a fraction that has denominator 8 and is equivalent to $\frac{1}{4}$

*In some cases, the old denominator does not divide evenly into the new given denominator. Then we often choose a **common** denominator and rewrite **both** fractions.*

— Procedure —
To Find an Equivalent Fraction With a Given Larger Denominator

Step 1 Check whether the old denominator divides evenly into the new (larger) denominator.

Step 2 If it does, divide the new denominator by the old denominator.

Step 3 Multiply the old numerator by this result. This is the new numerator.

Step 4 Use the new numerator and the new denominator to write the equivalent fraction.

Example EI.A.1

Find a fraction equivalent to $\frac{3}{5}$ with denominator 40.

Solution

Step 1 Check whether the old denominator divides evenly into the new denominator.

$$\frac{3}{5} = \frac{?}{40}$$

The old denominator, 5, divides evenly into the new denominator, 40.

Step 2 If it does, divide the new denominator by the old denominator.

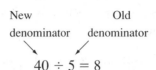

Divide 40 by 5. The result is 8.

$$40 \div 5 = 8$$

Step 3 Multiply the old numerator by this result.

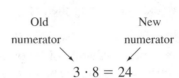

Multiply the old numerator, 3, by the result of the previous step, 8.

$$3 \cdot 8 = 24$$

Step 4 Use the new numerator and the new denominator to write the equivalent fraction.

The result of the previous step, 24, is the new numerator. The denominator is 40.

So, $\frac{3}{5} = \frac{24}{40}$.

Here is a compact way to show how to write $\frac{3}{5}$ with denominator 40:

$$\frac{3}{5} = \frac{3 \cdot 8}{5 \cdot 8} = \frac{24}{40}$$

Example EI.A.2

Find a fraction equivalent to $\frac{5}{12}$ with denominator 72.

Solution

Step 1 Check whether the old denominator divides evenly into the new denominator.

$$\frac{5}{12} = \frac{?}{72}$$

The old denominator, 12, divides evenly into the new denominator, 72.

Step 2 If it does, divide the new denominator by the old denominator.

Divide 72 by 12. The result is 6.

$$72 \div 12 = 6$$

Step 3 Multiply the old numerator by this result.

Multiply the old numerator, 5, by the result of the previous step, 6.

$$5 \cdot 6 = 30$$

Here is a compact way to show how to write $\frac{5}{12}$ with denominator 72:

$$\frac{5}{12} = \frac{5 \cdot 6}{12 \cdot 6} = \frac{30}{72}$$

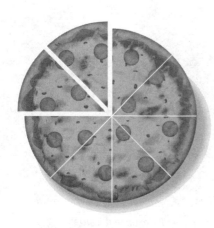

Step 4 *Use the new numerator and the new denominator to write the equivalent fraction.*

The result of the previous step, 30, is the new numerator. The denominator is 72.

$$= \frac{30}{72}$$

So, $\frac{5}{12} = \frac{30}{72}$.

In the last two examples, we started with a fraction and found an equivalent fraction with a larger denominator.

We will also need to do the reverse. That is, we will want to find a new fraction equivalent to a given fraction with a *smaller* denominator. This process is called **reducing** a fraction.

Sometimes you may be able to reduce a fraction by inspection. For example, using the pizza, we see that $\frac{2}{8} = \frac{1}{4}$.

Often, however, a fraction cannot be reduced this easily. In such cases we use a method that involves **prime factorization**. Now we will discuss prime factorization. Then we will use it to reduce fractions.

Prime Factorization

When two numbers are multiplied, each number is called a **factor**.

For example, in the product $2 \cdot 3$, both 2 and 3 are factors.

To find a **factorization** of a number means to write the number as a product.

For example, here are two factorizations of 6: $6 = 2 \cdot 3$ $6 = 1 \cdot 6$

A **prime number** is a whole number greater than 1 and divisible only by 1 and itself.

The first ten prime numbers are: 2, 3, 5, 7, 11, 13, 17, 19, 23, and 29

To find the prime factorization of a number, we write the number as the product of prime numbers.

— Procedure —
To Find the Prime Factorization of a Number

Step 1 Check to see if 2 is a factor of the number.
(That is, divide the number by 2. If the remainder is 0, then 2 is a factor).

If 2 is a factor, write the number as the product of 2 and another factor.

Step 2 If 2 is not a factor, try other prime numbers (3, 5, 7, 11, ...) until you find a prime number which is a factor of the original number. Write the original number as a product of this prime number and another factor.

Step 3 Check the other factor using the same procedure as in Steps 1 and 2.

Step 4 Continue this process until you can no longer factor. That is, continue dividing by prime numbers until you recognize the quotient as a prime number.

You can stop when the number you are dividing by is greater than the square root of the number you are dividing into.

Step 5 Write the original number as a product of the prime factors.

Example EI.A.3

Find the prime factorization of 60.

Solution

Step 1 Check to see if 2 is a factor of the number.

Divide 60 by 2.
The remainder is 0, so 2 is a factor of 60.
Write 60 as the product 2 · 30. $60 = \mathbf{2} \cdot 30$

Step 2 If 2 is not a factor, try other prime numbers (3, 5, 7, 11, ...).

Since 2 *is* a factor, we skip this step and proceed to Step 3.

Step 3 Check the other factor using the same procedure as in Steps 1 and 2.

Divide 30 by 2.
The remainder is 0, so 2 is a factor of 30.
Write 30 as the product 2 · 15. $60 = 2 \cdot \mathbf{2} \cdot \mathbf{15}$

Step 4 Continue this process until you can no longer factor.

Divide 15 by 2.
The remainder is not 0, so 2 is *not* a factor of 15.

Divide 15 by 3.
The remainder is 0, so 3 is a factor of 15.
Write 15 as the product $3 \cdot 5$. $60 = 2 \cdot 2 \cdot \mathbf{3} \cdot \mathbf{5}$

We do not need to look for more prime
factors because 5 is a prime number.

Step 5 Write the original number as a $60 = 2 \cdot 2 \cdot 3 \cdot 5$
        product of the prime factors.

So, the prime factorization of 60 is $2 \cdot 2 \cdot 3 \cdot 5$.

Here's a way to check our prime factorization of 60:

• *Is $2 \cdot 2 \cdot 3 \cdot 5 = 60$. Yes.* ✓

• *Does the factorization contain only prime numbers? Yes.* ✓

The factorization can be pictured
with a **factor tree**:

Example EI.A.4

Find the prime factorization of 53.

Solution

Step 1 Check to see if 2 is a factor of the number.

Divide 53 by 2. The remainder is
not 0, so 2 is **not** a factor of 53.

$$\begin{array}{r} 26 \\ 2\overline{)53} \\ \underline{4} \\ 13 \\ \underline{12} \\ 1 \end{array}$$

Step 2 If 2 is not a factor, try other
        prime numbers (3, 5, 7, 11, ...).

Divide 53 by 3. Since the remainder
is not 0, 3 is **not** a factor of 53.

Divide 53 by 5. Since the remainder
is not 0, 5 is **not** a factor of 53.

Divide 53 by 7. Since the remainder
is not 0, 7 is **not** a factor of 53.

$$\begin{array}{r} 17 \\ 3\overline{)53} \\ \underline{3} \\ 23 \\ \underline{21} \\ 2 \end{array} \qquad \begin{array}{r} 10 \\ 5\overline{)53} \\ \underline{5} \\ 3 \\ \underline{0} \\ 3 \end{array} \qquad \begin{array}{r} 7 \\ 7\overline{)53} \\ \underline{49} \\ 4 \end{array}$$

Use the $\sqrt{}$ key on your calculator to find the square root of 53.

$\sqrt{53} \approx 7.28.$

The next prime number is 11.
However, 11 is larger than the square root of 53, so we stop.

The only prime factor of 53 is 53 itself.
So, 53 is a prime number.

Greatest Common Factor (GCF)

When we reduce a fraction to lowest terms, it will often be useful to find the **greatest common factor (GCF)**.

The GCF of two or more whole numbers is the greatest whole number that divides evenly into each number.

For example, the GCF of 12 and 18 is 6 because 6 is the greatest whole number that divides evenly into both 12 and 18.

Sometimes we can find the GCF by inspection; that is, we can find the GCF by just looking at the numbers. In other cases, we will use this procedure.

The GCF of 8 and 10 is 2 because 2 is the greatest whole number that divides evenly into both 8 and 10.

We could also say that 2 is the greatest whole number that is a factor of both 8 and 10.

— Procedure —
To Find the Greatest Common Factor (GCF) of a Collection of Numbers

Step 1 Write the prime factorization of each number.

Step 2 List each common prime factor the **LEAST** number of times it appears in any factorization.

Step 3 Multiply the prime factors in the list.

If two numbers have no common prime factors, then their GCF is 1.

Example EI.A.5

Find the GCF of 30 and 75.

Solution

Step 1 Write the prime factorization of each number.

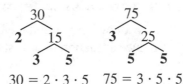

$$30 = 2 \cdot 3 \cdot 5 \qquad 75 = 3 \cdot 5 \cdot 5$$

Step 2 List each common prime factor the LEAST number of times it appears in any factorization.

The common prime factors of 30 and 75 are 3 and 5.

The **least** number of times that 3 appears is once.   3

The **least** number of times that 5 appears is once.   5

Step 3 Multiply the prime factors in the list. $3 \cdot 5 = 15$

Thus, the GCF of 30 and 75 is 15.

To make it easier to see the common factors, write the prime factorizations so the factors line up in columns.

The common factors are circled.

$$30 = 2 \cdot \textcircled{3} \cdot \textcircled{5}$$
$$75 = \textcircled{3} \cdot \textcircled{5} \cdot 5$$

Example EI.A.6

Find the GCF of 24, 84, and 108.

Solution

Step 1 Write the prime factorization of each number.

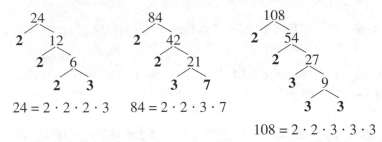

$$24 = 2 \cdot 2 \cdot 2 \cdot 3 \qquad 84 = 2 \cdot 2 \cdot 3 \cdot 7$$

$$108 = 2 \cdot 2 \cdot 3 \cdot 3 \cdot 3$$

Step 2 List each common prime factor the LEAST number of times it appears in any factorization.

The common prime factors of 24, 84, and 108 are 2 and 3.

The least number of times that 2 appears is twice.   2, 2

The least number of times that 3 appears is once.   3

Step 3 Multiply the prime factors in the list. $2 \cdot 2 \cdot 3 = 12$

Thus, the GCF of 24, 84, and 108 is 12.

Reducing to Lowest Terms

Now that we know how to find the GCF of two whole numbers, we are ready to reduce a fraction to lowest terms. Let's see what that means.

These fractions are equivalent fractions: $\dfrac{3}{5}, \dfrac{6}{10}, \dfrac{18}{30}$

Reducing a fraction to lowest terms does not mean that the value of the fraction is made smaller. The value of the fraction remains the same, but the numerator and denominator are made as small as possible.

The fraction $\dfrac{3}{5}$ is said to be **reduced to lowest terms** because its numerator and denominator have no common whole number factors other than 1.

The fraction $\dfrac{6}{10}$ is *not* in lowest terms $6 = 2 \cdot 3$
because 6 and 10 have a common factor, 2. $10 = 2 \cdot 5$

To write $\dfrac{6}{10}$ in lowest terms, we divide $\dfrac{6}{10} = \dfrac{6 \div 2}{10 \div 2} = \dfrac{3}{5}$
both 6 and 10 by their GCF, 2.

Step 1 Write the prime factorization of the numerator.

Step 2 Write the prime factorization of the denominator.

Step 3 Find the GCF of the numerator and the denominator.

Step 4 Divide the numerator and the denominator by this GCF.

Step 5 Write the resulting fraction.

Here's another way to reduce a fraction to lowest terms:

1. Factor the numerator and the denominator into prime factors.

2. Cancel all pairs of factors common to the numerator and the denominator.

Example EI.A.7

Reduce to lowest terms: $\dfrac{56}{70}$

Solution

Step 1 Write the prime factorization of the numerator.

$$56 = 2 \cdot 2 \cdot 2 \cdot 7$$

Step 2 Write the prime factorization of the denominator.

$$70 = 2 \cdot 5 \cdot 7$$

Step 3 Find the GCF of the numerator and the denominator.

$$2 \cdot 7 = \mathbf{14}$$

Step 4 Divide the numerator and the denominator by this GCF.

$$\frac{56}{70} = \frac{56 \div \mathbf{14}}{70 \div \mathbf{14}}$$

Step 5 Write the resulting fraction.

$$= \frac{4}{5}$$

So, in lowest terms, $\dfrac{56}{70} = \dfrac{4}{5}$.

We can also reduce by canceling prime factors:

$$\frac{56}{70} = \frac{\cancel{2} \cdot 2 \cdot 2 \cdot \cancel{7}}{\cancel{2} \cdot 5 \cdot \cancel{7}} = \frac{2 \cdot 2}{5} = \frac{4}{5}$$

Example EI.A.8

Reduce to lowest terms: $\dfrac{45}{120}$

Solution

Step 1 Write the prime factorization of the numerator.

$$45 = 3 \cdot 3 \cdot 5$$

Step 2 Write the prime factorization of the denominator.

$$120 = 2 \cdot 2 \cdot 2 \cdot 3 \cdot 5$$

Step 3 Find the GCF of the numerator and the denominator.

$$3 \cdot 5 = \mathbf{15}$$

Step 4 Divide the numerator and the denominator by this GCF.

$$\frac{45}{120} = \frac{45 \div \mathbf{15}}{120 \div \mathbf{15}}$$

Step 5 Write the resulting fraction.

$$= \frac{3}{8}$$

So, in lowest terms, $\dfrac{45}{120} = \dfrac{3}{8}$.

We can also reduce by canceling prime factors:

$$\frac{45}{120} = \frac{\cancel{3} \cdot 3 \cdot \cancel{5}}{2 \cdot 2 \cdot 2 \cdot \cancel{3} \cdot \cancel{5}} = \frac{3}{2 \cdot 2 \cdot 2} = \frac{3}{8}$$

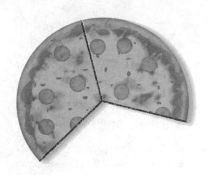

$\frac{1}{2}$ of $\frac{2}{3}$ of a pizza is $\frac{1}{3}$ of a pizza.

*If you prefer to reduce **after** you perform the multiplications, you can follow this procedure:*

* *Multiply the numerators to get the new numerator.*
* *Multiply the denominators to get the new denominator.*
* *Reduce the resulting fraction to lowest terms.*

Multiplying Fractions

Suppose you have $\frac{2}{3}$ of a pizza and you want to give half to a friend.

Each of you ends up with $\frac{1}{3}$ of the pizza.

Finding half of a quantity is equivalent to multiplying by $\frac{1}{2}$.

That is, you and your friend each end up with $\frac{1}{2} \cdot \frac{2}{3} = \frac{1}{3}$ of the pizza.

Here is a procedure for multiplying fractions.

— Procedure —
To Multiply Fractions

Step 1 Set up a new fraction as follows:
Write the numerator as a product of the original numerators.
Write the denominator as a product of the original denominators.

Step 2 Reduce by canceling factors common to the numerator and the denominator.

Step 3 Perform the remaining multiplication in the numerator.

Step 4 Perform the remaining multiplication in the denominator.

Example   El.A.9

Find: $\frac{12}{35} \cdot \frac{5}{18}$

Solution

*Step 1 Set up a new fraction:
Write the numerator as a product of the original numerators.
Write the denominator as a product of the original denominators.*

$$\frac{12}{35} \cdot \frac{5}{18}$$

$$= \frac{12 \cdot 5}{35 \cdot 18}$$

Step 2 Reduce by canceling factors common to the numerator and the denominator.

Here, we first factor 12, 35, and 18. Then we cancel factors common to the numerator and denominator.

$$\frac{12 \cdot 5}{35 \cdot 18} = \frac{\cancel{2} \cdot 2 \cdot \cancel{3} \cdot \cancel{5}}{\cancel{5} \cdot 7 \cdot \cancel{2} \cdot \cancel{3} \cdot 3}$$

Here's another way to cancel:

$$\frac{12 \cdot 5}{35 \cdot 18} = \frac{\cancel{12}^{2} \cdot \cancel{5}^{1}}{\cancel{35}_{7} \cdot \cancel{18}_{3}} = \frac{2 \cdot 1}{7 \cdot 3} = \frac{2}{21}$$

Step 3 Perform the remaining multiplication in the numerator.

$$= \frac{2}{7 \cdot 3}$$

Step 4 Perform the remaining multiplication in the denominator.

$$= \frac{2}{21}$$

So, $\frac{12}{35} \cdot \frac{5}{18} = \frac{2}{21}$.

Find: $6 \cdot \dfrac{10}{45}$

Solution

Step 1 *Set up a new fraction:*
Write the numerator as a product
of the original numerators.
Write the denominator as a product
of the original denominators.

$$6 \cdot \dfrac{10}{45}$$

First, write 6 as $\dfrac{6}{1}$.

$$= \dfrac{6}{1} \cdot \dfrac{10}{45}$$

Write the numerator as a product
and the denominator as a product.

$$= \dfrac{6 \cdot 10}{1 \cdot 45}$$

Step 2 *Reduce by canceling factors*
common to the numerator and
the denominator.

Here, we first factor 6, 10, and 45.
Then we cancel factors common to
the numerator and denominator.

$$\dfrac{6 \cdot 10}{1 \cdot 45} = \dfrac{2 \cdot \overset{1}{\cancel{3}} \cdot 2 \cdot \overset{1}{\cancel{5}}}{1 \cdot \underset{1}{\cancel{3}} \cdot 3 \cdot \underset{1}{\cancel{5}}}$$

Step 3 *Perform the remaining*
multiplication in the numerator.

$$= \dfrac{4}{1 \cdot 3}$$

Step 4 *Perform the remaining*
multiplication in the denominator.

$$= \dfrac{4}{3}$$

So, $6 \cdot \dfrac{10}{45} = \dfrac{4}{3}$.

Here's another way to cancel:

$$\dfrac{6 \cdot 10}{1 \cdot 45} = \dfrac{\overset{2}{\cancel{6}} \cdot \overset{2}{\cancel{10}}}{1 \cdot \underset{\underset{3}{\cancel{15}}}{\cancel{45}}} = \dfrac{2 \cdot 2}{1 \cdot 3} = \dfrac{4}{3}$$

The fraction $\dfrac{4}{3}$ may be left as is, or it may
be written as a mixed number.

$$\dfrac{4}{3} = 1\dfrac{1}{3}$$

Find: $\dfrac{8}{3} \cdot \dfrac{25}{60} \cdot \dfrac{12}{28}$

Solution

Step 1 *Set up a new fraction:*
Write the numerator as a product
of the original numerators.
Write the denominator as a product
of the original denominators.

$$\dfrac{8}{3} \cdot \dfrac{25}{60} \cdot \dfrac{12}{28}$$

$$= \dfrac{8 \cdot 25 \cdot 12}{3 \cdot 60 \cdot 28}$$

Step 2 *Reduce by canceling factors*
common to the numerator and
the denominator.

We use the prime factorization.

$$= \dfrac{\overbrace{2 \cdot 2 \cdot 2}^{8} \cdot \overbrace{5 \cdot 5}^{25} \cdot \overbrace{2 \cdot 2 \cdot 3}^{12}}{\underbrace{3}_{3} \cdot \underbrace{2 \cdot 2 \cdot 3 \cdot 5}_{60} \cdot \underbrace{2 \cdot 2 \cdot 7}_{28}}$$

Cancel factors common to the numerator and denominator.

$$= \frac{\overset{1}{\cancel{2}} \cdot \overset{1}{\cancel{2}} \cdot \overset{1}{\cancel{2}} \cdot \overset{1}{\cancel{5}} \cdot 5 \cdot \overset{1}{\cancel{2}} \cdot \overset{1}{\cancel{2}} \cdot \overset{1}{\cancel{3}}}{\underset{1}{\cancel{3}} \cdot \underset{1}{\cancel{2}} \cdot \underset{1}{\cancel{2}} \cdot 3 \cdot \underset{1}{\cancel{5}} \cdot \underset{1}{\cancel{2}} \cdot \underset{1}{\cancel{2}} \cdot 7}$$

$$= \frac{5 \cdot 2}{3 \cdot 7}$$

Step 3 Perform the remaining multiplication in the numerator.

$$= \frac{10}{3 \cdot 7}$$

Step 4 Perform the remaining multiplication in the denominator.

$$= \frac{10}{21}$$

So, $\dfrac{8}{3} \cdot \dfrac{25}{60} \cdot \dfrac{12}{28} = \dfrac{10}{21}$.

Dividing Fractions

In the previous section, we saw that if you had two-thirds of a pizza and wanted to share it equally with a friend, you would each get one-third of the pizza.

To picture this mathematically, we found one-half of two-thirds:

$$\mathbf{\frac{1}{2}} \cdot \frac{2}{3} = \frac{1}{3}$$

Here's another way to think about it. Divide two-thirds of a pizza into two equal parts. We write:

$$\frac{2}{3} \div \mathbf{2}$$

This suggests that dividing by 2 is equivalent to multiplying by $\dfrac{1}{2}$.

The numbers 2 and $\dfrac{1}{2}$ are **reciprocals** of one another.

Two numbers are reciprocals if their product is 1.

For example, $\dfrac{3}{4}$ and $\dfrac{4}{3}$ are reciprocals because their product is 1.

$$\frac{3}{4} \cdot \frac{4}{3} = \frac{12}{12} = 1$$

- To find the reciprocal of a fraction, invert the fraction. That is, exchange the numerator and denominator.

    For example, the reciprocal of $\mathbf{\dfrac{7}{2}}$ is $\mathbf{\dfrac{2}{7}}$.

$$\frac{7}{2} \cdot \frac{2}{7} = \frac{14}{14} = 1$$

- To find the reciprocal of a whole number, first write the number with denominator 1, then invert.

  For example, to find the reciprocal of 2, first write 2 as $\frac{2}{1}$.

  Then, invert $\frac{2}{1}$ to get $\frac{1}{2}$.

  Thus, the reciprocal of 2 is $\frac{1}{2}$. $2 \cdot \frac{1}{2} = \frac{2}{1} \cdot \frac{1}{2} = \frac{2}{2} = 1$

Example   **EI.A.12**

Find the reciprocal of each number, if possible.

  a. $\frac{5}{7}$ b. $\frac{13}{6}$ c. 12   d. $\frac{0}{4}$

Solution

a. The reciprocal of $\frac{5}{7}$ is $\frac{7}{5}$. $\frac{5}{7} \cdot \frac{7}{5} = \frac{35}{35} = 1$

b. The reciprocal of $\frac{13}{6}$ is $\frac{6}{13}$. $\frac{13}{6} \cdot \frac{6}{13} = \frac{78}{78} = 1$

c. To find the reciprocal of 12, first write 12 as $\frac{12}{1}$.

   Then, invert to obtain the reciprocal, $\frac{1}{12}$. $\frac{12}{1} \cdot \frac{1}{12} = \frac{12}{12} = 1$

d. If we exchange the numerator and denominator of $\frac{0}{4}$, the result is $\frac{4}{0}$.

   However, $\frac{4}{0}$ is undefined because division by 0 is not allowed.

   Therefore, $\frac{0}{4}$ does not have a reciprocal.

To divide one fraction by another, first rewrite the division problem as an equivalent multiplication problem.

— Procedure —
To Divide Fractions

Step 1 Invert the second fraction to find its reciprocal.

Step 2 Multiply the first fraction by this reciprocal.

Step 3 Finish the multiplication using the steps for multiplying fractions.

Example EI.A.13

Find: $\dfrac{5}{12} \div \dfrac{3}{8}$

Solution

$\dfrac{5}{12} \div \dfrac{3}{8}$

Step 1 Invert the second fraction to find its reciprocal.

The reciprocal of $\dfrac{3}{8}$ is $\dfrac{8}{3}$.

Step 2 Multiply the first fraction by this reciprocal.

$= \dfrac{5}{12} \cdot \dfrac{\mathbf{8}}{\mathbf{3}}$

Step 3 Finish the multiplication using the steps for multiplying fractions.

$= \dfrac{5 \cdot 8}{12 \cdot 3}$

Factor the numerator and denominator.

$= \dfrac{5 \cdot 2 \cdot 2 \cdot 2}{2 \cdot 2 \cdot 3 \cdot 3}$

Cancel common factors.

$= \dfrac{5 \cdot \overset{1}{\cancel{2}} \cdot \overset{1}{\cancel{2}} \cdot 2}{\underset{1}{\cancel{2}} \cdot \underset{1}{\cancel{2}} \cdot 3 \cdot 3}$

Simplify the numerator and denominator.

$= \dfrac{10}{9}$

You may write $\dfrac{10}{9}$ as $1\dfrac{1}{9}$.

So, $\dfrac{5}{12} \div \dfrac{3}{8} = \dfrac{10}{9}$.

Example EI.A.14

Find: $\dfrac{12}{17} \div 9$

Solution

$\dfrac{12}{17} \div 9$

Step 1 Invert the second fraction to find its reciprocal.

Write the whole number 9 as $\dfrac{9}{1}$.

The reciprocal of 9 is $\dfrac{1}{9}$.

Step 2 Multiply the first fraction by this reciprocal.

$= \dfrac{12}{17} \cdot \dfrac{\mathbf{1}}{\mathbf{9}}$

Step 3 Finish the multiplication using the steps for multiplying fractions.

$= \dfrac{12 \cdot 1}{17 \cdot 9}$

Factor the numerator and denominator.

$= \dfrac{2 \cdot 2 \cdot 3 \cdot 1}{17 \cdot 3 \cdot 3}$

Cancel common factors.

$= \dfrac{2 \cdot 2 \cdot \overset{1}{\cancel{3}} \cdot 1}{17 \cdot \underset{1}{\cancel{3}} \cdot 3}$

Simplify the numerator and denominator.

$= \dfrac{4}{51}$

So, $\dfrac{12}{17} \div 9 = \dfrac{4}{51}$.

Here is a summary of this concept from *Academic Systems Algebra*.

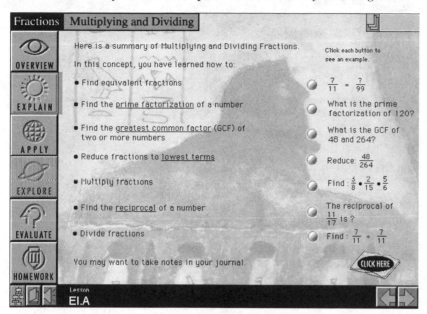

CONCEPT 2: ADDING AND SUBTRACTING

Adding and Subtracting Fractions With the Same Denominator

Suppose you have $\frac{1}{5}$ of a pizza and your friend has $\frac{2}{5}$ of the pizza.

Together you have $\frac{3}{5}$ of the pizza.

That is, $\frac{1}{5} + \frac{2}{5} = \frac{3}{5}$.

In general, to add or subtract two fractions that have the same denominator, add or subtract their numerators and keep the original denominator.

— Procedure —
To Add or Subtract Fractions With the Same Denominator

Step 1 Add or subtract the numerators. The denominator stays the same.

Step 2 Reduce to lowest terms.

Concept 2 has sections on

- **Adding and Subtracting Fractions With the Same Denominator**

- **Least Common Multiple (LCM)**

- **Least Common Denominator (LCD)**

- **Adding and Subtracting Fractions With Different Denominators**

Example EI.A.15

Find: $\dfrac{8}{15} + \dfrac{1}{15}$

Solution

$$\dfrac{8}{15} + \dfrac{1}{15}$$

Step 1 Add the numerators.

$$= \dfrac{8 + 1}{15} = \dfrac{9}{15}$$

Step 2 Reduce to lowest terms.

$$= \dfrac{3 \cdot 3}{3 \cdot 5}$$

Cancel the common factor, 3.

$$= \dfrac{3}{5}$$

So, $\dfrac{8}{15} + \dfrac{1}{15} = \dfrac{3}{5}$.

Example EI.A.16

Find: $\dfrac{19}{30} + \dfrac{7}{30} - \dfrac{1}{30}$

Solution

$$\dfrac{19}{30} + \dfrac{7}{30} - \dfrac{1}{30}$$

Step 1 Add or subtract the numerators.

$$= \dfrac{19 + 7 - 1}{30} = \dfrac{25}{30}$$

Step 2 Reduce to lowest terms.

$$= \dfrac{5 \cdot 5}{2 \cdot 3 \cdot 5}$$

Cancel the common factor, 5.

$$= \dfrac{5}{6}$$

So, $\dfrac{19}{30} + \dfrac{7}{30} - \dfrac{1}{30} = \dfrac{5}{6}$.

To add or subtract fractions with different denominators, first rewrite the fractions as equivalent fractions with the same denominator. To do this, we often find the **least common multiple** or **LCM** of the denominator.

Least Common Multiple (LCM)

The least common multiple, or LCM, of a collection of numbers is the number that is the smallest multiple of each number in the collection.

For example, let's find the LCM of 6 and 8;

To do this we'll list the first few multiples of each.

To find the multiples of 6 and 8, multiply each by the counting numbers.

$1 \cdot 6 = 6$	$1 \cdot 8 = 8$
$2 \cdot 6 = 12$	$2 \cdot 8 = 16$
$3 \cdot 6 = 18$	$3 \cdot 8 = 24$
$4 \cdot 6 = 24$	$4 \cdot 8 = 32$
$5 \cdot 6 = 30$	$5 \cdot 8 = 40$
$6 \cdot 6 = 36$	$6 \cdot 8 = 48$
$7 \cdot 6 = 42$	$7 \cdot 8 = 56$
$8 \cdot 6 = 48$	$8 \cdot 8 = 64$
$\vdots \quad \vdots$	$\vdots \quad \vdots$

Multiples of 6: 6, 12, 18, **24**, 30, 36, 42, **48**,…

Multiples of 8: 8, 16, **24**, 32, 40, **48**, 56, 64,…

A multiple of 6 that is also a multiple of 8 is called a **common multiple** of 6 and 8. The first two are 24 and 48. The smallest of these common multiples is 24, so 24 is the LCM of 6 and 8.

Notice that 24 is also the smallest number that is evenly divisible by both 6 and 8.

When we work with larger numbers or with more than two numbers, it is often time consuming to list their multiples.

Here is an efficient procedure for finding the LCM of a collection of numbers. This method uses the prime factors of each number.

— Procedure —
To Find the Least Common Multiple (LCM)
of a Collection of Numbers

Step 1 Write the prime factorization of each number.

Step 2 List each prime factor the **GREATEST** number of times it appears in any one factorization.

Step 3 Find the product of the prime numbers in Step 2.

Example EI.A.17

Find the LCM of 12 and 30.

Solution

Step 1 Write the prime factorization
of each number.

$12 = 2 \cdot 2 \cdot 3$
$30 = 2 \cdot 3 \cdot 5$

Step 2 List each prime factor the
GREATEST number of times it
appears in any one factorization.

2, 2, 3, 5

*Notice that 2 appears **twice** in the list. Here's why:*

*2 appears **twice** in the factorization of 12.*

*2 appears **once** in the factorization of 30.*

*The **greatest** number of times that 2 appears is twice.*

Step 3 Find the product of the prime
numbers in Step 2.

$2 \cdot 2 \cdot 3 \cdot 5 = 60$

So, the LCM of 12 and 30 is 60.
That is, 60 is the smallest number divisible by both 12 and 30.

Example EI.A.18

Find the LCM of 8, 15 and 36.

Solution

Step 1 Write the prime factorization
of each number.

$8 = 2 \cdot 2 \cdot 2$
$15 = 3 \cdot 5$
$36 = 2 \cdot 2 \cdot 3 \cdot 3$

Step 2 List each prime factor, the
GREATEST number of times it
appears in any one factorization.

2, 2, 2, 3, 3, 5

Step 3 Find the product of the prime
numbers in Step 2.

$2 \cdot 2 \cdot 2 \cdot 3 \cdot 3 \cdot 5 = 360$

So, the LCM of 8, 15, and 36 is 360.
360 is the smallest number divisible by 8, 15, and 36.

Least Common Denominator (LCD)

To add or subtract fractions with different denominators, first rewrite the fractions so they have the same denominator.

To obtain a **common denominator**, we often find the least common multiple of the denominators. We call this number the **least common denominator** (**LCD**) of the fractions.

Example **EI.A.19**

Find the LCD of $\dfrac{7}{15}$ and $\dfrac{5}{24}$.

Solution

The LCD of $\dfrac{7}{15}$ and $\dfrac{5}{24}$ is the LCM of 15 and 24.

Step 1 Write the prime factorization of each number.

$$15 = 3 \cdot 5$$
$$24 = 2 \cdot 2 \cdot 2 \cdot 3$$

Step 2 List each prime factor the GREATEST number of times it in any one factorization.

$$2, 2, 2, 3, 5$$

Step 3 Find the product of the prime appears numbers in step 2.

$$2 \cdot 2 \cdot 2 \cdot 3 \cdot 5 = 120$$

So, the least common denominator (LCD) of $\dfrac{7}{15}$ and $\dfrac{5}{24}$ is 120.

Adding and Subtracting Fractions With Different Denominators

Now that we know how to find the LCD of a collection of fractions, we are ready to add and subtract fractions with different denominators.

— Procedure —
To Add or Subtract Fractions with Different Denominators

Step 1 Find the LCD of the fractions.

Step 2 Write each fraction as an equivalent fraction with the LCD as its new denominator.

Step 3 Add (or subtract) the numerators. The denominator stays the same.

Step 4 Reduce to lowest terms.

Example ▌EI.A.20

Find: $\dfrac{5}{6} + \dfrac{7}{20}$

Solution

Step 1 Find the LCD of the fractions.

- *Write the prime factorization of each denominator.*

$$6 = 2 \cdot 3$$
$$20 = 2 \cdot 2 \cdot 5$$

- *List each prime factor the GREATEST number of times it appears in any one factorization.*

$$2, 2, 3, 5$$

- *Find the product of the prime numbers in Step 2.*

$$2 \cdot 2 \cdot 3 \cdot 5 = 60$$

Thus, the LCD of $\dfrac{5}{6}$ and $\dfrac{7}{20}$ is 60.

Step 2 Write each fraction as an equivalent fraction with the LCD as its new denominator.

Rewrite $\dfrac{5}{6}$ with denominator 60:

Divide 60 by 6. The result is 10.
Multiply numerator and denominator by 10.
The result is $\dfrac{50}{60}$.

$$\dfrac{5 \cdot 10}{6 \cdot 10} = \dfrac{50}{60}$$

Rewrite $\dfrac{7}{20}$ with denominator 60:

Divide 60 by 20. The result is 3.
Multiply numerator and denominator by 3.
The result is $\dfrac{21}{60}$.

$$\dfrac{7 \cdot 3}{20 \cdot 3} = \dfrac{21}{60}$$

Step 3 Add the numerators.
The denominator stays the same.

$$\dfrac{5}{6} + \dfrac{7}{20} = \dfrac{50}{60} + \dfrac{21}{60}$$
$$= \dfrac{71}{60}$$

Step 4 Reduce to lowest terms.

Find the prime factorizations of the numerator and denominator.
Note that 71 is a prime number.

$$= \dfrac{71}{2 \cdot 2 \cdot 3 \cdot 5}$$

Since the numerator and denominator have no common prime factors, $\dfrac{71}{60}$ cannot be reduced.

So, $\dfrac{5}{6} + \dfrac{7}{20} = \dfrac{71}{60}$.

The improper fraction can also be written as a mixed number:
$\dfrac{71}{60} = 1\dfrac{11}{60}$

Find: $\dfrac{3}{4} + \dfrac{7}{18} - \dfrac{5}{9}$

Solution

Step 1 Find the LCD of the fractions.

- *Write the prime factorization of each denominator.*

$$4 = 2 \cdot 2$$
$$18 = 2 \cdot 3 \cdot 3$$
$$9 = 3 \cdot 3$$

- *List each prime factor the GREATEST number of times it appears in any one factorization.*

$$2, 2, 3, 3$$

- *Find the product of the prime numbers in Step 2.*

$$2 \cdot 2 \cdot 3 \cdot 3 = 36$$

Thus, the LCD of $\dfrac{3}{4}$, $\dfrac{7}{18}$ and $\dfrac{5}{9}$ is 36.

Step 2 Write each fraction as an equivalent fraction with the LCD as its new denominator.

Rewrite $\dfrac{3}{4}$ with denominator 36.

Divide 36 by 4. The result is 9.
Multiply numerator and denominator by 9.
The result is $\dfrac{27}{36}$.

$$\dfrac{3 \cdot 9}{4 \cdot 9} = \dfrac{27}{36}$$

Rewrite $\dfrac{7}{18}$ with denominator 36.

Divide 36 by 18. The result is 2.
Multiply numerator and denominator by 2.
The result is $\dfrac{14}{36}$.

$$\dfrac{7 \cdot 2}{18 \cdot 2} = \dfrac{14}{36}$$

Rewrite $\dfrac{5}{9}$ with denominator 36.

Divide 36 by 9. The result is 4.
Multiply numerator and denominator by 4.
The result is $\dfrac{20}{36}$.

$$\dfrac{5 \cdot 4}{9 \cdot 4} = \dfrac{20}{36}$$

Step 3 Add and subtract the numerators. The denominator stays the same.

$$\dfrac{3}{4} + \dfrac{7}{18} - \dfrac{5}{9} = \dfrac{27}{36} + \dfrac{14}{36} - \dfrac{20}{36}$$
$$= \dfrac{21}{36}$$

Step 4 Reduce to lowest terms.

$$= \dfrac{3 \cdot 7}{2 \cdot 2 \cdot 3 \cdot 3}$$

Cancel the common factor, 3.

$$= \dfrac{\overset{1}{\cancel{3}} \cdot 7}{2 \cdot 2 \cdot \underset{1}{\cancel{3}} \cdot 3}$$
$$= \dfrac{7}{12}$$

So, $\dfrac{3}{4} + \dfrac{7}{18} - \dfrac{5}{9} = \dfrac{7}{12}$.

Here is a summary of this concept from *Academic Systems Algebra*.

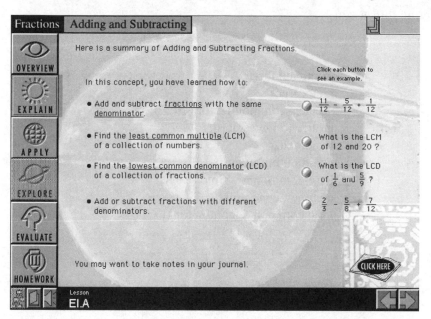

Here is a summary of Adding and Subtracting Fractions.

In this concept, you have learned how to:

Click each button to
see an example.

- Add and subtract fractions with the same denominator.
    $\frac{11}{12} - \frac{5}{12} + \frac{1}{12}$

- Find the least common multiple (LCM) of a collection of numbers.
    What is the LCM of 12 and 20 ?

- Find the lowest common denominator (LCD) of a collection of fractions.
    What is the LCD of $\frac{1}{6}$ and $\frac{5}{9}$?

- Add or subtract fractions with different denominators.
    $\frac{2}{3} - \frac{5}{8} + \frac{7}{12}$

You may want to take notes in your journal.

CLICK HERE

Lesson
EI.A

Checklist Lesson EI.A

Here is what you should know after completing this lesson.

Words and Phrases

fraction
fraction bar
denominator
numerator
equivalent fractions
reducing
prime factorization
factor
factorization

prime number
factor tree
greatest common factor (GCF)
reduce to lowest terms
reciprocals
common multiple
least common multiple (LCM)
common denominator
least common denominator (LCD)

Ideas and Procedures

❶ Equivalent Fractions
Find a fraction equivalent to a given fraction with a greater denominator.

Example EI.A.1

Find a fraction equivalent to $\frac{3}{5}$ with denominator 40.

See Also: Example EI.A.2
Apply 1-3

❷ Prime Numbers
List the first 10 prime numbers.

2, 3, 5, 7, 11, 13, 17, 19, 23, 29

❸ Prime Factorization
Find the prime factorization of a whole number.

Example EI.A.3
Find the prime factorization of 60.

See Also: Example EI.A.4
Apply 4-6

❹ Greatest Common Factor (GCF)
Find the GCF of a collection of numbers.

Example EI.A.6
Find the GCF of 24, 84, and 108.

See Also: Example EI.A.5
Apply 7-9

❺ Reduce to Lowest Terms
Reduce a fraction to lowest terms.

Example EI.A.8
Reduce to lowest terms: $\frac{45}{120}$

See Also: Example EI.A.7
Apply 10-12

❻ Multiply Fractions

Find the product of fractions.

Example EI.A.11

Find: $\dfrac{8}{3} \cdot \dfrac{25}{60} \cdot \dfrac{12}{28}$

See Also: Example EI.A.9, EI.A.10
          Apply 16-18, 25-28

❼ Reciprocal

Find the reciprocal of a number.

Example EI.A.12b

Find the reciprocal of $\dfrac{13}{6}$.

See Also: Example EI.A.12a, c, d
          Apply 13-15

❽ Divide Fractions

Find the quotient of fractions.

Example EI.A.13

Find: $\dfrac{5}{12} \div \dfrac{3}{8}$

See Also: Example EI.A.14
          Apply 19-24, 27, 28

❾ Least Common Multiple (LCM)

Find the LCM of a collection of numbers.

Example EI.A.18
Find the LCM of 8, 15, and 36.

See Also: Example EI.A.17
          Apply 31-33, 43-45

❿ Least Common Denominator (LCD)

Find the LCD of a collection of fractions.

Example EI.A.19

Find the LCD of $\dfrac{7}{15}$ and $\dfrac{5}{24}$.

See Also: Apply 34-36, 46-48

⓫ Add or Subtract Fractions

Find the sum or difference of fractions.

Example EI.A.21

Find: $\dfrac{3}{4} + \dfrac{7}{18} - \dfrac{5}{9}$

See Also: Example EI.A.15, EI.A.16, EI.A.20
          Apply 29, 30, 37-42, 49-56

Homework Problems

Circle the homework problems assigned to you by the computer, then complete them below.

☀ Explain

Multiplying and Dividing

1. Find the equivalent fraction:

   a. $\dfrac{3}{5} = \dfrac{?}{45}$

   b. $\dfrac{7}{8} = \dfrac{?}{120}$

2. Write the prime factorization of 84.

3. Find the greatest common factor of 18 and 72.

4. Reduce to lowest terms: $\dfrac{20}{72}$

5. Find the greatest common factor of 108 and 144.

6. Reduce to lowest terms: $\dfrac{64}{80}$

7. Find:

   a. $\dfrac{2}{3} \cdot \dfrac{5}{7}$

   b. $\dfrac{5}{12} \cdot \dfrac{8}{25}$

8. Find:

   a. $\dfrac{2}{3} \div \dfrac{5}{7}$

   b. $\dfrac{4}{21} \div \dfrac{8}{3}$

9. Find the reciprocal of 47.

10. Find:

    a. $\dfrac{5}{18} \cdot 3$

    b. $12 \div \dfrac{27}{5}$

11. Find: $\dfrac{15}{28} \cdot \dfrac{2}{11} \cdot \dfrac{7}{9}$

12. Find: $\dfrac{11}{28} \cdot \dfrac{5}{33} \div \dfrac{2}{7}$

Adding and Subtracting

13. Find: $\dfrac{11}{29} + \dfrac{9}{29}$

14. Find the least common multiple (LCM) of 3 and 4.

15. Find the least common denominator (LCD) of $\dfrac{5}{6}$ and $\dfrac{1}{4}$.

16. Find: $\dfrac{1}{6} + \dfrac{3}{4}$

17. Find: $\dfrac{17}{28} - \dfrac{5}{28}$

18. Find the least common multiple (LCM) of 15 and 36.

19. Find the least common denominator (LCD) of $\dfrac{5}{24}$ and $\dfrac{7}{32}$.

20. Find: $\dfrac{23}{28} - \dfrac{7}{12}$

21. Find: $\dfrac{8}{35} + \dfrac{21}{35} - \dfrac{4}{35}$

22. Find the least common multiple (LCM) of 6, 15, and 35.

23. Find the least common denominator (LCD) of $\dfrac{5}{24}, \dfrac{11}{15},$ and $\dfrac{1}{5}$.

24. Find: $\dfrac{4}{5} + \dfrac{5}{6} - \dfrac{7}{10}$

 **Apply**

Practice Problems

Here are some additional practice problems for you to try.

Multiplying and Dividing

1. Write the equivalent fraction: $\dfrac{2}{7} = \dfrac{?}{35}$

2. Write the equivalent fraction: $\dfrac{4}{9} = \dfrac{?}{27}$

3. Write the equivalent fraction: $\dfrac{3}{5} = \dfrac{18}{?}$

4. Write the prime factorization of 72.

5. Write the prime factorization of 45.

6. Write the prime factorization of 90.

7. Find the greatest common factor of 18 and 48.

8. Find the greatest common factor of 12 and 42.

9. Find the greatest common factor of 18, 24, 45.

10. Reduce to lowest terms: $\dfrac{15}{24}$

11. Reduce to lowest terms: $\dfrac{42}{56}$

12. Reduce to lowest terms: $\dfrac{56}{104}$

13. Find the reciprocal of 23.

14. Find the reciprocal of 35.

15. Find the reciprocal of $\dfrac{2}{3}$.

16. Find: $\dfrac{5}{6} \cdot \dfrac{18}{25}$

17. Find: $\dfrac{10}{21} \cdot \dfrac{3}{5}$

18. Find: $\dfrac{4}{5} \cdot \dfrac{10}{28}$

19. Find: $\dfrac{7}{20} \div \dfrac{7}{4}$

20. Find: $\dfrac{8}{25} \div \dfrac{8}{15}$

21. Find: $\dfrac{12}{42} \div \dfrac{6}{7}$

22. Find: $\dfrac{4}{5} \div 2$

23. Find: $\dfrac{6}{25} \div 3$

24. Find: $8 \div \dfrac{4}{5}$

25. Find: $\dfrac{2}{5} \cdot \dfrac{10}{12} \cdot \dfrac{4}{7}$

26. Find: $\dfrac{2}{5} \cdot \dfrac{15}{21} \cdot \dfrac{6}{11}$

27. Find: $\dfrac{3}{8} \cdot 4 \div \dfrac{3}{14}$

28. Find: $\dfrac{7}{16} \cdot 8 \div \dfrac{7}{12}$

Adding and Subtracting

29. Find: $\dfrac{3}{17} + \dfrac{9}{17} - \dfrac{7}{17}$

30. Find: $\dfrac{6}{23} + \dfrac{8}{23} - \dfrac{5}{23}$

31. Find the least common multiple (LCM) of 10 and 35.

32. Find the least common multiple (LCM) of 8 and 36.

33. Find the least common multiple (LCM) of 14 and 18.

34. Find the least common denominator (LCD) of $\dfrac{11}{20}$ and $\dfrac{13}{45}$.

35. Find the least common denominator (LCD) of $\dfrac{17}{21}$ and $\dfrac{3}{14}$.

36. Find the least common denominator (LCD) of $\dfrac{11}{18}$ and $\dfrac{15}{24}$.

37. Find: $\dfrac{2}{3} - \dfrac{5}{12}$

38. Find: $\dfrac{3}{5} - \dfrac{7}{15}$

39. Find: $\dfrac{8}{9} - \dfrac{5}{12}$

40. Find: $\dfrac{1}{2} + \dfrac{1}{8}$

41. Find: $\dfrac{1}{4} + \dfrac{5}{16}$

42. Find: $\dfrac{4}{15} + \dfrac{7}{8}$

43. Find the least common multiple (LCM) of 7, 14, and 21.

44. Find the least common multiple (LCM) of 10, 25, and 30.

45. Find the least common multiple (LCM) of 18, 21, and 36.

46. Find the least common denominator (LCD) of $\dfrac{1}{3}, \dfrac{3}{4},$ and $\dfrac{7}{15}$.

47. Find the least common denominator (LCD) of $\dfrac{1}{2}, \dfrac{2}{3},$ and $\dfrac{3}{10}$.

48. Find the least common denominator (LCD) of $\dfrac{3}{4}, \dfrac{7}{15},$ and $\dfrac{17}{24}$.

49. Find: $\dfrac{1}{12} + \dfrac{1}{5} + \dfrac{7}{10}$

50. Find: $\dfrac{1}{6} + \dfrac{1}{4} + \dfrac{3}{10}$

51. Find: $\dfrac{1}{3} + \dfrac{5}{18} + \dfrac{3}{16}$

52. Find: $\dfrac{5}{6} + \dfrac{7}{16} - 1$

53. Find: $\dfrac{7}{8} + \dfrac{5}{6} - 1$

54. Find: $\dfrac{3}{14} + 2 - \dfrac{17}{18}$

55. Find: $\dfrac{3}{5} + \dfrac{4}{7} - \dfrac{1}{4}$

56. Find: $\dfrac{5}{7} + \dfrac{2}{3} - \dfrac{1}{2}$

Evaluate

Practice Test

Take this practice test to be sure that you are prepared for the final quiz in Evaluate.

1. Find the greatest common factor (GCF) of 42 and 36.

2. Reduce to lowest terms: $\dfrac{20}{75}$

3. Find the reciprocal of $\dfrac{13}{45}$.

4. Find: $\dfrac{5}{8} \cdot \dfrac{18}{25} \div \dfrac{9}{7}$

5. Find the least common multiple (LCM) of 10 and 28.

6. Find the least common denominator (LCD) of $\dfrac{1}{6}$, $\dfrac{23}{30}$, and $\dfrac{3}{4}$.

7. Find: $\dfrac{1}{5} + \dfrac{1}{4}$

8. Find: $\dfrac{7}{9} + 5 - \dfrac{11}{12}$

LESSON EI.B
SIGNED NUMBERS

Overview

In this lesson, you will study positive and negative numbers. You will review how to combine them by addition, subtraction, multiplication, and division. You'll use these procedures throughout your study of algebra.

You will also review exponential notation, a shorthand way to indicate multiplication. Finally, you will review the rules that specify the order in which to perform calculations in expressions that contain several mathematical operations.

Explain

Concept 1 has sections on

- **Number Line**

- **Adding Numbers That Have the Same Sign**

- **Adding Numbers That Have Different Signs**

- **Subtracting Signed Numbers**

CONCEPT 1:
ADDING AND SUBTRACTING

Number Line

We often refer to positive numbers and negative numbers as **signed numbers**.

We can visualize the relationships among signed numbers by associating each number with a point on a **number line**.

Number line

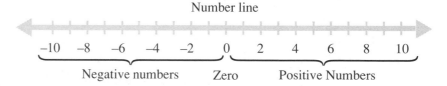

The negative numbers are located to the left of 0. The positive numbers are located to the right of 0. Each point on the number line corresponds to either a negative number, a positive number, or 0. The number 0 is neither negative nor positive.

To **plot** a point on a number line, we locate the point on the line. The number that corresponds to the point is called the **coordinate** of the point. For example, to plot -3 on the number line, place a dot at -3. The coordinate of that point is -3.

We can compare two numbers on a number line. The number on the **left** is **less than** the number on the **right**. For example, 5 is less than 8 since 5 lies to the left of 8. Likewise, -3 is less than -1 because -3 lies to the left of -1.

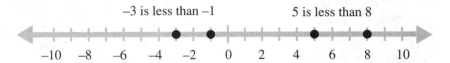

Example **EI.B.1**

Plot on a number line: $-8, -5, -\dfrac{3}{2}, 0, 4$

Solution

Place a dot at the approximate location of each number.

Example **EI.B.2**

State the coordinate of each labeled point:

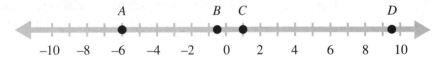

Solution

The coordinate of A is -6.
The coordinate of B is $-\dfrac{1}{2}$.

The coordinate of C is 1.
The coordinate of D is 9.5.

Adding Numbers That Have the Same Sign

A number line can help us add signed numbers.

For example, let's use a number line to add two positive numbers.
To calculate the sum $2 + 6$, start at 2 on the number line.
Then, since 6 is **positive**, move 6 units to the **right**. We are now at 8.

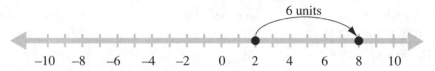

Thus, $2 + 6 = 8$.

This agrees with what we know from arithmetic.
Notice that we added two positive numbers and the result was also positive.

Now, let's use the number line to add two negative numbers.
To calculate $-1 + (-8)$, start at -1 on the number line.
Then, since -8 is **negative**, move 8 units to the **left**. We are now at -9.

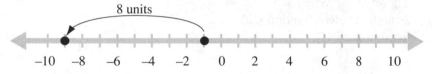

Thus, $-1 + (-8) = -9$.

Notice that we added two negative numbers and the result was also negative.

A number line helps us visualize how to add numbers that have the same sign. In practice, all we need is the following procedure.

— Procedure —
To Add Two Numbers That Have the Same Sign

Step 1 Ignore the signs and add the two numbers.

Step 2 Attach the original sign of the numbers.

Example EI.B.3

Find: $23 + 58$

Solution

Step 1 Ignore the signs and add the two numbers. $23 + 58 = 81$

Step 2 Attach the original sign of the numbers.

Attach a positive sign, $+$, since the
original numbers are both positive. $+81$

Therefore, $23 + 58 = +81$.

We usually omit the positive sign and write 81.

Example EI.B.4

Find: $-42 + (-17)$

Solution

Step 1 Ignore the signs and add the two numbers. $42 + 17 = 59$

Step 2 Attach the original sign of the numbers.

Attach a negative sign, $-$, since the
original numbers are both negative. -59

Therefore, $-42 + (-17) = -59$.

Example EI.B.5

Find: $-\dfrac{1}{6} + \left(-\dfrac{3}{4}\right)$

Solution

Step 1 Ignore the signs and add the two numbers.

The LCD of the fractions is 12.
Therefore, rewrite each fraction
as an equivalent fraction with
denominator 12.

$$\frac{1}{6} + \frac{3}{4} = \frac{1 \cdot 2}{6 \cdot 2} + \frac{3 \cdot 3}{4 \cdot 3}$$
$$= \frac{2}{12} + \frac{9}{12}$$
$$= \frac{11}{12}$$

Step 2 Attach the original sign of the numbers.

Attach a negative sign, $-$, since the
original numbers are both negative. $-\dfrac{11}{12}$

Therefore, $-\dfrac{1}{6} + \left(-\dfrac{3}{4}\right) = -\dfrac{11}{12}$.

Adding Numbers That Have Different Signs

The number line is also useful for determining the sum of numbers that
have different signs.

For example, to find $8 + (-6)$, start at 8 on the number line.
    Then, since -6 is **negative**, move 6 units to the **left**. We are now at 2.

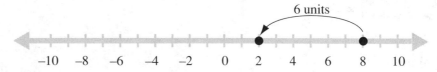

Thus, $8 + (-6) = 2$.

Likewise, to find $-10 + 7$, start at -10 on the number line.
Then, since 7 is **positive**, move 7 units to the **right**. We are now at -3.

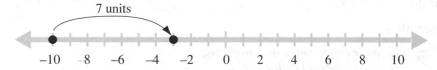

7 units

Thus, $-10 + 7 = -3$.

Instead of using a number line to add two numbers with different signs, we can use the following procedure.

— Procedure —
To Add Two Numbers That Have Different Signs

Step 1 Ignore the positive and negative signs and decide which is the greater number.

Step 2 Subtract the lesser number from the greater number.

Step 3 Attach the original sign of the greater number from step 1.

Example EI.B.6

Find: $86 + (-24)$

Solution

Step 1 Ignore the positive and negative signs and decide which is the greater number.   86 is greater than 24

Step 2 Subtract the lesser number from the greater number. $86 - 24 = 62$

Step 3 Attach the original sign of the greater number.

The greater number, 86, is positive.
So attach a positive sign, $+$. $+62$

Thus, $86 + (-24) = +62$.
We usually write $+62$ as 62.

Example EI.B.7

Find: $-58 + 35$

Solution

Step 1 Ignore the positive and negative signs and decide which is the greater number.

58 is greater than 35

Step 2 Subtract the lesser number from the greater number.

$58 - 35 = 23$

Step 3 Attach the original sign of the greater number.

Attach the sign of -58.
That is, attach a negative sign, $-$.

-23

Thus, $-58 + 35 = -23$.

Example EI.B.8

Find: $47 + (-16) + (-59) + 26$

Solution

One way to find this sum is to add the numbers, working from left to right.

$$47 + \underbrace{(-16) + (-59) + 26}$$
$$= \underbrace{31 \qquad + (-59)} + 26$$
$$= \qquad \underbrace{-28 \qquad + 26}$$
$$= \qquad\qquad -2$$

However, we can add numbers in any order. So, we can also do this problem by first adding the positive numbers, then adding the negative numbers, and finally adding the two sums.

Add the positive numbers, 47 and 26. $47 + 26 = 73$

Add the negative numbers, (-16) and (-59). $(-16) + (-59) = -75$

Add the two sums, 73 and (-75). $73 + (-75) = -2$

So, $47 + (-16) + (-59) + 26 = -2$.

Subtracting Signed Numbers

We know that $7 - 4$ is 3. $7 - 4 = 3$

Using the rules for the addition of signed numbers, we know that $7 + (-4)$ is also 3. $7 + (-4) = 3$

This suggests that we can rewrite a subtraction problem as an addition problem. $7 - 4 = 7 + (-4)$

We will now generalize this idea to subtract signed numbers. That is, we will rewrite a subtraction problem as an addition problem. Then we will follow the steps for adding signed numbers.

Be sure you understand the two uses of the $-$ sign:

* *In $7 - 4$, the $-$ indicates the **operation** of subtraction.*

* *In $7 + (-4)$, the $-$ indicates the **sign** of the number.*

— Procedure —
To Subtract One Signed Number from Another Signed Number

Step 1 Change the subtraction sign to an addition sign, and change the sign of the number being subtracted.

Step 2 Follow the steps for adding signed numbers.

Example EI.B.9

Find: $53 - 64$

Solution

Step 1 Change the subtraction sign $53 - 64$
to an addition sign, and change the
sign of the number being subtracted. $= 53 + (-64)$

Step 2 Follow the steps for adding
signed numbers.

53 and -64 have different signs.
Ignore the signs and subtract the
lesser number from the greater number. $64 - 53 = 11$

Attach the sign of -64.
That is, attach a negative sign, $-$. -11

So, $53 - 64 = -11$.

Example EI.B.10

Find: $32 - (-14)$

Solution

Step 1 Change the subtraction sign $32 - (-14)$
to an addition sign, and change the
sign of the number being subtracted. $= 32 + (+14)$

Step 2 Follow the steps for adding
signed numbers.

32 and $+14$ have the same sign.

Ignore the signs and add the numbers. $32 + 14 = 46$

Attach a positive sign, $+$, since both
numbers are positive. $+46$

So, $32 - (-14) = +46$.

We usually write $+46$ as 46.

Example EI.B.11

Find: $-126 - (-83)$

Solution

Step 1 Change the subtraction sign to an addition sign, and change the sign of the number being subtracted.

$$-126 - (-83)$$
$$= -126 + (+83)$$

Step 2 Follow the steps for adding signed numbers.

-126 and $+83$ have different signs. Ignore the signs and subtract the lesser number from the greater number.

$$126 - 83 = 43$$

Attach the sign of -126.
That is, attach a negative sign, $-$.

$$-43$$

So, $-126 - (-83) = -43$.

Example EI.B.12

Find: $-8 - (-2) - 4$

Solution

We can do the subtractions working from left to right.

$$-8 - (-2) - 4$$

To find $-8 - (-2)$, first change the subtraction to addition and change the sign of -2.

$$= -8 + (+2) - 4$$

Then, since -8 and $+2$ have different signs, ignore their signs and subtract.
Attach the sign of -8.

$$= -6 - 4$$

To find $-6 - 4$, first change the subtraction to addition and change the sign of $+4$.

$$= -6 + (-4)$$

Then, since -6 and -4 have the same sign, ignore their signs and and add.
Attach the original sign, $-$, of the numbers.

$$= -10$$

So, $-8 - (-2) - 4 = -10$.

Here is a summary of this concept from *Academic Systems Algebra*.

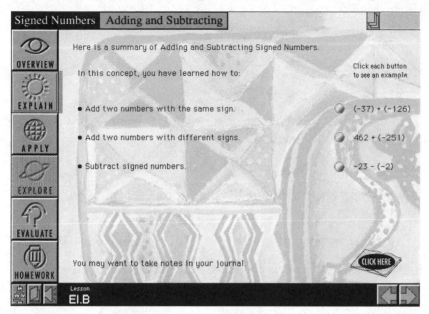

CONCEPT 2:
MULTIPLYING AND DIVIDING

Multiplying and Dividing Signed Numbers

We can write the product $4 \cdot 3$ using addition, like this:

$$4 \cdot 3 = 3 + 3 + 3 + 3 = 12$$

Notice that the product of two positive numbers is positive.

Similarly, we can find $4 \cdot (-3)$ by writing the product using addition:

$$4 \cdot (-3) = (-3) + (-3) + (-3) + (-3) = -12$$

This suggests that the product of a positive number and a negative number is a negative number. In fact, the product of two numbers with different signs is always negative.

What is the sign of the product of two negative numbers? To find out, we look for a pattern.

The following table shows some multiples of -3.

$$
\begin{array}{l}
\text{negative} \cdot \text{positive} \left\{
\begin{array}{rcr}
-3 \cdot 3 &=& -9 \\
-3 \cdot 2 &=& -6 \\
-3 \cdot 1 &=& -3
\end{array} \right\} \begin{array}{l}\text{We know these products}\\ \text{from the previous discussion.}\end{array} \\
\qquad\qquad\quad -3 \cdot 0 \;=\; 0 \quad \text{NOTICE: The products increase by 3.} \\
\text{negative} \cdot \text{negative} \left\{
\begin{array}{rcr}
-3 \cdot (-1) &=& \mathbf{3} \\
-3 \cdot (-2) &=& \mathbf{6} \\
-3 \cdot (-3) &=& \mathbf{9}
\end{array} \right\} \begin{array}{l}\text{To fit the pattern "increase by 3,"}\\ \text{these products must be } \mathbf{positive}.\end{array}
\end{array}
$$

Concept 2 has sections on

- **Multiplying and Dividing Signed Numbers**

- **Exponential Notation**

- **Properties of Real Numbers**

- **Distributive Property**

- **Order of Operations**

Notice that as the factors on the left decrease by 1, the products on the right increase by 3. Therefore, we have:

$$-3 \cdot (-1) = +3$$

$$-3 \cdot (-2) = +6$$

$$-3 \cdot (-3) = +9$$

This pattern suggests that the product of two negative numbers is a positive number. This is indeed true.

We summarize our results as follows:

If two numbers have the **same sign**, their product is **positive**.

positive · positive = positive	$2 \cdot 5 = 10$
negative · negative = positive	$(-2) \cdot (-5) = 10$

If two numbers have **different signs**, their product is **negative**.

positive · negative = negative	$2 \cdot (-5) = -10$
negative · positive = negative	$(-2) \cdot 5 = -10$

We also know that a division problem can be written as a multiplication problem.

For example, $6 \div 2$ can be written as $6 \cdot \dfrac{1}{2}$.

Therefore, it can be shown that the signs of quotients follow the same pattern as the signs of products.

We have the following:

If two numbers have the **same sign**, their quotient is **positive**.

positive ÷ positive = positive	$6 \div 3 = 2$
negative ÷ negative = positive	$(-6) \div (-3) = 2$

If two numbers have **different signs**, their quotient is **negative**.

positive ÷ negative = negative	$6 \div (-3) = -2$
negative ÷ positive = negative	$(-6) \div 3 = -2$

We can use these facts to write a procedure for multiplying or dividing two signed numbers.

— Procedure —
To Multiply or Divide Two Signed Numbers

Step 1 Ignore the signs and do the multiplication or division.

Step 2 Write the sign of the product or quotient:
- If the original signs are the **same**, the answer is **positive**.
- If the original signs are **different**, the answer is **negative**.

Example EI.B.13

Find: $(-8) \cdot (-11)$

Solution

Step 1 Ignore the signs and do the multiplication. $8 \cdot 11 = 88$

Step 2 Write the sign of the product.

The original signs are the same, $+88$
so the answer is positive.

Thus, $(-8) \cdot (-11) = 88$.

Example EI.B.14

Find: $72 \div (-18)$

Solution

Step 1 Ignore the signs and do the division. $72 \div 18 = 4$

Step 2 Write the sign of the quotient.

The original signs are different, -4
so the answer is negative.

Therefore, $72 \div (-18) = -4$.

Example EI.B.15

Find: $\dfrac{-5}{7} \cdot \dfrac{3}{11}$

Solution

**Step 1 Ignore the signs and
            do the multiplication.**

$$\frac{5}{7} \cdot \frac{3}{11} = \frac{5 \cdot 3}{7 \cdot 11} = \frac{15}{77}$$

Step 2 Write the sign of the product.

The original signs are different,
so the answer is negative. $\dfrac{-15}{77}$

So, $\dfrac{-5}{7} \cdot \dfrac{3}{11} = \dfrac{-15}{77}$.

*The negative sign in a fraction can be
written in front of the fraction, or in the
numerator, or in the denominator.*

For example,

$$-\frac{1}{2} = \frac{-1}{2} = \frac{1}{-2}$$

and,

$$\frac{-15}{77} = \frac{15}{-77} = -\frac{15}{77}$$

Example EI.B.16

Find: $-150 \div (-25)$

Solution

**Step 1 Ignore the signs and
            do the division.** $150 \div 25 = 6$

Step 2 Write the sign of the quotient.

The original signs are the same,
so the answer is positive. $+6$

So, $-150 \div (-25) = 6$.

Find: $-3 \cdot (-4) \cdot (-2) \cdot 5$

Solution

Here we have four factors.
   If we ignore the signs and do
   the multiplication, the result is 120. $3 \cdot 4 \cdot 2 \cdot 5 = 120$

Next we find the sign of the product.

   There are three negative signs.
   If we pair up two of them we
   get a positive product.

   We multiply that result by the next
   negative number and obtain a
   negative number.

   Finally, we multiply the negative
   number by a positive number, which
   results in a negative final product.

Therefore, $-3 \cdot (-4) \cdot (-2) \cdot 5 = -120$.

In a problem that contains only multiplication, if the number of negative factors is

• even, the answer is positive;
• odd, the answer is negative.

Exponential Notation

Sometimes we write a product where each factor is the same.

For example, to find the volume of a box measuring 4 ft. by 4 ft. by 4 ft., we find the product $4 \cdot 4 \cdot 4$.

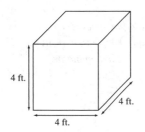

We can use **exponential notation** as a shorthand way to write such a product.

Using this notation, $4 \cdot 4 \cdot 4$ is written 4^3.

$$4^3 = 4 \cdot 4 \cdot 4 = 64$$

- 4 is called the **base**.
  It is the repeated factor.

- 3 is called the **exponent** or **power**.
  It tells us how many factors of the base occur in the product.

- 4^3 is read "four to the third power" or simply "four to the third."

We write: $4 \cdot 4 \cdot 4 = 4^3$

We often use special names for the exponents 2 and 3. For example:

• An exponent 2 is read "squared."
  5^2 can be read "five squared."

• An exponent 3 is read "cubed."
  4^3 can be read "four cubed."

Example EI.B.18

For each of the following, identify the base and the exponent.
Then, write each product using exponential notation.

a. $3 \cdot 3 \cdot 3 \cdot 3 \cdot 3$ b. $(-2) \cdot (-2) \cdot (-2) \cdot (-2)$

Solution

a.   Since 3 is the repeated factor, the base is 3. Because 3 appears as a   *3^5 is read "three to the fifth power" or*
factor 5 times, the exponent is 5. Written in exponential notation,   *"three to the fifth."*
we have:

$$\overbrace{3 \cdot 3 \cdot 3 \cdot 3 \cdot 3}^{\substack{5 \text{ factors,} \\ \text{each is } 3}} = 3^5$$

b.   Since -2 is the repeated factor, the base is -2. Because -2 appears   *$(-2)^4$ is read "negative two to the fourth*
as a factor 4 times, the exponent is 4. Written in exponential   *power" or "negative two to the fourth."*
notation, we have:

$$\overbrace{(-2)\,(-2)(-2)(-2)}^{4 \text{ factors}} = (-2)^4$$

Example EI.B.19

Write without an exponent and then calculate.

a. 10^3 b. $(-3)^2$ c. -3^2

Solution

a.   The base is 10 and the exponent is 3. 10^3
Therefore, the factor 10 occurs 3 times. $= 10 \cdot 10 \cdot 10$

Multiply. $= 1000$

So, $10^3 = 1000$.

b.   The base is -3 since the parentheses $(-3)^2$
enclose the negative sign as well as the 3.

The exponent is 2.

Therefore, the factor -3 occur 2 times. $= (-3) \cdot (-3)$

Multiply. $= 9$

So, $(-3)^2 = 9$.

A negative sign is part of the base of an exponential expression only when the sign and the number are both enclosed by parentheses.

For example, here the base is -3:
$$(-3)^2 = (-3)^2 = 9.$$

However, here the base is 3:
$$-3^2 = -3 \cdot 3 = -9.$$

c. The base is 3 since the negative sign is *not* grouped with the 3 inside parentheses.

The exponent is 2.

Therefore, the factor 3 occurs 2 times. -3^2
The sign of the product is negative. $= -3 \cdot 3$

Multiply. $= -9$

Thus, $-3^2 = -9$.

Properties of Real Numbers

Here are some properties of numbers that can help you compute more easily. Each property is true for all real numbers.

Commutative Property of Addition

When you add two numbers, regardless of the order, the sum is the same.

$$4 + 2 = 2 + 4$$
$$6 = 6$$

Commutative Property of Multiplication

When you multiply two numbers, regardless of the order, the product is the same.

$$5 \cdot 7 = 7 \cdot 5$$
$$35 = 35$$

Associative Property of Addition

When you add numbers, regardless of how you group (or associate) them, the sum is the same.

$$(2 + 3) + 4 = 2 + (3 + 4)$$
$$5 + 4 = 2 + 7$$
$$9 = 9$$

Associative Property of Multiplication

When you multiply numbers, regardless of how you group them, the product is the same.

$$(2 \cdot 3) \cdot 4 = 2 \cdot (3 \cdot 4)$$
$$6 \cdot 4 = 2 \cdot 12$$
$$24 = 24$$

The following properties involve the special numbers 0 and 1.

Identity Property of Addition

When we add 0 to any number, the result is the original number.
We call 0 the **additive identity**.

$$3 + 0 = 3$$
$$3 = 3$$

Inverse Property of Addition

For each number, we can find another number so that when we add the two numbers, the result is **0**.

$$5 + (-5) = 0$$
$$0 = 0$$

Two numbers whose sum is 0 are called **additive inverses** or **opposites**.

To find the opposite of a number, change its sign.

For example, the opposite of 8 is -8; the opposite of -5 is 5.

Identity Property of Multiplication

When we multiply a number by 1, the result is the original number.

$$7 \cdot 1 = 7$$
$$7 = 7$$

We call 1 the **multiplicative identity**.

Inverse Property of Multiplication

For each number except zero, we can find another number so that when we multiply the two numbers, the result is **1**.

$$4 \cdot \frac{1}{4} = 1$$
$$1 = 1$$

Two numbers whose product is 1 are called **multiplicative inverses** or **reciprocals**.

To find the reciprocal of a number, invert the number.

For example, the reciprocal of $\frac{2}{7}$ is $\frac{7}{2}$.

To find the reciprocal of 3, first write it as $\frac{3}{1}$. Then, invert to obtain $\frac{1}{3}$.

Distributive Property

Finally, let's look at one more property that will be very useful in algebra. The **Distributive Property** allows us to transform some types of multiplication problems into equivalent addition or subtraction problems.

For example, suppose we want to find $3 \cdot (6 - 2)$.
We can do this in two ways:

- First, subtract inside the parentheses. $3 \cdot (6 - 2) = 3 \cdot (\mathbf{4})$

  Then, multiply. $= 12$

- Or, first "distribute" the 3 to both the 6 and the 2. $3 \cdot (6 - 2) = \mathbf{3} \cdot 6 - \mathbf{3} \cdot 2$

  Then do the two multiplications. $=\ 18\ -\ 6$

  Finally, subtract. $= 12$

  Either way, the result is 12.

The Distributive Property is not often used in this way in arithmetic. However, as you will see, it is used quite often in algebra.

Order of Operations

When a problem contains more than one operation, we perform the operations in a specific order.

— Procedure —
To Use the Order of Operations to Simplify an Expression

Step 1 Do the operations inside grouping symbols.

Step 2 Simplify exponents and square roots.

Step 3 Do multiplication and division, working in order from left to right.

Step 4 Do addition and subtraction, working in order from left to right.

The **grouping symbols** referred to in Step 1 include the following:

parentheses	( )	$4 \cdot (2 + 1) = 4 \cdot 3$
brackets	[ ]	$5 - [6 - 4] = 5 - 2$
fraction bar $\longrightarrow \dfrac{a}{b}$		$\dfrac{2 + 4}{5 - 2} = \dfrac{6}{3}$
square root	$\sqrt{}$	$6 \cdot \sqrt{9 + 16} = 6 \cdot \sqrt{25}$

Example EI.B.20

Find: $2 + 3 \cdot 4 + 12 \div (3 \cdot 2)$

Solution $\hspace{3cm} 2 + 3 \cdot 4 + 12 \div (3 \cdot 2)$

Step 1 Do operations inside grouping symbols.

Inside the parenthesis, multiply 3 by 2. $\hspace{1cm} = 2 + 3 \cdot 4 + 12 \div \quad \mathbf{6}$

Step 2 Simplify exponents and square roots.

There are no exponents or square roots in this problem.

Step 3 Do multiplication and division, in order from left to right.

Multiply 3 by 4. $\hspace{2cm} = 2 + \mathbf{12} + 12 \div \quad 6$

Divide 12 by 6. $\hspace{2.3cm} = 2 + \ 12 + \quad \mathbf{2}$

Step 4 Do addition and subtraction, working in order from left to right.

Add 2 and 12. $\hspace{2.5cm} = \quad \mathbf{14} \quad + \quad 2$

Add 14 and 2. $\hspace{2.5cm} = \quad \quad 16$

So, $2 + 3 \cdot 4 + 12 \div (3 \cdot 2) = 16$.

Example EI.B.21

Find: $5 - [2 - (5 - 2) + 8]$

Solution $5 - [2 - (5 - 2) + 8]$

***Step 1 Do the operations inside
        grouping symbols.***

Do the work inside the innermost
grouping symbol first.
That is, calculate $5 - 2$. $= 5 - [2 -$ **(3)** $+ 8]$

Now, simplify inside the square brackets.
First, find $2 - 3$. $= 5 - [$ **−1** $+ 8]$

Next, calculate $-1 + 8$. $= 5 -$ **7**

Step 2 Simplify exponents and square roots.

There are no exponents or square roots
in this problem.

***Step 3 Do multiplication and division,
        working in order from left to right.***

There is no multiplication or division
in this problem.

Step 4 Do addition and subtraction, $= -2$
        working in order from left to right.

So, $5 - [2 - (5 - 2) + 8] = -2$.

Example EI.B.22

Find: $1 + 9^2 \div 3 - (8 - 3) \cdot 2$

Solution $1 + 9^2 \div 3 - (8 - 3) \cdot 2$

***Step 1 Do the operations inside
        grouping symbols.*** $= 1 + 9^2 \div 3 -$ **(5)** $\cdot 2$

***Step 2 Simplify exponents and
        square roots.*** $= 1 +$ **81** $\div 3 -$ (5) $\cdot 2$

***Step 3 Do multiplication and division,
        working in order from left to right.*** $= 1 +$ **27** $-$ (5) $\cdot 2$
                                                 $= 1 +$ 27 $-$ **10**

Step 4 Do addition and subtraction,
        working in order from left to right. $=$ 28 $- 10$
                                                 $=$ 18

So, $1 + 9^2 \div 3 - (8 - 3) \cdot 2 = 18$.

Example EI.B.23

Find: $25 - (4 + 2 \cdot 3^2)$

Solution $\qquad\qquad\qquad\qquad\qquad\qquad\qquad\qquad 25 - (4 + 2 \cdot 3^2)$

*Step 1 Do the operations inside
    grouping symbols.*

There are three operations inside
the parentheses. We must do the
operations in the proper order:

First, evaluate 3^2. $\qquad\qquad\qquad\qquad\qquad = 25 - (4 + 2 \cdot \mathbf{9})$

Then, multiply 2 by 9. $\qquad\qquad\qquad\qquad\quad = 25 - (4 + \mathbf{18})$

Finally, add 4 and 18. $\qquad\qquad\qquad\qquad\quad = 25 - \;\;\mathbf{22}$

Step 2 Simplify exponents and square roots.

No exponents or square roots
remain in this problem.

*Step 3 Do multiplication and division,
    working in order from left to right.*

No multiplication or division
remains in this problem.

*Step 4 Do addition and subtraction, $\qquad\qquad = 3$
    working in order from left to right.*

So, $25 - (4 + 2 \cdot 3^2) = 3$.

Example EI.B.24

Find: $3 \cdot \sqrt{18 - 2} + 2 \cdot 3^2$

Solution $\qquad\qquad\qquad\qquad\qquad\qquad\quad 3 \cdot \sqrt{18 - 2} + 2 \cdot 3^2$

*Step 1 Do the operations inside
    grouping symbols.* $\qquad\qquad\qquad = 3 \cdot \sqrt{16} \quad + 2 \cdot 3^2$

*Step 2 Simplify exponents and
    square roots.* $\qquad\qquad\qquad\qquad = 3 \cdot \mathbf{4} \qquad + 2 \cdot \mathbf{9}$

*Step 3 Do multiplication and division,
    working in order from left to right.* $\quad = \mathbf{12} \qquad\quad + 2 \cdot 9$
$\qquad\qquad\qquad\qquad\qquad\qquad\qquad\qquad\quad = 12 + \mathbf{18}$

*Step 4 Simplify addition and subtraction,
    working in order from left to right.* $\quad = 30$

So, $3 \cdot \sqrt{18 - 2} + 2 \cdot 3^2 = 30$.

Find: $3 + \dfrac{2 + 5^2}{4^3 - 5 \cdot (13 - 2)}$

Solution

$$3 + \dfrac{2 + 5^2}{4^3 - 5 \cdot (13 - 2)}$$

Step 1 Do the operations inside grouping symbols.

The fraction bar is a grouping symbol, so the first step is to simplify separately the numerator and the denominator.

Simplify the numerator by following the order of operations.

In the numerator, evaluate 5^2.

$$= 3 + \dfrac{2 + \mathbf{25}}{4^3 - 5 \cdot (13 - 2)}$$

In the numerator, add 2 and 25.

$$= 3 + \dfrac{\mathbf{27}}{4^3 - 5 \cdot (13 - 2)}$$

Now, simplify the denominator by following the order of operations.

In the denominator, subtract inside the parentheses.

$$= 3 + \dfrac{27}{4^3 - 5 \cdot \mathbf{11}}$$

In the denominator, evaluate 4^3.

$$= 3 + \dfrac{27}{\mathbf{64} - 5 \cdot 11}$$

In the denominator, multiply 5 by 11.

$$= 3 + \dfrac{27}{64 - \mathbf{55}}$$

In the denominator, find $64 - 55$.

$$= 3 + \dfrac{27}{\mathbf{9}}$$

Step 2 Simplify exponents and square roots.

There are no exponents or square roots in this problem.

Step 3 Do multiplication and division, working in order from left to right.

Divide 27 by 9.

$$= 3 + \mathbf{3}$$

Step 4 Do addition and subtraction, working in order from left to right.

$$= 6$$

So, $3 + \dfrac{2 + 5^2}{4^3 - 5 \cdot (13 - 2)} = 6$.

Here is a summary of this concept from *Academic Systems Algebra*.

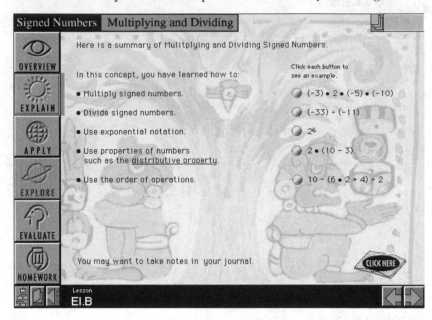

Signed Numbers | Multiplying and Dividing

OVERVIEW
EXPLAIN
APPLY
EXPLORE
EVALUATE
HOMEWORK

Here is a summary of Mulitplying and Dividing Signed Numbers.

In this concept, you have learned how to:

Click each button to
see an example.

• Multiply signed numbers.   ● $(-3) \bullet 2 \bullet (-5) \bullet (-10)$

• Divide signed numbers.   ● $(-33) \div (-11)$

• Use exponential notation.   ● 2^6

• Use properties of numbers
  such as the <u>distributive property</u>.   ● $2 \bullet (10 - 3)$

• Use the order of operations.   ● $10 - (6 \bullet 2 + 4) \div 2$

You may want to take notes in your journal.   CLICK HERE

Lesson
EI.B

Checklist Lesson EI.B

Here is what you should know after completing this lesson.

Words and Phrases

signed numbers
number line
plot
coordinate
exponential notation
base
exponent
power
Commutative Property of Addition
Commutative Property of Multiplication
Associative Property of Addition
Associative Property of Multiplication

Identity Property of Addition
additive identity
Inverse Property of Addition
additive inverse
opposites
Identity Property of Multiplication
multiplicative identity
Inverse Property of Multiplication
multiplicative inverse
reciprocal
Distributive Property
grouping symbols

Ideas and Procedures

❶ Number Line
Plot a point on a number line; find the coordinate of a point on a number line.

Example EI.B.1
   Plot on a number line: $-8, -5, -\frac{3}{2}, 0, 4$

See also: Example EI.B.2

❷ Add Signed Numbers
Find the sum of two signed numbers.

Example EI.B.7
   Find: $-58 + 35$

See also: Example EI.B.3-EI.B.6, EI.B.8
   Apply 1-5, 15-17

❸ Subtract Signed Numbers
Find the difference of two signed numbers.

Example EI.B.11
   Find: $-126 - (-83)$

See also: Example EI.B.9, EI.B.10, EI.B.12
   Apply 6-14, 15-28

❹ Multiply or Divide Signed Numbers
Find the product or quotient of signed numbers.

Example EI.B.17
   Find: $-3 \cdot (-4) \cdot (-2) \cdot 5$

See also: Example EI.B.13-EI.B.16
   Apply 29-37

⑤ Exponential Notation
Use exponential notation to write repeated multiplication.

Example EI.B.18
For each of the following, identify the base and the exponent. Then write each product using exponential notation.

a. $3 \cdot 3 \cdot 3 \cdot 3 \cdot 3$
b. $(-2) \cdot (-2) \cdot (-2) \cdot (-2)$

See also: Example EI.B.19
Apply 38-41

---

⑥ Properties of Real Numbers
Give an example of each property of real numbers.

Associative Property of Addition:
$2 + (3 + 4) = (2 + 3) + 4$

Associative Property of Multiplication:
$2 \cdot (3 \cdot 4) = (2 \cdot 3) \cdot 4$

Commutative Property of Addition:
$2 + 3 = 3 + 2$

Commutative Property of Multiplication:
$2 \cdot 3 = 3 \cdot 2$

Identity Property of Addition:
$5 + 0 = 5$

Identity Property of Multiplication:
$8 \cdot 1 = 8$

Inverse Property of Addition:
$-3 + 3 = 0$

Inverse Property of Multiplication:
$2 \cdot \frac{1}{2} = 1$

Distributive Property:
$2(5 + 3) = 2 \cdot 5 + 2 \cdot 3$

See also: Apply 42-44

---

⑦ Order of Operations
Apply the order of operations to simplify an arithmetic expression that contains several operations.

Example EI.B.22
Find: $1 + 9^2 \div 3 - (8 - 3) \cdot 2$

See Also: Example EI.B.20, EI.B.21, EI.B.23,
EI.B.24, EI.B.25
Apply 45-56

Homework

Homework Problems

Circle the homework problems assigned to you by the computer, then complete them below.

 Explain

Adding and Subtracting

Perform the indicated operations in questions $1 - 12$.

1. $25 + 13$

2. a. $-8 + 5$
   b. $-14 + 27$

3. a. $4 + 11 + 20$
   b. $24 + 17 + 31$

4. a. $-34 + 62$
   b. $-36 + 22$

5. $-31 + 45 + 7$

6. $-21 + 15 + 24$

7. a. $25 - 17$
   b. $38 - 29$

8. a. $9 - (-4)$
   b. $47 - (-18)$

9. a. $24 - 49$
   b. $53 - 76$

10. $77 - 49 - 8$

11. $47 + 65 - 73$

12. $-31 - (-61) - 20$

Multiplying and Dividing

13. Find:
    a. $(-7) \cdot 12$
    b. $(-12) \div 4$

14. Find:
    a. $(-7) \cdot (-20)$
    b. $(-108) \div (-9)$

15. Identify the base and the exponent: 13^{28}

16. Find: $(-12) \cdot (-5) \div (-4)$

17. Find: $36 \div (-4) \cdot (-8)$

18. Write without an exponent, then calculate: 2^7

19. Simplify: $(-4) \cdot (8 - 3)$

20. Find: $8 - 2 \cdot (4 - 1)$

21. Is $(139 - 47) - 258 = 139 - (47 - 258)$?

22. Find: $8 - 2 \cdot [11 - 3 \cdot (5 - 1)]$

23. Find: $3 \cdot 5^2$

24. Is $53 + (27 \cdot 44) = (53 + 27) \cdot (53 + 44)$?

Apply

Practice Problems

Here are some additional practice problems for you to try.

Adding and Subtracting

1. Find: $-6 + 10$

2. Find: $12 + (-7)$

3. Find: $-15 + 8$

4. Find: $15 + (-21)$

5. Find: $17 + (-27)$

6. Find: $-11 - 8$

7. Find: $-13 - 7$

8. Find: $-5 - 23$

9. Find: $-3 - 15$

10. Find: $-21 - 23$

11. Find: $-15 - 17$

12. Find: $-25 - (-15)$

13. Find: $-127 - (-15)$

14. Find: $-32 - (-43)$

15. Find: $4 - 14 + 11$

16. Find: $5 - 19 + 22$

17. Find: $10 + 23 - 44$

18. Find: $-3 - 7 - 9$

19. Find: $-2 - 14 - 37$

20. Find: $-34 - 18 - 23$

21. Find: $12 - 16 - 23$

22. Find: $14 - 20 - 32$

23. Find: $25 - 18 - 55$

24. Find: $10 - (-3) - 2$

25. Find: $15 - (-4) - 9$

26. Find: $26 - 18 - (-12)$

27. Find: $-24 - 3 - (-42)$

28. Find: $-18 - (-7) - 11$

Multiplying and Dividing

29. Find: $8 \cdot (-4)$

30. Find: $-9 \cdot (-6)$

31. Find: $-7 \cdot 6$

32. Find: $24 \div (-6)$

33. Find: $-27 \div 9$

34. Find: $-18 \div (-3)$

35. Find: $-90 \div 5 \cdot 2$

36. Find: $45 \div (-9) \cdot 3$

37. Find: $-18 \cdot (-2) \div 4$

38. Write without an exponent and then calculate: 3^4

39. Write without an exponent and then calculate: 4^3

40. Write without an exponent and then calculate: 5^4

41. Write without an exponent and then calculate: 2^6

42. Is $(32 - 15) - 10 = 32 - (15 - 10)$?

43. Is $(-16 - 4) - 11 = -16 - (4 - 11)$?

44. Is $(-20 - 2) - 8 = -20 - (2 - 8)$?

45. Simplify: $-3 \cdot (4 - 10)$

46. Simplify: $(6 - 2) \cdot (-5)$

47. Simplify: $-4 \cdot (7 - 8)$

48. Find: $3 \cdot 2^3$

49. Find: $5 \cdot 4^2$

50. Find: $-5 \cdot 4^2$

51. Find: $5 + (-3) \cdot (-9)$

52. Find: $10 - (-4) \cdot (-2)$

53. Find: $2 \cdot (-5) - (-15)$

54. Find: $[6 + (-8)] \cdot (-9 + 4)$

55. Find: $(7 - 13) \cdot (-12 + 8)$

56. Find: $[8 - (-3)] \cdot (5 - 9)$

Evaluate

Practice Test

Take this practice test to be sure that you are prepared for the final quiz in Evaluate.

1. Find:
    a. $8 + 11$
    b. $-23 + 12$
    c. $-13 + 28$

2. Find: $-40 + 18 + 7$

3. Find:
    a. $67 - 43$
    b. $-23 - 14$
    c. $34 - 61$

4. Find: $34 - 8 - (-13)$

5. Find:
    a. $34 \cdot 3$
    b. $(-14) \cdot (-6)$
    c. $(-50) \div 2$

6. Write using an exponent:
    $11 \cdot 11 \cdot 11 \cdot 11 \cdot 11 \cdot 11 \cdot 11 \cdot 11 \cdot 11$

7. Rewrite using the Distributive Property and simplify:
    $-4 \cdot (9 - 2)$

8. Simplify:
    a. $10 - 2 \cdot 3$
    b. $40 - 2 \cdot [6 - 3 (5 - 1)]$

TOPIC EI Cumulative Activities

Cumulative Review Problems

These problems combine all of the material you have covered so far in this course. You may want to test your understanding of this material before you move on to the next topic, or you may wish to do these problems to review for a test.

1. Find the equivalent fraction: $\frac{2}{7} = \frac{?}{56}$

2. Find: $\frac{1}{2} \cdot \frac{1}{9}$

3. Find: $4 - 6$

4. Find: $\frac{1}{2} + \frac{1}{3} - \frac{1}{4}$

5. Find: $8 \cdot 14$

6. Find: $56 \div (-7)$

7. Find the least common multiple (LCM) of 25 and 125.

8. Find: $-3 + 7$

9. Rewrite using the Commutative Property: $479 \cdot 261$

10. Write using an exponent: $18 \cdot 18 \cdot 18 \cdot 18$

11. Reduce to lowest terms: $\frac{8}{32}$

12. Find the reciprocal of 1000.

13. Find the least common denominator of $\frac{2378}{6}$ and $\frac{995}{10}$.

14. Find: $-9 + 2 + 4$

15. Find: $12 + 17$

16. Write the prime factorization of 54.

17. Find: $21 + (-15)$

18. Find: $(3 - 2 \cdot 4)^2$

19. Simplify using the Distributive Property: $4 \cdot (13 + 7)$

20. Find: $\frac{81}{55} \div \frac{9}{11}$

21. Find: $\frac{4}{7} - \left(-\frac{2}{5}\right)$

22. Find: $(-24) \cdot (-3)$

23. Identify the base and the exponent: 26^{11}

24. Find the greatest common factor of 18 and 36.

25. Find: $\frac{19}{7} - \frac{3}{2}$

26. Find: $(-3) \cdot (-15) \div (-5)$

27. Find the equivalent fraction: $\frac{11}{14} = \frac{?}{42}$

28. Find: $-23 + 15$

29. Reduce to lowest terms: $\frac{9}{15}$

30. Find: $11 + 19 + (-12)$

31. Find: $2 \cdot 9 + 45 \div 5$

32. Find: $\frac{3}{100} + \frac{7}{100}$

33. Find: $\frac{3}{16} - \frac{1}{8} - \frac{2}{32}$

34. Find: $7 - 9 \div 3$

35. Find: $\frac{3}{7} \cdot \frac{14}{6}$

36. Find: $-\frac{5}{4} + \frac{2}{4}$

37. Simplify: $\left(-\frac{2}{7}\right) \cdot \left(\frac{21}{4} + \frac{28}{16}\right)$

38. Find: $20 \div \frac{2}{7}$

39. Find the least common multiple (LCM) of 14 and 8.

40. Find: $(-12) \div 8$

41. Find the reciprocal of $\frac{13}{87}$.

42. Find: $-\frac{11}{129} + \frac{24}{129} - \frac{5}{129}$

43. Find the least common denominator (LCD) of $\frac{1}{16}$ and $\frac{19}{40}$.

44. Write using an exponent:
$(-2) \cdot (-2) \cdot (-2) \cdot (-2) \cdot (-2) \cdot (-2)$

45. Find: $\frac{78}{17} \div \frac{26}{5}$

46. Reduce to lowest terms: $\frac{32}{50}$

47. Find the greatest common factor (GCF) of 50 and 125.

48. Find: $\frac{5}{12} - \frac{1}{12} + \frac{3}{12}$

49. Write the prime factorization of 363.

50. Find: $\left(-\frac{13}{7}\right) \cdot \left(-\frac{5}{39}\right)$

TOPIC 1
REAL NUMBERS

Throughout history, numbers have helped us understand and describe the world. In this topic, you will examine the real numbers, fractions, factoring, and the properties of real numbers. This review will provide you with a firm foundation for your study of algebra.

On the computer, this topic begins with a glimpse of mathematics in the fifth century BC somewhere along the shores of the Aegean Sea.

Lesson 1.1 The Real Numbers

Concept 1: Number Line and Notation
The Real Numbers
The Number Line
Sets
Comparison Symbols
Absolute Value
Multiplication Symbols
Exponents

Lesson 1.2 Factoring and Fractions

Concept 1: GCF and LCM
Prime Numbers
The Greatest Common Factor (GCF)
The Least Common Multiple (LCM)

Concept 2: Fractions
Reducing a Fraction to Lowest Terms
Multiplying Fractions
Dividing Fractions
Adding and Subtracting Fractions

Lesson 1.3 Arithmetic of Numbers

Concept 1: Operations on Numbers
Opposites
Adding Numbers
Subtracting Numbers
Multiplying Numbers
Dividing Numbers
Order of Operations
Properties of Numbers and Definitions

LESSON 1.1
THE REAL NUMBERS

 ## Overview

Numbers have been important to people since ancient times. Early cultures in Australia, South America, and South Africa all had basic counting systems. Later civilizations, including those of the Egyptians, Babylonians, Chinese, Greeks, and Mayans had sophisticated number systems, some of which form the basis of mathematics today.

You will begin your study of algebra by learning about different types of numbers. You will also learn to use a number line to compare numbers and to find distances. Finally, you will learn some mathematical notation.

 ## Explain

Concept 1 has sections on

- **The Real Numbers**
- **The Number Line**
- **Sets**
- **Comparison Symbols**
- **Absolute Value**
- **Multiplication Symbols**
- **Exponents**

CONCEPT 1: NUMBER LINE AND NOTATION

The Real Numbers

People in ancient civilizations used only the counting numbers 1, 2, 3, 4, and so on. As their lives became more complex, they found they needed additional numbers to solve new problems and explain new situations.

The types of numbers that have arisen over time—natural numbers, whole numbers, integers, rational numbers, irrational numbers, and real numbers—have given people the tools they need to solve problems in an increasingly complex life.

The table below lists the different types of numbers used in elementary algebra.

Types of Numbers	Description	Examples
Natural Numbers	Also known as the **counting numbers**.	1, 2, 3, 4, …
Whole Numbers	Zero and the natural numbers.	0, 1, 2, 3, 4, …
Integers	The whole numbers and their opposites.	… −3, −2, −1, 0, 1, 2, 3, …
Rational Numbers	Numbers that may be written as the ratio of two integers, where the denominator is not 0. When written as a decimal, the decimal portion either repeats or terminates.	$-\dfrac{1}{7}, \dfrac{4}{5}, 3 = \dfrac{3}{1}, 0 = \dfrac{0}{2}$ $5.34 = \dfrac{534}{100}, \dfrac{3}{4} = 0.75$ $\dfrac{4}{11} = 0.3636…$
Irrational Numbers	Numbers that cannot be written as the ratio of two integers. When written as a decimal, the decimal portion never repeats or terminates.	$\sqrt{2} = 1.41421…$ $\pi = 3.14159…$ $-\sqrt{5} = -2.23606…$ $\sqrt[3]{-3} = -1.44224…$
Real Numbers	The rational and irrational numbers combined.	Each of the numbers above is an example of a real number.

The following diagram may help you see the relationship among the different types of numbers.

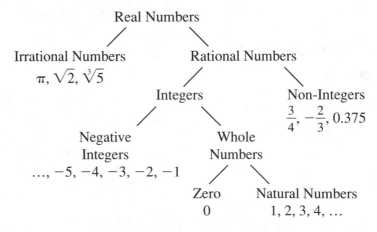

Notice that the **real numbers** include all the other numbers.

The **rational numbers** contain the **integers**, the **whole numbers**, and the **natural numbers**. That is because integers, whole numbers, and natural numbers are also rational numbers.

The Number Line

Sometimes it is helpful to picture numbers on a **number line**. A number line looks like a thermometer laid on its side with the positive numbers (temperatures above 0) on the right and the negative numbers (temperatures below 0) on the left.

Number line

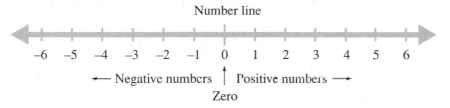

← Negative numbers | Positive numbers →

Zero

Each point on the number line corresponds to a real number.

For example, the point A on the number line corresponds to the real number **4** because point A lies four units to the right of zero.

The location of a point is called its **coordinate**.

The coordinate of point A is 4.

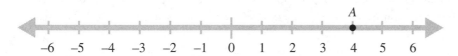

Example 1.1.1

Estimate the coordinate of each point.

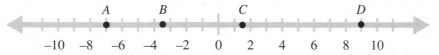

Solution

Point A and Point D each correspond to integers. Point B and Point C each lie between two integers, so we estimate their coordinates.

$A = -7 \qquad B \approx -3.5 \qquad C \approx 1.5 \qquad D = 9$

The symbol $\approx$ means "is approximately equal to."

Each real number corresponds to a point on the number line. When we locate the corresponding point on the number line, we say that we **plot** the point.

Example **1.1.2**

Plot the following numbers on a number line: $-7.6, -5, -\frac{5}{3}, 0, 2, 2\pi$.

Solution

Find the approximate location of each number and place a dot at that point. Recall that $\pi \approx 3.14\ldots$, so 2π is approximately 6.28.

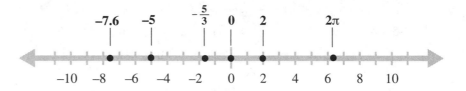

Sets

A collection of numbers, such as the real numbers or the integers, is called a **set**.

Each number in a set is called a **member** or an **element** of the set.

For example, suppose a set consists of the numbers $-4, 0, 6,$ and 15.
To show that this is a set, we enclose the elements in braces, { }, and write

$$\{-4, 0, 6, 15\}.$$

To refer to a set, we often use a single letter such as S. Using this notation we write

$$S = \{-4, 0, 6, 15\}.$$

To show that 6 is a member of S, we write $6 \in S$.

To show that 7 is **not** a member of S, we write $7 \notin S$.

A set that contains no elements is called the **empty set** or the **null set**. The empty set is denoted by the Greek letter phi, $\varnothing$, or by empty braces { }.

A **subset** is a set contained within another set.
That is, set S is a subset of set T if each element of S also belongs to T.

For example, consider the following three sets:

$A = \{1, 2, 3, 4, 5, 6, 7, 8\}$

$B = \{4, 7, 8\}$

$C = \{4, 5, 6, 7\}$

- B is a subset of A because each element of B is also an element of A. To indicate that B is a subset of A, we write $B \subset A$.

- B is **not** a subset of C because B contains 8, an element not found in C. To show that B is **not** a subset of C, we write $B \not\subset C$.

Example 1.1.3

Consider these two sets: $F = \{-12, 0, 4, 7, 13\}$
$$G = \{0, 4\}$$

Which of the following statements are true?

a. $7 \in F$ b. $3 \notin G$ c. $F \subset G$

Solution

a. **True.** The number 7 is an element of set F.

b. **True.** The number 3 is not an element of set G.

c. **False.** F is not a subset of G. The set F has elements that do not belong to G.

For example, $-12 \in F$. But $-12 \notin G$.

However, $G \subset F$ since each element of G is also an element of F.

Comparison Symbols

When we compare two numbers on a number line, the number on the left is less than the number on the right.

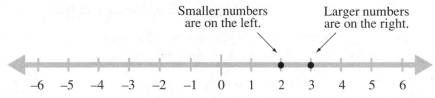

Smaller numbers are on the left.

Larger numbers are on the right.

For example, 2 lies to the left of 3 on the number line, so 2 is less than 3. Using symbols, we write $2 < 3$.

We can also state that 3 is greater than 2.
Using symbols, we write $3 > 2$.
This also means that 3 lies to the right of 2 on the number line.

When we use the inequality symbols $>$ or $<$, the pointed end of the symbol always points to the smaller number.

For example, to indicate "four is less than seven," we write $4 < 7$. The inequality symbol, $<$, points to 4 because 4 is the smaller number.

The symbols shown below are frequently used to compare two numbers.

Symbol	Meaning	Examples	
=	is equal to	$3 = 3$	$\frac{1}{2} = 0.5$
≠	is not equal to	$5 \neq 7$	$\frac{1}{5} \neq 0.1$
<	is less than	$2 < 9$	$-5 < -3$
>	is greater than	$7 > 1$	$-2 > -6$
≤	is less than or equal to	$4 \leq 5$	$4 \leq 4$
≥	is greater than or equal to	$5 \geq 4$	$4 \geq 4$

Example 1.1.4

Which of the following statements are true?

a. $-4 > -2$ b. $-7 < 3$ c. $5 < 5$ d. $5 \leq 5$ e. $6 \leq 8$

Solution

a. **False.** $-4 > -2$ is read "negative four is greater than negative two."
   This is false because -4 lies to the left of -2 on the number line.

b. **True.** $-7 < 3$ is read "negative seven is less than three."
   This is true because -7 lies to the left of 3 on the number line.

c. **False.** $5 < 5$ is read "five is less than five."
   This is false because 5 is not less than itself.

d. **True.** $5 \leq 5$ is read "five is less than or equal to five."
   This means "either 5 is less than 5 or 5 is equal to 5." Since "5 is equal to 5" is true, the entire statement is true.

   (An "or" statement is true if either part is true.)

e. **True.** $6 \leq 8$ is read "six is less than or equal to eight."
   This means "either 6 is less than 8 or 6 is equal to 8." Since "6 is less than 8" is true, the entire statement is true.

Absolute Value

The **absolute value** of a number is the distance of the number from zero on a number line.

We indicate the absolute value of a number by placing vertical bars on each side of the number.

For example, $|\,7\,| = 7$ because 7 lies 7 units from 0 on the number line.

Likewise, $|-7\,| = 7$ because -7 also lies 7 units from 0.

$$|-7| = 7 \qquad |7| = 7$$

7 units from 0   7 units from 0

$$-9\ -8\ -7\ -6\ -5\ -4\ -3\ -2\ -1\ \ 0\ \ 1\ \ 2\ \ 3\ \ 4\ \ 5\ \ 6\ \ 7\ \ 8\ \ 9$$

Example 1.1.5

Find:

a. $|-2\,|$ b. $|\,8\,|$ c. $|\,0\,|$ d. $-|\,6\,|$ e. $-|-12\,|$

Solution

a. $|-2\,| = \mathbf{2}$ because -2 lies **2** units from 0 on the number line.

b. $|\,8\,| = \mathbf{8}$ because 8 lies **8** units from 0 on the number line.

c. $|\,0\,| = \mathbf{0}$ because 0 lies **0** units from 0 on the number line.

d. $-|\,6\,| = -6$. The absolute value of 6 is 6. The negative sign in front of the absolute value symbol makes the final result -6.

e. $-|-12\,| = -12$. The absolute value of -12 is 12. The negative sign in front of the absolute value symbol makes the final result -12.

Example 1.1.6

Which of the following statements are true?

a. $|-18\,| < 10$ b. $5.8 \geq |-7.6\,|$ c. $\left|\dfrac{21}{3}\right| = |-7\,|$

d. $|\,6.3\,| \leq |-9.5\,|$

Solution

To decide whether a statement is true, we first write an equivalent statement without absolute value symbols.

a.   **False.** $|-18\,| < 10$ is equivalent to $18 < 10$.
18 is **not** less than 10.

b.   **False.** $5.8 \geq |-7.6\,|$ is equivalent to $5.8 \geq 7.6$.
5.8 is **not** greater than or equal to 7.6.

c.   **True.** $\left|\dfrac{21}{3}\right| = |-7\,|$ is equivalent to $\dfrac{21}{3} = 7$.

$\dfrac{21}{3}$ means $21 \div 3$, which is equal to 7.

d.   **True.** $|\,6.3\,| \leq |-9.5\,|$ is equivalent to $6.3 \leq 9.5$.
6.3 is less than or equal to 9.5.

Multiplication Symbols

When two numbers are multiplied the resulting number is their **product**.

We can indicate multiplication with a variety of symbols:

a cross	$\times$
a dot	$\cdot$
parentheses	( )

For example, the product of 4 and 5 may be written as

$$4 \times 5 \quad 4 \cdot 5 \quad 4(5) \quad (4)5 \quad (4)(5) \quad (4) \cdot (5)$$

Each number being multiplied is called a **factor**.

For example, in the multiplication **4 · 5 = 20**,

4 is a factor and **5** is a factor;

4 · 5 is a product and **20** is a product.

Exponents

Exponents are used to indicate repeated multiplication of the same number.

For example, to show $5 \cdot 5 \cdot 5 \cdot 5$ we write 5^4.

Here, 5 is called the **base**.

The 4 is called the **exponent** or **power**. The exponent indicates the number of times the base occurs as a factor.

$$\underset{\text{Base}}{\overset{\text{Exponent}}{5^4}} = 5 \cdot \underbrace{5 \cdot 5 \cdot 5}_{\text{4 factors}} = \underset{\text{Product}}{625}$$

Here are some examples of ways to read exponents:

5^4 is read "five to the fourth power" or simply "five to the fourth."

5^3 is read "five to the third" or "five cubed."

5^2 is read "five to the second" or "five squared."

Example 1.1.7

Find the value of 5^3.

Solution

The base is **5** and the exponent is **3**. 5^3

This means the factor **5** occurs **3** times. $= 5 \cdot 5 \cdot 5$

Therefore, $5^3 = 125$. $= 125$

Example 1.1.8

Rewrite $10 \cdot 10 \cdot 10 \cdot 10 \cdot 10$ using an exponent.

Solution

The factors **10** occurs **5** times.

Therefore, the base is **10** and the exponent is **5**.

We write 10^5.

That is, $10 \cdot 10 \cdot 10 \cdot 10 \cdot 10 = 10^5$.

Example 1.1.9

Find: $2^5 \cdot 3^4$.

Solution

When exponents and multiplication are $2^5 = 2 \cdot 2 \cdot 2 \cdot 2 \cdot 2$
both present, we first work with the exponents. $3^4 = 3 \cdot 3 \cdot 3 \cdot 3$

Then, we do the multiplication. $2^5 \cdot 3^4$
$$= 32 \cdot 81$$
$$= 2592$$

So, $2^5 \cdot 3^4 = 2592$.

Example 1.1.10

In a warehouse boxes are stacked in layers. Each layer is 6 boxes wide and 6 boxes deep. The boxes are stacked 6 high. Each box contains 6 shirts. How many shirts are there in all?

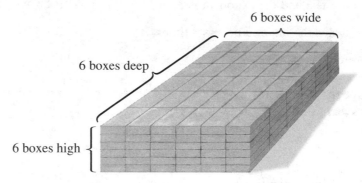

6 boxes wide

6 boxes deep

6 boxes high

Solution

Looking at the picture, you can see that

- there are $6 \cdot 6$ boxes in each layer;

- there are 6 layers so there are $6 \cdot (6 \cdot 6)$ boxes in the stack;

- there are 6 shirts in each box so there are $6 \cdot [6 \cdot (6 \cdot 6)]$ shirts in the stack.

Therefore, there are $6^4 = 1296$ shirts in the stack.

Here is a summary of this concept from *Academic Systems Algebra*.

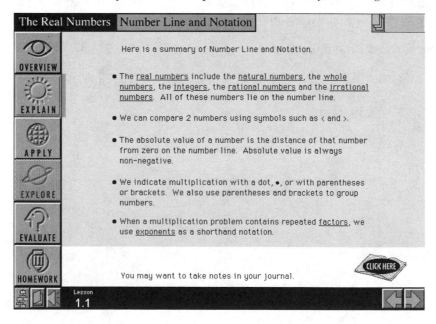

The Real Numbers | Number Line and Notation

OVERVIEW
EXPLAIN
APPLY
EXPLORE
EVALUATE
HOMEWORK

Here is a summary of Number Line and Notation.

- The <u>real numbers</u> include the <u>natural numbers</u>, the <u>whole numbers</u>, the <u>integers</u>, the <u>rational numbers</u> and the <u>irrational numbers</u>. All of these numbers lie on the number line.

- We can compare 2 numbers using symbols such as < and >.

- The absolute value of a number is the distance of that number from zero on the number line. Absolute value is always non-negative.

- We indicate multiplication with a dot, •, or with parentheses or brackets. We also use parentheses and brackets to group numbers.

- When a multiplication problem contains repeated <u>factors</u>, we use <u>exponents</u> as a shorthand notation.

CLICK HERE

You may want to take notes in your journal.

Lesson 1.1

✓ Checklist Lesson 1.1

Here is what you should know after completing this lesson.

Words and Phrases

natural numbers (counting numbers)
whole numbers
integers
rational numbers
irrational numbers
real numbers
number line
plot
coordinate
set
member

element
empty set
null set
subset
absolute value
product
factor
base
exponent
power

Ideas and Procedures

❶ Real Numbers

State the characteristics of different types of numbers.

Natural numbers: 1, 2, 3, 4, ...

Whole numbers: 0, 1, 2, 3, 4, ...

Integers: ...−4, −3, −2, −1, 0, 1, 2, 3, 4, ...

Rational numbers: $-\frac{1}{7}, \frac{0}{3}, \frac{4}{5}, 3, \frac{9}{2}, 5.34, \frac{4}{11}$

Irrational numbers: $\sqrt{2}, \pi, \sqrt[3]{-5}$

Real numbers: Rational and irrational numbers combined.

❷ Number Line

Draw a number line.
Plots points on a number line.
Find the coordinates of points on a number line.

Example 1.1.2
Plot the following numbers on a number line:
$-7.6, -5, -\frac{5}{3}, 0, 2, 2\pi$

See also: Example 1.1.1

❸ Sets

Determine if one set is a subset of another.

Example 1.1.3
Consider these two sets: $F = \{-12, 0, 4, 7, 13\}$
$G = \{0, 4\}$

Which of the following statements are true?
a. $7 \in F$ b. $3 \notin G$ c. $F \subset G$

See also: Apply 16, 17, 18

❹ **Comparison Symbols**
State the meanings of the following symbols:
$=, \neq, <, >, \leq, \geq$.
Use these symbols to state a relationship between two numbers.

Example 1.1.4
Which of the following statements are true?
a. $-4 > -2$ b. $-7 < 3$ c. $5 < 5$ d. $5 \leq 5$
e. $6 \leq 8$

See also: Apply 1, 2, 3

❺ **Absolute Value**
Define absolute value and evaluate expressions written in absolute value notation.

Example 1.1.5
Find:
a. $|-2|$ b. $|8|$ c. $|0|$ d. $-|6|$ e. $-|-12|$

See also: Example 1.1.6
Apply 4, 5, 6, 19, 20, 21

❻ **Exponents**
Evaluate expressions written in exponential notation.
Use exponential notation to write repeated multiplication.

Example 1.1.9
Find: $2^5 \cdot 3^4$.
See also: Example 1.1.7, 1.1.8, 1.1.10
Apply 7-15, 19-24

 **Homework**

Homework Problems

Circle the homework problems assigned to you by the computer, then complete them below.

 Explain

Number Line and Notation

1. Which of the following statements are true?

   $3 < 12$ $4 \le 4$

   $5 = \frac{20}{4}$ $6 \neq 7$

   $-2 < -6$

2. Find the absolute values:

   a. $|7|$

   b. $|-3|$

   c. $|0.4|$

   d. $|-1.6|$

   e. $|-0.72|$

3. Find the value of 5^4.

4. Which of the following statements are true?

   $2 \neq 3$ $-8 < -4$

   $9 > 6$ $2 \ge \frac{5}{8}$

   $8 < 4$

5. Find the absolute values:

   a. $|9|$

   b. $|-17|$

   c. $|2.3|$

   d. $|-4.8|$

   e. $|-0.485|$

6. Rewrite using exponents: $6 \cdot 6 \cdot 6 \cdot 6 \cdot 6$

7. Find: $|-2^3|$

8. Find: $3^2 \cdot 4^3$

9. Restaurants buy eggs in bulk by the box. Each box of eggs contains 12 cartons. Each carton has 12 rows and each row contains 12 eggs. Which of the following expresses the number of eggs in a box?

   $12 \cdot 3$

   12^3

   3^{12}

   $12(12 + 12 + 12)$

   $12 + 12 + 12$

10. In a small town, 7 sisters each had 7 baskets.
    In each basket, there were 7 cats.
    Each cat had 7 kittens.
    In total, how many kittens were there?

11. Rewrite using exponents: $2 \cdot 2 \cdot 2 \cdot 2 \cdot 7 \cdot 7 \cdot 7$

12. Find: $3^3 \cdot 5^2$

 **Apply**

Practice Problems

Here are some additional practice problems for you to try.

Number Line and Notation

1. Which of the following statements are true?
   $9 = 9$
   $5 > 5$
   $7 \le 11$
   $15 \le 15$
   $2 < 0$

2. Which of the following statements are true?
   $5 \ne 5$
   $6 \le 6$
   $7 < 7$
   $12 \ge 12$
   $1 > 0$

3. Which of the following statements are true?
   $7 \ne 7$
   $4 < 4$
   $6 \le 12$
   $9 \ge 9$
   $10 > 15$

4. Find the absolute values.
   a. $|7|$
   b. $|-9|$
   c. $|0.25|$
   d. $|2.3|$
   e. $|-7.45|$

5. Find the absolute values.
   a. $|0|$
   b. $|100|$
   c. $|-0.001|$
   d. $|4.33|$
   e. $|-2.497|$

6. Find the absolute values.
   a. $|26|$
   b. $|3|$
   c. $|0.5|$
   d. $|1.9|$
   e. $|-5.18|$

7. Find: 8^2

8. Find: 5^3

9. Find: 7^3

10. Find: 2^7

11. Find: 3^5

12. Find: 2^5

13. Rewrite using exponents: $7 \cdot 7 \cdot 7 \cdot 7 \cdot 7 \cdot 7 \cdot 7 \cdot 7$

14. Rewrite using exponents: $10 \cdot 10 \cdot 10 \cdot 10$

15. Rewrite using exponents: $8 \cdot 8 \cdot 8 \cdot 8 \cdot 8$

16. Given the sets P and Q below, determine whether the following statements are true or false.
    $$P = \{3, 5, 7, 9, 11\}$$
    $$Q = \{1, 3, 6, 9, 12, 15\}$$
    a. $P \subset Q$
    b. $Q \not\subset P$
    c. $3 \notin P$
    d. $3 \in Q$

17. Given the sets S and T below, determine whether the following statements are true or false.
    $$S = \{2, 4, 6, 8, 10, 12, 14\}$$
    $$T = \{4, 8, 12\}$$
    a. $T \subset S$
    b. $S \subset T$
    c. $4 \in S$
    d. $4 \in T$

18. Given the sets R and S below, determine whether the following statements are true or false.

$R = \{1, 2, 5, 7, 8, 9\}$

$S = \{1, 2, 5\}$

a. $S \subset R$

b. $R \not\subset S$

c. $2 \in R$

d. $2 \in S$

19. Find: $|-4^3|$

20. Find: $|-5^2| - |3^3|$

21. Find: $|3^2| - |2^3|$

22. Find: $3^4 \cdot 2^3$

23. Find: $5^3 \cdot 4^2$

24. Find: $2^4 \cdot 9^2$

Practice Test

Take this practice test to be sure that you are prepared for the final quiz in Evaluate.

1. Circle the true statements.

    $3 > -4$

    $-5 > -7$

    $2 < 2$

    $0 \geq 3$

    $-6 \leq -6$

    $-1 \geq -1$

2. Find the absolute values:

    a. $|8|$

    b. $|-12.18|$

    c. $|-0.23|$

    d. $|15|$

    e. $|3.7|$

3. Which of the symbols, $>, <, \geq, \leq, =,$ and $\neq$, could replace the ? below to make a true statement?

    $-7\ ?\ -9$

4. Which of the following is a rational number between 0 and 1?

    $(0.91)^2$

    $\sqrt{0.91}$

    $\dfrac{1}{\sqrt{2}}$

    $-\left|\dfrac{2}{3}\right|$

5. The population of a colony of insects raised in a laboratory doubles every week. If you start with 2 insects, you will have 4 insects after 1 week, 8 insects after 2 weeks, and so on. How many insects will you have after 4 weeks?

    $5 \cdot 2$

    4^2

    $2 + 2 + 2 + 2$

    2^4

    2^5

6. Find: $4^2 + 3^3$

7. Find the points on the given number line which have an absolute value less than 2.

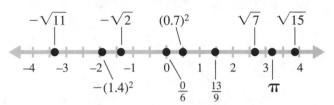

8. Given the sets A and B below, determine whether the following statements are true or false.

    $$A = \{1, 2, 3, 5, 7, 9\}$$
    $$B = \{3, 5, 9\}$$

    a. $A \subset B$

    b. $B \subset A$

    c. $7 \in A$

    d. $7 \in B$

LESSON 1.2
FACTORING AND FRACTIONS

 Overview

We often use fractions in everyday conversations. For example, you might say you ate $\frac{1}{2}$ of a pizza or you jogged $\frac{3}{4}$ of a mile.

In this lesson you will review some techniques to help you add, subtract, multiply, and divide fractions.

 Explain

Concept 1 has sections on

- **Prime Numbers**
- **The Greatest Common Factor (GCF)**
- **The Least Common Multiple (LCM)**

CONCEPT 1:
GCF AND LCM

Prime Numbers

A **prime number** is a whole number greater than 1 that is evenly divisible by only 1 and itself.

For example, 37 is a prime number because the only positive integers that divide 37 (with remainder zero) are 1 and 37.

The first few prime numbers are

2, 3, 5, 7, 11, 13, 17, 19, 23, 29, …

To find the **prime factorization** of a number, write the number as the product of prime numbers. This may be done using a **factor tree**.

Example 1.2.1

Find the prime factorization of 120.

Solution

Write 120 as a product of two whole numbers, for example, $10 \cdot 12$.

Write 10 as the product of two whole numbers, $2 \cdot 5$, and write 12 as $2 \cdot 6$.

Finally, write 6 as the product of $2 \cdot 3$. Now each branch of the tree ends with a prime number.

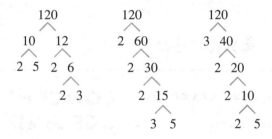

$$120 = 2 \cdot 5 \cdot 2 \cdot 2 \cdot 3$$

The prime factorization of 120 is the product of these prime numbers.

The standard way of writing the product is to place the factors in order from least to greatest: $\qquad 120 = 2 \cdot 2 \cdot 2 \cdot 3 \cdot 5$

You may also write the prime factorization using exponents: $\qquad 120 = 2^3 \cdot 3 \cdot 5$

There are several possible factor trees for 120, including:

Each factor tree results in the same prime factorization: $\qquad 120 = 2 \cdot 2 \cdot 2 \cdot 3 \cdot 5$

The Greatest Common Factor (GCF)

Let's look at the factors of 30 and 36.

$$30 = 1 \cdot 30 \qquad\qquad 36 = 1 \cdot 36$$
$$30 = 2 \cdot 15 \qquad\qquad 36 = 2 \cdot 18$$
$$30 = 3 \cdot 10 \qquad\qquad 36 = 3 \cdot 12$$
$$30 = 5 \cdot 6 \qquad\qquad 36 = 4 \cdot 9$$
$$\qquad\qquad\qquad\qquad 36 = 6 \cdot 6$$

The whole number factors of 30 are **1**, **2**, **3**, 5, **6**, 10, 15, and 30.

The whole number factors of 36 are **1**, **2**, **3**, 4, **6**, 9, 12, 18, and 36.

The factors of 30 that are also factors of 36 are called **common factors** of 30 and 36.
These are **1**, **2**, **3**, and **6**.

The greatest of these common factors is 6.

We say 6 is the **greatest common factor (GCF)** of 30 and 36.

You can think of this in two ways:

- 6 is the largest whole number that is a factor of both 30 and 36.

- 6 is the largest whole number that divides evenly into both 30 and 36.

To find the GCF of 30 and 36, we listed all whole number factors of each number.
We can also find the GCF by using the prime factors of each number.

— Procedure —
To Find the Greatest Common Factor (GCF) of a Collection of Numbers

Step 1 Write the prime factorization of each number.

Step 2 List each common prime factor the LEAST number of times it appears in any factorization.

Step 3 Multiply the prime factors in the list.

If two numbers have no common prime factors, then their GCF is 1.

Example 1.2.2

Find the GCF of 68 and 102.

Solution

Step 1 Write the prime factorization of each number.

$68 = 2 \cdot 2 \cdot 17$
$102 = 2 \cdot 3 \cdot 17$

Step 2 List each common prime factor the LEAST number of times it appears in any factorization.

The common prime factors of 68 and 102 are 2 and 17.

2 appears twice in the factorization of 68.
2 appears once in the factorization of 102.
The **least** number of times that 2 appears is once.   **2**

17 appears once in the factorization of 68.
17 appears once in the factorization of 102.
The *least* number of times that 17 appears is once.   **17**

Step 3 Multiply the prime factors in the list. $2 \cdot 17 = 34$

The GCF of 68 and 102 is 34.

```
  68              102
  /\              /\
2  34           2  51
   /\              /\
  2  17           3  17
```

To make it easier to see the common factors, write the prime factorizations so that the factors line up in columns. The common factors are circled.

$68 = 2 \cdot 2 \quad \cdot 17$
$102 = 2 \quad \cdot 3 \cdot 17$

Example 1.2.3

Find the GCF of 50 and 63.

Solution

Step 1 Write the prime factorization of each number.

$50 = 2 \cdot 5 \cdot 5$
$63 = 3 \cdot 3 \cdot 7$

50
2   25
  5 5

63
3   21
  3 7

Step 2 List each common prime factor the LEAST number of times it appears in any factorization.

The numbers 50 and 63 have no common prime factors.

$50 = 2 \qquad \cdot 5 \cdot 5$
$63 = \quad 3 \cdot 3 \qquad \cdot 7$

Because 50 and 63 have no common prime factors their GCF is 1.

Example 1.2.4

Find the GCF of 56, 84, and 196.

Solution

Step 1 Write the prime factorization of each number.

$56 = \mathbf{2 \cdot 2 \cdot 2} \quad \cdot \mathbf{7}$
$84 = \mathbf{2 \cdot 2} \quad \cdot 3 \cdot \mathbf{7}$
$196 = \mathbf{2 \cdot 2} \qquad \cdot \mathbf{7} \cdot 7$

Step 2 List each common prime factor the LEAST number of times it appears in any factorization.

The common prime factors of 56, 84, and 196 are 2 and 7.

The least number of times that 2 appears is twice. **2, 2**

The least number of times that 7 appears is once. **7**

Step 3 Multiply the prime factors in the list. $2 \cdot 2 \cdot 7 = 28$

The GCF of 56, 84, and 196 is 28.

Example 1.2.5

A company produces snack-size boxes of raisins. They plan to shrinkwrap a bundle of boxes for sale to a grocery store. The store wants to sell the raisin snacks in 3 sizes: a bag of 24 boxes, a bag of 60 boxes, and a bag of 120 boxes.

How many raisin boxes should the manufacturer place in each shrinkwrapped package so the store can bag the packages without opening any of them?

Solution

The company needs to package bundles so that 24, 60, and 120 are all multiples of the number of boxes in each bundle. That is, the number of boxes in a bundle should be the GCF of 24, 60, and 120.

Step 1 Write the prime factorization of each number.

$$24 = 2 \cdot 2 \cdot 2 \cdot 3$$
$$60 = 2 \cdot 2 \quad\ \cdot 3 \cdot 5$$
$$120 = 2 \cdot 2 \cdot 2 \cdot 3 \cdot 5$$

Step 2 List each common prime factor the LEAST number of times it appears in any factorization.

The common prime factors are 2 and 3.

The least number of times   **2, 2**
that 2 occurs is twice.

The least number of times   **3**
that 3 occurs is once.

Step 3 Multiply the prime factors in the list. $2 \cdot 2 \cdot 3 = 12$

The manufacturer should place 12 boxes in each shrinkwrapped bundle. Since 24, 60, and 120 are each a multiple of 12, any order can be filled with shrinkwrapped bundles.

The Least Common Multiple (LCM)

To find the **multiples** of a number, multiply the number by the counting numbers 1, 2, 3, 4, and so on.

For example, let's look at some multiples of 4 and some multiples of 6.

$$
\begin{array}{ll}
4 \cdot 1 = 4 & 6 \cdot 1 = 6 \\
4 \cdot 2 = 8 & 6 \cdot 2 = \mathbf{12} \\
4 \cdot 3 = \mathbf{12} & 6 \cdot 3 = 18 \\
4 \cdot 4 = 16 & 6 \cdot 4 = \mathbf{24} \\
4 \cdot 5 = 20 & 6 \cdot 5 = 30 \\
4 \cdot 6 = \mathbf{24} & 6 \cdot 6 = \mathbf{36} \\
4 \cdot 7 = 28 & 6 \cdot 7 = 42 \\
4 \cdot 8 = 32 & 6 \cdot 8 = 48 \\
4 \cdot 9 = \mathbf{36} & 6 \cdot 9 = 54
\end{array}
$$

The first nine multiples of 4 are 4, 8, **12**, 16, 20, **24**, 28, 32, and **36**.

The first nine multiples of 6 are 6, **12**, 18, **24**, 30, **36**, 42, 48, and 54.

A multiple of 4 that is also a multiple of 6 is called a **common multiple** of 4 and 6.

The first three common multiples of 4 and 6 are: 12, 24, and 36.

The smallest of these common multiples is 12, so 12 is called the **least common multiple (LCM)** of 4 and 6.

You can think of this in two ways:

- 12 is the smallest whole number that is a multiple of both 4 and 6.

- 12 is the smallest whole number that is evenly divisible by both 4 and 6.

To find the LCM of 4 and 6, we listed the first few multiples of each number.

We can also find the LCM by using the prime factors of each number.

— Procedure —
To Find the Least Common Multiple (LCM)
of a Collection of Numbers

Step 1 Write the prime factorization of each number.

Step 2 List each prime factor the GREATEST number of times it appears in any factorization.

Step 3 Multiply the prime factors in the list.

Example 1.2.6

Find the LCM of 12 and 42.

Solution

Step 1 Write the prime factorization of each number.

$12 = 2 \cdot 2 \cdot 3$
$42 = 2 \quad \cdot 3 \cdot 7$

Step 2 List each prime factor the GREATEST number of times it appears in any factorization.

2, 2, 3, 7

Step 3 Multiply the prime factors in the list. $2 \cdot 2 \cdot 3 \cdot 7 = 84$

The LCM of 12 and 42 is 84.

*Notice that 2 appears **twice** in the list. Here's why:*
2 appears twice in the factorization of 12.
2 appears once in the factorization of 42.
*The **greatest** number of times that 2 appears is twice.*

Notice that 84 is a multiple of both 12 and 42.

$$84 = \underbrace{2 \cdot 2 \cdot 3}_{12} \cdot 7 \qquad 84 = 2 \cdot \underbrace{2 \cdot 3 \cdot 7}_{42}$$

Example 1.2.7

Find the LCM of 18 and 30.

Solution

Step 1 Write the prime factorization of each number.

$18 = 2 \cdot 3 \cdot 3$
$30 = 2 \cdot 3 \quad \cdot 5$

Step 2 List each prime factor the GREATEST number of times it appears in any factorization.

2, 3, 3, 5

Step 3 Multiply the prime factors in the list. $2 \cdot 3 \cdot 3 \cdot 5 = 90$

The LCM of 18 and 30 is 90.

Notice that 90 is a multiple of both 18 and 30 because $18 \cdot 5 = 90$ and $30 \cdot 3 = 90$.

Example 1.2.8

Find the LCM of 12, 90, and 105.

Solution

Step 1 Write the prime factorization of each number.

$12 = 2 \cdot 2 \cdot 3$
$90 = 2 \quad \cdot 3 \cdot 3 \cdot 5$
$105 = \quad\quad 3 \quad \cdot 5 \cdot 7$

Step 2 List each prime factor the GREATEST number of times it appears in any factorization

2, 2, 3, 3, 5, 7.

Step 3 Multiply the prime factors in the list. $2 \cdot 2 \cdot 3 \cdot 3 \cdot 5 \cdot 7 = 1260$

The LCM of 12, 90, and 105 is 1260.

Consider the numbers 4 and 6.

- *You may be able to find the GCF by asking, "What is the largest whole number that evenly divides both 4 and 6?" If 2 pops into your head, great; if not, use prime factoring.*

- *You may be able to find the LCM by asking, "What is the smallest whole number that can be divided evenly by both 4 and 6?" If 12 pops into your head, great; if not, use prime factoring.*

Note the relationship between the GCF and the LCM.

For a given collection of numbers,

- the **GCF** is the **largest** whole number that is a **factor** of each number in the collection;
- the **LCM** is the **smallest** whole number that is a **multiple** of each number in the collection.

Example 1.2.9

Find the GCF and LCM of 8, 12, and 20.

Solution

GCF	**LCM**
Step 1 Write the prime factorization of each number.	*Step 1 Write the prime factorization of each number.*

$$8 = 2 \cdot 2 \cdot 2$$
$$12 = 2 \cdot 2 \quad \cdot 3$$
$$20 = 2 \cdot 2 \qquad \cdot 5$$

$$8 = 2 \cdot 2 \cdot 2$$
$$12 = 2 \cdot 2 \quad \cdot 3$$
$$20 = 2 \cdot 2 \qquad \cdot 5$$

Step 2 List each common prime factor the LEAST number of times it appears in any factorization.

2, 2

Step 2 List each prime factor the GREATEST number of times it appears in any factorization.

2, 2, 2, 3, 5

Step 3 Multiply the prime factors in the list.

$$2 \cdot 2 = 4$$

Step 3 Multiply the prime factors in the list.

$$2 \cdot 2 \cdot 2 \cdot 3 \cdot 5 = 120$$

So, the GCF of 8, 12, and 20 is 4. That is, 4 is the **largest** number that divides evenly into 8, 12, and 20.

The LCM of 8, 12, and 20 is 120. That is, 120 is the **smallest** number that can be divided evenly by 8, 12, and 20.

Here is a summary of this concept from *Academic Systems Algebra*.

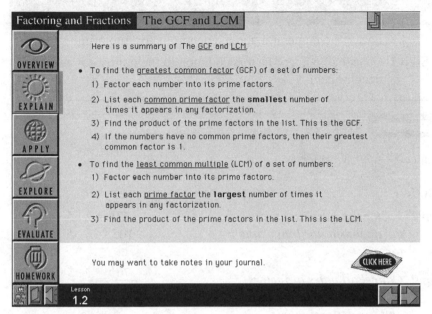

CONCEPT 2: FRACTIONS

Reducing a Fraction to Lowest Terms

Fractions are numbers that are written in the form $\frac{a}{b}$, where b is not zero.

A fraction may be interpreted as division. For example, the fraction $\frac{3}{5}$

may be interpreted as a shorthand way of writing $3 \div 5$.

Equivalent fractions are fractions that represent the same quantity.

For example, these fractions are equivalent fractions:

$$\frac{1}{2}, \frac{2}{4}, \text{ and } \frac{43}{86}$$

In **lowest terms**, each fraction may be written as $\frac{1}{2}$.

A fraction is **reduced to lowest terms** when the GCF of the numerator and denominator is 1.

Fractions are usually written in lowest terms in order to simplify calculations.

Concept 2 has sections on

- **Reducing a Fraction to Lowest Terms**
- **Multiplying Fractions**
- **Dividing Fractions**
- **Adding and Subtracting Fractions**

```
┌─────────────────────────────────────────────────────┐
│                   — Procedure —                       │
│          To Reduce a Fraction to Lowest Terms         │
├─────────────────────────────────────────────────────┤
│  Step 1  Factor the numerator and the denominator     │
│          into prime factors.                          │
│                                                       │
│  Step 2  Cancel all pairs of factors common to the    │
│          numerator and the denominator.               │
└─────────────────────────────────────────────────────┘
```

Example 1.2.10

Reduce $\dfrac{70}{105}$ to lowest terms.

Solution

Step 1 Factor the numerator and the denominator into prime factors.

$70 = 2 \cdot 5 \cdot 7$
$105 = 3 \cdot 5 \cdot 7$

Step 2 Cancel all pairs of factors common to the numerator and the denominator.

$$\frac{70}{105} = \frac{2 \cdot \cancel{5} \cdot \cancel{7}}{3 \cdot \cancel{5} \cdot \cancel{7}}$$
$$= \frac{2}{3}$$

So, $\dfrac{70}{105} = \dfrac{2}{3}$.

When you cancel pairs of common factors, you use the fact that a number divided by itself is 1.

To see this we write the problem like this:

$$\frac{70}{105} = \frac{2 \cdot 5 \cdot 7}{3 \cdot 5 \cdot 7}$$
$$= \frac{2}{3} \cdot \frac{5}{5} \cdot \frac{7}{7}$$
$$= \frac{2}{3} \cdot 1 \cdot 1$$
$$= \frac{2}{3}$$

Example 1.2.11

Reduce $\dfrac{84}{150}$ to lowest terms.

Solution

Step 1 Factor the numerator and the denominator into prime factors.

$84 = 2 \cdot 2 \cdot 3 \cdot 7$
$150 = 2 \cdot 3 \cdot 5 \cdot 5$

Step 2 Cancel all pairs of factors common to the numerator and the denominator.

$$\frac{84}{150} = \frac{\cancel{2} \cdot 2 \cdot \cancel{3} \cdot 7}{\cancel{2} \cdot \cancel{3} \cdot 5 \cdot 5}$$
$$= \frac{2 \cdot 7}{5 \cdot 5}$$
$$= \frac{14}{25}$$

So, $\dfrac{84}{150} = \dfrac{14}{25}$.

We can always use prime factorization to reduce a fraction to lowest terms. However, there is a short cut that can save time.

If you notice that the numerator and denominator have a common factor (other than 1), then you can reduce the fraction by dividing the numerator and the denominator by that factor.

For example, consider the fraction $\dfrac{12}{18}$.

6 is a common factor of the numerator and the denominator.

Divide 12 by 6 and divide 18 by 6.

$$\frac{12}{18} = \frac{12 \div 6}{18 \div 6}$$
$$= \frac{2}{3}$$

Since the fraction $\frac{2}{3}$ is now in lowest terms, we know that the GCF of 12 and 18 is 6.

Therefore, $\frac{12}{18}$ reduced to lowest terms is $\frac{2}{3}$.

Example **1.2.12**

Reduce $\frac{200}{600}$ to lowest terms.

Solution

Notice that 100 is a common factor of 200 and 600. Divide 200 by 100 and divide 600 by 100.

$$\frac{200}{600} = \frac{200 \div 100}{600 \div 100}$$
$$= \frac{2}{6}$$

$\frac{200}{600}$ can also be reduced by dividing the numerator and denominator by 200.

The result is $\frac{2}{6}$.

But, don't stop here. You can reduce $\frac{2}{6}$.

The numerator and denominator each have a common factor, 2.

So divide the numerator and denominator by 2.

$$\frac{2}{6} = \frac{2 \div 2}{6 \div 2}$$
$$= \frac{1}{3}$$

Prime factorization gives the same result.
$$\frac{200}{600} = \frac{\cancel{2} \cdot \cancel{2} \cdot \cancel{2} \cdot \cancel{5} \cdot \cancel{5}}{\cancel{2} \cdot \cancel{2} \cdot \cancel{2} \cdot 3 \cdot \cancel{5} \cdot \cancel{5}} = \frac{1}{3}$$

Therefore, $\frac{200}{600} = \frac{1}{3}$.

Multiplying Fractions

When we multiply fractions, we use the same skills we used to reduce a fraction to lowest terms.

— Procedure —
To Multiply Fractions

Step 1 Factor each numerator and denominator into prime factors.

Step 2 Cancel each pair of factors common to a numerator and a denominator.

Step 3 Multiply the numerators. Then multiply the denominators.

Example 1.2.13

Find: $\dfrac{18}{25} \cdot \dfrac{30}{24}$

Solution

Step 1 Factor each numerator and denominator into prime factors.

$$\dfrac{18}{25} \cdot \dfrac{30}{24} = \dfrac{2 \cdot 3 \cdot 3}{5 \cdot 5} \cdot \dfrac{2 \cdot 3 \cdot 5}{2 \cdot 2 \cdot 2 \cdot 3}$$

Step 2 Cancel each pair of factors common to a numerator and a denominator.

$$= \dfrac{\cancel{2} \cdot 3 \cdot 3}{\underset{1}{\cancel{5}} \cdot 5} \cdot \dfrac{\cancel{2} \cdot \cancel{3} \cdot \cancel{5}}{\underset{1}{\cancel{2}} \cdot \underset{1}{\cancel{2}} \cdot 2 \cdot \underset{1}{\cancel{3}}}$$

$$= \dfrac{3 \cdot 3}{5} \cdot \dfrac{1}{2}$$

Step 3 Multiply the numerators. Then multiply the denominators.

$$= \dfrac{3 \cdot 3 \cdot 1}{5 \cdot 2}$$

$$= \dfrac{9}{10}$$

Therefore, $\dfrac{18}{25} \cdot \dfrac{30}{24} = \dfrac{9}{10}$.

Example 1.2.14

Find: $\dfrac{9}{20} \cdot 6 \cdot \dfrac{25}{15}$

Solution

Recall that a whole number may be written as a fraction with denominator 1.

Therefore, write 6 as $\dfrac{6}{1}$.

$$\dfrac{9}{20} \cdot 6 \cdot \dfrac{25}{15} = \dfrac{9}{20} \cdot \dfrac{6}{1} \cdot \dfrac{25}{15}$$

Notice that you may cancel common factors within the same fraction or between fractions. The only requirement is that one factor is in any numerator and its twin is in any denominator.

Step 1 Factor each numerator and denominator into prime factors.

$$= \dfrac{3 \cdot 3}{2 \cdot 2 \cdot 5} \cdot \dfrac{2 \cdot 3}{1} \cdot \dfrac{5 \cdot 5}{3 \cdot 5}$$

Step 2 Cancel each pair of factors common to a numerator and a denominator.

$$= \dfrac{3 \cdot 3}{2 \cdot \underset{1}{\cancel{2}} \cdot \underset{1}{\cancel{5}}} \cdot \dfrac{\cancel{2} \cdot \cancel{3}}{1} \cdot \dfrac{\cancel{5} \cdot \cancel{5}}{\underset{1}{\cancel{3}} \cdot \underset{1}{\cancel{5}}}$$

Step 3 Multiply the numerators. Then multiply the denominators.

$$= \dfrac{3 \cdot 3 \cdot 1 \cdot 1}{2 \cdot 1 \cdot 1}$$

The answer may be left as an improper fraction, $\dfrac{9}{2}$, or written as the mixed number $4\dfrac{1}{2}$.

$$= \dfrac{9}{2}$$

Therefore, $\dfrac{9}{20} \cdot 6 \cdot \dfrac{25}{15} = \dfrac{9}{2}$.

Dividing Fractions

To divide one fraction by another we convert the division into an equivalent multiplication.

— Procedure —
To Divide Fractions

Step 1 Invert the second fraction and replace the division symbol, $\div$, with the multiplication symbol, $\cdot$.

Step 2 Multiply the resulting fractions.

Example 1.2.15

Find: $\dfrac{20}{3} \div \dfrac{50}{9}$

Solution

Step 1 Invert the second fraction and replace $\div$ with $\cdot$.

$$\frac{20}{3} \div \frac{50}{9} = \frac{20}{3} \cdot \frac{9}{50}$$

Step 2 Multiply the resulting fractions.

$$= \frac{2 \cdot 2 \cdot \cancel{5}}{\cancel{3}} \cdot \frac{\cancel{3} \cdot 3}{\cancel{2} \cdot \cancel{5} \cdot 5}$$

$$= \frac{2 \cdot 3}{5}$$

$$= \frac{6}{5}$$

The answer may be left as $\dfrac{6}{5}$ or written as $1\dfrac{1}{5}$.

Therefore, $\dfrac{20}{3} \div \dfrac{50}{9} = \dfrac{6}{5}$.

Example 1.2.16

Find: $\dfrac{42}{91} \div \dfrac{51}{65}$

Solution

Step 1 Invert the second fraction and replace $\div$ with $\cdot$.

$$\frac{42}{91} \div \frac{51}{65} = \frac{42}{91} \cdot \frac{65}{51}$$

Step 2 Multiply the resulting fractions.

$$= \frac{2 \cdot \cancel{3} \cdot \cancel{7}}{\cancel{7} \cdot \cancel{13}} \cdot \frac{5 \cdot \cancel{13}}{\cancel{3} \cdot 17}$$

$$= \frac{2 \cdot 5}{17}$$

$$= \frac{10}{17}$$

So, $\dfrac{42}{91} \div \dfrac{51}{65} = \dfrac{10}{17}$.

Example 1.2.17

Find: $\frac{24}{30} \div 4$

Solution

Recall that 4 may be written as $\frac{4}{1}$.

$$\frac{24}{30} \div 4 = \frac{24}{30} \div \frac{4}{1}$$

**Step 1 Invert the second fraction
and replace $\div$ with $\cdot$.**

$$= \frac{24}{30} \cdot \frac{1}{4}$$

Step 2 Multiply the resulting fractions.

$$= \frac{\cancel{2} \cdot \cancel{2} \cdot \cancel{2} \cdot \cancel{3}}{\underset{1}{\cancel{2}} \cdot \underset{1}{\cancel{3}} \cdot 5} \cdot \frac{1}{\underset{1}{\cancel{2}} \cdot \underset{1}{\cancel{2}}}$$

$$= \frac{1}{5}$$

Thus, $\frac{24}{30} \div 4 = \frac{1}{5}$.

Adding and Subtracting Fractions

Let's begin by considering fractions that have the same denominator.

**— Procedure —
To Add or Subtract Fractions With the Same Denominator**

Step 1 Add or subtract the numerators. The denominator stays the same.

Step 2 Reduce to lowest terms.

Example 1.2.18

Find: $\frac{5}{16} + \frac{7}{16}$

Solution

The fractions have the same denominator.

**Step 1 Add the numerators.
The denominator stays the same.**

$$\frac{5}{16} + \frac{7}{16} = \frac{5 + 7}{16}$$

$$= \frac{12}{16}$$

Step 2 Reduce to lowest terms.

The GCF of 12 and 16 is 4.
Divide numerator and denominator by 4.

$$= \frac{12 \div 4}{16 \div 4}$$

$$= \frac{3}{4}$$

So, $\frac{5}{16} + \frac{7}{16} = \frac{3}{4}$.

Example | **1.2.19**

Find: $\dfrac{27}{32} - \dfrac{9}{32}$

Solution

The fractions have the same denominator.

Step 1 Subtract the numerators.
 The denominator stays the same.

$$\frac{27}{32} - \frac{9}{32} = \frac{27 - 9}{32}$$

$$= \frac{18}{32}$$

Step 2 Reduce to lowest terms.

The GCF of 18 and 32 is 2.
Divide numerator and denominator by 2.

$$= \frac{18 \div 2}{32 \div 2}$$

$$= \frac{9}{16}$$

Therefore, $\dfrac{27}{32} - \dfrac{9}{32} = \dfrac{9}{16}$.

To add fractions with *different* denominators, we first rewrite the fractions so that they have the same denominator.

To obtain a **common denominator**, it is often convenient to find the **least common denominator (LCD)** of the fractions. The LCD is the LCM of the denominators.

— Procedure —
To Add or Subtract Fractions With Different Denominators

Step 1 Find the LCD of the fractions.

Step 2 Write each fraction as an equivalent fraction with the LCD as the denominator.

Step 3 Add or subtract the numerators. The denominator stays the same.

Step 4 Reduce to lowest terms.

Example 1.2.20

Find: $\dfrac{3}{10} + \dfrac{9}{14}$

Solution

Step 1 Find the LCD of the fractions.

To find the LCD of the fractions, find the LCM of their denominators.

- Write the prime factorization of each denominator.

$$10 = 2 \cdot 5$$
$$14 = 2 \cdot 7$$

- List each prime factor the GREATEST number of times it appears in any factorization.

$$2, 5, 7$$

- Find the product of the prime factors in the list.

$$2 \cdot 5 \cdot 7 = \mathbf{70}$$

So, the LCD of $\dfrac{3}{10}$ and $\dfrac{9}{14}$ is 70.

Step 2 Write each fraction as an equivalent fraction with the LCD as the denominator.

To write $\dfrac{3}{10}$ as a fraction with denominator 70,

When we multiply $\dfrac{3}{10}$ by $\dfrac{7}{7}$, we actually multiply $\dfrac{3}{10}$ by 1.

multiply the numerator and the denominator by 7, like this:

$$\dfrac{3}{10} = \dfrac{3}{10} \cdot \dfrac{7}{7} = \dfrac{21}{70}$$

Likewise, to write $\dfrac{9}{14}$ as an equivalent fraction with denominator 70, multiply $\dfrac{9}{14}$ by $\dfrac{5}{5}$, like this:

$$\dfrac{9}{14} = \dfrac{9}{14} \cdot \dfrac{5}{5} = \dfrac{45}{70}$$

The whole process looks like this: $\dfrac{3}{10} + \dfrac{9}{14} = \dfrac{3}{10} \cdot \dfrac{7}{7} + \dfrac{9}{14} \cdot \dfrac{5}{5}$

Step 3 Add the numerators.

$$= \dfrac{21}{70} + \dfrac{45}{70}$$

$$= \dfrac{66}{70}$$

Step 4 Reduce to lowest terms.

Divide out the GCF of 2.

$$= \dfrac{66 \div 2}{70 \div 2}$$

$$= \dfrac{33}{35}$$

Thus, $\dfrac{3}{10} + \dfrac{9}{14} = \dfrac{33}{35}$.

Example 1.2.21

Find: $2\frac{3}{8} + \frac{1}{4}$

Solution

First, write $2\frac{3}{8}$ as an improper fraction. $2\frac{3}{8} = \frac{2 \cdot 8 + 3}{8} = \frac{19}{8}$

Now we find $\frac{19}{8} + \frac{1}{4}$.

Step 1 Find the LCD of the fractions.

One way to find the LCM of 8 and 4 is to ask "What is the smallest number that is evenly divisible by both 8 and 4?"

The answer is 8. Therefore, the LCD of $\frac{19}{8}$ and $\frac{1}{4}$ is 8.

Step 2 Write each fraction as an equivalent fraction with the LCD as the denominator.

$\frac{19}{8}$ already has the LCD, 8, as its denominator.

To rewrite $\frac{1}{4}$ with denominator 8,

multiply $\frac{1}{4} \cdot \frac{2}{2}$.

$$\frac{19}{8} + \frac{1}{4} = \frac{19}{8} + \frac{1}{4} \cdot \frac{2}{2}$$
$$= \frac{19}{8} + \frac{2}{8}$$

Step 3 Add the numerators.

$$= \frac{21}{8}$$

Step 4 Reduce to lowest terms.

Because 8 and 21 have no common factors (other than 1) this fraction cannot be reduced.

Therefore, $2\frac{3}{8} + \frac{1}{4} = \frac{21}{8}$.

The answer may be left as $\frac{21}{8}$ or written as $2\frac{5}{8}$

Here is a summary of this concept from *Academic Systems Algebra*.

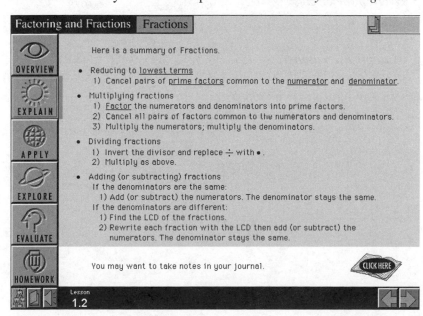

Sample Problems

In the online exploration, you used overlapping circles to make some observations about the GCF and LCM of two numbers. Here are some additional exploration problems.

Example 1.2.22

Use overlapping circles to find the GCF of 990 and 1078.

Solution

Step 1 Write the prime factorization of each number.

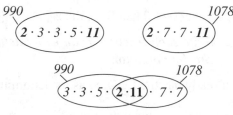

Step 2 Overlap the circles.

Step 3 Multiply the numbers where the circles overlap. $2 \cdot 11 = \mathbf{22}$

So, the GCF of 990 and 1078 is **22**.

Example 1.2.23

Use overlapping circles to find the LCM of 990 and 1078.

Solution

Step 1 Write the prime factorization of each number.

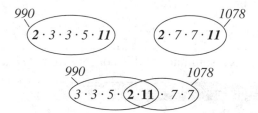

Step 2 Overlap the circles.

Step 3 Multiply the numbers in the joined circles. $3 \cdot 3 \cdot 5 \cdot 2 \cdot 11 \cdot 7 \cdot 7 = \mathbf{48{,}510}$

So, the LCM of 990 and 1078 is **48,510**.

Here is a summary of this Exploration from *Academic Systems Algebra*.

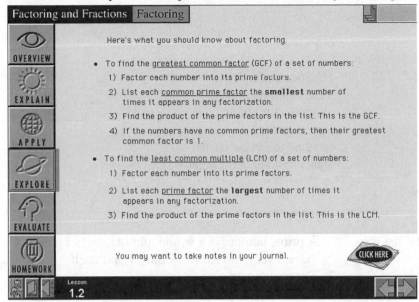

Factoring and Fractions   Factoring

OVERVIEW
EXPLAIN
APPLY
EXPLORE
EVALUATE
HOMEWORK

Here's what you should know about factoring.

- To find the <u>greatest common factor</u> (GCF) of a set of numbers:

  1) Factor each number into its prime factors.

  2) List each <u>common prime factor</u> the **smallest** number of times it appears in any factorization.

  3) Find the product of the prime factors in the list. This is the GCF.

  4) If the numbers have no common prime factors, then their greatest common factor is 1.

- To find the <u>least common multiple</u> (LCM) of a set of numbers:

  1) Factor each number into its prime factors.

  2) List each <u>prime factor</u> the **largest** number of times it appears in any factorization.

  3) Find the product of the prime factors in the list. This is the LCM.

You may want to take notes in your journal.   CLICK HERE

Lesson
1.2

Checklist Lesson 1.2

Here is what you should know after completing this lesson.

Words and Phrases

prime number
prime factorization
factor tree
common factors
greatest common factor (GCF)
multiples

common multiples
least common multiple (LCM)
equivalent fractions
lowest terms
reduced to lowest terms
least common denominator (LCD)

Ideas and Procedures

❶ Prime Number
State the definition of a prime number and list the first ten prime numbers.

A prime number is a whole number greater than 1 that is evenly divisible by only 1 and itself.
The first ten prime numbers are:
2, 3, 5, 7, 11, 13, 17, 19, 23, and 29

❷ Prime Factorization
Write a number as the product of prime numbers.

Example 1.2.1
Find the prime factorization of 120.

❸ Greatest Common Factor (GCF)
Find the greatest common factor of a set of numbers.

Example 1.2.4
Find the GCF of 56, 84, and 196.

See also: Example 1.2.2, 1.2.3, 1.2.5, 1.2.9, 1.2.22
Apply 1-28

❹ Least Common Multiple (LCM)
Find the least common multiple of a set of numbers.

Example 1.2.8
Find the LCM of 12, 90, and 105.

See also: Example 1.2.6, 1.2.7, 1.2.9, 1.2.23
Apply 1-28

❺ Reduce a Fraction
Reduce a fraction to lowest terms.

Example 1.2.11
Reduce $\dfrac{84}{150}$ to lowest terms.
See also: Example 1.2.10, 1.2.12
Apply 29, 30, 31

❻ Multiply Fractions
Write the product of fractions in lowest terms.

Example 1.2.13
Find: $\dfrac{18}{12} \cdot \dfrac{30}{24}$
See also: Example 1.2.14
Apply 32, 33, 34

❼ Divide Fractions

Write the quotient of fractions in lowest terms.

Example 1.2.15
 Find: $\dfrac{20}{3} \div \dfrac{50}{9}$
See also: Example 1.2.16, 1.2.17
 Apply 35-40

❽ Add Fractions

Write the sum of fractions in lowest terms.

Example 1.2.20
 Find: $\dfrac{3}{10} + \dfrac{9}{14}$
See also: Example 1.2.18, 1.2.21
 Apply 41, 42, 45-50

❾ Subtract Fractions

Write the difference of fractions in lowest terms.

Example 1.2.19
 Find: $\dfrac{27}{32} - \dfrac{9}{32}$
See also: Apply 43, 44, 51-56

Homework

Homework Problems

Circle the homework problems assigned to you by the computer, then complete them below.

Explain

The GCF and LCM

1. Find the LCM of 4 and 6.

2. Find the GCF of 9 and 12.

3. Find the GCF of 18 and 24.

4. Find the LCM of 8 and 12.

5. Find the LCM of 36 and 54.

6. Find the GCF of 27 and 32.

7. Find the GCF of 45 and 60.

8. Find the LCM of 28 and 30.

9. A baker expects to use 126 eggs in one week. He can either order cartons which contain 8 eggs or cartons which contain 18 eggs, but not both. If he doesn't want any eggs left over at the end of the week, which size carton should he order?

10. There will be 256 guests at a wedding reception and the bride wants all the tables to be the same size. If she can rent tables which seat 5, 6, or 8 people, what size table should she rent?

11. Find the GCF of 18, 25 and 30.

12. Find the LCM of 9, 11 and 33.

Fractions

13. Write in lowest terms: $\frac{28}{32}$

14. Find: $\frac{4}{5} \cdot \frac{7}{10}$

15. Find: $\frac{2}{11} + \frac{5}{11}$

16. Write in lowest terms: $\frac{25}{30}$

17. Find: $\frac{7}{20} \div \frac{14}{15}$

18. Find: $5\frac{11}{17} - 2\frac{4}{17}$

19. Find: $\frac{49}{30} \cdot \frac{20}{21}$

20. Find: $3\frac{1}{6} + 2\frac{3}{8}$

21. Stock prices are recorded in eighths of a dollar. If the price of a stock is $31\frac{1}{8}$ and it loses $\frac{1}{4}$ of a dollar, what is its new price?

22. The Triple Crown is a series of three horse races— The Kentucky Derby, The Preakness Stakes, and The Belmont Stakes. The Kentucky Derby is $\frac{5}{4}$ miles, The Preakness Stakes is $\frac{19}{16}$ miles, and The Belmont Stakes is $\frac{3}{2}$ miles. What is the total distance of the three races?

23. Find: $9\frac{11}{12} - 4\frac{5}{18}$

24. Find: $\frac{63}{50} \div \frac{42}{25}$

Explore

25. Draw the appropriately overlapped circles to find the GCF of 252 and 525.

26. Draw the appropriately overlapped circles to find the LCM of 252 and 525.

27. Draw the appropriately overlapped circles to find the GCF of 540 and 315.

28. Draw the appropriately overlapped circles to find the LCM of 540 and 315.

29. Draw the appropriately overlapped circles to find the GCF of 280 and 784.

30. Draw the appropriately overlapped circles to find the LCM of 280 and 784.

 **Apply**

Practice Problems

Here are some additional practice problems for you to try.

The GCF and LCM

1. Find the GCF and LCM of 8 and 18.

2. Find the GCF and LCM of 10 and 36.

3. Find the GCF and LCM of 6 and 14.

4. Find the GCF and LCM of 22 and 45.

5. Find the GCF and LCM of 18 and 25.

6. Find the GCF and LCM of 24 and 35.

7. Find the GCF and LCM of 16 and 48.

8. Find the GCF and LCM of 18 and 54.

9. Find the GCF and LCM of 56 and 84.

10. Find the GCF and LCM of 36 and 88.

11. Find the GCF and LCM of 48 and 60.

12. Find the GCF and LCM of 24 and 60.

13. Find the GCF and LCM of 48 and 108.

14. Find the GCF and LCM of 32 and 48.

15. Find the GCF and LCM of 35 and 98.

16. Find the GCF and LCM of 132 and 330.

17. Find the GCF and LCM of 42 and 105.

18. Find the GCF and LCM of 40 and 50.

19. Find the GCF and LCM of 63 and 72.

20. Find the GCF and LCM of 36 and 45.

21. Find the GCF and LCM of 57 and 95.

22. Find the GCF and LCM of 51 and 68.

23. Find the GCF and LCM of 12, 16 and 36.

24. Find the GCF and LCM of 36, 45 and 108.

25. Find the GCF and LCM of 5, 10, and 14.

26. Find the GCF and LCM of 48, 72 and 120.

27. Find the GCF and LCM of 56, 96 and 152.

28. Find the GCF and LCM of 24, 56 and 96.

Fractions

29. Write in lowest terms: $\dfrac{36}{108}$

30. Write in lowest terms: $\dfrac{72}{256}$

31. Write in lowest terms: $\dfrac{18}{105}$

32. Find: $\dfrac{35}{48} \cdot \dfrac{96}{105}$

33. Find: $\dfrac{42}{55} \cdot \dfrac{33}{56}$

34. Find: $\dfrac{15}{28} \cdot \dfrac{21}{100}$

35. Find: $\dfrac{5}{6} \div \dfrac{5}{9}$

36. Find: $\dfrac{12}{25} \div \dfrac{6}{15}$

37. Find: $\dfrac{15}{42} \div \dfrac{10}{21}$

38. Find: $\dfrac{27}{52} \div \dfrac{81}{39}$

39. Find: $\dfrac{56}{75} \div \dfrac{64}{225}$

40. Find: $\dfrac{25}{42} \div \dfrac{125}{24}$

41. Find: $\dfrac{8}{11} + \dfrac{2}{11}$

42. Find: $\dfrac{9}{13} + \dfrac{4}{13}$

43. Find: $\dfrac{11}{19} - \dfrac{7}{19}$

44. Find: $\dfrac{15}{23} - \dfrac{9}{23}$

45. Find: $\dfrac{3}{8} + \dfrac{3}{10}$

46. Find: $\dfrac{4}{15} + \dfrac{4}{9}$

47. Find: $\dfrac{5}{9} + \dfrac{5}{12}$

48. Find: $\dfrac{7}{30} + \dfrac{9}{35}$

49. Find: $\dfrac{8}{25} + \dfrac{11}{20}$

50. Find: $\dfrac{15}{42} + \dfrac{16}{35}$

51. Find: $\dfrac{7}{9} - \dfrac{1}{5}$

52. Find: $\dfrac{3}{4} - \dfrac{1}{3}$

53. Find: $\dfrac{7}{8} - \dfrac{2}{7}$

54. Find: $\dfrac{17}{18} - \dfrac{4}{15}$

55. Find: $\dfrac{12}{25} - \dfrac{4}{15}$

56. Find: $\dfrac{15}{16} - \dfrac{11}{24}$

Practice Test

Take this practice test to be sure that you are prepared for the final quiz in Evaluate.

1. Find the prime factorizations of 12, 28 and 40.

2. Find the GCF of 12, 28 and 40.

3. Find the LCM of 12, 28 and 40.

4. Write $\dfrac{18}{48}$ in lowest terms.

5. Circle the prime factors of each number in the factor trees below.

    ```
        42          55          63
        /\          /\          /\
      2 · 21       5 · 11      3 · 21
          /\                       /\
         3 · 7                    3 · 7
    ```

6. If Sarah runs $\dfrac{2}{3}$ of a mile, how much farther must she run to go $2\dfrac{1}{2}$ miles?

7. Find the GCF of 54 and 66.

8. Find the LCM of 15 and 50.

9. Find the least common denominator of the fractions $\dfrac{7}{24}$ and $\dfrac{2}{9}$ by finding the LCM of their denominators.

10. Find: $\dfrac{5}{9} \div \dfrac{25}{12}$

11. What are the common prime factors of 56 and 70?

    ```
    56                          70
      \                        /
      (2 · 2 · 2 · 7)    (2 · 5 · 7)
    ```

12. Find the LCM and GCF of 42 and 70.

LESSON 1.3
ARITHMETIC OF NUMBERS

 Overview

An ancient Egyptian document, found by an archeologist in the 19th century began with the promise that it contained "a thorough study of all things, insight into all that exists, (and) knowledge of all obscure secrets." However, it turned out the document was a guide to mathematics, and the "secrets" were how to multiply and divide.

While knowledge of this "secret" may not give you "insight into all that exists," it can help you in your daily life.

In this lesson, you will learn how to add, subtract, multiply, and divide real numbers. You will also learn the correct order of operations on numbers when there is more than one operation to perform.

 Explain

Concept 1 has sections on

- **Opposites**
- **Adding Numbers**
- **Subtracting Numbers**
- **Multiplying Numbers**
- **Dividing Numbers**
- **Order of Operations**
- **Properties of Numbers and Definitions**

CONCEPT 1: OPERATIONS ON NUMBERS

Opposites

Two numbers with the same absolute value, but different signs, are called **opposites** of each other.

For example, 6 and −6 are opposites of each other.

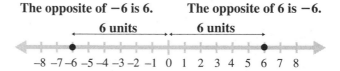

The opposite of −6 is 6.   The opposite of 6 is −6.

On a number line, opposites lie an equal distance from 0 on **opposite** sides of 0.

The sum of a number and its opposite is zero.

Here are two examples:

Number	+	Opposite	=	Zero
−6	+	6	=	0
2.1	+	(–2.1)	=	0

Adding Numbers

We begin by adding two numbers that have the same sign.

— Procedure —
To Add Two Numbers With the Same Sign

Step 1 Find the absolute value of each number.

Step 2 Add the absolute values.

Step 3 Attach the sign of the original numbers to the result.

Example 1.3.1

Find: 35 + 7

Solution

Numbers written without a sign are positive. So, 35 and 7 have the same sign.

Step 1 Find the absolute value of each number. $|35| = 35$
$|7| = 7$

Step 2 Add the absolute values. $35 + 7 = 42$

Step 3 Attach the sign of the original numbers to the result.

The original numbers are positive
so attach a positive sign, +.   +42

Therefore, $35 + 7 = +42$.

We usually write a positive number without its sign, so we write the answer as 42.

Here's a way to think about the sum 35 + 7.

*Suppose you have $35 in your checking account and you deposit of $7.
The new balance is $35 + $7 = $42.*

Example 1.3.2

Find: $-5 + (-23)$

Solution

-5 and -23 have the same sign.

Step 1 **Find the absolute value of each number.** $|-5| = 5$
$|-23| = 23$

Step 2 **Add the absolute values.** $5 + 23 = 28$

Step 3 **Attach the sign of the original numbers to the result.**

The original numbers are negative
so attach a negative sign, $-$. -28

Therefore, $-5 + (-23) = -28$.

Here's a way to think about the sum $-5 + (-23)$.

Suppose your checking account is overdrawn by $5 (that is, your balance is $-$$5). If you write a check for $23, it would be like adding $-$$23 to your account. If the check clears, the new balance will be $-$$5 + (-$$23) = -$$28. Your account is overdrawn by $28.

To add two numbers that have different signs, we perform a subtraction.

— Procedure —
To Add Two Numbers With Different Signs

Step 1 Find the absolute value of each number.

Step 2 Subtract the smaller absolute value from the larger absolute value.

Step 3 Attach the sign of the original number that has the larger absolute value.

Example 1.3.3

Find: $56 + (-16)$

Solution

The numbers have different signs.

Step 1 **Find the absolute value of each number.** $|56| = 56$
$|-16| = 16$

Step 2 **Subtract the smaller absolute value from the larger absolute value.** $56 - 16 = 40$

Step 3 **Attach the sign of the original number that has the larger absolute value.**

Since 56 has the larger absolute value
and 56 is positive, attach a positive sign. $+40$

Therefore, $56 + (-16) = 40$.

Here's a way to think about the sum $56 + (-16)$.

Suppose you have $56 in your checking account and you write a check for $16.

This adds $-$$16 to your account. The new balance is $56 + (-$$16) = $40.

Example 1.3.4

Find: $-72 + 8$

Solution

The signs of the numbers are different.

Here's a way to think about the sum $-72 + 8$.

Suppose your checking account is overdrawn by \$72.
That is, the balance is $-\$72$.

If you deposit \$8 the new balance is $-\$72 + \$8 = -\$64$.
Your account is now overdrawn by \$64.

Step 1 *Find the absolute value of each number.*

$$|-72| = 72$$
$$|8| = 8$$

Step 2 *Subtract the smaller absolute value from the larger absolute value.*

$$72 - 8 = 64$$

Step 3 *Attach the sign of the original number that has the larger absolute value.*

Since -72 has the larger absolute value and -72 is negative, attach a negative sign. -64

Therefore, $-72 + 8 = -64$.

Subtracting Numbers

To subtract a number, we add its opposite.

— Procedure —
To Subtract One Number from Another Number

Step 1 Change the subtraction sign ($-$) to an addition sign ($+$) AND change the sign of the number being subtracted.

Step 2 Follow the procedure for adding two numbers.

Example 1.3.5

Find: $-37 - 22$

Solution

Step 1 *Change the subtraction sign ($-$) to an addition sign ($+$) AND change the sign of the number being subtracted.*

$$-37 - 22$$
$$= -37 + (-22)$$

Step 2 *Follow the procedure for adding two numbers.*

Both -37 and -22 are negative numbers, so their sum is negative. $= -59$

So, $-37 - 22 = -59$.

Example `1.3.6`

Find: $73 - (-15)$

Solution

*Step 1 Change the subtraction sign (−)
to an addition sign (+) AND change
the sign of the number being
subtracted.*

$$73 - (-15)$$
$$= 73 + (+15)$$

*Step 2 Follow the procedure for adding
two numbers.*

$$= 88$$

So, $73 - (-15) = 88$.

Multiplying Numbers

We know from arithmetic that when we multiply two positive numbers, the result is a positive number.

To determine the sign when we multiply a positive number and a negative number, we look at a pattern. In particular, we look at some multiples of 2.

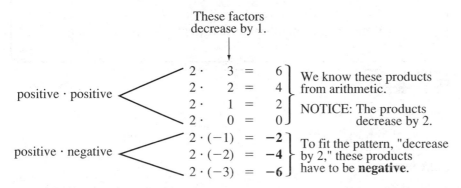

This pattern predicts that the product of a positive number and a negative number is a negative number.

We follow a similar approach to predict the product of two negative numbers. But this time, we use -2 for the first factor.

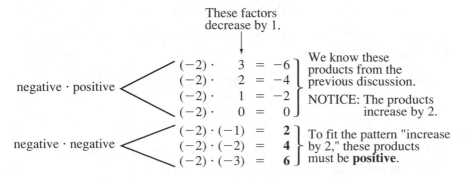

Thus, we predict that the product of two negative numbers is a positive number.

It can be shown that our predictions are correct.

If two numbers have the **same sign**,
their product is **positive**.

positive ·positive = positive	$3 \cdot 5 = 15$
negative · negative = positive	$(-3) \cdot (-5) = 15$

If two numbers have **different signs**,
their product is **negative**.

positive · negative = negative	$3 \cdot (-5) = -15$
negative ·positive = negative	$(-3) \cdot 5 = -15$

This provides us with a procedure for multiplying two numbers.

— Procedure —
To Multiply Two Numbers

Step 1 Multiply the absolute values of the numbers.

Step 2 Attach a sign to the product as follows:

- If the original numbers have the same sign, attach a positive sign.

- If the original numbers have different signs, attach a negative sign.

Example 1.3.7

Find the following products:

a. $-2 \cdot 3$ b. $-5 \cdot (-4)$ c. $7 \cdot (-3)$ d. $0 \cdot (-2)$

Solution

For each problem, we first multiplied the absolute values of the numbers. Then we determined the sign of the product.

a. The signs are different so the product is negative. $-2 \cdot 3 = -6$

b. The signs are the same so the product is positive. $-5 \cdot (-4) = 20$

c. The signs are different so the product is negative. $7 \cdot (-3) = -21$

d. Zero has no sign. It is neither negative nor positive. $0 \cdot (-2) = 0$

Dividing Numbers

To divide 6 by 3, we can multiply 6 by $\frac{1}{3}$, the reciprocal of 3.

$$6 \div 3 = \frac{6}{3} = \left(\frac{6}{1}\right) \cdot \left(\frac{1}{3}\right)$$

Division and multiplication are closely related, so the sign rules for division are the same as those for multiplication.

If two numbers have the **same sign**,
their quotient is **positive**.

$$\text{positive} \div \text{positive} = \text{positive} \qquad 20 \div 5 = 4$$
$$\text{negative} \div \text{negative} = \text{positive} \qquad (-20) \div (-5) = 4$$

If two numbers have **different signs**,
their quotient is **negative**.

$$\text{positive} \div \text{negative} = \text{negative} \qquad 20 \div (-5) = -4$$
$$\text{negative} \div \text{positive} = \text{negative} \qquad (-20) \div 5 = -4$$

The procedure for division is similar to the procedure for multiplication.

— Procedure —
To Divide One Number by Another (Nonzero) Number

Step 1 Divide the absolute values of the numbers.

Step 2 Attach a sign to the quotient as follows:

- If the original numbers have the same sign, attach a positive sign.

- If the original numbers have different signs, attach a negative sign.

Example 1.3.8

Find the following quotients:

a. $-12 \div 4$ b. $-8 \div (-2)$ c. $\dfrac{30}{-6}$ d. $-18/(-3)$

e. $0/2$ f. $\dfrac{8}{0}$

Solution

For each problem, we first divided the absolute values of the numbers.
Then we determined the sign of the quotient.

a. The signs are different so the quotient is negative. $-12 \div 4 = -3$

b. The signs are the same so the quotient is positive. $-8 \div (-2) = 4$

c. The signs are different so the quotient is negative. $\dfrac{30}{-6} = -5$

d. The signs are the same so the quotient is positive. $-18/(-3) = 6$

e. Zero has no sign. It is neither negative nor positive. $0/2 = 0$

f. Division by 0 is not defined. $\dfrac{8}{0} = \text{undefined}$

On your calculator, enter $8 \div 0 =$.

The display reads – E – or Error. In this way, the calculator indicates that division by 0 is not defined.

Order of Operations

When an expression contains more than one operation, we have to know which operation to do first.

For example, what is $2 + 5 \cdot 3$?

Here there are two operations, addition and multiplication.

- If we add first, we have $7 \cdot 3$, which is 21.

- If we multiply first, we have $2 + 15$, which is 17.

To see which operation we should do first, let's consider a practical example. Suppose you buy a loaf of bread for $2 and 5 boxes of cereal for $3 each. Mathematically, this would be written as $2 + 5 \cdot 3$.

$$
\begin{array}{rcl}
\text{Total} & & \text{Cost of} \quad \text{Cost of} \\
\text{cost} & = & \text{bread} \; + \; \text{cereal} \\
& = & 2 \;\; + \;\; 5 \cdot 3 \\
& = & 2 \;\; + \;\; 15 \\
& = & 17
\end{array}
$$

You spent $2 on the bread and $15 on the cereal for a total of $17. This implies that we must do the multiplication before the addition.

To avoid confusion, mathematicians have agreed upon an order in which to perform mathematical operations.

We use the following procedure to simplify an expression that contains more than one operation.

— Procedure —
To Use the Order of Operations to Simplify an Expression

Step 1 Simplify expressions inside grouping symbols.

Step 2 Simplify exponents, square roots, and absolute values.

Step 3 Simplify multiplication and division, working in order from left to right.

Step 4 Simplify addition and subtraction, working in order from left to right.

The **grouping symbols** referred to in **Step 1** include:

Symbol	Name	Example
( )	parentheses	$6 \div (\mathbf{2 + 1}) = 6 \div \mathbf{3} = 2$
[ ]	brackets	$12 - [\mathbf{6 - 4}] = 12 - \mathbf{2} = 10$
$\frac{a}{b}$	fraction bar	$\frac{\mathbf{2 + 4}}{\mathbf{5 - 2}} = \frac{\mathbf{6}}{\mathbf{3}} = 2$
| |	absolute value	$3 \cdot \|\mathbf{1 - 5}\| = 3 \cdot \|\mathbf{-4}\| = 3 \cdot \mathbf{4} = 12$
$\sqrt{\ }$	radical	$6 \cdot \sqrt{\mathbf{9 + 16}} = 6 \cdot \sqrt{\mathbf{25}} = 6 \cdot \mathbf{5} = 30$

Example 1.3.9

Find: $1 + 4^2 \div 2 - (7 - 2) \cdot 3$

Solution

Step 1 Simplify expressions inside grouping symbols.
$$1 + 4^2 \div 2 - (7 - 2) \cdot 3$$
$$= 1 + 4^2 \div 2 - \mathbf{5} \cdot 3$$

Step 2 Simplify exponents, square roots, and absolute values.
$$= 1 + \mathbf{16} \div 2 - 5 \cdot 3$$

Step 3 Simplify multiplication and division, working in order from left to right.
$$= 1 + \mathbf{8} - 5 \cdot 3$$
$$= 1 + 8 - \mathbf{15}$$

Step 4 Simplify addition and subtraction, working in order from left to right.
$$= \mathbf{9} - 15$$
$$= \mathbf{-6}$$

So, $1 + 4^2 \div 2 - (7 - 2) \cdot 3 = -6$.

Example 1.3.10

Find: $\sqrt{20 - 4} + 6^2 \div (5 - 1) - 2 \cdot (11 - 3)$

Solution

Step 1 Simplify expressions inside grouping symbols.
$$\sqrt{20 - 4} + 6^2 \div (5 - 1) - 2 \cdot (11 - 3)$$
$$= \sqrt{\mathbf{16}} + 6^2 \div \mathbf{4} - 2 \cdot \mathbf{8}$$

Step 2 Simplify exponents, square roots, and absolute values.
$$= \mathbf{4} + \mathbf{36} \div 4 - 2 \cdot 8$$

Step 3 Simplify multiplication and division, working in order from left to right.
$$= 4 + \mathbf{9} - 2 \cdot 8$$
$$= 4 + 9 - \mathbf{16}$$

Step 4 Simplify addition and subtraction, working in order from left to right.
$$= \mathbf{13} - 16$$
$$= \mathbf{-3}$$

So, $\sqrt{20 - 4} + 6^2 \div (5 - 1) - 2 \cdot (11 - 3) = -3$.

Example 1.3.11

Simplify: $60 \div 4 \cdot [1 - (2 - 6)]$

Solution

Step 1 Simplify expressions inside grouping symbols.

When grouping symbols are nested
inside one another, work first within
the innermost grouping symbols.

$$60 \div 4 \cdot [1 - (2 - 6)]$$
$$= 60 \div 4 \cdot [1 - (\mathbf{-4})]$$
$$= 60 \div 4 \cdot [\mathbf{5}]$$

**Step 2 Simplify exponents, square roots,
and absolute values.**

There are none to simplify.

**Step 3 Simplify multiplication and division,
working in order from left to right.**

Note that we do the division before
the multiplication. That's because as we
work from left to right, the division
comes before the multiplication.

$$= \mathbf{15} \cdot 5$$
$$= \mathbf{75}$$

**Step 4 Simplify addition and subtraction,
working in order from left to right.**

There are none to simplify.

So, $60 \div 4 \cdot [1 - (2 - 6)] = 75$.

Example 1.3.12

Simplify: $8 - \dfrac{7 - 2^3 \cdot 9}{18 \div 2 \cdot 3 - 7 \cdot 2}$

Solution

Step 1 Simplify expressions inside grouping symbols.

The fraction bar acts as a grouping
symbol. So, first simplify the
numerator and the denominator.

$$8 - \frac{7 - 2^3 \cdot 9}{18 \div 2 \cdot 3 - 7 \cdot 2}$$

*We use the order of operations to simplify
the numerator and denominator.*

- *Simplify exponents, square
  roots, and absolute values.*

$$= 8 - \frac{7 - \mathbf{8} \cdot 9}{18 \div 2 \cdot 3 - 7 \cdot 2}$$

- *Simplify multiplication and
  division, working in order
  from left to right.*

$$= 8 - \frac{7 - \mathbf{72}}{\mathbf{9} \cdot 3 - 7 \cdot 2}$$

$$= 8 - \frac{7 - 72}{\mathbf{27} - \mathbf{14}}$$

- *Simplify addition and
  subtraction, working
  in order from left to right.*

$$= 8 - \frac{\mathbf{-65}}{\mathbf{13}}$$

***Step 2 Simplify exponents, square
        roots, and absolute values.***

There are none to simplify.

***Step 3 Simplify multiplication and
        division, working in order
        from left to right.*** $= 8 - (-5)$

***Step 4 Simplify addition and
        subtraction, working
        in order from left to right.*** $= 13$

So, $8 - \dfrac{7 \quad 2^3 \cdot 9}{18 \div 2 \cdot 3 - 7 \cdot 2} = 13.$

Properties of Numbers and Definitions

In the following, a, b and c represent real numbers.

Commutative Property

Commutative Property of Addition	**Commutative Property of Multiplication**
When you *add* two numbers, regardless of the *order*, the sum is the same.	When you *multiply* two numbers, regardless of the *order*, the product is the same.
$5 + 7 = 7 + 5$ $\qquad$ $a + b = b + a$	$5 \cdot 7 = 7 \cdot 5$ $\qquad$ $a \cdot b = b \cdot a$

*Subtraction and division are not
commutative. For example, $5 - 3 = 2$,
but $3 - 5 = -2$. Likewise, $6 \div 2 = 3$,
but $2 \div 6 = \frac{1}{3}$*

Associative Property

Associative Property of Addition	**Associative Property of Multiplication**
When you *add* numbers, regardless of how you *group* (or associate) them, the sum is the same.	When you *multiply* numbers, regardless of how you *group* (or associate) them, the product is the same.
$2 + (3 + 4) = (2 + 3) + 4$ $a + (b + c) = (a + b) + c$	$2 \cdot (3 \cdot 4) = (2 \cdot 3) \cdot 4$ $a \cdot (b \cdot c) = (a \cdot b) \cdot c$

Distributive Property

This property allows us to convert a product into an equivalent sum.

$$2 \cdot (3 + 4) = 2 \cdot 3 + 2 \cdot 4$$
$$a \cdot (b + c) = a \cdot b + a \cdot c$$

Identities

Additive Identity
(Addition Property of 0)

The sum of a number and zero is the number itself.

$$3 + 0 = 3$$
$$a + 0 = a$$

0 is called the **additive identity**.

Multiplicative Identity
(Multiplication Property of 1)

The product of a number and one is the number itself.

$$3 \cdot 1 = 3$$
$$a \cdot 1 = a$$

1 is called the **multiplicative identity**.

Multiplication Property of 0

The product of any number and 0 is 0.

$$3 \cdot 0 = 0$$
$$a \cdot 0 = 0$$

Inverses

Additive Inverse
(Opposite)

The sum of a number and its opposite is 0.

$$7 + (-7) = 0$$

$$a + (-a) = 0$$

The opposite of a number is also called the **additive inverse** of the number.

Multiplicative Inverse
(Reciprocal)

The product of a number and its reciprocal is 1.

$$7 \cdot \frac{1}{7} = 1$$

$$a \cdot \frac{1}{a} = 1 \ \ (\text{Here, } a \neq 0.)$$

The reciprocal of a number is also called the **multiplicative inverse** of the number.

(Zero does not have a reciprocal because you may not divide by zero.)

These properties will be very useful as you study algebra. They are also useful when solving arithmetic problems.

Example 1.3.13

Find: $2 \cdot 2 \cdot 13 \cdot 5$

Solution

Using the Order of Operations, multiply working left to right.

$$2 \cdot 2 \cdot 13 \cdot 5$$
$$= \mathbf{4} \cdot 13 \cdot 5$$
$$= \mathbf{52} \cdot 5$$
$$= 260$$

Using the Properties of Numbers, we can group the factors in any order we wish. Let's use the Associative and Commutative Properties to group the factors 2 and 5 together.

Use the Commutative Property to rearrange the order of the factors.

$$2 \cdot 2 \cdot 13 \cdot 5$$
$$= 2 \cdot \mathbf{5} \cdot 2 \cdot 13$$

Use the Associative Property to group the factors 2 and 5 together.

$$= (\mathbf{2 \cdot 5}) \cdot 2 \cdot 13$$

Simplify inside the parentheses.

$$= \mathbf{10} \cdot 2 \cdot 13$$

Then multiply.

$$= 20 \cdot 13$$
$$= 260$$

Notice that by grouping the factors 2 and 5 together to get 10, we can more easily perform this multiplication.

Example 1.3.14

Tom needs to buy some lumber to repair a deck. For every board that is 8 feet long, he also needs a 10 foot board. He needs three boards of each length to fix the deck. What is the total length of all the boards?

Solution

There are three 8-foot boards and three 10-foot boards. So the total length of all the boards is $8 + 8 + 8 + 10 + 10 + 10$.

Here are three ways to find this sum.

Method 1:

Use the Order of Operations to add the lengths of the individual boards from left to right.

$$8 + 8 + 8 + 10 + 10 + 10$$
$$= \ \mathbf{16} \ + 8 + 10 + 10 + 10$$
$$= \ \ \ \ \ \ \mathbf{24} \ \ \ + 10 + 10 + 10$$
$$= \ \ \ \ \ \ \ \ \ \ \ \mathbf{34} \ \ \ \ + 10 + 10$$
$$= \ \ \ \ \ \ \ \ \ \ \ \ \ \ \ \ \mathbf{44} \ \ \ \ \ + 10$$
$$= \mathbf{54}$$

Method 2:

Use the Associative Property to group the 8-foot boards together and the 10-foot boards together.

$$8 + 8 + 8 + 10 + 10 + 10$$
$$= (8 + 8 + 8) + (10 + 10 + 10)$$
$$= \ \ \ \ \mathbf{24} \ \ \ \ + \ \ \ \ \ \mathbf{30}$$
$$= \ \ \ \ \ \ \ \ \ \ \ \ \ \mathbf{54}$$

Method 3:

Use the Commutative and Associative Properties to rearrange the numbers into groups of 8- and 10-foot boards.

$$8 + 8 + 8 + 10 + 10 + 10$$
$$= 8 + 10 + 8 + 10 + 8 + 10$$
$$= (8 + 10) + (8 + 10) + (8 + 10)$$
$$= \ \ \mathbf{18} \ \ \ + \ \ \mathbf{18} \ \ \ + \ \ \mathbf{18}$$
$$= \ \ \ \ \ \ \ \ \ \ \ \ \ \mathbf{54}$$

The total length of the boards is 54 feet.

Here is a summary of this concept from *Academic Systems Algebra*.

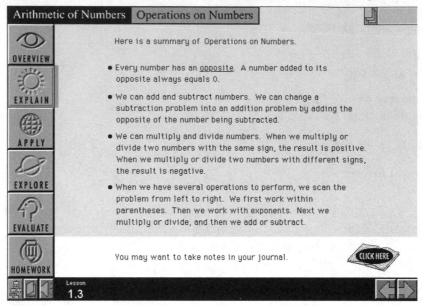

Arithmetic of Numbers	Operations on Numbers

OVERVIEW

EXPLAIN

APPLY

EXPLORE

EVALUATE

HOMEWORK

Here is a summary of Operations on Numbers.

- Every number has an <u>opposite</u>. A number added to its opposite always equals 0.

- We can add and subtract numbers. We can change a subtraction problem into an addition problem by adding the opposite of the number being subtracted.

- We can multiply and divide numbers. When we multiply or divide two numbers with the same sign, the result is positive. When we multiply or divide two numbers with different signs, the result is negative.

- When we have several operations to perform, we scan the problem from left to right. We first work within parentheses. Then we work with exponents. Next we multiply or divide, and then we add or subtract.

You may want to take notes in your journal.

CLICK HERE

Lesson 1.3

 **Explore**

Sample Problems

In the online Explore, you used several properties of real numbers. Here are some additional exploration problems.

Example | **1.3.15**

Determine which property justifies each of the following:

a. $(5 + 3) \cdot 2 = 2 \cdot (5 + 3)$
b. $(2 + 4)(3 + 7) = (2 + 4) \cdot 3 + (2 + 4) \cdot 7$
c. $(3 \cdot 4) \cdot 5 = 3 \cdot (4 \cdot 5)$
d. $8 + 0 = 0 + 8$
e. $8 + 0 = 8$

Solution

a. $(5 + 3) \cdot 2 = 2 \cdot (5 + 3)$ illustrates the Commutative Property of Multiplication. The order of the factors, $(5 + 3)$ and 2, is reversed.

b. $(2 + 4)(3 + 7) = (2 + 4) \cdot 3 + (2 + 4) \cdot 7$ illustrates the Distributive Property. The factor $(2 + 4)$ is distributed to each term of the sum $(3 + 7)$.

c. $(3 \cdot 4) \cdot 5 = 3 \cdot (4 \cdot 5)$ illustrates the Associative Property of Multiplication. The parentheses were moved to change the groupings of the factors.

d. $8 + 0 = 0 + 8$ illustrates the Commutative Property of Addition. The order of the terms in the sum is changed.

e. $8 + 0 = 8$ illustrates the Addition Property of 0. Zero is added to 8 and the result is 8, the original number.

Here is a summary of this Exploration from *Academic Systems Algebra*.

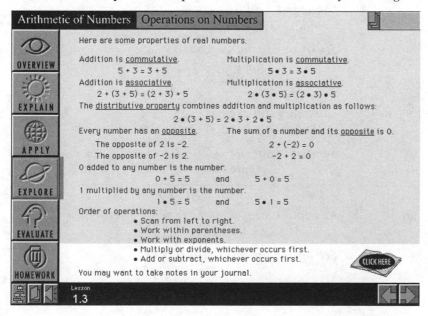

Checklist Lesson 1.3

Here is what you should know after completing this lesson.

Words and Phrases

opposite
grouping symbols
Commutative Property
Associative Property
Distributive Property
Addition Property of 0

additive identity
Multiplication Property of 1
multiplicative identity
Multiplication Property of 0
additive inverse
multiplicative inverse (reciprocal)

Ideas and Procedures

❶ **Adding Numbers**
Find the sum of real numbers.

Example 1.3.3
   Find: $56 + (-16)$

See also: Example 1.3.1, 1.3.2, 1.3.4
          Apply 1, 2, 3

❷ **Subtracting Numbers**
Find the difference of real numbers.

Example 1.3.6
   Find: $73 - (-15)$

See also: Example 1.3.5
          Apply 4, 5, 6

❸ **Multiplying Numbers**
Find the product of real numbers.

Example 1.3.7c
   Find: $7 \cdot (-3)$

See also: Example 1.3.7a, b, d
          Apply 7-12

❹ **Dividing Numbers**
Find the quotient of real numbers.

Example 1.3.8d
   Find: $-18/(-3)$

See also: Example 1.3.8a, b, c, e, f
          Apply 13-18

❺ **Order of Operations**
Simplify an expression that contains more than one mathematical operation.

Example 1.3.9
   Find: $1 + 4^2 \div 2 - (7 - 2) \cdot 3$

See also: Example 1.3.10, 1.3.11, 1.3.12
          Apply 19-28

❻ **Properties of Numbers**
Apply properties of numbers to simplify an expression.

Example 1.3.13
   Find: $2 \cdot 2 \cdot 13 \cdot 5$

See also: Example 1.3.14, 1.3.15

Homework

Homework Problems

Circle the homework problems assigned to you by the computer, then complete them below.

 Explain

Operations on Numbers

Simplify the expressions in problems 1 through 8.

1. $-381 + 97$

2. $(4) \cdot (-8)$

3. $8 \div (9 - 5) + 7$

4. $-442 - (-126)$

5. $(-68) \div 17$

6. $(6 - 1) + 5 \cdot 3^2 - 8$

7. $-215 + [31 - (3 \cdot 2)]$

8. $(-12) \cdot (-7)$

9. Hiro bought 4 loaves of bread for $2.25 a loaf, 2 pounds of cheese for $3.50 a pound, and a dozen oranges for $.20 each. If he paid with a $20 bill, how much change did he get?

10. Betsy bought 4 cartons of ice cream for $2.25 a carton, 7 jars of chocolate sauce for $1.95 each, and a can of whipped cream for $1.43. If she started out the day with $12.37 in her checking account and wrote a check for all her purchases, how much did she have in her account at the end of the day?

Simplify the expressions in problems 11 and 12.

11. $42 \div [(2 \cdot 3) - (5 \cdot 2) + 1]$

12. $(6 - 3) \cdot 5 - (9 + 7) \div 2^3 + 4$

Explore

13. Simplify the following expressions:

    a. $2 + 8 \cdot 3$ d. $\frac{3}{4}(16 - 2)$

    b. $3 \cdot 5 + 3 \cdot 3$ e. $(3 - 5) \cdot 8 - 9 \div (6 - 3)$

    c. $6 + 3 \cdot 2^3$ f. $3 - 5 \cdot 8 - 9 \div 3 - 6$

14. Is the statement below true or false? Explain your reasoning.

    The product of a positive number and its opposite is positive.

15. Simplify the following expressions:

    a. $16 - 1 \cdot (13 - 9 \div 3)$

    b. $[(15 - 6 \div 2) \cdot 2 - 4] \div 2$

    c. $[(3 + 8) \cdot 2] \div 11 - 2$

    d. $3 \cdot (9 - 2) + 3 \cdot (9 + 2)$

    e. $\frac{2}{3}(17 - 26)$

    f. $\frac{3}{8}(13 + 5)$

16. Calculate the value of this expression:

    $(-3[6 - (-4)^2] + 3 \cdot 6) \div 2$

17. Is the statement below true or false? Explain your reasoning.

    The product of any two negative numbers is positive.

18. Determine which property justifies the following:

    $5(6 - 8) + 2 = 5 \cdot 6 + 5 \cdot (-8) + 2$

    Commutative Property of Addition
    Commutative Property of Multiplication
    Associative Property of Addition
    Associative Property of Multiplication
    Distributive Property

Apply

Practice Problems

Here are some additional practice problems for you to try.

Operations on Numbers

1. Find: $-34 + 82$

2. Find: $-22 + 10$

3. Find: $-73 + 39$

4. Find: $15 - (-43)$

5. Find: $-63 - (-18)$

6. Find: $-9 - (-36)$

7. Find: $4 \cdot (-15)$

8. Find: $-6 \cdot 24$

9. Find: $-5 \cdot 13$

10. Find: $-5 \cdot (-7)$

11. Find: $-12 \cdot (-28)$

12. Find: $-36 \cdot (-18)$

13. Find: $84 \div (-14)$

14. Find: $-136 \div 8$

15. Find: $-256 \div 64$

16. Find: $-78 \div (-13)$

17. Find: $-135 \div (-15)$

18. Find: $-132 \div (-11)$

19. Find: $3 \cdot 5 - 8$

20. Find: $8 + 2 \cdot 7$

21. Find: $26 \div [10 - (3 \cdot 4)]$

22. Find: $54 \div [3 - (2 \cdot 3)]$

23. Find: $6 \cdot (3 - 5)^2 + 24$

24. Find: $81 \div (10 - 7)^3 - 36$

25. Find: $72 \div (7 - 4)^2 + 11$

26. Find: $36 \div (5 - 2)^2 + 6 \cdot 7$

27. Find: $(-20 + 4) \div 2^3 - 3 \cdot 4^2$

28. Find: $(29 - 5) \div 2^2 + 3 \cdot 4$

Evaluate

Practice Test

Take this practice test to be sure that you are prepared for the final quiz in Evaluate.

1. Simplify the following expressions:
   a. $-6 - (-7)$
   b. $-4 - 1$
   c. $3 + (-9)$
   d. $-6 + 5$
   e. $-1 + (-12)$
   f. $7 - (-3)$

2. Simplify the following expressions:
   a. $(-8) \cdot (-4)$
   b. $8 \cdot (-4)$
   c. $(-8) \cdot 4$
   d. $(-8) \div (-4)$
   e. $8 \div (-4)$
   f. $(-8) \div 4$

3. Calculate the value of the expression
   $-2[5 - (-3)^2] + 4 \cdot 6$.

4. Determine whether each of the following statements is true.
   a. The sum of a positive number and its opposite is less than 1.
   b. The sum of a number and its opposite is negative.
   c. The product of a non-zero number and its opposite is negative.
   d. The sum of any two negative numbers is positive.

5. Determine the property that justifies each one of the highlighted steps below.
   $$= 2[(3 + 4) + (-3)]$$
   $$= \mathbf{2[3 + (4 + (-3))]}$$
   $$= \mathbf{2[3 + ((-3) + 4)]}$$
   $$= \mathbf{2[(3 + (-3)) + 4]}$$
   $$= 2[0 + 4]$$
   $$= 2[4]$$
   $$= 8$$

6. Yoko received $30.25 in credit when she returned a dress at a store. She then bought two pairs of jeans there for a total of $37.50. How much does she now owe the store?

7. Determine which property justifies the following:
   $$5(10 + (-2)) = 5(10) + 5(-2)$$
   Commutative Property of Addition
   Commutative Property of Multiplication
   Associative Property of Addition
   Associative Property of Multiplication
   Distributive Property
   Additive Inverse
   Multiplicative Inverse

8. Find the value of $[-(5 - 12)] \cdot (-1)$. Plot this value on the number line.

TOPIC 1 Cumulative Activities

Cumulative Review Problems

These problems combine all of the material you have covered so far in this course. You may want to test your understanding of this material before you move on to the next topic, or you may wish to do these problems to review for a test.

1. Circle the true statements.

    $-3(2) < -2(3)$

    $\dfrac{10}{12} = \dfrac{5}{6}$

    $\dfrac{2}{5} < 5$

    $9 < 5 + 3$

    $|-8| \geq |7|$

2. Find: $2^5 \cdot 3^2$

3. Find the GCF of 39 and 41.

4. Find: $\dfrac{15}{28} \cdot \dfrac{12}{25}$

5. Find: $\dfrac{6}{7} - \dfrac{1}{7}$

6. Find: $5^2(4 + 2) + 3^4$

7. Circle the true statements.

    $\dfrac{12}{15} \neq \dfrac{3}{4}$

    $|6| < |-14|$

    $2(5) < 2(8)$

    $(-2)(5) < (-2)(8)$

    $\dfrac{3}{8} \div \dfrac{9}{11} = \dfrac{8}{3} \cdot \dfrac{9}{11}$

8. Rewrite using exponents: $5 \cdot 5 \cdot 5 \cdot 7 \cdot 7 \cdot 7 \cdot 7$

9. Write in lowest terms: $\dfrac{56}{63}$

10. Find: $\dfrac{2}{9} + \dfrac{5}{9}$

11. Find: $(2 - 7) \cdot (8 + 4) - 112$

12. Circle the true statements.

    $12 \geq 12$

    $|-3| < |-2|$

    $\dfrac{9}{4} > 3$

    $|0| = 0$

    $\dfrac{5}{7} \cdot \dfrac{2}{9} = \dfrac{5}{7} \div \dfrac{9}{2}$

13. Find the LCM of 15 and 16.

14. Find: $\dfrac{56}{45} \div \dfrac{14}{75}$

15. Find: $6[(4 + 2) - 5(3 - 1) + 7]$

16. Find: $6^3 \cdot 4^2$

17. Find: $\dfrac{14}{15} \cdot \dfrac{20}{21}$

18. Find: $7^3 - 15[(5 - 2) \cdot 3 - 1]$

19. Plot the points $\sqrt{17}$, π, 4, and $\sqrt{8}$ on the number line below. Then order the points from smallest to largest.

20. Find: $\dfrac{17}{30} + \dfrac{29}{24}$

21. Circle the true statements.

    The opposite of -3 is 3.

    The correct order of operations is to add before you subtract.

    A negative number divided by a positive number is negative.

    The multiplicative inverse of 7 is $-\dfrac{1}{7}$.

22. Find: $\dfrac{3}{14} + \dfrac{7}{18}$

23. Find the LCM of 6 and 9.

24. Find the GCF of 45 and 36. Write your answer using exponents.

25. Find: $\dfrac{11}{18} \div \dfrac{25}{6}$

26. Write in lowest terms: $\dfrac{90}{126}$

27. Find: $\dfrac{7}{15} - \dfrac{19}{25}$

28. Circle the true statements.

$\dfrac{3}{4} + \dfrac{1}{6} = \dfrac{4}{10}$

$\dfrac{3}{4} \cdot \dfrac{1}{6} = \dfrac{3}{24}$

$-2 > 0$

$|-5 + 2| \le |2 - 5|$

$\dfrac{2}{3} \ne \dfrac{5}{6}$

29. Find the GCF of 88 and 121.

30. Find the GCF of 90 and 315. Write your answer using exponents.

TOPIC 2
SOLVING LINEAR EQUATIONS AND INEQUALITIES

When you solve a problem in algebra, there is often some quantity that you are asked to find. It may be a person's age, the distance a car has traveled, or perhaps the number of olives in a container. The unknown quantity is represented by a letter called a variable.

In this topic, you will learn about variables and algebraic expressions. Algebraic expressions are used in equations and inequalities, which in turn can be used to model real world situations. Such models are useful for solving problems in many important fields such as business, the life sciences, and the social sciences.

Lesson 2.1 Algebraic Expressions

Concept 1: Simplifying Expressions
Definitions
Simplifying Algebraic Expressions
Evaluating Algebraic Expressions

Lesson 2.2 Solving Linear Equations

Concept 1: Solving Equations I
Definitions
The Solution of a Linear Equation
Principles of Equality
Combining the Principles to Solve Linear
    Equations

Concept 2: Solving Equations II
Solving Linear Equations That Contain
    Fractions
Solving Linear Equations That Have Variables
    on Both Sides
Solving Linear Equations That Contain
    Parentheses
A General Procedure for Solving a Linear
    Equation
Identities and Equations with No Solution
Formulas

Lesson 2.3 Problem Solving

Concept 1: Number and Age
Translating Words into Algebra
A General Procedure for Solving Word
    Problems
Number Problems
Age Problems

Concept 2: Geometry
Geometry Problems

Lesson 2.4 Linear Inequalities

Concept 1: Solving Inequalities
Linear Inequalities
Graphing the Solutions of a Linear Inequality
Solving Linear Inequalities Using Addition and
    Subtraction
Solving Linear Inequalities Using
    Multiplication and Division
Compound Linear Inequalities
Solving Compound Linear Inequalities

LESSON 2.1
ALGEBRAIC EXPRESSIONS

 Overview

In algebra, a letter may be used to represent an unspecified number. For example, to represent the width of a rectangle, you might use the letter x. The letter x is called a variable.

Algebra makes use of variables. In this lesson you will learn about variables and how to use them in mathematical expressions. You will also simplify and evaluate expressions containing variables.

 Explain

Concept 1 has sections on

- **Definitions**

- **Simplifying Algebraic Expressions**

- **Evaluating Algebraic Expressions**

CONCEPT 1: SIMPLIFYING EXPRESSIONS

Definitions

An **algebraic expression** is a collection of numerals, letters, operators (such as $+$, $-$, $\cdot$, and $\div$), and grouping symbols.

Here's an example of an algebraic expression:

$$3x^2 - 8 + xy^3$$

The different parts of an expression are given special names.

- A **term** is a quantity joined to other quantities by the operation of addition or subtraction.

When a term is subtracted, a negative sign is attached to the individual term.

A term includes the sign $(+$ or $-)$ that precedes it.

For example, the expression $3x^2 - 8 + xy^3$ has three terms:

$$+3x^2, \quad -8, \quad +xy^3$$

- A **variable** is a symbol used to represent a quantity whose value we do not know or whose value may change. We typically use letters such as x and y for variables.

For example, the expression $3x^2 - 8 + xy^3$ has two variables, x and y.

$$3x^2 - 8 + \mathbf{xy^3}$$

- A **constant term** is a term that does not contain a variable.

For example, the expression $3x^2 - 8 + xy^3$ has one constant term, -8.

$$3x^2 - \mathbf{8} + xy^3$$

- A **coefficient** is the numeric part of a term.

If the numeric part of the term is not written explicitly, the coefficient is 1.

For example, consider the expression $3x^2 - 8 + xy^3$:
In the term $3x^2$, the coefficient is 3.
In the term -8, the coefficient is -8.
In the term xy^3, the coefficient is 1.

$$3x^2 - 8 + \mathbf{1}xy^3$$

Example 2.1.1

Given the expression $-4w + 25wx^3 - 15 - x^2$, identify each of the following:

a. terms   b. variables   c. constant terms   d. coefficients

Solution

a. The terms are $-4w$, $25wx^3$, -15, and $-x^2$.
   Terms are joined by $+$ and $-$.

b. The variables are w and x.

c. The constant term is -15. A constant term does not contain a variable.

d. The coefficient of the term $-4w$ is -4.
   The coefficient of the term $25wx^3$ is 25.
   The coefficient of the term -15 is -15.
   The coefficient of the term $-x^2$ is -1 because $-x^2$ may be written $-1x^2$.

Simplifying Algebraic Expressions

Like terms are terms that have the same variables raised to the same powers. Constant terms are considered like terms.

For example,

- $3x$ and $-4.2x$ are like terms.

- $8x^2y^3$ and x^2y^3 are like terms.

- $-\frac{2}{5}x^3y$ and $3.5yx^3$ are like terms.

- 5 and -3 are like terms because they are constant terms.

However, $4x^2y^3$ and $7x^3y^2$ are **not** like terms. This is because in $4x^2y^3$, the variable x is raised to the second power, while in $7x^3y^2$, the variable x is raised to the third power.

Similarly, in each term the variable y has a different exponent.

To combine like terms we add their coefficients.

To do so, we use the Distributive Property in reverse:

$$2x + 3x$$
$$= (2 + 3)x$$
$$= 5x$$

When we **simplify an expression**, we rewrite it in a form that is usually easier to work with. To do this, we perform operations such as removing parentheses and combining like terms. Once all of the mathematical operations have been carried out, the expression is said to be completely simplified.

This example may help you:

2 dogs + 3 dogs = 5 dogs
2 miles + 3 miles = 5 miles
2x + 3x = 5x

Be careful. We can combine like terms only: 2x + 3x = 5x

However, 2x + 3y are not like terms. That is: 2x + 3y ≠ 5xy

Example 2.1.2

Simplify each expression.

a. $8x + 3x - 2x$ b. $12w^4 - 5w^3 - w^4$ c. $-7x^2 + 9x + 5x^2 - 2x$

Solution

a.   All three terms are like terms. $8x + 3x - 2x$
      Combine their coefficients. $= (8 + 3 - 2)x$
                                          $= 9x$

b. Only the first and last terms are like terms.
    Note that the coefficient of the term $-w^4$ is -1.
    Use the Commutative Property to write the like terms next to each other.
    Combine like terms.

    Therefore, $12w^4 - 5w^3 - w^4$ simplifies to $11w^4 - 5w^3$.

$$12w^4 - 5w^3 - w^4$$
$$= 12w^4 - 5w^3 - \mathbf{1}w^4$$
$$= \mathbf{12}w^4 - \mathbf{1}w^4 - 5w^3$$
$$= [\mathbf{12 + (-1)}]w^4 - 5w^3$$
$$= 11w^4 - 5w^3$$

c. There are two pairs of like terms, the x^2-terms and the x-terms.
    Use the Commutative Property to write the like terms next to each other.
    Combine like terms.

$$-7x^2 + 9x + 5x^2 - 2x$$
$$= -7x^2 + 5x^2 + 9x - 2x$$
$$= \mathbf{-2}x^2 + \mathbf{7}x$$

    Therefore, $-7x^2 + 9x + 5x^2 - 2x$ simplifies to $-2x^2 + 7x$.

When an expression contains parentheses, we often use the Distributive Property to remove them. Then, we combine like terms to simplify the expression.

Recall that the Distributive Property is $a(b + c) = ab + ac$. (Here a, b, and c are real numbers.)

Example **2.1.3**

Simplify.

a. $3(4x + 2)$ b. $-2(5 - x)$ c. $(x + 3)2$ d. $-(2x - 3)$

Solution

a. Distribute the 3 to each term inside the parentheses.
    Simplify.

$$3(4x + 2)$$
$$= \mathbf{3}(4x) + \mathbf{3}(2)$$
$$= 12x + 6$$

    Therefore, $3(4x + 2)$ simplifies to $12x + 6$.

b. Be careful with the negative signs.
    Distribute the -2 to each term inside the parentheses.
    Simplify.

$$-2(5 - x)$$
$$= \mathbf{-2}(5) - (\mathbf{-2})(x)$$
$$= -10 + 2x$$

    Therefore, $-2(5 - x)$ simplifies to $-10 + 2x$.

Because multiplication is commutative, the Distributive Property may also be stated as $(b + c)a = ab + ac$.

c. Distribute the 2 to each term inside the parentheses.
    Simplify.

$$(x + 3)2$$
$$= x(\mathbf{2}) + 3(\mathbf{2})$$
$$= 2x + 6$$

    Therefore, $(x + 3)2$ simplifies to $2x + 6$.

d. A negative sign in front of the parentheses means -1 times the expression inside the parentheses.

$$-(2x - 3)$$

$$= -\mathbf{1}(2x - 3)$$

When we distribute -1, we change the sign of each term inside the parentheses.

Distribute the -1.

$$= -\mathbf{1}(2x) - (-\mathbf{1})(3)$$

Simplify.

$$= -2x + 3$$

Therefore, $-(2x - 3)$ simplifies to $-2x + 3$.

Here is a procedure for simplifying expressions.

— Procedure —
To Simplify an Expression

Step 1 Use the Distributive Property to remove parentheses.

Step 2 Use the Commutative Property to move like terms next to each other.

Step 3 Combine like terms.

Example 2.1.4

Simplify: $3(xy - 7) - 4y(x + 5) + 8y$

Solution

Step 1 Use the Distributive Property to remove parentheses.

$$3(xy - 7) - 4y(x + 5) + 8y$$

Distribute 3. Then, distribute $-4y$.

$$= \mathbf{3} \cdot xy - \mathbf{3} \cdot 7 - \mathbf{4y} \cdot x - \mathbf{4y} \cdot 5 + 8y$$

Simplify.

$$= 3xy - 21 - 4xy - 20y + 8y$$

Step 2 Use the Commutative Property to move like terms next to each other.

$$= 3xy - 4xy - 20y + 8y - 21$$

Step 3 Combine like terms.

$$= -\mathbf{1}xy - \mathbf{12}y - 21$$

We usually do not write coefficients 1 or -1, so we write the answer as $-xy - 12y - 21$.

Example 2.1.5

Simplify: $9x - (3x - 4) + 5x$

Solution

Step 1 Use the Distributive Property to remove parentheses.	$9x - (3x - 4) + 5x$
Note that the minus sign in front of the parentheses means multiply each term inside the parentheses by -1.	$= 9x - 3x + 4 + 5x$
Step 2 Use the Commutative Property to move like terms next to each other.	$= 9x - 3x + 5x + 4$
Step 3 Combine like terms.	$= 11x + 4$

So, $9x - (3x - 4) + 5x$ simplifies to $11x + 4$.

— Caution —
Not All Parentheses Indicate the Distributive Property

It may be tempting to distribute the 2 in $10 - 2(7x \cdot 3)$.

However, the operation inside the parentheses is multiplication, not addition, so we may not use the Distributive Property here.

To simplify this expression, use the order of operations. That is, do the work inside the parentheses first, then combine like terms.

	$= 10 - 2(7x \cdot 3)$
Multiply inside parentheses.	$= 10 - 2(\mathbf{21x})$
Multiply.	$= 10 - \mathbf{42x}$

Evaluating Algebraic Expressions

To **evaluate an expression**, we first replace each variable with a given number. Then we simplify the result.

Example 2.1.6

Evaluate $8x - 5y + 9$ when $x = -2$ and $y = 6$.

Solution			
	$8x$	$- 5y$	$+ 9$
Replace x with -2 and y with 6.	$8(\mathbf{-2})$	$- 5(\mathbf{6})$	$+ 9$
Multiply.	$= \mathbf{-16}$	$- \mathbf{30}$	$+ 9$
Add and subtract.	$= -37$		

When $x = -2$ and $y = 6$, the expression $8x - 5y + 9$ has the value -37.

Example 2.1.7 Evaluate $-x^2 - 5xy + 8$ when $x = 3$ and $y = -4$.

Solution

$$-x^2 - 5xy + 8$$

Replace x with 3 and y with -4.

$$-(3)^2 - 5(3)(-4) + 8$$

Multiply.

$$= -9 - (-60) + 8$$

Add and subtract.

$$= 59$$

To evaluate $-(3)^2$, we use the order of operations.

$$-(3)^2 = -(9) = -9$$

$\uparrow$ $\uparrow$

Find 3^2.   Multiply by -1.

When $x = 3$ and $y = -4$, the expression $-x^2 - 5xy + 8$ has the value 59.

Example 2.1.8

An object falls d feet in t seconds as given by the formula $d = \frac{1}{2}gt^2$.

Here, g represents the acceleration due to gravity. On the surface of the earth, g is about 32 feet/sec^2.

Note that $sec \cdot sec = sec^2$.
We read sec^2 as "seconds squared."

Melissa drops a rock off a bridge. The rock hits the river below 3 seconds later. How high is the bridge?

Solution

The height of the bridge is the same as the distance the rock falls in 3 seconds.

$$d = \frac{1}{2}gt^2$$

Replace g with 32 feet/sec^2 and t with 3 sec.

$$= \frac{1}{2} \cdot \frac{\mathbf{32\ feet}}{\mathbf{1\ sec^2}} \cdot (\mathbf{3\ sec})^2$$

Calculate the square.

$$= \frac{1}{2} \cdot \frac{32\ feet}{1\ \cancel{sec^2}} \cdot 9\ \cancel{sec^2}$$

Cancel the units.

$$= \frac{1}{2}(32)(9)\ feet$$

$$= 144\ feet$$

The rock fell about 144 feet, so the bridge is 144 feet high.

When we simplify an expression, the new expression is equivalent to the original expression. That is, if we use the same numbers to replace the variables in both the original expression and the simplified expression, we obtain the same value.

For example, let's simplify: $= 8x + 2(x - 1) - 6x$

Distribute the 2. $= 8x + \mathbf{2x - 2} - 6x$

Combine like terms. $= \mathbf{4x} - 2$

Now replace x with any number. For example, let $x = 5$.

Original Form	Simplified Form
$8x + 2(x - 1) - 6x$	$4x - 2$
$8(\mathbf{5}) + 2(\mathbf{5} - 1) - 6(\mathbf{5})$	$4(\mathbf{5}) - 2$
$= 8(5) + 2(\mathbf{4}) - 6(5)$	$= \mathbf{20} - 2$
$= \mathbf{40 + 8 - 30}$	$= 18$
$= 18$	

Notice that both expressions simplify to the same value, 18.

Example 2.1.9

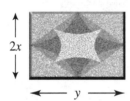

Sue decides to use tiles of two different sizes to create a pattern by her front door.

The small tiles are squares.

The large tiles are rectangles. The width of a large tile is twice the width of a small tile.

Sue will use 6 small tiles and 3 large tiles.

Let x represent the width of a small tile. Therefore, the area of a small tile is $x \cdot x = x^2$.

Let y represent the length of a large tile. Therefore, the area of a large tile is $2x \cdot y = 2xy$.

The area of the tiles may be represented as follows:

Total area = (area of 6 small tiles) + (area of 3 large tiles)

$$= \quad 6(x^2) \quad + \quad 3(2xy)$$

$$= 6x^2 + 6xy$$

a. Find the total area when $x = 5$ inches and $y = 12$ inches.

b. Find the total cost of the tiles if each tile costs $0.25 per square inch.

Solution

a. To evaluate $6x^2 + 6xy$, $6x^2 + 6xy$
    replace x with 5 inches
    and y with 12 inches. $= 6(\textbf{5 inches})^2 + 6(\textbf{5 inches})(\textbf{12 inches})$

    Then, simplify. $= 6(\textbf{25 inches}^2) + 6(\textbf{60 inches}^2)$ *Note that inch · inch = inch².*
    $= \textbf{150}\text{ inches}^2 + \textbf{360}\text{ inches}^2$ *We read inch² as "square inches."*
    $= 510\text{ inches}^2$

The total area of the tiles is 510 square inches.

b. To find the total cost, multiply the cost of one square inch of tile by
    the total square inches needed.

    Total cost $=$ ($0.25 per square inch) · (510 square inches)

    $$= \frac{\$0.25}{1 \text{ square inch}} \cdot \frac{510 \text{ square inches}}{1}$$

    $= \$127.50$

The tiles will cost $127.50.

Here is a summary of this concept from *Academic Systems Algebra*.

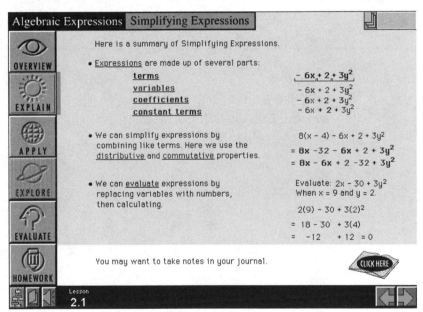

Checklist Lesson 2.1

Here is what you should know after completing this lesson.

Words and Phrases

algebraic expression

term

variable

constant term

coefficient

like terms

simplify an expression

evaluate an expression

Ideas and Procedures

❶ **Parts of an Expression**

Identify the parts of algebraic expression

Example 2.1.1

Given the expression $-4w + 25wx^3 - 15 - x^2$, identify the terms, variables, constant terms, and coefficients.

See also: Apply 1, 2

❷ **Simplify an Expression**

Simplify an algebraic expression.

Example 2.1.4

Simplify: $3(xy - 7) - 4y(x + 5) + 8y$

See also: Example 2.1.2, 2.1.3, 2.1.5
Apply 3-20

❸ **Evaluate an Expression**

Evaluate an algebraic expression for given values of the variables.

Example 2.1.7

Evaluate $-x^2 - 5xy + 8$ when $x = 3$ and $y = -4$.

See also: Example 2.1.6, 2.1.8, 2.1.9
Apply 21-28

Homework

Homework Problems

Circle the homework problems assigned to you by the computer, then complete them below.

 Explain

Simplifying Expressions

1. What are the constants in the expression
$11 + 4y - 6 + 2x - 1$?

2. Simplify the expression
$2x - 5 + 4y + 3x - 7y + 4$.

3. Evaluate the expression $4x - 7$ when $x = -3$.

4. What are the terms in the expression
$3xy - 5x + 8 - y - x^2y$?

5. Simplify the expression $5 + 3(x - 1)$.

6. Evaluate the expression $2x + 3y + 5$ when $x = 2$
and $y = 1$.

7. Simplify the expression $3(y - 4) + 4y(x + 2) + 5$.

8. Evaluate the expression $3xy - 2x + 1 - y$ when
$x = -1$ and $y = 2$.

9. Melissa bought 3 gallons of white paint for $11.00 per gallon, 2 quarts of blue paint for $7.00 per quart, and 1 brush for $6.00. How much did she spend all together?

   Hint: The amount she spent can be expressed as:
   $3(11) + 2(7) + 1(6)$

10. Mr. Burton is in charge of the cookie sale for his daughter's Girl Scout troop. When the girls turned in their money, he collected 6 twenty-dollar bills, 8 ten-dollar bills, 17 five-dollar bills, and 25 one-dollar bills. How much money did he collect all together?

    Hint: The amount of money he collected can be expressed as:
    $6(20) + 8(10) + 17(5) + 25(1)$

11. Simplify the expression
$7(2 - x) - 8 - 2(y - 3x) + 4y$.

12. Evaluate the expression $xy^2 - 4y + 2 - 3x$ when
$x = 3$ and $y = -2$.

 **Apply**

Practice Problems

Here are some additional practice problems for you to try.

Simplifying Expressions

1. What are the terms in the expression $6x^3 + 5xy^2 - y + 25$?

2. What are the terms in the expression $3a^3 - 2a^2b + 7b^2 - 6$?

3. Simplify: $2(3y + 7) - 10$

4. Simplify: $8 - 4(a + 3)$

5. Simplify: $3 - 5(x - 7)$

6. Simplify: $7b + 10 + 3b - 17$

7. Simplify: $-4x - 15 + 9x - 12$

8. Simplify: $6a - 13 - 5a + 15$

9. Simplify: $2(y - 3) + 5(y + 4)$

10. Simplify: $5a(b - 7) - 2(3a + 4)$

11. Simplify: $4(x + 5) - 3x(y + 3)$

12. Simplify: $7(b^2 + 2b) - 3(b - 5)$

13. Simplify: $12(x - 3) - 7(2x^2 + 6x)$

14. Simplify: $11(a + 1) + 8(a^2 - 3a)$

15. Simplify: $10(y + 7) - 12 + 3(y^2 + 2y)$

16. Simplify: $15(2 - b) + 32 - 9(3b - b^2)$

17. Simplify: $15(x - 2) + 24 - 10(3x - x^2)$

18. Simplify: $4b(a + 5) - 7a - 2(3ab - b^2)$

19. Simplify: $7m(n - 6) + 10m + 3(n^2 - 8mn)$

20. Simplify: $5x(6 - y) + 5x + 4(y^2 - 2xy)$

21. Evaluate $7a - 3b + 9$ when $a = -3$ and $b = -4$.

22. Evaluate $8m + n - 17$ when $m = 5$ and $n = -1$.

23. Evaluate $3x + 4y - 5$ when $x = 6$ and $y = -2$.

24. Evaluate $3a^2 - 7a - 6b$ when $a = 23$ and $b = 11$.

25. Evaluate $10m + 2n - 8n^2$ when $m = 5$ and $n = -4$.

26. Evaluate $2x^2 - x - 2y$ when $x = 5$ and $y = 10$.

27. Evaluate $3x^3 - 6xy - 5xz + 4z - 1$ when $x = 2$, $y = -4$, and $z = 7$.

28. Evaluate $2a^3 - 7ab + 3ac - 10c + 8$ when $a = -2$, $b = 3$, and $c = 5$

Evaluate

Practice Test

Take this practice test to be sure that you are prepared for the final quiz in Evaluate.

1. What are the coefficients in the expression $2x^2y - y + 7xy - 4y^3 + 12$?

2. Simplify the following expression by using the distributive property and combining like terms:
$7(x + 3) + 2(9 - x)$

3. Simplify the following expression by using the distributive property and combining like terms:
$y(3 - y) + 5(x + y^2) - x(2 - 7y)$

4. Evaluate the expression $2x^3 - 4x^2 + 7x - 6$ when $x = 2$.

5. Evaluate the expression $5x + 2xy - 5y^2$ when $x = 3$ and $y = -2$.

6. Simplify the following expression by using the distributive property and combining like terms:
$y(6 + y) - 5(y^2 - 1) + 2$

7. Evaluate the expression $4x^2y + y - 5xy^2 - 15$ when $x = 5$ and $y = 3$.

8. Simplify the following expression by using the distributive property and combining like terms:
$x^2(3 + y) - 2x(5 - x) + 6x^2y$

LESSON 2.2
SOLVING LINEAR EQUATIONS

 Overview

Suppose a friend hands you 25 olives and a container with an unknown number of olives inside. She tells you she has just handed you a total of 67 olives.

Using this information you can figure out the number of olives in the container.

One way to do so is to set up and solve an equation.

Solving an equation for an unknown, like the number of olives in the container, is an important part of algebra. In this lesson you will study a particular type of equation, the linear equation.

 Explain

Concept 1 has sections on

- **Definitions**

- **The Solution of a Linear Equation**

- **Principles of Equality**

- **Combining the Principles to Solve Linear Equations**

CONCEPT 1: SOLVING EQUATIONS I

Definitions

Recall that an expression is a collection of numerals, letters, operators, and grouping symbols.

Here are two examples of expressions:

$$14x - 10$$
$$3(12x + 6)$$

An **equation** is a mathematical statement that consists of two expressions joined by an equals sign, $=$.

Here is an example of an equation:

$$14x - 10 = 3(12x + 6)$$

An equation is like an English sentence.

- Some sentences are **false**.
  For example: "A week has 12 days."

  Some equations are **false**.
  For example: $1 + 2 = 4$

- Some sentences are **true**.
  For example: "A week has 7 days."

  Some equations are **true**.
  For example: $1 + 2 = 3$

- Some sentences are **conditionally true**.
  For example: "There are 31 days in a month."
  This is true for January, March, May, July, August, October, and December.
  Otherwise, this statement is false.

  Some equations are **conditionally true**.
  For example: $x + 2 = 3$

  If the value of x is 1, this equation is true.
  Otherwise, this equation is false.

  An equation that is true for some values of the variable and false for others is called a **conditional equation**.

There are many different types of equations. One type is the **linear equation in one variable**. This is an equation that can be written in the general form

$$ax + b = c$$

The letter x is often used for the variable in an equation. However, other letters may also be used for the variable. For example, 5y − 6 = 9 is a linear equation. So is 4z = −10.

where a, b, and c are real numbers, $a \neq 0$, and x is a variable that represents an unknown quantity.

In a linear equation, the variable always has exponent 1. If no exponent is written, it's understood to be 1. That is, x has the same meaning as x^1.

An equation that is not linear is called a non-linear equation.

The Solution of a Linear Equation

A **solution** of an equation is a number that, when substituted for the variable, makes the equation true. The solution is said to **satisfy** the equation.

Example 2.2.1

Is $x = -3$ a solution of the equation $3x + 10 = 4 + x$?

Solution $3x + 10 = 4 + x$

Replace x with -3.   Is $3(-3) + 10 = 4 + (-3)$?

Simplify each side of the equation.   Is $-9 + 10 = 1$?

The result is a true statement.   Is $1 = 1$? **Yes**

Therefore, $x = -3$ is a solution of
the equation $3x + 10 = 4 + x$.

The solution, -3 satisfies the equation.

Example 2.2.2

Is $p = 7$ a solution of the equation $5(p - 6) = -5$?

Solution $5(p - 6) = -5$

Replace p with 7.   Is $5(7 - 6) = -5$?

Simplify each side of the equation.   Is $5(1) = -5$?

The result is a false statement.   Is $5 = -5$? **No**

Therefore, $p = 7$ is NOT a solution
of $5(p - 6) = -5$.

The number 7 does NOT satisfy the equation.

— Note —
Some Differences Between an Expression and an Equation

Expression	Equation
• An expression **never** contains an equals sign.	• An equations **always** contains an equals sign.
• We **simplify** an expression.	• We **solve** an equation.
For example, we simplify $4x + 2x$ to get $6x$.	For example, we solve $4x + 2x = 6$ to get $x = 1$.

Principles of Equality

Equivalent equations are equations that have the same solutions. For example, the following equations are equivalent because 4 is a solution of each.

$2x + 6 = 14$
$2x = 8$
$x = 4$

In the last example, notice that the variable, x, is by itself on one side of the equation. A constant, 4, is on the other side.

An equation can be solved by transforming it into an equivalent equation with the variable isolated on one side and a constant on the other.

Four principles of equality can be used to transform an equation.

The first principle is the Addition Principle of Equality.

— Principle —
Addition Principle of Equality

English: If we add the same quantity to both sides of an equation, we obtain an equivalent equation.

Algebra: If $a = b$, then $a + c = b + c$.
(a, b, and c are real numbers.)

Example: If $x = 5$, then $x + 2 = 5 + 2$.

Example 2.2.3

Solve: $x - 6 = -8$

Solution

We will use the Addition Principle of Equality to get x by itself on one side of the equation.

$$x - 6 = -8$$

To isolate x, add 6 to both sides of the equation.

$$x - 6 + \mathbf{6} = -8 + \mathbf{6}$$

Simplify.

$$x + 0 = -2$$

$$x = -2$$

Check

Now we check that $x = -2$ is a solution of the original equation.

$$x - 6 = -8$$

In the original equation, replace x with -2.   Is $\mathbf{-2} - 6 = -8$?

The result is a true statement.   Is $\quad -8 = -8$? **Yes**

The solution of the equation is $x = -2$.

The Subtraction Principle is similar to the Addition Principle.

— Principle —
Subtraction Principle of Equality

English: If we subtract the same quantity from both sides of an equation, we obtain an equivalent equation.

Algebra: If $a = b$, then $a - c = b - c$.
(a, b, and c are real numbers.)

Example: If $x = 5$, then $x - 2 = 5 - 2$.

Example 2.2.4

Solve: $5 + x = -4$

Solution

We will use the Subtraction Principle of Equality to get x by itself on one side of the equation.

$$5 + x = -4$$

To isolate x, subtract 5 from both sides of the equation.

$$5 + x \; \mathbf{5} = -4 - \mathbf{5}$$

Simplify.

$$x + 0 = -9$$

$$x = -9$$

The solution of the equation is $x = -9$.

You may want to check the solution.

We may also use division to transform an equation.

— Principle —
Division Principle of Equality

English: If we divide both sides of an equation by the same non-zero quantity, we obtain an equivalent equation.

Algebra: If $a = b$, then $a \div c = b \div c$.
(a, b, and c are real numbers; $c \neq 0$.)

Example: If $x = 5$, then $x \div 2 = 5 \div 2$.

Example 2.2.5

Solve: $-21 = 7x$

Solution

We will use the Division Principle of Equality to get x by itself on one side of the equation.

$$-21 = 7x$$

To make the coefficient of the variable 1, divide both sides of the equation by 7.

$$\frac{-21}{7} = \frac{7x}{7}$$

Simplify.

$$-3 = 1x$$
$$-3 = x$$

The solution of the equation is $x = -3$.

You may want to check the solution.

```
 ┌──────────────────────────────────────────────────┐
 │                  — Principle —                     │
 │        Multiplication Principle of Equality        │
 ├──────────────────────────────────────────────────┤
```

English: If we multiply both sides of an equation by the same non-zero quantity, we obtain an equivalent equation.

Algebra: If $a = b$, then $a \cdot c = b \cdot c$.
(a, b, and c are real numbers; $c \neq 0$.)

Example: If $x = 5$, then $x \cdot 2 = 5 \cdot 2$.

Example **2.2.6**   Solve: $-\dfrac{x}{2} = 3$

Solution

We will use the Multiplication Principle of Equality to get x by itself on one side of the equation.

$$-\frac{x}{2} = 3$$

When we multiply the left side by -2, we "cancel" the -2 in the denominator. The result is $\frac{x}{1}$ which is x.

To make the coefficient of the variable 1, multiply both sides of the equation by -2.

$$(-2) \cdot \left(-\frac{x}{2}\right) = (-2) \cdot (3)$$

Simplify.

$$x = -6$$

The solution of the equation is $x = -6$.

You may want to check the solution.

Combining the Principles to Solve Linear Equations

It is often necessary to use more than one of the principles of equality to solve an equation. When that is the case, follow this order:

• First, use addition or subtraction to get all terms with a variable on one side and the constant terms on the other side.

• Second, use multiplication or division to make the coefficient of the variable 1.

Example **2.2.7**

Solve: $2x - 7 = -15$

Solution

$$2x - 7 = -15$$

To isolate the x-term, add 7 to both sides of the equation.

$$2x - 7 + 7 = -15 + 7$$

Simplify.

$$2x = -8$$

To make the coefficient of the variable 1, divide both sides of the equation by 2.

$$\frac{2x}{2} = \frac{-8}{2}$$

Simplify.

$$x = -4$$

The solution of the equation is $x = -4$.

Example 2.2.8

Solve: $15 - w = 42$

Solution

To isolate the variable term, subtract 15 from both sides of the equation.	$15 - w = 42$ $15 - w - \mathbf{15} = 42 - \mathbf{15}$
Simplify.	$-w = 27$
Note that $-w$ means $-1w$.	$-\mathbf{1}w = 27$
To make the coefficient of the variable 1, divide both sides of the equation by -1.	$\dfrac{-1w}{-1} = \dfrac{27}{-1}$
Simplify.	$w = -27$

The solution of the equation is $w = -27$.

Example 2.2.9

Tony wants to find the thickness, T, of the screw head shown. Write an equation that represents this situation. Then, solve the equation for T.

Solution

Here are two ways to write the equation.

$$\text{Unknown length} = \text{Total length} - \text{Known length}$$
$$T = 3.875 \text{ cm} - 3.448 \text{ cm}$$
$$T = 0.427 \text{ cm}$$

or

$$\text{Total length} = \text{Unknown length} + \text{Known length}$$
$$3.875 \text{ cm} = T + 3.448 \text{ cm}$$
$$3.875 - 3.448 = T + 3.448 - 3.448$$
$$0.427 \text{ cm} = T$$

The thickness, T, of the screw head is 0.427 cm.

Example 2.2.10

To sell a house, a real estate company charges the owner a commission of 7% of the selling price.

a. After paying the commission the owner received $152,520. What was the selling price of the house?

b. How much was the commission?

Solution

a. The amount received by the owner can be written as an equation:

$$\text{Amount Received} = \text{Selling Price} - \text{Commission}$$

Amount Received: We are told that the amount received is $152,520.

Selling Price: This is what we are asked to find. So, we represent the selling price with a variable, x.

Commission: The commission is based on the selling price. Here, the commission is 7% of the selling price, that is, 7% of x.

We write 7% as a decimal: $7\% = \dfrac{7}{100} = 0.07$

Therefore, the commission, 7% of x, is $0.07x$.

Now, put these expressions in the equation and solve for x.

	Amount = Selling Price − Commission
	$\$152,520 =$ x $-$ 7% of x
We write x as $1.00x$.	$152,520 =$ $1.00x$ $-$ $0.07x$
Combine like terms.	$152,520 =$ **$0.93x$**
To isolate x, divide both sides of the equation by 0.93.	$\dfrac{152,520}{0.93} = \dfrac{0.93x}{0.93}$
Simplify.	$164,000 =$ x

The selling price was $164,000.

b. The commission is $0.07x$. $0.07x$

Replace x with 164,000. $= 0.07 \cdot (\textbf{164,000})$

Simplify. $= 11,480$

The commission was $11,480.

Here is a summary of this concept from *Academic Systems Algebra*.

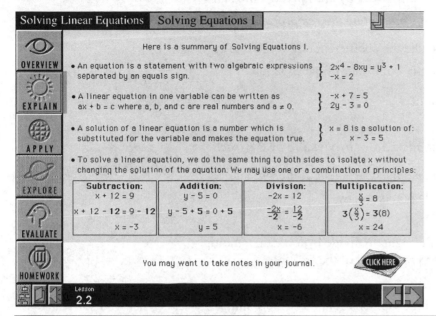

CONCEPT 2:
SOLVING EQUATIONS II

Solving Linear Equations That Contain Fractions

Let's look at an equation where the coefficient of the variable is a fraction.

For example, $\frac{3}{5}x = 12$.

There are several ways to solve this type of equation.

Example 2.2.11

Solve: $\frac{3}{5}x = 12$

Solution

Here are three ways to solve this equation.

Method 1: Solve by clearing the fraction:

$$\frac{3}{5}x = 12$$

To clear the fraction, multiply both sides
of the equation by 5.

$$5 \cdot \left(\frac{3}{5}x\right) = 5 \cdot (12)$$

Simplify.

$$\overset{1}{\cancel{5}} \cdot \left(\frac{3}{\cancel{5}}x\right) = 60$$

$$3x = 60$$

Divide both sides by 3.

$$\frac{3x}{3} = \frac{60}{3}$$

Simplify.

$$x = 20$$

Concept 2 has sections on

- **Solving Linear Equations That Contain Fractions**

- **Solving Linear Equations That Have Variables on Both Sides**

- **Solving Linear Equations That Contain Parentheses**

- **A General Procedure for Solving a Linear Equation**

- **Identities and Equations with No Solution**

- **Formulas**

Method 2: Solve by multiplying both sides $\frac{3}{5}x = 12$
of the equation by the reciprocal of $\frac{3}{5}$:

To make the coefficient of the variable 1,
multiply both sides of the equation by $\frac{5}{3}$. $\frac{5}{3} \cdot \left(\frac{3}{5}x\right) = \frac{5}{3} \cdot 12$

Simplify. $1x = 20$

     $x = 20$

Method 3: Solve by dividing by the fraction: $\frac{3}{5}x = 12$

To make the coefficient of the variable 1,
divide both sides by $\frac{3}{5}$. $\dfrac{\frac{3}{5}x}{\frac{3}{5}} = \dfrac{12}{\frac{3}{5}}$

On the right, to divide by a fraction, multiply
by the reciprocal of the fraction. $1x = 12 \cdot \dfrac{5}{3}$

     $x = 20$

All three methods give the same solution, $x = 20$. When you solve an
equation, choose the method that is easiest for you.

Solving Linear Equations that Have Variables on Both Sides

When variables are present on both sides of the equals sign, use the
Addition Principle of Equality to move all of the variables to one side of
the equation.

Example 2.2.12

Solve: $2x - 3 = 5 + 3x$

Solution $2x - 3 = 5 + 3x$

To get all the x terms on one side,
subtract $2x$ from both sides of the
equation. $2x - 3 - \mathbf{2x} = 5 + 3x - \mathbf{2x}$

Simplify. $-3 = 5 + x$

To get x by itself, subtract 5 from
both sides of the equation. $-3 - \mathbf{5} = 5 + x - \mathbf{5}$

Simplify. $-8 = x$

The solution is $x = -8$.

Solving Linear Equations that Contain Parentheses

Some equations may contain expressions with parentheses. In those situations, we first simplify each expression using the Distributive Property. Then we use the principles of equality to complete the solution.

Example 2.2.13

Solve: $4(x - 5) = -3(x + 2) + 5x - 10$

Solution

First, simplify each side of the equation.

$$4(x - 5) = -3(x + 2) + 5x - 10$$

Use the Distributive Property to remove parentheses on each side.

$$4x - 20 = -3x - 6 + 5x - 10$$

Combine like terms on each side.

$$4x - 20 = 2x - 16$$

Now, apply the principles of equality.

To get the x-terms on the left, subtract $2x$ from both sides of the equation.

$$4x - 20 - 2x = 2x - 16 - 2x$$

We chose to place the x-terms on the left side of the equation. You could also place them on the right side by subtracting 4x from both sides.

Simplify.

$$2x - 20 = -16$$

To get the constants on the right, add 20 to both sides.

$$2x - 20 + 20 = -16 + 20$$

Simplify.

$$2x = 4$$

To make the coefficient of the variable 1, divide both sides of the equation by 2.

$$\frac{2x}{2} = \frac{4}{2}$$

Simplify.

$$x = 2$$

The solution is $x = 2$.

A General Procedure for Solving a Linear Equation

We have discussed several techniques for solving linear equations. For most equations there is no single "correct" way to find the solution. However, you may find the following procedure useful.

— Procedure —
To Solve A Linear Equation

Step 1 If fractions are present, multiply both sides of the equation by the LCD of all the fractions.

Step 2 Simplify each side of the equation.

Step 3 Use addition and subtraction to get all terms with the variable on one side and all constant terms on the other side of the equation. Then, simplify each side of the equation.

Step 4 Divide both sides of the equation by the coefficient of the variable.

Step 5 Check your solution in the original equation.

Example 2.2.14

Solve: $6 - \frac{2}{3}x = \frac{1}{4}(2x - 4)$

Solution

Step 1 Multiply both sides of the equation $\quad 6 - \frac{2}{3}x = \frac{1}{4}(2x - 4)$
by the LCD of all the fractions.

The LCD of $\frac{2}{3}$ and $\frac{1}{4}$ is 12.

Multiply both sides by 12. $\quad \mathbf{12 \cdot \left(6 - \frac{2}{3}x\right) = 12 \cdot \left(\frac{1}{4}(2x - 4)\right)}$

Step 2 Simplify each side of the equation.

On the left side, distribute
the 12. On the right side,
multiply $\frac{1}{4}$ by 12. $\qquad \mathbf{12 \cdot 6 - 12 \cdot \left(\frac{2}{3}x\right) = \left(12 \cdot \frac{1}{4}\right)(2x - 4)}$

Multiply. $\qquad\qquad\qquad\qquad \mathbf{72 - 8x} = 3(2x - 4)$

Distribute the 3. $\qquad\qquad\qquad 72 - 8x = \mathbf{6x - 12}$

Step 3 *Use addition and subtraction to get all terms with the variable on one side and all the constant terms on the other side of the equation. Then, simplify each side of the equation.*

To get the x-terms on the right
side, add $8x$ to both sides. $72 - 8x + \mathbf{8x} = 6x - 12 + \mathbf{8x}$

Simplify. $72 = \mathbf{14x} - 12$

To get the constant terms on the
left side, add 12 to both sides. $72 + \mathbf{12} = 14x - 12 + \mathbf{12}$

Simplify. $\mathbf{84} = 14x$

Step 4 *Divide both sides of the equation by the coefficient of the variable.*

Divide both sides of the equation by 14. $\dfrac{84}{\mathbf{14}} = \dfrac{14x}{\mathbf{14}}$

Simplify. $6 = x$

Step 5 *Check your solution in the original equation.*

$$6 - \frac{2}{3}x = \frac{1}{4}(2x - 4)$$

Replace x with 6 in the original
equation. Then simplify each side.   Is $6 - \dfrac{2}{3}(\mathbf{6}) = \dfrac{1}{4}(2(\mathbf{6}) - 4)$?

Multiply.   Is $6 - \mathbf{4} = \dfrac{1}{4}(\mathbf{12} - 4)$?

Simplify.   Is $\mathbf{2} = \dfrac{1}{4}(\mathbf{8})$?

                                        Is $2 = 2$? **Yes**

The statement $2 = 2$ is true, so the solution of the equation is $x = 6$.

Identities and Equations with No Solution

Up to this point, each equation we have worked with has had a solution. That is, there is some value of the variable that makes the equation true.

Some equations do NOT have a solution.

For example, the equation $x + 1 = x$ does NOT have a solution.

This equation states that a number, x, increased by 1, is equal to itself. This is not possible. There is no value of x to make the equation true.

Example 2.2.15

Solve: $x + 2(x + 4) = 3x + 1$

Solution

Step 1 Multiply both sides of the equation $x + 2(x + 4) = 3x + 1$
by the LCD of all the fractions.

There are no fractions, so skip this step.

Step 2 Simplify each side of the equation.

Distribute the 2. $\qquad\qquad\qquad\qquad\qquad x + \mathbf{2x + 8} = 3x + 1$

Combine like terms. $\qquad\qquad\qquad\qquad\quad \mathbf{3x} + 8 = 3x + 1$

***Step 3 Use addition and subtraction to get all terms with the variable on
one side and all the constant terms on the other side of the
equation. Then, simplify each side of the equation.***

To get the x-terms on the right,
subtract $3x$ from both sides. $\qquad\qquad\quad 3x + 8 - \mathbf{3x} = 3x + 1 - \mathbf{3x}$

Simplify. $\qquad\qquad\qquad\qquad\qquad\qquad\qquad 8 = 1$

*The statement 8 = 1 is a false statement, which is sometimes called a **contradiction**.*

The statement $8 = 1$ is false. No value of x will make the equation true.
Therefore, the original equation does not have a solution.

There are also equations for which every value of the variable is a
solution. Such an equation is called an **identity**.

For example, the equation $x + 1 = 1 + x$ is an identity. This equation
states that any number, x, increased by 1, is equal to 1 increased by that
number. This is true for every real number, x.

Example 2.2.16

Solve: $12 + 4y = 3(y + 4) + y$

Solution

Step 1 Multiply both sides of the equation $\qquad 12 + 4y = 3(y + 4) + y$
by the LCD of all the fractions.

There are no fractions, so skip this step.

Step 2 Simplify each side of the equation.

Distribute the 3. $\qquad\qquad\qquad\qquad\qquad 12 + 4y = \mathbf{3y + 12} + y$

Combine like terms. $\qquad\qquad\qquad\qquad\quad 12 + 4y = \mathbf{4y} + 12$

Step 3 *Use addition and subtraction to get all terms with the variable on one side and all the constant terms on the other side of the equation. Then, simplify each side of the equation.*

To get the y-terms on the right, subtract $4y$ from both sides.

$$12 + 4y - \mathbf{4y} = 4y + 12 - \mathbf{4y}$$

Simplify.

$$12 = 12$$

The statement $12 = 12$ is an identity.
Therefore, the original equation is also an identity.
Any value of y will make the equation true.

The solution of the equation is all real numbers.

— Note —
How to Recognize an Identity and an Equation with No Solution

When you solve a linear equation, if the simplified equation is

- a false statement, such as $8 = 1$, the equation has no solution.

- a true statement, such as $12 = 12$, the equation is an identity. The solution of the equation is all real numbers.

Formulas

A **formula** is an equation that contains at least two variables. In an applied problem, a formula tells us the mathematical relationship between the quantities represented by the variables.

For example:

The formula $d = rt$ gives the relationship between the distance traveled, d, the rate of travel, r, and the time of travel, t.

We say that this formula is solved for d in terms of r and t.

Suppose we know the rate of a car is 50 miles per hour and the car has been traveling for 3 hours.

We can use $d = rt$ to calculate the distance the car has traveled.

$$d = rt$$
$$d = 150 \text{ miles}$$
$$d = \frac{50 \text{ miles}}{1 \text{ hour}} \cdot \frac{3 \text{ hours}}{1}$$

Sometimes it's useful to solve a formula for a specific variable. To do this, we use the same methods that we used to solve an equation with one variable.

For example, if we know the distance a car traveled and the time it took to travel that distance, we can solve $d = rt$ for r to get a formula for the rate.

$$d = rt$$

Divide both sides by t.

$$\frac{d}{t} = \frac{r\cancel{t}}{\cancel{t}}$$

$$\frac{d}{t} = r$$

We usually write the isolated variable on the left:

$$r = \frac{d}{t}$$

We say that this formula is solved for r in terms of d and t.

When more than one operation is involved, we still follow the same procedure.

For example, we know how to solve an equation such as $3x + 1 = 7$. To solve the formula $ax + b = c$ for x, we would follow the same steps.

Solve the equation $3x + 1 = 7$ for x	Solve the formula $ax + b = c$ for x
Step 1 There are no fractions, so skip this step.	**Step 1** There are no fractions, so skip this step.
Step 2 Each side of the equation is simplified.	**Step 2** Each side of the equation is simplified.
Step 3 To get the constant terms on the right, subtract 1 from both sides. $3x + 1 - 1 = 7 - 1$ $3x = 6$	**Step 3** To get the constant terms on the right, subtract b from both sides. $ax + b - b = c - b$ $ax = c - b$
Step 4 Divide both sides by the coefficient of the variable. $\frac{3x}{3} = \frac{6}{3}$ $x = 2$	**Step 4** Divide both sides by the coefficient of the variable. $\frac{ax}{a} = \frac{c - b}{a}$ $x = \frac{c - b}{a}$ The equation is solved for x in terms of a, b, and c.

Example **2.2.17**

The volume of a cone is given by the formula $v = \frac{1}{3}\pi r^2 h$, where r is the radius of the base of the cone and h is the height. Solve this formula for h.

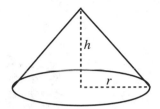

Solution

Step 1 Multiply both sides of the equation by the LCD of all the fractions.

The LCD of the fractions is 3. $\qquad v = \frac{1}{3}\pi r^2 h$

Multiply both sides by **3**. $\qquad \mathbf{3} \cdot (v) = \mathbf{3} \cdot \left(\frac{1}{3}\pi r^2 h\right)$

Step 2 Simplify each side of the equation. $\qquad 3v = \pi r^2 h$

Step 3 Use addition and subtraction to get all terms with the variable on one side and all the constant terms on the other side of the equation. Then, simplify each side of the equation.

The variable term, $\pi r^2 h$, is already isolated on the right side of the equation.

Step 4 Divide both sides of the equation by the coefficient of the variable.

We are solving for h.
Here, h is multiplied by πr^2.
Therefore, divide both sides by πr^2. $\qquad \dfrac{3v}{\pi r^2} = \dfrac{\pi r^2 h}{\pi r^2}$

Simplify. $\qquad \dfrac{3v}{\pi r^2} = h$

Now h is isolated on one side, so the formula is solved for h.

We usually write the isolated variable on the left side of the equation.

Therefore, the preferred form for the formula is $\qquad h = \dfrac{3v}{\pi r^2}$.

$$3v = \pi r^2 h$$

The right side of this equation contains two variables, r and h. We are solving for h, so πr^2 is the coefficient of h because it is multiplied by h. To solve the equation for h, we divide both sides of the equation by the coefficient πr^2.

Step 5 Check your solution in the original equation.

To check, replace h with $\dfrac{3v}{\pi r^2}$ and simplify. $\qquad v = \frac{1}{3}\pi r^2 h$

Is $v = \frac{1}{3}\pi r^2\left(\dfrac{\mathbf{3v}}{\pi r^2}\right)$?

Is $v = \dfrac{1 \cdot \cancel{\pi} \cdot \cancel{r^2} \cdot \cancel{3} \cdot v}{\cancel{3} \cdot \cancel{\pi} \cdot \cancel{r^2}}$?

Is $v = v$? **Yes**

The solution is $h = \dfrac{3v}{\pi r^2}$.

Example **2.2.18**

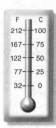

The relation between the Fahrenheit temperature scale
and the Celsius scale is given by $C = \frac{5}{9}(F - 32)$.
This formula is solved for C in terms of F.

Solve this equation for F in terms of C.

Solution

Step 1 Multiply both sides of the equation by the LCD of all the fractions.

For this equation, it will be easier
to multiply not by the LCD, 9, but
by $\frac{9}{5}$, the reciprocal of the given

fraction, $\frac{5}{9}$.

$$C = \frac{5}{9}(F - 32)$$

$$\frac{9}{5}(C) = \frac{9}{5}\left(\frac{5}{9}(F - 32)\right)$$

$$\frac{9}{5}C = \left(\frac{9}{5} \cdot \frac{5}{9}\right)(F - 32)$$

Step 2 Simplify each side of the equation.
$$\frac{9}{5}C = F - 32$$

Step 3 Use addition and subtraction to get all terms with the variable on one side and all the constant terms on the other side of the equation. Then, simplify each side of the equation.

To isolate F, add 32 to both sides.
$$\frac{9}{5}C + \mathbf{32} = F - 32 + \mathbf{32}$$

$$\frac{9}{5}C + 32 = F$$

Step 4 Divide both sides of the equation by the coefficient of the variable.

We are solving for F.
Its coefficient is already 1.
We write the final answer with F,
the isolated variable, on the left.
$$F = \frac{9}{5}C + 32$$

Step 5 Check your solution in the original equation.

We leave the check to you.

Example **2.2.19**

Solve for y: $x + 6 = -\frac{3}{2}(y - 10)$

Solution

Step 1 Multiply both sides of the equation by the LCD of all the fractions.

The LCD of the fractions is 2.
$$x + 6 = -\frac{3}{2}(y - 10)$$

Multiply each side by 2.
$$\mathbf{2} \cdot (x + 6) = \mathbf{2} \cdot \left(-\frac{3}{2}(y - 10)\right)$$

Step 2 Simplify each side of the equation.

On the left side, distribute 2 to the terms inside the parentheses.

$$2 \cdot (x + 6) = \left(\mathbf{2} \cdot \left(-\frac{3}{2}\right)\right)(y - 10)$$

On the right side, the 2 cancels with the denominator of $-\frac{3}{2}$.

$$\mathbf{2x + 12} = -3(y - 10)$$

Distribute -3 to the terms inside the parentheses.

$$2x + 12 = \mathbf{-3y + 30}$$

Step 3 Use addition and subtraction to get all terms with the variable on one side and all the constant terms on the other side of the equation. Then, simplify each side of the equation.

To isolate the y-terms, subtract 30 from both sides.

$$2x + 12 \mathbf{- 30} = -3y + 30 \mathbf{- 30}$$
$$2x \mathbf{- 18} = -3y$$

Step 4 Divide both sides of the equation by the coefficient of the variable.

Divide both sides by -3.

$$\frac{2x - 18}{\mathbf{-3}} = \frac{-3y}{\mathbf{-3}}$$

On the left, break up the fraction into two fractions.

$$\frac{2x}{-3} + \frac{-18}{-3} = y$$

Simplify.

$$-\frac{2}{3}x + 6 = y$$

Write the final answer with the isolated variable on the left.

The solution is $y = -\frac{2}{3}x + 6$.

Step 5 Check your solution in the original equation.

We leave the check to you.

Here is a summary of this concept from *Academic Systems Algebra*.

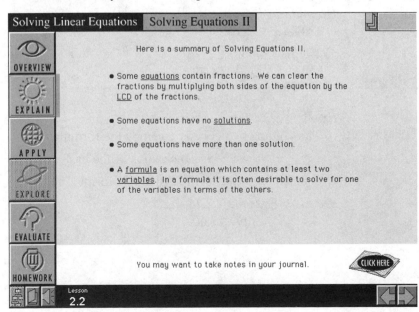

Solving Linear Equations | Solving Equations II

OVERVIEW

EXPLAIN

APPLY

EXPLORE

EVALUATE

HOMEWORK

Here is a summary of Solving Equations II.

• Some equations contain fractions. We can clear the fractions by multiplying both sides of the equation by the LCD of the fractions.

• Some equations have no solutions.

• Some equations have more than one solution.

• A formula is an equation which contains at least two variables. In a formula it is often desirable to solve for one of the variables in terms of the others.

You may want to take notes in your journal.   CLICK HERE

Lesson 2.2

Checklist Lesson 2.2

Here is what you should know after completing this lesson.

Words and Phrases

equation
conditional equation
linear equation in one variable
non-linear equation
solution

satisfy
equivalent equations
identity
formula

Ideas and Procedures

❶ Solution of an Equation
Determine whether a value is a solution of an equation.

Example 2.2.2
   Is $p = 7$ a solution of the equation $5(p - 6) = -5$?

See Also: Example 2.2.1
   Apply 1, 2

❷ Solve an Equation
Find the solution of an equation

Example 2.2.7
   Solve: $2x - 7 = -15$

See Also: Example 2.2.3-2.2.6, 2.2.8-2.2.10, 2.2.12,
   and 2.2.13
   Apply 3-34

❸ Solve an Equation That Contains Fractions
Find the solution of an equation that contains fractions.

Example 2.2.14
   Solve: $6 - \frac{2}{3}x = \frac{1}{4}(2x - 4)$

See Also: Example 2.2.11
   Apply 35-43

❹ Identities and Equations with No Solution
Determine whether an equation is an identity, or has no solution.

Example 2.2.15
   Solve: $x + 2(x + 4) = 3x + 1$

See Also: Example 2.2.16
   Apply 44-52

❺ Formulas
Solve a formula for a specified variable.

Example 2.2.17
   The volume of a cone is given by the formula
   $v = \frac{1}{3}\pi r^2 h$, where r is the radius of the base of the
   cone and h is the height. Solve this formula for h.

See Also: Example 2.2.18, 2.2.19
   Apply 53-60

Homework

Homework Problems

Circle the homework problems assigned to you by the computer, then complete them below.

☀ Explain

Solving Equations I

1. Solve for x: $x + 15 = 37$

2. Is $y = 77$ a solution of the equation $y - 23 = 54$?

3. Solve for t: $9t = 108$

4. Solve for w: $-7 = w + 29$

5. Solve for v: $\frac{1}{3}v = 2$

6. Solve for x: $2x + 3 = 17$

7. Solve for y: $-1 = \frac{1}{4}y + 2$

8. Is $s = 4$ a solution of the equation $5s - 4 = 11$?

9. Francisco bought eight bottles of juice for $12.00. How much did a single bottle of juice cost?

10. Vanessa took the $50 she got for birthday money and went to buy fish. If she got six angel fish and had $14 left over, how much did one angel fish cost?

11. Solve for z: $4z + 13 = 1$

12. Solve for x: $-3 = \frac{1}{7}x - 6$

Solving Equations II

13. Solve for y: $\frac{2}{3}y = 2$

14. Solve for x: $\frac{1}{3}(x + 8) = 7$

15. Solve for x: $x + 1 = x - 3$

16. Solve for x: $\frac{2}{5}(x - 3) = \frac{3}{5}x$

17. Solve for z: $-\frac{2}{3}(2z + 3) = \frac{1}{2}(1 - z)$

18. Solve for w: $4(w + 1) - 3w = w + 4$

19. The formula to find the circumference of a circle is $C = 2\pi r$, where C is the circumference of a circle and r is the radius. Solve the formula $C = 2\pi r$ for r.

20. Solve for y: $\frac{1}{2}y + 2 = \frac{1}{6}(3y - 9)$

21. Solve for x: $-3(2x + 1) = 7(2 - x)$

22. The math score on a college entrance exam can be written as $S = 200 + 20R - 5W$, where S is the score, R is the number of right answers, and W is the number of wrong answers. Dana's score on the test was 525 and he answered 19 questions correctly. How many questions did he answer incorrectly?

23. Solve for z: $\frac{1}{3}(4z - 3) = 4x - 5$

24. A formula which relates the measure of the interior angles of a regular polygon to the number of sides of the polygon is $360 + an = 180n$, where n is the number of sides and a is the measure of the interior angle. Solve this equation for a.

25. Apply the distributive property to remove the parentheses on both sides of the equation $9(x + 5) = 6(2x + 7)$, then solve for x.

26. Solve for x: $\frac{3x}{7} + 2 = 8$

27. Find the least common multiple of the denominators of the fractions in the equation $\frac{5}{6}y = \frac{3}{14}(4y + 3)$, then use it to solve the equation.

28. Apply the distributive property to remove the parentheses on both sides of the equation $-2(5 - 3x) = 4(x - 7)$, then solve for x.

29. Solve for z: $-7 = \frac{2}{3}z - 5$

30. Find the least common multiple of the denominators of the fractions in the equation $\frac{5}{12}(7 + x) = \frac{7}{18}(x + 8)$, then use it to solve the equation.

 **Apply**

Practice Problems

Here are some additional practice problems for you to try.

Solving Equations I

1. Is $x = 3$ a solution of $x - 7 = 4$?

2. Is $y = -5$ a solution of $y + 3 = -2$?

3. Solve for a: $a + 5 = 23$

4. Solve for x: $x + 6 = 19$

5. Solve for b: $b - 10 = 14$

6. Solve for m: $m - 9 = 24$

7. Solve for z: $z - 7 = 12$

8. Solve for x: $15 - x = 8$

9. Solve for x: $24 - x = 16$

10. Solve for t: $21 - t = 11$

11. Solve for r: $3r + 2 = 17$

12. Solve for s: $7s + 12 = 26$

13. Solve for a: $5a + 3 = 23$

14. Solve for m: $5m - 9 = 41$

15. Solve for p: $6p - 11 = 13$

16. Solve for k: $8k - 5 = 19$

17. Solve for b: $4b - 5 = -21$

18. Pralve for b: $9b + 3 = -42$

19. Solve for n: $3n - 12 = -33$

20. Solve for h: $12 + 5h = -38$

21. Solve for q: $14 + 7q = -42$

22. Solve for v: $16 + 4v = -20$

23. Solve for c: $22 - 4c = 42$

24. Solve for d: $56 - 5d = 31$

25. Solve for x: $16 - 3x = 22$

26. Solve for k: $-10 - 6k = 26$

27. Solve for f: $-25 - 9f = 11$

Solving Equations II

28. Solve for y: $-7 - 3y = 8$

29. Solve for h: $10h - 9 = 6h + 3$

30. Solve for y: $12y - 13 = 7y + 12$

31. Solve for t: $3(t - 6) = -8(1 - t)$

32. Solve for u: $-6(2u - 3) = 5(u - 10)$

33. Solve for c: $-7(2c + 5) = 3(c - 6)$

34. Solve for x: $4(x + 3) = -5(3x - 10)$

35. Solve for p: $\frac{1}{4}(p - 5) = 3$

36. Solve for r: $\frac{1}{8}(r + 3) = 6$

37. Solve for y: $-\frac{2}{3}(4 - y) = 6$

38. Solve for z: $\frac{3}{4}(z + 3) = 9$

39. Solve for c: $\frac{1}{2}(c + 8) = \frac{1}{4}c$

40. Solve for b: $-\frac{1}{3}(4 - b) = \frac{1}{7}b$

41. Solve for a: $\frac{1}{5}a + 8 = -\frac{3}{5}(a - 15)$

42. Solve for m: $12 - \frac{3}{10}m = \frac{7}{10}(m + 20)$

43. Solve for n: $\frac{1}{8}n + 6 = -\frac{5}{8}(n - 16)$

44. Solve for b: $-\frac{1}{3}(15 - 6b) = 2b - 5$

45. Solve for r: $5r + 2 = \frac{1}{7}(35r + 14)$

46. Solve for p: $\frac{1}{2}(6p + 12) = 3p + 6$

47. Solve for t: $-8\left(\frac{1}{4}t - 4\right) = 12 - 2t$

48. Solve for y: $3\left(5 + \frac{1}{6}y\right) = 8 + \frac{1}{2}y$

49. Solve for x: $6\left(3 + \frac{1}{2}x\right) = 3x + 7$

50. Solve for d: $\frac{4}{3}d + 16 = \frac{4}{3}(d + 12)$

51. Solve for z: $\frac{5}{4}z - 10 = -\frac{5}{4}(8 - z)$

52. Solve for w: $\frac{3}{2}w + 12 = \frac{3}{2}(w + 8)$

53. Solve for z: $4z - 3y = 8$

54. Solve for c: $5b - 2c = 10$

55. Solve for x: $3y - \frac{1}{3}x = 4$

56. Solve for t: $\frac{1}{2}t + 3v = 5$

57. The formula for the area of a triangle is
$A = \frac{1}{2} \cdot b \cdot h$, where A is the area of the triangle,
b is the length of its base, and h is its height. Solve this formula for b.

58. The formula for the area of a trapezoid is
$A = \frac{1}{2}h(a + b)$, where A is the area of the trapezoid, a and b are the lengths of its two bases, and h is its height. Solve this formula for a.

59. The formula for the volume of a pyramid with a rectangular base is $V = \frac{1}{3}lwh$, where V is the volume of the pyramid, l is the length of its base, w is the width of its base and h is the height of the pyramid. Solve this formula for w.

60. The formula for the volume of a cylinder is
$V = \pi r^2 h$, where V is the volume, r is the radius of the base, and h is the height of the cylinder. Solve this formula for h.

 **Evaluate**

Practice Test

Take this practice test to be sure that you are prepared for the final quiz in Evaluate.

1. Solve for x: $x + 16 = 5$

2. To isolate z in the equation $-\frac{1}{2}z = 6$, by what number do you multiply both sides of the equation?

3. Solve for y: $-2y = 18$

4. Solve for x: $3x - 4 = 11$

5. Solve for x: $3(2x + 4) = 2(3x + 6)$

6. Solve for y: $2(y - 10) = 10 + 2y$

7. To solve the equation $8x - 2 = 6 - 2x$, you might begin by adding $2x$ to both sides of the equation. What would be the resulting equation?

8. Solve for z: $\frac{1}{4}(z + 3) = 1$

9. What is the resulting equation when you use the distributive property to remove parentheses from the equation $5(3x - 2) = 2(x + 3)$?

10. Solve for x: $\frac{2}{3}(4x - 1) = \frac{2}{9}(5x + 4)$

11. Solve for y: $8x - y = 5$

12. Solve for x: $8x - y = 5$

LESSON 2.3
PROBLEM SOLVING

 Overview

You may not realize it, but you use mathematics in every day life—whether it's figuring out the least expensive brands to buy in a grocery store or finding the measurements of a fence that you plan to build. In fact, you may discover that the more mathematics you know, the more you use it.

In this lesson, you will apply what you have learned about solving equations to solve word problems that involve numbers, age, and geometry.

 Explain

Concept 1 has sections on

- **Translating Words into Algebra**

- **A General Procedure for Solving Word Problems**

- **Number Problems**

- **Age Problems**

CONCEPT 1:
NUMBER AND AGE

Translating Words into Algebra

Many people study algebra to help them solve problems that are expressed in English. We call such problems **word problems**.

An important part of solving a word problem is translating between English and algebra. So, the first step in learning to solve a word problem is to study these translations.

Many problems contain key words that will help you recognize the mathematical operations involved.

Addition

English	Algebra
The **sum** of a number and 4.	$x + 4$
Seven **more than** a number.	$x + 7$
Six **increased by** a number.	$6 + x$
A number **added to** 8.	$8 + x$
A number **plus** four.	$x + 4$

Subtraction

Be careful with subtraction. The order is important. Three less than a number is $x - 3$ not $3 - x$.

English	Algebra
The **difference** of a number and 3.	$x - 3$
The **difference** of 3 and a number.	$3 - x$
Five **less than** a number.	$x - 5$
A number **decreased by** 3.	$x - 3$
A number **subtracted from** 8.	$8 - x$
Eight **subtracted from** a number.	$x - 8$
Two **minus** a number.	$2 - x$

Multiplication

English	Algebra
The **product** of 3 and a number.	$3x$
Three-fourths **of** a number.	$\frac{3}{4}x$
Four **times** a number.	$4x$
A number **multiplied** by 6.	$x6$ or $6x$
Double a number.	$2x$
Twice a number.	$2x$

Division

Like subtraction, the order is important for division as well.

English	Algebra
The **quotient** of a number and 3.	$x \div 3$ or $\frac{x}{3}$
The **quotient** of 3 and a number.	$3 \div x$ or $\frac{3}{x}$
A number **divided by** 6.	$x \div 6$ or $\frac{x}{6}$
Six **divided by** a number.	$6 \div x$ or $\frac{6}{x}$

A General Procedure for Solving Word Problems

Many word problems have the same basic structure. For these, a set of general steps may help you to find the solution. The following steps will help you translate the words into an equation. Then you can solve the equation and determine if your solution is correct.

— Procedure —
General Procedure for Solving a Word Problem

Step 1 List the quantities to be found. Use English phrases.

Step 2 Represent these quantities algebraically.

Step 3 Write an equation that describes the problem.

Step 4 Solve the equation.

Step 5 Check that the numbers work in the original problem.

Number Problems

Number problems involve relationships between numbers. Problems such as these will help you develop the skills you need to solve more complex application problems.

Example 2.3.1

The sum of two numbers is 82. The larger number is 17 less than twice the smaller number. What are the two numbers?

Solution

Step 1 List the quantities to be found. Use English phrases.

Two numbers.

Step 2 Represent these quantities algebraically.

We may let the variable represent either number. However, since the larger number is described in terms of the smaller number, it is easiest to let the variable represent the smaller number.

Let x represent the smaller number. $x =$ smaller number

The larger number is 17 less than
twice the smaller number. $2x - 17 =$ larger number

Step 3 Write an equation that describes the problem.

The sum of two numbers is 82. $\dfrac{\text{smaller}}{\text{number}} + \dfrac{\text{larger}}{\text{number}} = 82$

Substitute the expressions from Step 2. $x + 2x - 17 = 82$

Step 4 Solve the equation.

Combine like terms on the left side.	$3x - 17 = 82$
Add 17 to both sides.	$3x = 99$
Divide both sides by 3.	$x = 33$

The smaller number, x, is 33.

The larger number is $2x - 17$.

To calculate the larger number
substitute 33 for x and simplify.

$$2x - 17$$
$$= 2(33) - 17$$
$$= 66 - 17$$
$$= 49$$

The larger number, $2x - 17$, is **49**.

Therefore, the numbers are **33** and **49**.

Step 5 Check that the numbers work in the original problem.

Condition	***Check***
• The sum of the numbers is 82.	• $33 + 49 = 82$ ✓
• The larger number is 17 less than twice the smaller number.	• Twice 33 is 66. Seventeen less than 66 is 49. ✓

Some number problems involve consecutive integers.

English Examples	***Algebraic Expressions***
• 16, 17, and 18 are **consecutive integers**. Start with 16 and add 1 to get the next consecutive integer, 17.	• If x is an integer, then $x, x + 1$ $x + 2, ...$ is a sequence of consecutive integers.
• 16, 18, and 20 are **consecutive *even* integers**. Start with 16 and add 2 to get the next consecutive **even** integer, 18.	• If x is an **even** integer, then x, $x + 2, x + 4, ...$ is a sequence of consecutive **even** integers.
• 17, 19, and 21 are **consecutive *odd* integers**. Start with 17 and add 2 to get the next consecutive **odd** integer, 19.	• If x is an **odd** integer, then x, $x + 2, x + 4, ...$ is a sequence of consecutive **odd** integers.

If x is even, then x + 2 and x + 4 are also even.

If x is odd, then x + 2 and x + 4 are also odd.

Example 2.3.2

The sum of three consecutive odd integers is 21 less than four times the smallest of the integers. What are the three integers?

Solution

Step 1 List the quantities to be found. Use English phrases.

   Three consecutive odd integers.

Step 2 Represent these quantities algebraically.

   Let x represent the smallest of
the three integers. x = smallest of the three integers

   The next consecutive odd
integer is 2 more than x. $x + 2$ = next odd integer

   The next consecutive odd
integer is 2 more than $x + 2$. $x + 4$ = next odd integer

Step 3 Write an equation that describes the problem.

   The sum is 21 less than
four times the smallest of $\dfrac{\text{sum of the}}{\text{three integers}} = 4 \cdot \left(\dfrac{\text{smallest}}{\text{integer}}\right) - 21$
the integers.

   Substitute the expressions $x + (x + 2) + (x + 4) = 4 \cdot x - 21$
from Step 2.

Step 4 Solve the equation.

Combine like terms on the left side.	$3x + 6 = 4x - 21$
Add 21 to both sides.	$3x + 27 = 4x$
Subtract $3x$ from both sides.	$27 = x$

The smallest of the three integers, x, is 27.

The next consecutive odd integer is $x + 2$.	$x + 2$
Replace x with 27.	$= (27) + 2$
Simplify.	$= 29$

The next consecutive odd integer is $x + 4$.	$x + 4$
Replace x with 27.	$= (27) + 4$
Simplify.	$= 31$

The three consecutive odd integers are 27, 29, and 31.

Step 5 *Check that the numbers work in the original problem.*

Condition	Check
• The numbers are consecutive odd integers.	• 27, 29, and 31 are consecutive odd integers. ✓
• Their sum is 21 less than four times the smallest of the integers.	• The sum of the integers is $27 + 29 + 31 = 87$. Four times the smallest is $4(27) = 108$. Twenty-one less than 108 is $108 - 21 = 87$. ✓

Age Problems

Age problems give you practice writing expressions where the relative sizes of numbers are stated in unusual ways.

Example 2.3.3

Lloyd is 7 years older than Frank. In 5 years, the sum of their ages will be 57. How old is each of them now?

Solution

Step 1 *List the quantities to be found. Use English phrases.*

Lloyd's age today and Frank's age today.

Step 2 *Represent these quantities algebraically.*

The problem gives Lloyd's age in terms of Frank's age. Therefore, let f represent Frank's age today. f = Frank's age today

Lloyd is 7 years older than Frank. $f + 7$ = Lloyd's age today

The problem also refers to their ages 5 years from now.

In 5 years Frank's age will be 5 more than his age is today. $f + 5$ = Frank's age in 5 years

In 5 years Lloyd's age will be 5 more than his age is today. $(f + 7) + 5 = f + 12 = $ Lloyd's age in 5 years

Step 3 *Write an equation that describes the problem.*

In 5 years, the sum of their ages will be 57. $\text{Frank's age in 5 years} + \text{Lloyd's age in 5 years} = 57$

Substitute the expressions from Step 2. $(f + 5) + (f + 12) = 57$

Step 4 Solve the equation.

Combine like terms on the left side.	$2f + 17 = 57$
Subtract 17 from both sides.	$2f = 40$
Divide both sides by 2.	$f = 20$

Frank's age today, f, is 20.

Lloyd's age today is $f + 7$.	$f + 7$
Replace f with 20.	$= (20) + 7$
Simplify.	$= 27$

Frank's age today is 20 and Lloyd's age today is 27.

Step 5 Check that the numbers work in the original problem.

Condition

- Lloyd is 7 years older than Frank.

- In 5 years, the sum of their ages will be 57.

Check

- Lloyd's age, 27, is 7 more than Frank's age, 20. ✓

- In 5 years, Frank's age will be $20 + 5 = 25$.
  In 5 years, Lloyd's age will be $27 + 5 = 32$.
  The sum of their ages in five years is $25 + 32 = 57$. ✓

Example 2.3.4

Maria is 8 years older than Tony. Three years ago, Maria was 4 years less than twice Tony's age. How old was Tony then?

Solution

Step 1 List the quantities to be found. Use English phrases.

Tony's age 3 years ago.

Step 2 Represent these quantities algebraically.

To find Tony's age 3 years ago, we use information about Tony and Maria today.

Since Maria's age today is given in terms of Tony's age today, let t represent Tony's age today.v	$t =$ Tony's age today
Maria is 8 years older than Tony.	$t + 8 =$ Maria's age today
Maria's age 3 years ago is 3 less than her age today.	$(t + 8) - 3 = t + 5 = $ Maria's age 3 years ago
Tony's age 3 years ago is 3 less than his age today.	$t - 3 =$ Tony's age 3 years ago

Step 3 Write an equation that describes the problem.

Three years ago, Maria was 4 years less than twice Tony's age.

$$\frac{\text{Maria's age}}{\text{3 years ago}} = 2 \cdot \frac{\text{Tony's age}}{\text{3 years ago}} - 4$$

Substitute the expressions from Step 2.

$$t + 5 = 2 \cdot (t - 3) - 4$$

Step 4 Solve the equation.

To remove the parentheses on the right side, distribute 2.

$$t + 5 = 2t - 6 - 4$$

Combine like terms.

$$t + 5 = 2t - 10$$

Subtract t from both sides.

$$5 = t - 10$$

Add 10 to both sides.

$$15 = t$$

Tony's age today, t, is 15 years.

The problem asks for Tony's age 3 years ago.

Tony's age 3 years ago is $t - 3$ which is $15 - 3 = 12$ years.

Step 5 Check that the numbers work in the original problem.

To check the condition, we need to know Maria's age. Maria is 8 years older than Tony, so her age today is $15 + 8 = 23$ years.

Condition	Check
• Three years ago, Maria was 4 years less than twice Tony's age.	• Maria's age three years ago was $23 - 3 = 20$. Tony's age three years ago was 12; twice this is 24. Maria's age three years ago, 20, is 4 less than 24. ✓

Here is a summary of this concept from *Academic Systems Algebra*.

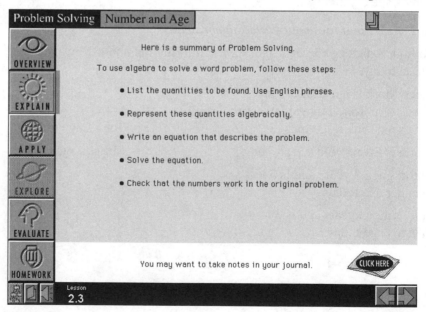

CONCEPT 2: GEOMETRY

Geometry Problems

Geometry problems make use of facts and formulas that involve the angles, areas, and perimeters of geometric figures such as triangles, rectangles, and circles. In these problems you are often required to use a formula or a fact that is not stated in the problem. You will have to recall these facts and formulas or look them up in a reference book.

We solve geometry problems using the same steps that we used to solve number and age problems.

Example 2.3.5

In isosceles triangle ABC, the measure of one angle is 30° (thirty degrees) greater than the measure of each of the other two angles. What is the measure of each angle?

Solution

An isosceles triangle has two sides of equal length and two angles of equal measure.

A sketch can help us visualize the problem.

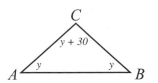

Sides of equal length

Angles of equal measure

Step 1 List the quantities to be found. Use English phrases.

The measures of the three angles.

Step 2 Represent these quantities algebraically.

Two of the angles have the same measure.

Let y represent the degree measure of each of the equal angles, A and B.

$$y = \text{measure of angle } A$$
$$y = \text{measure of angle } B$$

The measure of the third angle is 30° greater than the measure of each of the other angles.

$$y + 30 = \text{measure of angle } C$$

Step 3 Write an equation that describes the problem.

To solve this problem, we need to use a fact about the sum of the angle measures of a triangle. (This fact was not given.)

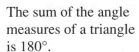

The sum of the angle measures of a triangle is 180°.

$$\text{measure of angle } A + \text{measure of angle } B + \text{measure of angle } C = 180$$

Substitute the expressions from Step 2.

$$y + y + (y + 30) = 180$$

Step 4 Solve the equation.

Combine like terms on the left side.	$3y + 30 = 180$
Subtract 30 from both sides.	$3y = \mathbf{150}$
Divide both sides by 3.	$y = 50$

Angle *A* and angle *B* each measure 50°.

The measure of angle *C* is $y + 30$.	$y + 30$
Replace *y* with 50.	$= (\mathbf{50}) + 30$
Simplify.	$= 80$

The measures of the angles are 50°, 50°, and 80°.

Step 5 Check that the numbers work in the original problem.

Condition	*Check*
• The sum of the angles is 180°. (This condition was used, but not stated.)	• $50° + 50° + 80° = 180°$ ✓
• The triangle is isosceles.	• Two of the angles have equal measure, 50°. ✓
• The measure of one angle is 30° greater than the measure of each of the other two angles.	• The measure of the third angle is 80°. This is 30° more than 50°, the measure of each of the other two angles. ✓

Example 2.3.6

The length of a rectangle is 3 feet less than twice its width. If the perimeter of the rectangle is 30 feet, find the width and length.

Solution

A sketch can help us visualize this problem.

Step 1 List the quantities to be found. Use English phrases.

The width and length of the rectangle.

Step 2 Represent these quantities algebraically.

Since the length is given in terms of the width, let *w* represent the width in feet.	$w = \text{width}$
The length is 3 less than twice the width.	$2w - 3 = \text{length}$

Step 3 Write an equation that describes the problem.

The perimeter is the distance around the outside of the rectangle. The perimeter of this rectangle is 30 feet.

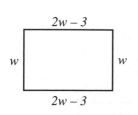

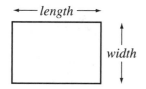

Perimeter can also be written as
$P = 2 \cdot (length) + 2 \cdot (width)$

Substitute the expressions from Step 2.

$$\text{Perimeter} = \text{width} + \text{length} + \text{width} + \text{length}$$
$$30 = w + (2w - 3) + w + (2w - 3)$$

Step 4 Solve the equation.

Combine like terms.	$30 = 6w - 6$
Add 6 to both sides.	$36 = 6w$
Divide both sides by 6.	$6 = w$

The width is 6 feet.

The length is $2w - 3$.	$= 2w - 3$
Replace w with 6.	$= 2(6) - 3$
Simplify.	$= 9$

The width is 6 feet and the length is 9 feet.

Step 5 Check that the numbers work in the original problem.

Condition

- The length of a rectangle is 3 feet less than twice its width.

- The perimeter of the rectangle is 30 feet.

Check

- Twice the width is:
  $2 \cdot (6 \text{ feet}) = 12 \text{ feet}$
  The length, 9 feet, is 3 feet less than this. ✓

- The distance around the outside of the rectangle is:
  $6 + 9 + 6 + 9 = 30 \text{ feet}$ ✓

Example 2.3.7

The longest side of a triangle is 16 inches longer than the shortest side. The remaining side is 2 inches shorter than the longest side. The perimeter of the triangle is 60 inches. What is the length of each side?

Solution

A sketch can help us visualize this problem.

Step 1 List the quantities to be found. Use English phrases.

The length of each side of the triangle.

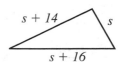

Step 2 Represent these quantities algebraically.

Let s represent the length of the shortest side.

$$s = \text{length of shortest side}$$

The length of the longest side is 16 inches more than s.

$$s + 16 = \text{length of longest side}$$

The length of the remaining side is 2 inches less than $s + 16$.

$$(s + 16) - 2 = s + 14 = \text{length of remaining side}$$

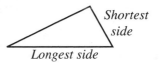

Step 3 Write an equation that describes the problem.

The perimeter is the distance around the outside of the triangle.

$$\text{Perimeter} = \begin{array}{c}\text{length of}\\ \text{shortest}\\ \text{side}\end{array} + \begin{array}{c}\text{length of}\\ \text{longest}\\ \text{side}\end{array} + \begin{array}{c}\text{length of}\\ \text{remaining}\\ \text{side}\end{array}$$

Substitute the expressions
from Step 2. $\qquad 60 = (s) + (s + 16) + (s + 14)$

Step 4 Solve the equation.

Combine like terms.	$60 = 3s + 30$
Subtract 30 from both sides.	$30 = 3s$
Divide both sides by 3.	$10 = s$

The length of the shortest side, s, is 10 inches.

The length of the longest side is $s + 16$, which is $10 + 16 = 26$ inches.

The length of the remaining side is $s + 14$, which is $10 + 14 = 24$ inches.

Step 5 Check that the numbers work in the original problem.

Condition	**Check**
• The longest side of a triangle is 16 inches longer than the shortest side.	• The length of the longest side is 26 inches. This is 16 inches longer than the length of the shortest side, 10 inches. ✓
• The remaining side is 2 inches shorter than the longest side.	• The remaining side is 24 inches long. This is 2 inches shorter than the length of the longest side, 26 inches. ✓
• The perimeter of the triangle is 60 inches.	• The distance around the outside of the triangle is: $10 + 26 + 24 = 60$ inches ✓

Example 2.3.8

A regular hexagon has the same perimeter as a given square. If the length of each side of the square is 13 inches, how long is each side of the hexagon? (A regular hexagon has 6 sides that are all the same length.)

Solution

A sketch might be helpful in visualizing this problem.

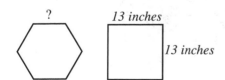

Step 1 List the quantities to be found. Use English phrases.

The length of each side of the hexagon.

Step 2 Represent these quantities algebraically.

Let h represent the length of each side of the hexagon.

Step 3 Write an equation that describes the problem.

The hexagon and the square have the same perimeter.

 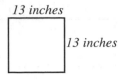

$$\text{Perimeter of hexagon} = \text{Perimeter of square}$$
$$h + h + h + h + h + h = 13 + 13 + 13 + 13$$

Step 4 Solve the equation.

Combine like terms on each side. $\qquad\qquad 6h = 52$

Divide both sides by 6. $\qquad\qquad\qquad h = \dfrac{52}{6}$

Convert the fraction to a mixed number. $\qquad h = 8\dfrac{2}{3}$

The length of each side of the hexagon is $8\dfrac{2}{3}$ inches.

Step 5 Check that the numbers work in the original problem.

Condition	**Check**

- A regular hexagon has the same perimeter as a square.
- The perimeter of the hexagon is $6 \cdot \left(8\dfrac{2}{3} \text{ inches}\right) = 52$ inches.

  The perimeter of the square is $4 \cdot 13$ inches $= 52$ inches. ✓

Example 2.3.9

Martha plans to build a rectangular fence along her house to enclose a garden. The length of the fence will be three times its width. The wall of her house forms one side of the garden. Martha uses 30 feet of fencing for the other three sides of the garden.

What is the length and the width of the garden?

Solution

A sketch can help us visualize this problem.

Step 1 List the quantities to be found. Use English phrases.

The length and the width of the garden.

Step 2 Represent these quantities algebraically.

Let w represent the width of the garden. $\qquad w = \text{width}$

The length is 3 times the width. $\qquad\qquad 3w = \text{length}$

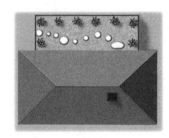

$3w = \text{length}$

$w = \text{width}$

Step 3 Write an equation that describes the problem.

The house forms one side of the garden, so the fence encloses only three sides of the garden.

$$\underset{\text{of fencing}}{\text{total amount}} = \text{width} + \text{length} + \text{width}$$

Substitute the expressions from Step 2.

$$30 = \quad w \quad + \quad 3w \quad + \quad w$$

Step 4 Solve the equation.

Combine like terms on the right. $30 = 5w$
Divide both sides by 5. $6 = w$

The width, w, is 6 feet.

The length, $3w$, is $3 \cdot (6 \text{ feet}) = 18$ feet.

Step 5 Check that the numbers work in the original problem.

Condition	Check
• The length is three times the width.	• The length, 18 feet, is three times the width, 6 feet. ✓
• The total length of the fence is 30 feet.	• $6 + 18 + 6 = 30$ feet ✓

Here is a summary of this concept from *Academic Systems Algebra*.

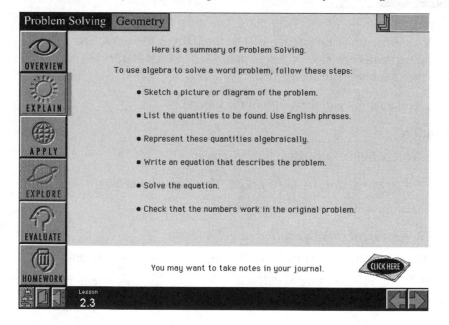

Checklist Lesson 2.3

Here is what you should know after completing this lesson.

Words and Phrases

word problems
consecutive integers

consecutive even integers
consecutive odd integers

Ideas and Procedures

❶ **Translate Words Into Algebra**
Translate key words such as sum, difference, twice, and quotient to construct algebraic expressions from English phrases.

See the chart at the beginning of Lesson 2.3.

❷ **Number Problems**
Solve word problems that involve relationships between numbers.

Example 2.3.2
The sum of three consecutive odd integers is 21 less than four times the smallest of the integers. What are the three integers?

See also: Example 2.3.1
Apply 1-14

❸ **Age Problems**
Solve word problems that involve relationships between ages of people.

Example 2.3.4
Maria is 6 years older than Tony. Three years ago, Maria was 4 years less than twice Tony's age. How old was Tony then?

See also: Example 2.3.3
Apply 15-28

❹ **Geometry Problems**
Solve word problems which make use of facts and formulas that involve the angles, areas, and perimeters of geometric figures such as triangles, rectangles, and circles.

Example 2.3.6
The length of a rectangle is 3 feet less than twice its width. If the perimeter of the rectangle is 30 feet, find the width and length.

See also: Example 2.3.5, 2.3.7, 2.3.8, 2.3.9
Apply 29-56

Homework Problems

Circle the homework problems assigned to you by the computer, then complete them below.

 Explain

Number and Age

1. The sum of four consecutive integers is -118. What are the four numbers?

2. The sum of three consecutive odd integers is -9. What is the largest integer?

3. The sum of three consecutive odd integers is 81. What are the three integers?

4. Latoya is twice as old as her cousin was 3 years ago. If the sum of their ages now is 15, how old is each one of them?

5. Mount Everest is the tallest mountain in the world. It is 237 meters higher than K2, the second tallest mountain. If the sum of their heights is 17,459 meters, how tall is each mountain?

6. Eleven years ago Hye was four times as old as her brother. In 1 year she will be twice as old as he is now. What are their ages now?

7. A molecule of octane has 26 atoms. If there are 6 fewer hydrogen atoms than 3 times the number of carbon atoms, how many atoms of each does it contain?

8. Ariel is 2 years older than twice Juan's age and Felix is 6 years older than Juan. If the sum of their ages is 80, how old is each person?

9. One number is 9 more than 3 times another. If their sum is 53, what is the smaller number?

10. When John F. Kennedy was sworn in as President, he was 1 year older than Teddy Roosevelt was when Roosevelt took the office. If the sum of their ages when each became President was 85, how old was Kennedy when he was sworn in?

11. The average surface temperature on Earth (in degrees Celsius) is 70 degrees more than the average surface temperature on Mars. If the sum of the average temperatures on the two planets is -20 degrees, what is the average surface temperature on Mars?

12. Toshihiko is 4 years more than twice as old as Kyoko. If the sum of their ages is 79, how old is Kyoko?

Geometry

13. The length of the longest leg of a triangle is twice the length of the shortest leg. The remaining leg is 2 inches longer than the shortest leg. If the perimeter of the triangle is 26 inches, how long is each leg?

14. A regular hexagon (which has 6 sides all the same length) has the same perimeter as a square. If the length of a side of the hexagon is 10 centimeters, how long is one side of the square?

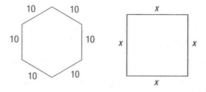

15. The length of a rectangle is 7 inches less than 3 times its width. If the perimeter of the rectangle is 50 inches, what are its dimensions?

16. The distance around one circular track is three times as far as the distance around a second circular track. If the sum of the distances around both tracks is 80π yards, what is the distance around the larger track?

17. If one side of a square is increased by 11 feet and an adjacent side is decreased by 5 feet, a rectangle is formed whose perimeter is 52 feet. Find the length of a side of the original square.

18. The measure of the smallest angle of a right triangle is 15 degrees less than half the measure of the next smallest angle. What is the measure of each angle?

19. The length of a rectangle is 12 feet less than three times its width. If the perimeter of the rectangle is 24 feet, what are its dimensions?

20. A regular pentagon (which has 5 sides all the same length) has the same perimeter as a regular hexagon (which has 6 sides all the same length). If the length of a side of the hexagon is 15 feet, how long is one side of the pentagon?

 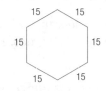

21. When the unequal side of an isosceles triangle (which has two equal sides) is increased by 3 inches, the triangle becomes an equilateral triangle (which has three equal sides). If the perimeter of the triangle is initially 18 inches, how long is each side of the original triangle?

22. The measure of one angle of a triangle is 20 degrees more than the measure of the smallest angle. The measure of another angle is 8 degrees less than twice the measure of the smallest angle. What is the measure of each angle?

23. A rectangular track was being built so that the length of one of the short sides was half the length of one of the long sides. The track was supposed to be 300 yards around. At the last minute, the plans for the track were changed and a semicircle (half a circle) was added at each of the short ends. What is the distance around the track after the plans were modified?

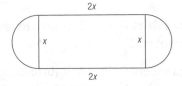

24. A regular octagon (which has 8 sides all the same length) has the same perimeter as a regular hexagon (which has 6 sides all the same length). If the length of one of the sides of the octagon is 1 inch less than a side of the hexagon, what is the length of a side of each figure?

 **Apply**

Practice Problems

Here are some additional practice problems for you to try.

Number and Age

1. The sum of two numbers is 42. One number plus 2 times the other number is 57. What are the numbers?

2. The sum of two numbers is 43. One number plus three times the other number is 65. What are the numbers?

3. The sum of two numbers is 45. Their difference is 9. What are the numbers?

4. The sum of two numbers is 24. Their difference is 52. What are the numbers?

5. The sum of two numbers is 16. Their difference is 40. What are the numbers?

6. The difference between two numbers is 55. Four times the smaller number plus five times the larger number is 176. What are the numbers?

7. The difference between two numbers is -38. Two times the smaller number minus five times the larger number is -217. What are the numbers?

8. The difference between two numbers is 80. Three times the smaller number plus four times the larger number is -334. What are the numbers?

9. The sum of three consecutive integers is 96. What are the numbers?

10. The sum of four consecutive integers is -226. What are the numbers?

11. The sum of four consecutive integers is 114. What are the numbers?

12. The sum of three consecutive even integers is 444. What are the numbers?

13. The sum of four consecutive even integers is -316. What are the numbers?

14. The sum of four consecutive odd integers is -32. What are the numbers?

15. David is 3 years older than Sean. The sum of their ages is 15. How old is Sean?

16. Alexandra is 8 years younger than Natasha. The sum of their ages is 30. How old is Alexandra?

17. Jeremy is six years older than Barbara. The sum of their ages is 68. How old is Barbara?

18. Carl is 9 years older than his cousin Jenny. If the sum of their ages is 77, how old is each one of them?

19. Miriam is ten years younger than her husband Edward. If the sum of their ages is 106, how old is each one of them?

20. Pietro is 12 years younger than Annietta. If the sum of their ages is 62, how old is each one of them?

21. Mark is three times as old as Luke. In 5 years Mark will be two times as old as Luke is in 5 years. How old is each one now?

22. Serge is five times as old as his daughter Katia. In 12 years Serge will be three times as old as Katia is in 12 years. How old is each one now?

23. Svetlana is four times as old as Boris. In 10 years Svetlana will be three times as old as Boris is in 10 years. How old is each one now?

24. Brandon is three times as old as Caitlin. Eighteen years ago, Brandon was six times as old as Caitlin was eighteen years ago. How old is each one now?

25. Masato is twice as old as Kim. Ten years ago, Masato was three times as old as Kim was ten years ago. How old is each one now?

26. Gerhard is twice as old as Isolde. Sixteen years ago, Gerhard was four times as old as Isolde was sixteen years ago. How old is each one now?

27. In 7 years, Maria will be four times as old as Angelica will be then. The sum of their ages now is 71. How old will each of them be in 5 years?

28. In 5 years, Alessandro will be three times as old as Frederico will be then. The sum of their ages now is 86. How old will each of them be in 3 years?

Geometry

29. An isosceles triangle has two angles whose measures are equal. If the largest angle of the triangle measures 85 degrees, what are the measures of the other two equal angles?

30. If the largest angle of an isosceles triangle measures 68 degrees, what are the measures of the other two equal angles?

31. The sum of the angle measures of a triangle is 180°. The smallest angle in a triangle is 64 degrees less than the measure of the largest angle. The measure of the remaining angle is 8 degrees more than the measure of the smallest angle. What is the measure of each angle?

32. The measure of the smallest angle in a triangle is 50 degrees less than the measure of the largest angle. The measure of the remaining angle is 10 degrees more than the measure of the smallest angle. What is the measure of each angle?

33. The measure of the largest angle in a triangle is 55 degrees more than the smallest angle. The measure of the remaining angle is 5 degrees less than the measure of the largest angle. What is the measure of each angle?

34. The shortest side of a triangle is 3 inches shorter than the longest side. The remaining side is 2 inches longer than the shortest side. The perimeter of the triangle is 20 inches. What is the length of each side? (Note: The perimeter of a figure is the distance around the outside of the figure.)

35. The longest side of a triangle is 12 cm longer than the shortest side. The remaining side is 2 cm shorter than the longest side. The perimeter of the triangle is 31 cm. What is the length of each side?

36. The longest side of a triangle is 7 cm longer than the shortest side. The remaining side is 3 cm shorter than the longest side. The perimeter of the triangle is 29 cm. What is the length of each side?

37. The shortest side of an isosceles triangle is 4 cm shorter than the length of each of the equal sides. The perimeter of the triangle is 26 cm. What is the length of each side?

38. The shortest side of an isosceles triangle is 5 inches shorter than the length of each of the equal sides. The perimeter of the triangle is 43 inches. What is the length of each side?

39. The shortest side of an isosceles triangle is half the length of each of the equal sides. The perimeter of the triangle is 80 inches. What is the length of each side?

40. The length of a rectangle is 10 cm longer than its width. The perimeter of the rectangle is 68 cm. What are the length and width of the rectangle? (Note: The perimeter of a rectangle is the distance around the outside of the rectangle.)

41. The width of a rectangle is 4 inches shorter than its length. The perimeter of the rectangle is 36 inches. What are the length and width of the rectangle?

42. The width of a rectangle is 9 cm shorter than its length. The perimeter of the rectangle is 40 cm. What are the length and width of the rectangle?

43. The length of a rectangle is 10 cm less than five times its width. The perimeter of the rectangle is 52 cm. What are the length and width of the rectangle?

44. The length of a rectangle is 23 cm less than three times its width. The perimeter of the rectangle is 82 cm. What are the length and width of the rectangle?

45. The length of a rectangle is 2 inches more than twice its width. The perimeter of the rectangle is 28 inches. What are the length and width of the rectangle?

46. The width of a rectangle is 52 inches less that four times its length. The perimeter of the rectangle is 51 inches. What are the length and width of the rectangle?

47. The width of a rectangle is 25 inches less than 3 times its length. The perimeter of the rectangle is 38 inches. What are the length and width of the rectangle?

48. The width of a rectangle is 3 more than half its length. The perimeter of the rectangle is 60 cm. What are the length and width of the rectangle?

49. The perimeter of an equilateral triangle (which has three sides, all the same length) is four times the perimeter of a regular hexagon (which has 6 sides, all the same length). The length of a side of the triangle is 10 cm more than six times the length of a side of the hexagon. What is the perimeter of the triangle? What is the perimeter of the hexagon?

50. The perimeter of a square is three times the perimeter of a regular hexagon (which has 6 sides all the same length). The length of a side of the square is 2 inches more than four times the length of a side of the hexagon. What is the perimeter of the square? What is the perimeter of the hexagon?

51. The length of a rectangular playground is four times its width. The perimeter of the playground is 250 feet. What is the area of the play ground? (Note: The area of a rectangle is found by multiplying its length by its width.)

52. The length of a rectangular park is five times its width. The perimeter of the park is 108 miles. What is the area of the park?

53. The length of a rectangular floor is six times its width. The perimeter of the floor is 210 feet. What is the area of the floor?

54. The length of a rectangular pool is 4 m more than twice its width. The perimeter of the pool is 20 m. What is the area of the pool?

55. The length of a rectangular garden is 3 feet more than twice its width. The perimeter of the garden is 78 feet. What is the area of the garden?

56. The width of a rectangular window is 10 feet less than twice its length. The perimeter of the window is 28 feet. What is the area of the window?

Evaluate

Practice Test

Take this practice test to be sure that you are prepared for the final quiz in Evaluate.

1. One number is 3 more than another. Twice the larger number minus the smaller number is 15. What are the two numbers?

2. Abe and his younger sister are 3 years apart in age. If the sum of their ages will be 35 next year, what are their ages now?

3. Five years ago, Felipe was half of Carolina's age. At that time, the sum of their ages was 30. How old is Felipe now?

4. The sum of three consecutive odd integers is 5 less than 4 times the smallest such integer. What are the three odd integers?

5. A rectangular park was built so that its length is 3 times its width. The perimeter of the park is 24 yards. What are the width and length of the park?

6. The measure of one angle of a triangle is 10 degrees more than the measure of the smallest angle. The measure of the third angle is 50 degrees more than the measure of the smallest angle. What are the measures of the angles of the triangle?

7. The distance around a rectangular city block is 280 yards. If the length of the block is 10 yards less than twice its width, what are the dimensions of the block?

8. The perimeter of a certain square is the same as the perimeter of a certain equilateral triangle. (An equilateral triangle is a triangle in which all three sides have the same length.) Each side of the triangle is 1 inch longer than a side of the square. How long is a side of the square? How long is a side of the triangle?

LESSON 2.4
LINEAR INEQUALITIES

 Overview

Most of the equations that you have solved so far have had exactly one solution. However, some problems have more than one solution.

For example, Keisha is trying to earn an A in her math class. She has done well on the first two exams, and wonders what score she needs to achieve on the final exam in order to earn an A.

In this lesson, you will learn about linear inequalities, which can help you solve a problem like Keisha's.

 Explain

Concept 1 has sections on

- **Linear Inequalities**

- **Graphing the Solutions of a Linear Inequality**

- **Solving Linear Inequalities Using Addition and Subtraction**

- **Solving Linear Inequalities Using Multiplication and Division**

- **Compound Linear Inequalities**

- **Solving Compound Linear Inequalities**

CONCEPT 1: SOLVING INEQUALITIES

Linear Inequalities

An equation is a mathematical statement that consists of two expressions joined by an equals sign, $=$. Here is an example: $x - 3 = 2$.

An **inequality** is a mathematical statement that consists of two (or more) expressions joined by an inequality symbol: $<$, $\leq$, $>$, or $\geq$. Here is an example: $x - 3 < 2$.

A **solution of an inequality** is a number that, when substituted for the variable, makes the inequality true.

Example 2.4.1

Determine if 6 is a solution of each inequality.

a. $x > -4$ b. $x < 5$ c. $x \leq 6$

Solution

a. $6 > -4$ is a true statement, so 6 is a solution of $x > -4$.

b. $6 < 5$ is a false statement, so 6 is NOT a solution of $x < 5$.

c. $6 \leq 6$ is a true statement (because $6 = 6$), so 6 is a solution of $x \leq 6$.

A linear equation, such as $x - 3 = 2$, typically has exactly one solution. The solution of this equation is $x = 5$.

A linear inequality, such as $x \leq 6$, typically has infinitely many solutions.

The solutions of this inequality include -8.2, 0, $\frac{1}{2}$, and 3.

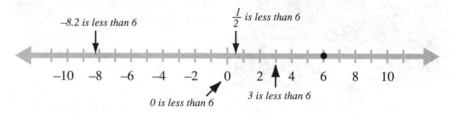

Graphing the Solutions of a Linear Inequality

Since it is impossible to list all the solutions of an inequality, we often graph the solutions on a number line.

Example 2.4.2

Graph: $x \leq 5$

Solution

The graph of $x \leq 5$ consists of the point that represents 5 and the points that represent all numbers less than 5.

To show that 5 is a solution, place a closed circle, •, at 5.

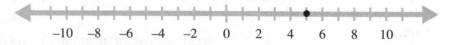

To show that all numbers less than 5 are solutions, draw an arrow starting at the closed circle and pointing to the left.

Example 2.4.3

Graph: $-4 < x$

Solution

The graph consists of the points that represent all the numbers that -4 is less than. This does not include -4.

To show that -4 is not a solution, place an open circle, O, at -4.

-4 is less than numbers such as $-2, 0, 5,$ and 18. These numbers lie to the right of -4 on the number line. Therefore, draw the arrow to the right.

Be careful. The direction of the inequality symbol does not necessarily indicate the direction of the arrow on the number line.

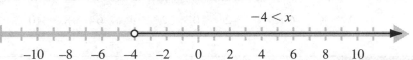

$-4 < x$

— Note —
Closed Circle ● Versus Open Circle ○

The inequality $x \geq 3$ is read "x is greater than or equal to three." The phrase "or equal to three" means that 3 is a solution. We use a closed circle, ●, at 3 to show this.

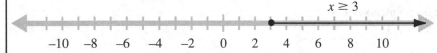

$x \geq 3$

The inequality $x > 3$ is read "x is greater than three." The phrase "or equal to" is not included, so 3 is not a solution. We use an open circle, ○, to show this.

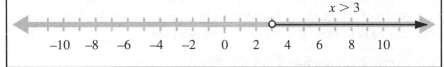

$x > 3$

Solving Linear Inequalities Using Addition and Subtraction

Solving an inequality is similar to solving an equation because equations and inequalities share many of the same principles.

For example, if we add or subtract the same quantity on both sides of an inequality, the result is an equivalent inequality.

Example 2.4.4

Solve the inequality $x - 2 \geq -6$. Then graph its solution.

Solution

Add 2 to both sides.

Simplify.

$$x - 2 \geq -6$$
$$x - 2 + 2 \geq -6 + 2$$
$$x \geq -4$$

The solution is $x \geq -4$.

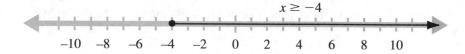

Example 2.4.5

Solve the inequality $x + 3 < 5$. Then graph its solution.

Solution

Subtract 3 from both sides.

Simplify.

$$x + 3 < 5$$
$$x + 3 - 3 < 5 - 3$$
$$x < 2$$

The solution is $x < 2$.

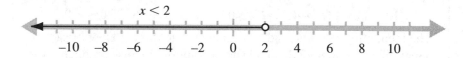

Because an inequality may have infinitely many solutions, it is not possible to check them all. However, it is a good idea to check one or two solutions to determine if the answer is reasonable.

In Example 2.4.5, we found that the solutions of $x + 3 < 5$ are the numbers less than 2. Since 0 is less than 2, we should obtain a true statement when we substitute 0 for x.

$$x + 3 < 5$$
$$\mathbf{0} + 3 < 5$$
$$3 < 5 \quad \textbf{True} \checkmark$$

Since 4 is greater than 2, we should obtain a false statement when we substitute 4 for x.

$$x + 3 < 5$$
$$\mathbf{4} + 3 < 5$$
$$7 < 5 \quad \textbf{False} \checkmark$$

Solving Linear Inequalities Using Multiplication and Division

As was the case with equations, we may multiply or divide both sides of an inequality by the same **positive** quantity and the result will be an equivalent inequality.

However, when we multiply or divide both sides of an inequality by a **negative** number, we **reverse** the direction of the inequality symbol. This is necessary so that the new inequality results in an equivalent statement.

An example may help to clarify this.
Let's begin with a true inequality statement. $\qquad\qquad 2 < 5$ **True**

If we multiply both sides by a positive number, 3 for example, the resulting inequality remains true.

$$\mathbf{3} \cdot 2 < \mathbf{3} \cdot 5$$
$$6 < 15 \ \ \textbf{True}$$

However, if we multiply both sides by a negative number, -3 for example, the resulting inequality is false.

$$2 < 5 \ \ \textbf{True}$$
$$-\mathbf{3} \cdot 2 < -\mathbf{3} \cdot 5$$
$$-6 < -15 \ \ \textbf{False}$$

When we multiply (or divide) by a negative number we must reverse the direction of the inequality symbol. $\qquad -6 > -15 \ \ \textbf{True}$

Example 2.4.6

Solve: $6x \le 18$. Then, graph its solution.

Solution $\qquad\qquad\qquad\qquad\qquad 6x \le 18$

Divide both sides by 6. $\qquad\qquad\qquad \dfrac{6x}{6} \le \dfrac{18}{6}$

We divide both sides by a positive number, 6, so the direction of the inequality symbol stays the same.

Simplify. $\qquad\qquad\qquad\qquad\qquad x \le 3$

The solution is $x \le 3$.

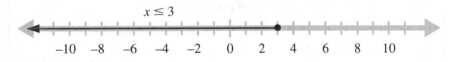

Example 2.4.7

Solve: $-\dfrac{2}{3}x > 4$. Then, graph its solution.

Solution $\qquad\qquad\qquad\qquad\qquad -\dfrac{2}{3}x > 4$

Multiply both sides by $-\dfrac{3}{2}$.

Because we are multiplying by a negative number we must reverse the direction of the inequality symbol.

$$\left(-\frac{\mathbf{3}}{\mathbf{2}}\right) \cdot \left(-\frac{2}{3}x\right) < \left(-\frac{\mathbf{3}}{\mathbf{2}}\right) \cdot 4$$

Simplify. $\qquad\qquad\qquad\qquad\qquad x < -6$

The solution is $x < -6$.

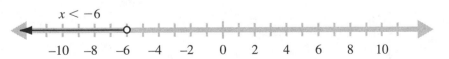

Principles of Inequality

In the examples below, a, b, and c are real numbers.

Addition Principle

If we add the same quantity to both sides of an inequality, we obtain an equivalent inequality.

If $a < b$ then $a + c < b + c$.
If $3 < 5$ then $3 + 2 < 5 + 2$.

Subtraction Principle

If we subtract the same quantity from both sides of an inequality, we obtain an equivalent inequality.

If $a < b$ then $a - c < b - c$.
If $3 < 5$ then $3 - 2 < 5 - 2$.

Multiplication Principle

If we multiply both sides of an inequality by the same **positive** number, we obtain an equivalent inequality.

If $a < b$ then $a \cdot c < b \cdot c$ when c is **positive.**
If $3 < 5$ then $3 \cdot 2 < 5 \cdot 2$.

If we multiply both sides of an inequality by the same **negative** number, we **reverse the direction** of the inequality symbol to obtain an equivalent inequality.

If $a < b$ then $a \cdot c > b \cdot c$ when c is **negative.**
If $3 < 5$ then $3 \cdot (-2) > 5 \cdot (-2)$.

Division Principle

If we divide both sides of an inequality by the same **positive** number, we obtain an equivalent inequality.

If $a < b$ then $a \div c < b \div c$ when c is **positive.**
If $3 < 5$ then $3 \div 2 < 5 \div 2$.

If we divide both sides of an inequality by the same **negative** number, we **reverse the direction** of the inequality symbol to obtain an equivalent inequality.

If $a < b$ then $a \div c > b \div c$ when c is **negative.**
If $3 < 5$ then $3 \div (-2) > 5 \div (-2)$.

Example 2.4.8

Solve: $-3w + 13 < 34$

Solution $\qquad\qquad\qquad\qquad -3w + 13 < 34$

Subtract 13 from both sides. $\qquad -3w + 13 - \mathbf{13} < 34 - \mathbf{13}$

Simplify. $\qquad\qquad\qquad\qquad\qquad -3w < 21$

Divide both sides by -3.
Because we divide by a **negative**
number, we **reverse the direction**
of the inequality symbol. $\qquad\qquad \dfrac{-3w}{-\mathbf{3}} > \dfrac{21}{-\mathbf{3}}$

Simplify. $\qquad\qquad\qquad\qquad\qquad w > -7$

The solution is $w > -7$.

Example 2.4.9

Solve: $3 > \dfrac{3}{4}m + \dfrac{5}{2}$

Solution $\qquad\qquad\qquad\qquad\qquad 3 > \dfrac{3}{4}m + \dfrac{5}{2}$

Multiply both sides by 4, the LCD
of all the fractions. $\qquad \mathbf{4} \cdot (3) > \mathbf{4} \cdot \left(\dfrac{3}{4}m + \dfrac{5}{2} \right)$

We multiply both sides by a positive number, 4, so the direction of the inequality symbol stays the same.

Simplify. $\qquad\qquad\qquad\qquad\qquad 12 > 3m + 10$

Subtract 10 from both sides. $\qquad 12 - \mathbf{10} > 3m + 10 - \mathbf{10}$

Simplify. $\qquad\qquad\qquad\qquad\qquad 2 > 3m$

Divide both sides by 3. $\qquad\qquad\qquad \dfrac{2}{3} > \dfrac{3m}{\mathbf{3}}$

Simplify. $\qquad\qquad\qquad\qquad\qquad \dfrac{2}{3} > m$

The solution is $\dfrac{2}{3} > m$.

This is read "$\dfrac{2}{3}$ is greater than m."

The solution may also be written as $m < \dfrac{2}{3}$.

That is, m is less than $\dfrac{2}{3}$.

Example 2.4.10

Walt must average at least 70 on three algebra exams to pass the course. His scores on the first two exams were 82 and 56. What is the lowest score Walt can earn on the third exam and still pass the course?

Solution

Step 1 List the quantities to be found. Use English phrases.

The lowest score Walt can earn on the third exam and still have an average of at least 70.

Step 2 Represent these quantities algebraically.

Let t represent the score on the third exam.

t = Walt's score on the third exam

Step 3 Write an inequality that describes the problem.

The average of the exam scores must be greater than or equal to 70.

exam average ≥ 70

To find the average of 3 scores, add the scores and divide by 3.

$\dfrac{82 + 56 + t}{3} \geq 70$

Step 4 Solve the inequality.

To clear the fraction, multiply both sides by 3.

$3 \cdot \left(\dfrac{82 + 56 + t}{3} \right) \geq 3 \cdot (70)$

Simplify.

$82 + 56 + t \geq 210$

Combine like terms.

$138 + t \geq 210$

Subtract 138 from both sides.

$t \geq 72$

To pass the course, the lowest score Walt can earn on the third exam is 72.

Step 5 Check that the numbers work in the original problem.

Condition	*Check*
• The average of the three exam scores must be at least 70.	• If Walt scores 72 on the third exam his average will be: $\dfrac{82 + 56 + 72}{3} = 70$ If his third exam score is greater than 72, then his exam average will be greater than 70. ✓

Compound Linear Inequalities

Some problems require the use of more than one inequality. An inequality that contains two inequality symbols is called a **compound inequality**.

For example, to be eligible to play Pee Wee hockey, a child must meet two conditions: the child must be at least 5 years old and less than 9 years old.

If we let y represent the age (in years) of the child, then these conditions may be written as two inequalities connected by the word *and*.

$$5 \leq y \text{ and } y < 9$$

The word *and* means that both conditions must be met.

The two individual inequalities may be written as a compound inequality:

$$5 \leq y < 9$$

The graphs of the two separate inequalities may be combined to form a single graph that represents all the solutions of the compound inequality.

The graph of numbers 5 and above is:

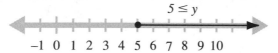

The graph of numbers below 9 is:

$$y < 9$$

The graph of the numbers on BOTH of the above graphs is:

$$5 \leq y < 9$$

Solving Compound Linear Inequalities

The equations and inequalities we have studied so far each had a left side and a right side. Compound inequalities, however, have three parts: a left side, a middle part, and a right side.

A compound inequality is solved when the variable has been isolated in the middle part.

To solve a compound inequality, apply the same operations to each part.

Example 2.4.11

Solve $-11 \le 3n - 5 < 2$. Then, graph the solution.

Solution

Apply the solution steps to all three parts of the inequality.

$$-11 \le \quad 3n - 5 \quad < 2$$

Add 5 to each part.

$$-11 + \mathbf{5} \le 3n - 5 + \mathbf{5} < 2 + \mathbf{5}$$

Simplify.

$$-6 \le \quad 3n \quad < 7$$

Divide each part by 3.

$$\frac{-6}{\mathbf{3}} \le \quad \frac{3n}{\mathbf{3}} \quad < \frac{7}{\mathbf{3}}$$

Simplify.

$$-2 \le \quad n \quad < \frac{7}{3}$$

The solution is $-2 \le n < \frac{7}{3}$.

To graph the solution, first plot -2 and then plot $\frac{7}{3}$.

Be sure to use a closed circle at -2 and an open circle at $\frac{7}{3}$.

Then, draw a line between the points to indicate that the solutions lie between -2 and $\frac{7}{3}$.

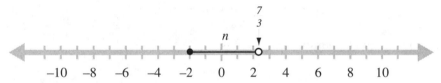

Example 2.4.12

Solve $-\frac{16}{3} < -\frac{2}{3}x - 4 \le 2$. Then, graph the solution.

Solution

$$-\frac{16}{3} < \quad -\frac{2}{3}x - 4 \quad \le 2$$

Multiply each part by 3, the LCD of the fractions.

$$\mathbf{3} \cdot \left(-\frac{16}{3}\right) < \mathbf{3} \cdot \left(-\frac{2}{3}x - 4\right) \le \mathbf{3} \cdot (2)$$

Simplify.

$$-16 < \quad -2x - 12 \quad \le 6$$

Add 12 to each part.

$$-16 + \mathbf{12} < -2x - 12 + \mathbf{12} \le 6 + \mathbf{12}$$

Simplify.

$$-4 < \quad -2x \quad \le 18$$

Divide each part by -2. We **reverse** the directions of **both** inequality symbols because we divide by a **negative** number.

$$\frac{-4}{\mathbf{-2}} > \quad \frac{-2x}{\mathbf{-2}} \quad \ge \frac{18}{\mathbf{-2}}$$

Simplify.

$$2 > \quad x \quad \ge -9$$

The solution is $2 > x \ge -9$.

We usually write a compound inequality with the smallest number on the left. To do this, we note the following:

The compound inequality $2 > x \geq -9$ means $2 > x$ and $x \geq -9$.

$2 > x$ is equivalent to $x < 2$.

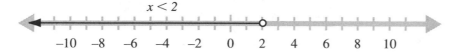

$x \geq -9$ is equivalent to $-9 \leq x$.

We may combine $-9 \leq x$ and $x < 2$ into a single compound inequality $-9 \leq x < 2$.

In other words, we can rewrite $2 > x \geq -9$ by interchanging the numbers 2 and -9 AND changing the direction of the inequality symbols.

Here is a summary of this concept from *Academic Systems Algebra*.

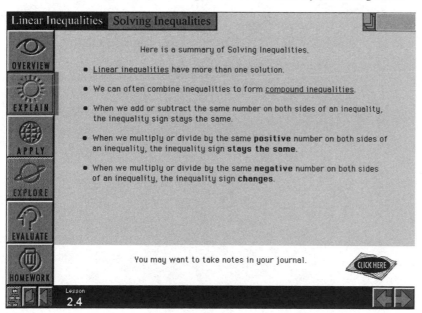

Checklist Lesson 2.4

Here is what you should know after completing this lesson.

Words and Phrases

inequality
solution of an inequality

compound inequality

Ideas and Procedures

❶ Solution of an Inequality
Determine whether a given value is a solution of a given inequality.

Example 2.4.1c
  Determine if 6 is a solution of $x \leq 6$.

See Also: Example 2.4.1a, b

❷ Graph an Inequality
Graph an inequality on a number line.

Example 2.4.3
  Graph: $-4 < x$

See Also: Example 2.4.2

❸ Solve an Inequality
Find the solution of an inequality.

Example 2.4.9
  Solve: $3 > \frac{3}{4}m + \frac{5}{2}$

See Also: Example 2.4.4-2.4.8, 2.4.10
      Apply 1-22

❹ Solve a Compound Inequality
Find the solution of a compound inequality.

Example 2.4.11
  Solve $-11 \leq 3n - 5 < 2$. Then, graph the solution.

See Also: Example 2.4.12
      Apply 23-28

Homework

Homework Problems

Circle the homework problems assigned to you by the computer, then complete them below.

 Explain

Solving Inequalities

1. Solve for x: $x - 7 < 2$

2. Solve for x: $15 < 5x$

3. Solve for x: $-3 \leq x + 1 \leq 5$

4. Solve for x: $18 < 2x + 4$

5. Solve for x: $6x < -18$

6. Solve for x: $-5 \leq 2x - 3 < -2$

7. Solve for x: $-2 < 6 - 4x$

8. Solve for x: $4 - x < x + 2$

9. Mohammad took $40 out of his savings account to go shopping for a birthday present. He needs $3.00 for parking and $12.50 for gas. Write an inequality to represent the amount he can spend on the present and still have enough money to pay for parking and gas.

10. Donna's new car gets 22 miles per gallon (mpg) in the city and 34 mpg on the highway. Write a compound inequality which represents the number of miles she can drive on 14 gallons of gas.

11. Solve for x: $\frac{3x + 1}{2} - 5 < -1$

12. Solve for x: $\frac{8}{5} < 2 - x < 6$

13. Graph the solutions of each inequality: $x - 2 \leq 5$ and $x - 2 < 5$. Explain how the solutions of the inequalities differ.

14. Graph the solutions of the compound inequality $-2 < 3x + 7 \leq 10$.

15. Graph the solutions of the compound inequality $1 < -\frac{2}{5}x + 3 < 5$.

16. Graph the solution of each inequality: $4 - 3x \leq -5$ and $4 - 3x < -5$. Explain how the solutions of the inequalities differ.

17. Graph the solutions of the compound inequality $-14 < 2 - 4x < 0$.

18. Graph the solutions of the compound inequality $\frac{1}{2} \geq \frac{2}{3}x - 2 > -\frac{4}{7}$.

 **Apply**

Practice Problems

Here are some additional practice problems for you to try.

Solving Inequalities

1. Solve for x: $x + 6 \leq 10$

2. Solve for y: $y + 7 \geq 9$

3. Solve for a: $a - 3 > 9$

4. Solve for w: $w - 6 \leq 3$

5. Solve for b: $3b < 18$

6. Solve for a: $4a \leq 36$

7. Solve for c: $5c \geq -25$

8. Solve for m: $-2m \leq 24$

9. Solve for d: $-4d > 5$

10. Solve for k: $-3k < -9$

11. Solve for x: $3x + 7 < 13$

12. Solve for y: $4y + 7 \geq 15$

13. Solve for z: $8z + 15 > 39$

14. Solve for m: $6m - 8 > -32$

15. Solve for a: $5a - 7 < -8$

16. Solve for h: $7h - 12 \leq 37$

17. Solve for x: $9 - x < 1$

18. Solve for x: $7 - x > 2$

19. Solve for p: $18 - p \geq 20$

20. Solve for y: $6 - 3y \geq 9$

21. Solve for z: $5 - 4z < 37$

22. Solve for y: $9 - 6y \leq -45$

23. Solve for y: $-6 \leq y + 5 < 13$

24. Solve for y: $-4 < y - 2 \leq 10$

25. Solve for z: $-15 < z - 14 < 25$

26. Solve for z: $16 \leq 7 - 2z < 23$

27. Solve for x: $15 \leq 8 - 3x \leq 20$

28. Solve for k: $-15 < 8 - 4k \leq -8$

Evaluate

Practice Test

Take this practice test to be sure that you are prepared for the final quiz in Evaluate.

1. Solve for x: $x - 3 < 4$

2. Solve for z: $3z - 7 \leq 5$

3. Solve for x: $7x + 2 < 6x + 5$

4. Solve for y: $9y + 11 > 8y - 3$

5. Solve for x: $9 - 4x \geq -19$

6. Solve for x: $\frac{1}{2}x + 4 \geq x$

7. Solve for z: $10 < 2z + 10 < 20$

8. At her job, Sonal can choose to work a different number of hours each day, but she must average at least 8 hours per day. This week she worked 10 hours on Monday, 6 hours on Tuesday, 7 hours on Wednesday, and 8 hours on Thursday. How many hours must she work on Friday to maintain or exceed her 8 hour average?

TOPIC 2 Cumulative Activities

Cumulative Review Problems

These problems combine all of the material you have covered so far in this course. You may want to test your understanding of this material before you move on to the next topic, or you may wish to do these problems to review for a test.

1. Simplify the expression
   $2x^2y - 5y + 6x^2y + 4x - 3y$.

2. Solve for y: $2y + 5 = 4\left(\frac{1}{2}y + 3\right)$

3. Solve for x: $-4 < 4x + 3 < 7$

4. Write using exponents:
   $3 \cdot 3 \cdot 5 \cdot 5 \cdot 5 \cdot 5 \cdot 17 \cdot 17 \cdot 17$

5. Suppose you have two numbers and the second number is 2 less than 3 times the first. If the sum of the two numbers is 34, what are the numbers?

6. Solve for x: $3(x + 2) = 12$

7. Solve for y: $-1 \le 6y - 4 < 12$

8. Simplify: $4 \cdot 3^2[7 - (3 + 4)] - 6$

9. Simplify the expression
   $2(x^2y^2 - 3x) + 4xy - 3(7x + x^2y^2) - 2$.

10. Circle the graph that represents the inequality
    $x - 7 < -3$.

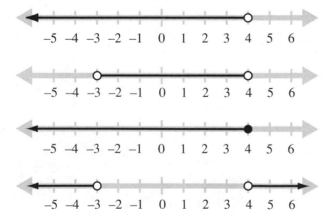

11. Find: $\dfrac{5}{9} \div \dfrac{10}{3}$

12. Simplify the expression
    $7xy^3 - 4xy^2 - 5x + xy^3 + 3x - 2xy^2$.

13. Solve for y: $5y - 2 \ge 23$, then graph its solution on the number line below.

14. One number is 8 less than 5 times another. If the sum of the two numbers is -2, what are the numbers?

15. Solve for z: $z + 5 = 8$

16. Reduce $\dfrac{54}{36}$ to lowest terms.

17. Evaluate the expression $xy^2 + 2xy - 3 + 5y$ when $x = 2$ and $y = -3$.

18. Find the GCF of 76 and 57.

19. Bjorn is 3 years older than Ivar was 5 years ago. If the sum of their ages now is 66, how old is each person?

20. Solve for y: $3 < 7 - 2y \le 6$, then graph its solution on the number line below.

21. The formula to find the area of a circle is $A = \pi r^2$, where A is the area and r is the radius. Solve the formula $A = \pi r^2$ for r.

22. Given the expression $4x^3y - 3 + 2y^2 - 7x + 12$,
    a. what are the terms?
    b. what are the variables?
    c. what are the coefficients?
    d. what are the constants?

23. The length of one side of a square is decreased by 2 meters and the length of an adjacent side is increased by 1 meter. In the resulting rectangle, the length is twice the width. How long was a side of the original square?

24. Evaluate the expression $5x - 3x^2y + 4 - 2y$ when $x = -3$ and $y = 1$.

25. Solve for x: $2x + 1 = -5 + 2(x + 3)$

26. Solve for z: $-8 \leq 3z + 10 \leq 16$, then graph its solution on the number line below.

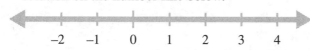

27. Find: $\dfrac{2}{3} + \dfrac{3}{4}$

28. Find the LCM of 16 and 42.

29. Solve for y: $\dfrac{1}{3}(3 - y) = \dfrac{5}{6}(3 + y)$

30. Solve for x: $\dfrac{1}{4}x + 5 = \dfrac{1}{2}(x - 2)$

TOPIC 3
INTRODUCTION TO GRAPHING

Graphs are used extensively to visualize numerical information. In this topic you will learn about one of the most widely used graphing systems, the Cartesian coordinate system. You will use the Cartesian coordinate system to find the coordinates of a point, to plot a point, and to find the rise and run in moving from one point to another.

Lesson 3.1 Introduction to Graphing

Concept 1: Plotting Points
The Cartesian Coordinate System
Finding the Coordinates of a Point
Plotting a Point

Concept 2: Rise and Run
Definition of Rise and Run
Finding the Rise and Run

Concept 3: The Distance Formula
The Distance Between Two Points on a Number Line
The Pythagorean Theorem
The Distance Formula
The Equation of a Circle

LESSON 3.1
INTRODUCTION TO GRAPHING

 Overview

A graph may be used to display different kinds of information. Nurses, sportswriters, car mechanics, engineers, bookkeepers, and scientists all use graphs in their work.

A graph is often used as a way to record observations. After the observations are recorded, the graph can be used to better understand how different quantities are related. Graphs can also be helpful in predicting future outcomes.

In this lesson you will learn about the most widely used graphing system—the Cartesian coordinate system. You will learn to plot points and how to find the horizontal and vertical change between two points. You will also learn how to calculate the distance between two points and how to find the equation of a circle.

 Explain

Concept 1 has sections on

- **The Cartesian Coordinate System**

- **Finding the Coordinates of a Point**

- **Plotting a Point**

CONCEPT 1: PLOTTING POINTS

The Cartesian Coordinate System

Suppose we know the sum of two numbers is 6.
We can represent this situation with the equation $x + y = 6$.

There infinitely many possibilities for x and y. For example:

$$
\begin{array}{lll}
1 \text{ and } 5 & -4 \text{ and } 10 & 0 \text{ and } 6 \\
1 + 5 = 6 & -4 + 10 = 6 & 0 + 6 = 6
\end{array}
$$

We can visualize this relationship between x and y using two number lines, one for x and the other for y.

First, draw a horizontal number line.
This is usually called the **x-axis** and is labeled with the variable x.

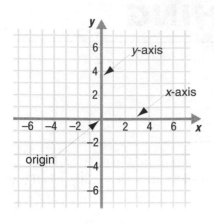

Next, draw a vertical number line perpendicular to the *x*-axis.

The two number lines should intersect at their zeros.

The vertical number line is usually called the **y-axis** and is labeled with the variable *y*.

The point of intersection, the zero of each number line, is called the **origin**.

To make it easier to locate a point, we draw a rectangular grid as a background.

The axes and the grid define a flat surface called the **xy-plane**.

The number lines and grid form a **rectangular coordinate system**. We typically use *x* and *y* for the variables, so a rectangular coordinate system is often called an **xy-coordinate system**. The French mathematician Rene Descartes (1596-1650) is credited with developing this type of coordinate system, so it is also referred to as the **Cartesian coordinate system**.

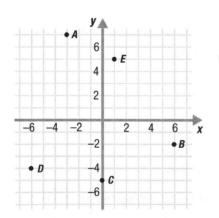

The *x*- and *y*-axes divide the plane into four regions called **quadrants**. We label these with Roman numerals I, II, III, and IV in a counter-clockwise direction beginning in the upper right.

Quadrant	Sign of x	Sign of y
I	positive	positive
II	negative	positive
III	negative	negative
IV	positive	negative

A point on an axis does not lie in a quadrant.

Example **3.1.1**

State the quadrant in which each labeled point lies.

a. A   b. B   c. C   d. D

Solution

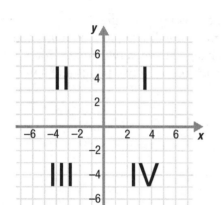

a. Quadrant II. Point *A* lies in the upper left quadrant.

b. Quadrant IV. Point *B* lies in the lower right quadrant.

c. None. Points on either axis do not lie in a quadrant.

d. Quadrant III. Point *D* lies in the lower left quadrant.

e. Quadrant I. Point *E* lies in the upper right quadrant.

Finding the Coordinates of a Point

Each point in the *xy*-plane has two numbers associated with it.

- The **x-coordinate** or **abscissa** tells how far the point lies to the left or right of the *y*-axis.

- The **y-coordinate** or **ordinate** tells how far the point lies above or below the *x*-axis.

The *x*- and *y*-coordinates are often written as an ordered pair inside parentheses, like this: (x, y).

The first number always represents the *x*-coordinate.

The second number always represents the *y*-coordinate.

Since the order in which the pair of numbers is written is so important, (x, y) is called an **ordered pair**.

For example:

The point $(-3, 4)$ has *x*-coordinate -3 and *y*-coordinate 4. This point is located 3 units to the left of the *y*-axis and 4 units above the *x*-axis.

The point $(4, -3)$ has *x*-coordinate 4 and *y*-coordinate -3. This point is located 4 units to the right of the *y*-axis and 3 units below the *x*-axis.

To find the coordinates of a point, we note its location relative to the *x*- and *y*-axes.

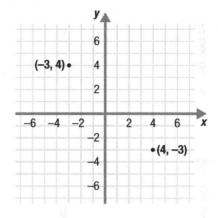

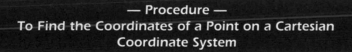

— Procedure —
To Find the Coordinates of a Point on a Cartesian Coordinate System

Step 1 Draw (or imagine) a vertical line through the point. The line intersects the *x*-axis at the *x*-coordinate.

Step 2 Draw (or imagine) a horizontal line through the point. The line intersects the *y*-axis at the *y*-coordinate.

Step 3 Write the coordinates as an ordered pair: (*x*-coordinate, *y*-coordinate).

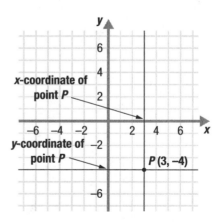

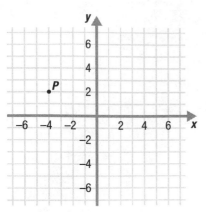

Example **3.1.2**

Find the coordinates of point *P*.

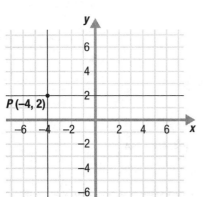

Solution

Step 1 Draw (or imagine) a vertical line through the point.

This line meets the *x*-axis at -4. The *x*-coordinate is -4.

Step 2 Draw (or imagine) a horizontal line through the point.

This line meets the *y*-axis at 2. The *y*-coordinate is 2.

Step 3 Write the coordinates as an ordered pair.

The coordinates of the point *P* are $(-4, 2)$.

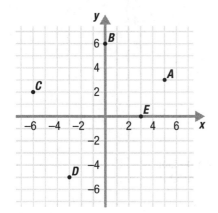

Example **3.1.3**

Find the coordinates of each labeled point on the graph.

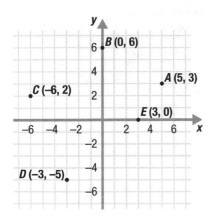

Solution

Point *A* has coordinates (5, 3).

Point *B* has coordinates (0, 6).

Point *C* has coordinates $(-6, 2)$.

Point *D* has coordinates $(-3, -5)$.

Point *E* has coordinates (3, 0).

Plotting Points

If the x-coordinate and the y-coordinate of a point are given, we can plot the point on a Cartesian coordinate system.

```
─────────────── Procedure ───────────────
    To Plot a Point on a Cartesian Coordinate System
```

Step 1 Draw (or imagine) a vertical line through the x-coordinate of the point.

Step 2 Draw (or imagine) a horizontal line through the y-coordinate of the point.

Step 3 Place a dot where the lines intersect.

Example 3.1.4

Plot the point (3, 7) on a Cartesian coordinate system.

Solution

Step 1 Draw (or imagine) a vertical line through the x-coordinate of the point.

Draw a vertical line through the x-axis at 3.

Step 2 Draw (or imagine) a horizontal line through the y-coordinate of the point.

Draw a horizontal line through the y-axis at 7.

Step 3 Place a dot where the lines intersect.

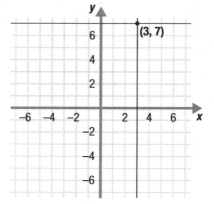

Example 3.1.5

Plot each point on a Cartesian coordinate system.

a. $(-3, -5)$ b. $(-2, 0)$ c. $(0, -3)$

d. $(5, -2.5)$ e. $\left(-6, 4\frac{1}{2}\right)$

Solution

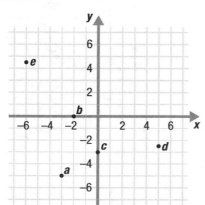

t time (hours)	d distance (miles)
0	0
1	40
2	80
3	120

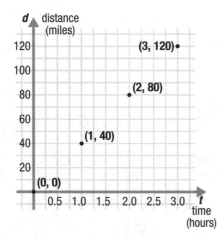

Example 3.1.6

The data in the table represent the total distance traveled by a car in 0 hour, 1 hour, 2 hours, and 3 hours. Plot the data on a Cartesian coordinate system.

Solution

The data correspond to these points: (0, 0), (1, 40), (2, 80), (3, 120)

To plot these points, we change the way we display the coordinate system.

Horizontal axis:

• The first column in the data table represents time, so we label the horizontal axis t instead of x.

• The times are between 0 and 3 hours, so we change the scale of the horizontal axis so each mark represents 0.25 hours.

• There are no negative times, so we do not show much of the negative horizontal axis.

Vertical axis:

• The second column in the data table represents distance, so we label the vertical axis with the letter d instead of y.

• Since the distances range from 0 to 120 miles we change the scale of the vertical axis so that each mark represents 10 miles.

• There are no negative distances, so we do not show much of the negative vertical axis.

The four points are plotted on the graph.

Example 3.1.7

The Gross National Product (GNP) of the United States is a measure of the vitality of the nation's economy. Use the information in the table to plot the ordered pairs in the form (*year*, *GNP*).

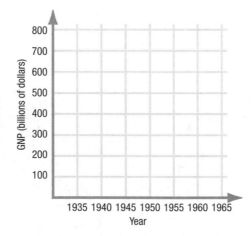

Year	GNP (billions of dollars)
1935	73
1940	101
1945	223
1950	294
1955	415
1960	527
1965	720

Solution

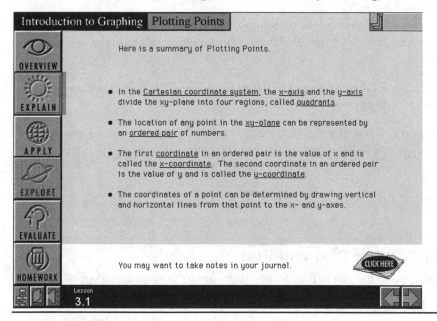

Here is a summary of this concept from *Academic Systems Algebra*.

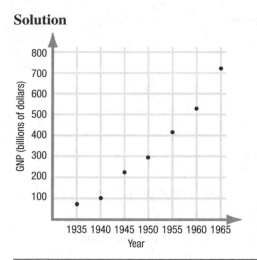

Introduction to Graphing | Plotting Points

OVERVIEW

EXPLAIN

APPLY

EXPLORE

EVALUATE

HOMEWORK

Here is a summary of Plotting Points.

• In the Cartesian coordinate system, the x-axis and the y-axis divide the xy-plane into four regions, called quadrants.

• The location of any point in the xy-plane can be represented by an ordered pair of numbers.

• The first coordinate in an ordered pair is the value of x and is called the x-coordinate. The second coordinate in an ordered pair is the value of y and is called the y-coordinate.

• The coordinates of a point can be determined by drawing vertical and horizontal lines from that point to the x- and y-axes.

You may want to take notes in your journal. CLICK HERE

Lesson 3.1

CONCEPT 2: RISE AND RUN

Concept 2 has sections on

▪ **Definition of Rise and Run**

▪ **Finding the Rise and Run**

Definition of Rise and Run

Suppose a car is traveling at a constant speed of 40 miles per hour. If we let d represent the miles traveled and t represent the hours traveled, then the relationship between d and t is given by:

$$d = 40t$$

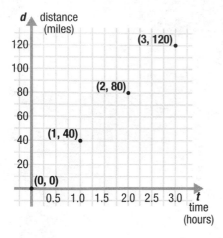

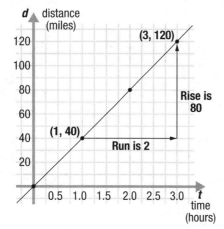

Here is a data table and a graph of the data.

t time (hours)	d distance (miles)	ordered pairs
0	0	(0, 0)
1	40	(1, 40)
2	80	(2, 80)
3	120	(3, 120)

In the second graph, we connect the points with a line to show all the solutions of $d = 40t$.

The coordinates of each point on the line satisfies the equation.

Now we will look at the vertical and horizontal changes that occur as we move from one point to another on the graph.

The **rise** is the vertical change in moving from one point to another on the graph. For this graph, the rise represents the change in the distance traveled.

For example, the rise from (1, 40) to (3, 120) is 80. This represents a change in distance of 80 miles.

The **run** is the horizontal change in moving from one point to another on the graph. For this graph, the run represents the change in the time traveled.

For example, the run from (1, 40) to (3, 120) is 2. This represents a change in time of 2 hours.

Finding the Rise and Run

The rise and the run between two given points may be found in two ways:

Use the graph:
- To find the rise, count the vertical units moved in going from the first point to the second point.
- To find the run, count the horizontal units moved in going from the first point to the second point.

Use algebra:
- To find the rise, subtract the y-coordinate of the first point from the y-coordinate of the second point.
- To find the run, subtract the x-coordinate of the first point from the x-coordinate of the second point.

Example **3.1.8**

Find the rise and the run in moving from point P_1 to point P_2 on the graph.

In $P_1(x_1, y_1)$, the P stands for "point" and the small 1 written a bit below and to the right of P indicates point 1. The small 1 is called a subscript. It is part of the name for the point.

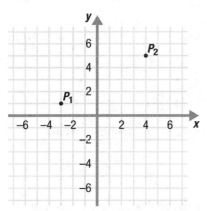

Solution

We may find the rise and the run in two ways.

Use the graph:

*   To find the run, on the graph count the number of units of horizontal change when moving from P_1 to P_2.

    The run is 7.

*   To find the rise, count the number of vertical units when moving from P_1 to P_2.

    The rise is 4.

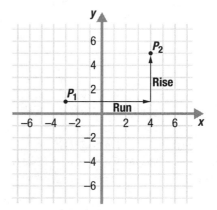

Use algebra:

The coordinates of P_1 are $(-3, 1)$.
The coordinates of P_2 are $(4, 5)$.

*   To find the rise, subtract the
    y-coordinates. That is, find $y_2 - y_1$.

$$\text{rise} = y_2 - y_1$$
$$= 5 - 1$$
$$= 4$$

Note that the y-coordinate of the starting point, y_1, is subtracted from the y-coordinate of the ending point, y_2.

*   To find the run, subtract the
    x-coordinates. That is, find $x_2 - x_1$.

$$\text{run} = x_2 - x_1$$
$$= 4 - (-3)$$
$$= 4 + 3$$
$$= 7$$

Example **3.1.9**

a. Use the graph to find the rise and the run in moving from $(-2, 1)$ to $(4, -3)$.

b. Use the graph to find the rise and the run in moving the other way, from $(4, -3)$ to $(-2, 1)$.

Solution

a. We are starting at $(-2, 1)$ and moving to $(4, -3)$.

To find the rise, count the number of vertical units when moving from $(-2, 1)$ to $(4, -3)$.

The rise is -4.

To find the run, count the number of horizontal units when moving from $(-2, 1)$ to $(4, -3)$.

The run is 6.

b. We are starting at $(4, -3)$ and moving to $(-2, 1)$.

To find the rise, count the number of vertical units when moving from $(4, -3)$ to $(-2, 1)$.

The rise is 4.

To find the run, count the number of horizontal units when moving from $(4, -3)$ to $(-2, 1)$.

The run is -6.

The run from $(4, -3)$ to $(-2, 1)$ is -6. This is the opposite of the run from $(-2, 1)$ to $(4, -3)$.

Here is a summary of this concept from *Academic Systems Algebra*.

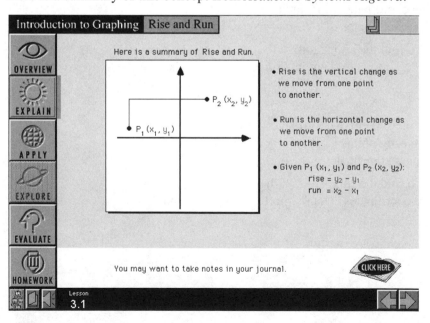

CONCEPT 3:
THE DISTANCE FORMULA

The Distance Between Two Points on a Number Line

If a and b are any two points on a number line, then the distance between a and b is given by $|a - b|$ or $|b - a|$. Absolute value is used because distance is cannot be a negative number.

Example 3.1.10

Find the distance on a number line between -6 and 4.

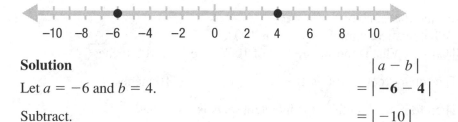

Solution $|a - b|$

Let $a = -6$ and $b = 4$. $= |-6 - 4|$

Subtract. $= |-10|$

Find the absolute value. $= 10$

We could also find the distance between -6 and 4 by computing $|4 - (-6)|$.

The distance between -6 and 4 is 10 units.

We have just found the distance between two points on a number line.

To find the distance between two points in the xy-plane we first review a theorem named after Pythagoras, a sixth-century BC Greek mathematician and philosopher.

The Pythagorean Theorem

A 90° angle is a **right angle**, so a triangle that contains a 90° angle is called a **right triangle**. The side opposite the right angle is the **hypotenuse** of the triangle.

Let a and b represent the lengths of the sides that form the right angle. Let c represent the length of the hypotenuse.

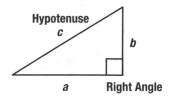

The **Pythagorean Theorem** states the relationship between the lengths of the sides of a right triangle.

— Formula —
Pythagorean Theorem

If a and b are the lengths of the sides that form the right angle in a right triangle and c is the length of the hypoteneuse, then:
$$c^2 = a^2 + b^2$$

If we know the lengths of two sides of a right triangle, we can use the Pythagorean Theorem to find the length of the third side.

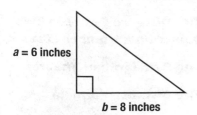

a = 6 inches

b = 8 inches

Example 3.1.11

Given a right triangle with sides of length 6 inches and 8 inches, find the length of the hypotenuse.

Solution $c^2 = a^2 + b^2$

In the Pythagorean Theorem, substitute
6 inches for a and 8 inches for b. $c^2 = (\mathbf{6 \text{ inches}})^2 + (\mathbf{8 \text{ inches}})^2$

Calculate the squares. $= 36 \text{ inches}^2 + 64 \text{ inches}^2$

Add. $= 100 \text{ inches}^2$

The value of c^2 is 100.

To find the value of c we ask,
"What positive number squared is 100?"
That is, "What is the square root of 100?" $c = \sqrt{100 \text{ inches}^2}$

The square root of 100 is 10. $c = 10 \text{ inches}$

Therefore, the length of the hypotenuse, c, is 10 inches.

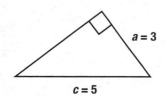

a = 3

c = 5

Example 3.1.12

Given a right triangle where one leg has length 3 units and the hypotenuse has length 5 units, find the length of the third side.

Solution $c^2 = a^2 + b^2$

In the Pythagorean Theorem, substitute
3 for a and 5 for c. $\mathbf{5}^2 = (\mathbf{3})^2 + b^2$

Calculate the squares. $25 = 9 + b^2$

Subtract 9 from both sides. $16 = b^2$

We found that b^2 is 16.
The square root of 16 is 4. $4 = b$

Therefore, the length of the third side, b, is 4 units.

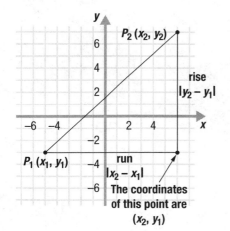

rise
$|y_2 - y_1|$

run
$|x_2 - x_1|$

The coordinates
of this point are
(x_2, y_1)

The Distance Formula

Now we will use the Pythagorean Theorem to find a formula we can use to find the distance between two points in the xy-plane.

Consider any two points in the xy-plane. Let's label them $P_1(x_1, y_1)$ and $P_2(x_2, y_2)$.

We draw a right triangle with P_1 and P_2 as the ends of the hypotenuse.

The length of the horizontal side of the triangle is the run from P_1 to P_2. That run is $|x_2 - x_1|$. We use absolute value because the length cannot be negative.

Likewise, the length of the vertical side of the triangle is the rise between P_1 and P_2. That rise is $|y_2 - y_1|$.

In the Pythagorean Theorem: $\qquad\qquad c^2 = a^2 + b^2$

Substitute the run, $|x_2 - x_1|$, for a.

Substitute the rise, $|y_2 - y_1|$, for b. $\qquad c^2 = |x_2 - x_1|^2 + |y_2 - y_1|^2$

When we square a quantity, we get a positive number. So we do not need the absolute value symbols. We replace them with parentheses. $\qquad c^2 = (x_2 - x_1)^2 + (y_2 - y_1)^2$

To find c, we take the square root. $\qquad c = \sqrt{(x_2 - x_1)^2 + (y_2 - y_1)^2}$

We call this result the distance formula.

— Formula —
The Distance Formula

Let $P_1(x_1, y_1)$ and $P_2(x_2, y_2)$ represent any two points in the xy-plane.

The distance, d, between P_1 and P_2 is given by
$$d = \sqrt{(x_2 - x_1)^2 + (y_2 - y_1)^2}$$

Example 3.1.13

Use the distance formula to find the distance between the points $(5, 0)$ and $(-2, -8)$.

Solution

Let (x_1, y_1) be $(5, 0)$ and (x_2, y_2) be $(-2, -8)$. $\qquad d = \sqrt{(x_2 - x_1)^2 + (y_2 - y_1)^2}$

Substitute these values into the distance formula. $\qquad d = \sqrt{(-2 - 5)^2 + (-8 - 0)^2}$

Simplify. $\qquad\qquad d = \sqrt{(-7)^2 + (-8)^2}$

$\qquad\qquad\qquad\qquad\qquad d = \sqrt{49 + 64}$

$\qquad\qquad\qquad\qquad\qquad d = \sqrt{113}$

The distance, d, is $\sqrt{113}$ units.

We obtain the same answer if we use $(5, 0)$ for (x_2, y_2) and $(-2, -8)$ for (x_1, y_1).

The Equation of a Circle

A **circle** is the set of all points equidistant from a single fixed point in a plane. The single fixed point is called the **center** of the circle. The distance from the center to any point on the circle is called the **radius**.

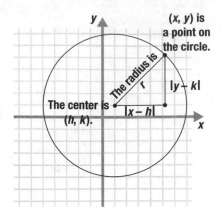

The center is (h, k).
The radius is r
(x, y) is a point on the circle.
$|y - k|$
$|x - h|$

This circle is drawn on a Cartesian coordinate system.

In the figure:

- The ordered pair (h, k) is the center of the circle.

- The ordered pair (x, y) represents any point on the circle.

- The radius, r, is the distance between the center of the circle, (h, k), and any point on the circle, (x, y).

Now we may use the distance formula to express the distance between the center of the circle and any point on the circle. That distance is the radius of the circle.

$$\text{distance} = \sqrt{(x_2 - x_1)^2 + (y_2 - y_1)^2}$$

In the distance formula, make the following substitutions:

$\text{distance} = r$
$(x_1, y_1) = (h, k)$
$(x_2, y_2) = (x, y)$

$$r = \sqrt{(x - h)^2 + (y - k)^2}$$

To remove the square root, square both sides.

$$r^2 = (x - h)^2 + (y - k)^2$$

The result is the **equation of a circle**.

This equation is usually written with r^2 on the right.

— Formula —
The Equation of a Circle

The equation of a circle in the xy-plane is given by

$$(x - h)^2 + (y - k)^2 = r^2$$

where the point (h, k) is the center of the circle, (x, y) is any point on the circle, and r is the radius of the circle.

Example 3.1.14

Find the equation of the circle with center at $(-4, 3)$ and radius 2.

Solution $(x - h)^2 + (y - k)^2 = r^2$

In the equation of a circle,
substitute -4 for h, 3 for k, and 2 for r. $[x - (-4)]^2 + (y - 3)^2 = (2)^2$

Simplify. $(x + 4)^2 + (y - 3)^2 = 4$

The equation of the circle is $(x + 4)^2 + (y - 3)^2 = 4$.

Example 3.1.15

Find the center and the radius of the circle whose equation is
$(x - 5)^2 + (y + 3)^2 = 16$.

Solution

The given equation has almost the same form as the standard equation of a circle.

$$(x - h)^2 + (y - k)^2 = r^2$$
$$(x - 5)^2 + (y + 3)^2 = 16$$

$x - 5$ has the form $x - h$. Therefore, h is 5.

$y + 3$ does not have the form $y - k$.
Rewrite $y + 3$ as $y - (-3)$.

$$(x - 5)^2 + [y - (-3)]^2 = 16$$

Therefore, k is -3.

r^2 is 16.

Therefore, r is $\sqrt{16} = 4$.

The center of the circle, (h, k), is $(5, -3)$. The radius, r, is 4.

Example 3.1.16

Find the center and the radius of the circle with equation
$(x + 1)^2 + y^2 = 20$.

Solution

The given equation has almost the same form as the standard equation of a circle.

$$(x - h)^2 + (y - k)^2 = r^2$$
$$(x + 1)^2 + y^2 = 20$$

Rewrite $x + 1$ as $x - (-1)$.

$$[x - (-1)]^2 + y^2 = 20$$

Rewrite y^2 as $(y - 0)^2$.

$$[x - (-1)]^2 + (y - 0)^2 = 20$$

Now, we can identify h, k, and r.

$x - (-1)$ has the form $x - h$. Therefore, h is -1.

$y - 0$ has the form $y - k$. Therefore, k is 0.

r^2 is 20. Therefore, r is $\sqrt{20}$.

The center of the circle, (h, k), is $(-1, 0)$. The radius is $\sqrt{20}$.

We can also write $\sqrt{20}$ as $2\sqrt{5}$.

Here is a summary of this concept from *Academic Systems Algebra*.

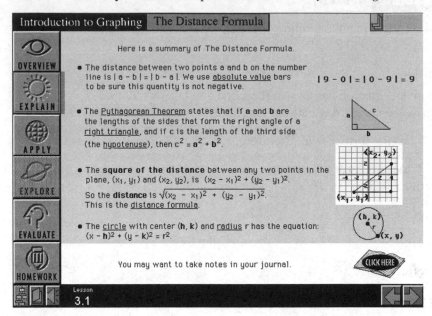

Here is a summary of The Distance Formula.

- The distance between two points a and b on the number line is $|a - b| = |b - a|$. We use <u>absolute value</u> bars to be sure this quantity is not negative.

  $|9 - 0| = |0 - 9| = 9$

- The <u>Pythagorean Theorem</u> states that if **a** and **b** are the lengths of the sides that form the right angle of a <u>right triangle</u>, and if c is the length of the third side (the <u>hypotenuse</u>), then $c^2 = a^2 + b^2$.

- The **square of the distance** between any two points in the plane, (x_1, y_1) and (x_2, y_2), is $(x_2 - x_1)^2 + (y_2 - y_1)^2$.

  So the **distance** is $\sqrt{(x_2 - x_1)^2 + (y_2 - y_1)^2}$. This is the <u>distance formula</u>.

- The <u>circle</u> with center (**h**, **k**) and <u>radius</u> r has the equation: $(x - h)^2 + (y - k)^2 = r^2$.

You may want to take notes in your journal.

CLICK HERE

Lesson
3.1

Checklist Lesson 3.1

Here is what you should know after completing this lesson.

Words and Phrases

x-axis
y-axis
origin
xy-plane
rectangular coordinate system
xy-coordinate system
Cartesian coordinate system
quadrant
x-coordinate
abscissa
y-coordinate
ordinate

ordered pair
rise
run
right angle
right triangle
hypotenuse
Pythagorean Theorem
distance formula
circle
center
radius
equation of a circle

Ideas and Procedures

❶ **Cartesian Coordinate System**
Label and describe the parts of the Cartesian coordinate system.

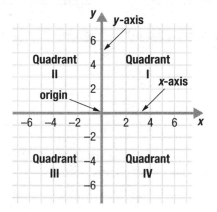

❷ **Quadrant**
State in which quadrant a given point lies.

Example 3.1.1
State the quadrant in which each labeled point lies.

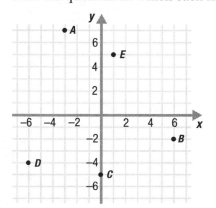

See also: Apply 25-28

❸ Coordinates of a Point

Find the coordinates of a point on a Cartesian coordinate system.

Example 3.1.3

Find the coordinates of each labeled point on the graph.

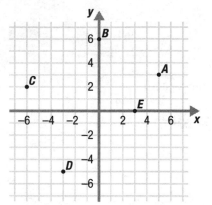

See also: Example 3.1.2

Apply 16-24

❹ Plot Points

Plot points on a Cartesian coordinate system.

Example 3.1.4

Plot the point (3, 7) on a Cartesian coordinate system.

See also: Example 3.1.5, 3.1.6, 3.1.7

Apply 1-15

❺ Rise and Run

Find the rise and the run in moving from one point to another on a Cartesian coordinate system.

Example 3.1.8

Find the rise and the run in moving from point P_1 to point P_2.

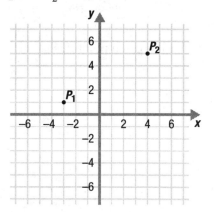

See also: Example 3.1.9

Apply 29-56

❻ Distance Between Two Points on a Number Line

Find the distance between two points on a number line.

Example 3.1.10
Find the distance on a number line between -6 and 4.

---

❼ Pythagorean Theorem

State the Pythagorean Theorem.

If a and b are the lengths of the sides that form the right angle in a right triangle, and c is the length of the hypotenuse, then
$$c^2 = a^2 + b^2.$$

Use the Pythagorean Theorem to find the length of a side of a right triangle.

Example 3.1.12
Given a right triangle where one leg has length 3 units and the hypotenuse has length 5 units, find the length of the third side.

See also: Example 3.1.11
Apply 57-60, 73-78

---

❽ Distance Formula

State the formula for the distance between two points on a Cartesian coordinate system.

Let $P_1(x_1, y_1)$ and $P_2(x_2, y_2)$ represent any two points in the xy-plane. The distance between P_1 and P_2 is given by:
$$d = \sqrt{(x_2 - x_1)^2 + (y_2 - y_1)^2}$$

Use the distance formula to find the distance between two points.

Example 3.1.13
Use the distance formula to find the distance between the points $(5, 0)$ and $(-2, -8)$.

See also: Apply 67-72

---

❾ Equation of a Circle

State the equation of a circle on a Cartesian coordinate system.

$$(x - h)^2 + (y - k)^2 = r^2$$
where (h, k) is the center of the circle, (x, y) is any point on the circle, and r is the radius of the circle.

Find the center and radius of a circle given its equation.
Find the equation of a circle given its center and radius.

Example 3.1.15
Find the center and the radius of the circle whose equation is $(x - 5)^2 + (y + 3)^2 = 16$.

See also: Example 3.1.14, 3.1.16
Apply 61-66, 79-84

Homework

Homework Problems

Circle the homework problems assigned to you by the computer, then complete them below.

 **Explain**

Plotting Points

Use Figure 3.1.1 to answer questions 1 through 8.

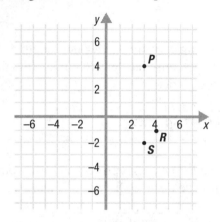

Figure 3.1.1

1. Find the coordinates of point *P*.

2. Plot the point $Q(-2, 5)$.

3. In what quadrant does the point $R(4, -1)$ lie?

4. Find the coordinates of point *S*.

5. Plot the point $T(-3, 6)$.

6. Plot a point which lies in Quadrant III.

7. Plot the point $U(0, 5)$.

8. Plot a point in Quadrant I whose *x*-coordinate is 4.

9. For selected years, the number of farms in the United States is listed in the table below. Use this information to plot the ordered pairs (*year, number of farms*) on the grid in Figure 3.1.2.

Year	Number of Farms (in thousands)	Number of Average Acres per Farm
1940	6,102	175
1950	5,388	216
1960	3,962	297
1970	2,954	373
1980	2,440	426
1990	2,143	461

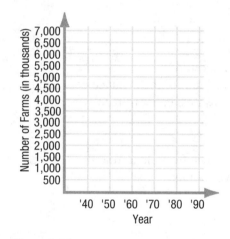

Figure 3.1.2

10. Using the data provided in question 9, plot the ordered pairs (*year, average number of acres per farm*) on the grid in Figure 3.1.3.

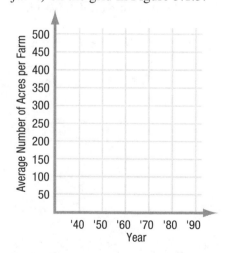

Figure 3.1.3

11. Plot the point $V(-3, 0)$.

12. Plot a point which does not lie in any quadrant.

Rise and Run

13. Draw one vertical and one horizontal line to show the rise and the run in moving from $P_1(1, 3)$ to $P_2(4, 6)$.

14. Plot the points $Q_1(-2, 3)$ and $Q_2(3, 4)$. Draw one vertical and one horizontal line to find the rise and the run in moving from Q_1 to Q_2.

15. Use rise $= y_2 - y_1$ and run $= x_2 - x_1$ to find the rise and the run in moving from $R_1(2, 5)$ to $R_2(5, 7)$.

16. Find the rise and the run in moving from $S_1(6, 7)$ to $S_2(2, -4)$ by drawing one vertical and one horizontal line on the graph.

17. Find the rise and the run from $T_1(-1, -4)$ to $T_2(-5, -8)$ by subtracting the appropriate coordinates.

18. Which is greater, the rise from $U_1(-9, -6)$ to $U_2(-1, 5)$ or the rise from $V_1(0, -6)$ to $V_2(10, 2)$?

19. Find the rise and the run from $W_1(-7, 11)$ to $W_2(17, 19)$ by subtracting the appropriate coordinates.

20. Given $P_1(1, 2)$, find the coordinates of P_2 if the rise from P_1 to P_2 is 2 and the run is 5. Use the grid in Figure 3.1.4.

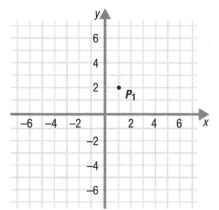

Figure 3.1.4

21. Plotted in Figure 3.1.5 is the federal minimum hourly wage rate (for nonfarm workers) for selected years. Use this information to determine which five-year period had the greatest rise in minimum wage. (You can refer to the table for more accurate numbers.)

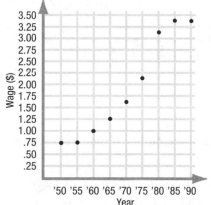

Year	Wage
1950	$0.75
1955	$0.75
1960	$1.00
1965	$1.25
1970	$1.60
1975	$2.10
1980	$3.10
1985	$3.35
1990	$3.35

Figure 3.1.5

22. Use the graph and table in question 21 to determine which five-year period had the smallest rise in minimum wage.

23. Find the rise and the run from $P_1(-68, -32)$ to $P_2(17, 94)$ by subtracting the appropriate coordinates.

24. Starting at $P_1(-3, -6)$, find the coordinates of P_2 if the rise from P_1 to P_2 is 8 and the run is 7.

The Distance Formula

25. If $a = 5$ and $b = 12$, use the Pythagorean Theorem to find c, the length of the hypotenuse of the right triangle shown in Figure 3.1.6.

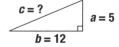

Figure 3.1.6

26. What is the equation of a circle whose center is at $(2, 3)$ and whose radius is 4?

27. Using the distance formula, find the distance between $(0, 0)$ and $(5, 2)$.

28. Use the Pythagorean Theorem to find the distance between (0, 0) and (6, 8). See Figure 3.1.7.

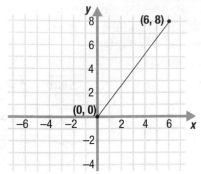

Figure 3.1.7

29. Find the center and the radius of the circle whose equation is $(x + 5)^2 + (y - 7)^2 = 2^2$.

30. Using the distance formula, find the distance between $(-2, 4)$ and $(-1, -7)$.

31. Use the Pythagorean Theorem to find the distance between $(-2, -1)$ and $(5, -6)$. See Figure 3.1.8.

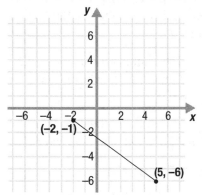

Figure 3.1.8

32. Find the center and the radius of the circle whose equation is: $(x - 6)^2 + (y + 1)^2 = 16$.

33. A fullback takes the ball from his 5 yard line (30 yards from the sideline) to his 45 yard line (50 yards from the same sideline). How many yards did he actually run? (You can express your answer as the square of the distance.) Start by finding a and b as shown in Figure 3.1.9. Then find c.

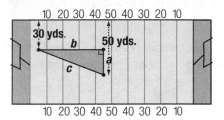

Figure 3.1.9

34. Marilena has been taking a shortcut across a lawn as shown in Figure 3.1.10. If the two lengths of the sidewalk measure 6 ft. and 8 ft., how much distance does Marilena save by taking the shortcut?

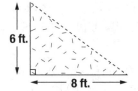

Figure 3.1.10

35. Write the equation of the circle with radius 5 whose center is at $(-3, 2)$.

36. Using the distance formula, find the distance between $(-4, 4)$ and $(5, -8)$.

 **Apply**

Practice Problems

Here are some additional practice problems for you to try.

Plotting Points

1. Plot the point $(3, 5)$.

2. Plot the point $(6, 1)$.

3. Plot the point $(4, 1)$.

4. Plot the point $(-3, 4)$.

5. Plot the point $(-5, 6)$.

6. Plot the point $(-1, 2)$.

7. Plot the point $(-1, -5)$.

8. Plot the point $(-6, -2)$.

9. Plot the point $(-3, -5)$.

10. Plot the point $(1, -6)$.

11. Plot the point $(4, -4)$.

12. Plot the point $(4, -2)$.

13. Plot the point $(0, -3)$.

14. Plot the point $(2, 0)$.

15. Plot the point $(-3, 0)$.

16. Find the coordinates of the point P.

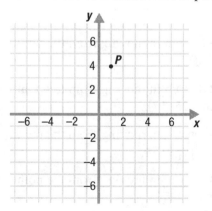

17. Find the coordinates of the point T.

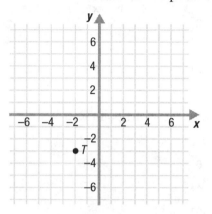

18. Find the coordinates of the point Q.

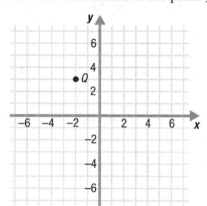

19. Find the coordinates of the point M.

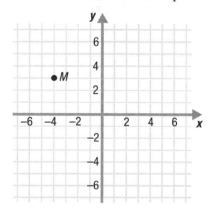

20. Find the coordinates of the point N.

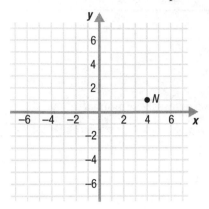

23. Find the coordinates of the point R.

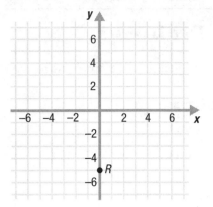

21. Find the coordinates of the point R.

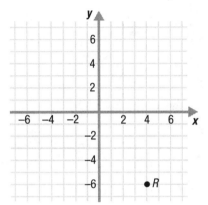

24. Find the coordinates of the point S.

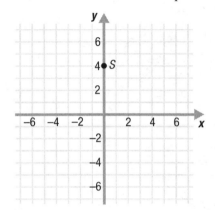

22. Find the coordinates of the point Q.

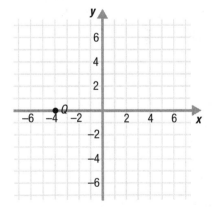

25. In what quadrant does the point $(-4, 3)$ lie?

26. In what quadrant does the point $(-2, -3)$ lie?

27. In what quadrant does the point $(1, -3)$ lie?

28. In what quadrant does the point $(4, 2)$ lie?

Rise and Run

29. Find the rise and the run in moving from the point $(1, 5)$ to the point $(9, 7)$.

30. Find the rise and the run in moving from the point $(12, 8)$ to the point $(25, 17)$.

31. Find the rise and the run in moving from the point $(11, 5)$ to the point $(2, 9)$.

32. Find the rise and the run in moving from the point $(4, 3)$ to the point $(2, -7)$.

33. Find the rise and the run in moving from the point $(0, -6)$ to the point $(8, 5)$.

34. Find the rise and the run in moving from the point $(2, 5)$ to the point $(11, 9)$.

35. Find the rise and the run in moving from the point $(3, -10)$ to the point $(0, -4)$.

36. Find the rise and the run in moving from the point $(-21, -16)$ to the point $(-19, -13)$.

37. Find the rise and the run in moving from the point $(-2, -5)$ to the point $(4, -2)$.

38. Find the rise and the run in moving from the point $(4, 0)$ to the point $(9, 5)$.

39. Find the rise and the run in moving from the point $(8, -1)$ to the point $(0, -7)$.

40. Find the rise and the run in moving from the point $(2, 0)$ to the point $(-5, 2)$.

41. Find the rise and the run in moving from the point $(-5, -9)$ to the point $(8, 2)$.

42. Find the rise and the run in moving from the point $(-10, -4)$ to the point $(1, 8)$.

43. Find the rise and the run in moving from the point $(-4, -4)$ to the point $(6, 3)$.

44. Find the rise and the run in moving from the point $(23, 17)$ to the point $(1, -3)$.

45. Find the rise and the run in moving from the point $(15, -16)$ to the point $(43, 31)$.

46. Find the rise and the run in moving from the point $(11, -7)$ to the point $(35, 24)$.

47. Find the rise and the run in moving from the point $(-13, -29)$ to the point $(0, -7)$.

48. Find the rise and the run in moving from the point $(-85, -57)$ to the point $(0, 3)$.

49. Find the rise and the run in moving from the point $(-27, -14)$ to the point $(0, 12)$.

50. Which is greater, the rise from $P_1(9, 13)$ to $P_2(21, 17)$ or the rise from $Q_1(-3, -5)$ to $Q_2(4, 16)$?

51. Which is greater, the run from $P_1(7, 12)$ to $P_2(19, 13)$ or the run from $Q_1(-1, 5)$ to $Q_2(3, 39)$?

52. Given $P_1(11, 14)$, find the coordinates of P_2 if the rise from P_1 to P_2 is 3 and the run is 9.

53. Given $P_1(8, 9)$, find the coordinates of P_2 if the rise from P_1 to P_2 is 4 and the run is 7.

54. Given $P_1(-4, -7)$, find the coordinates of P_2 if the rise from P_1 to P_2 is 6 and the run is 2.

55. Given $P_1(-16, 7)$, find the coordinates of P_2 if the rise from P_1 to P_2 is 13 and the run is 17.

56. Given $P_1(-3, -6)$, find the coordinates of P_2 if the rise from P_1 to P_2 is 6 and the run is 8.

The Distance Formula

57. If $a = 12$ and $b = 16$, use the Pythagorean Theorem to find c, the length of the hypotenuse of the right triangle shown below.

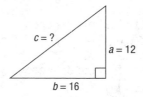

58. If $a = 9$ and $b = 12$, use the Pythagorean Theorem to find c, the length of the hypotenuse of the right triangle shown below.

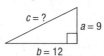

59. If $a = 15$ and $b = 36$, use the Pythagorean Theorem to find c, the length of the hypotenuse of the right triangle shown below.

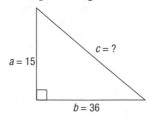

60. If $a = 20$ and $b = 48$, use the Pythagorean Theorem to find c, the length of the hypotenuse of the right triangle shown below.

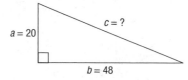

61. What is the equation of the circle whose center is at $(2, -3)$ and whose radius is 4?

62. What is the equation of the circle whose center is at $(-4, -5)$ and whose radius is 7?

63. What is the equation of the circle whose center is at $(-3, 1)$ and has radius 5?

64. Write the equation of the circle whose center is at $(1, 6)$ and has radius 10.

65. Write the equation of the circle whose center is at $(-3, 7)$ and has radius 8.

66. Write the equation of the circle whose center is at $(3, 10)$ and has radius 8.

67. Use the distance formula to find the distance between the points $(3, 6)$ and $(9, 13)$.

68. Use the distance formula to find the distance between the points $(4, -7)$ and $(-2, 3)$.

69. Use the distance formula to find the distance between the points $(7, 2)$ and $(-8, 3)$.

70. Use the distance formula to find the distance between the points $(-11, -5)$ and $(4, -7)$.

71. Use the distance formula to find the distance between the points $(-1, 7)$ and $(-10, -2)$.

72. Use the distance formula to find the distance between the points $(-10, -3)$ and $(4, -2)$.

73. Use the Pythagorean Theorem to find the distance between $(-4, 0)$ and $(-1, 4)$.

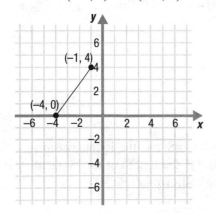

74. Use the Pythagorean Theorem to find the distance between $(0, 0)$ and $(3, 4)$.

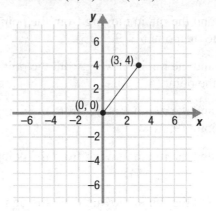

75. Use the Pythagorean Theorem to find the distance between $(-2, -5)$ and $(4, 3)$.

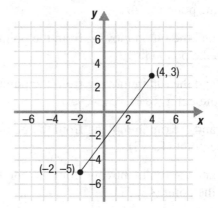

76. Use the Pythagorean Theorem to find the distance between $(-1, -6)$ and $(4, 6)$.

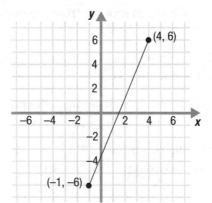

77. Use the Pythagorean Theorem to find the distance between $(7, 2)$ and $(-5, -3)$.

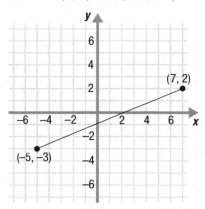

78. Use the Pythagorean Theorem to find the distance between $(-5, 5)$ and $(7, 0)$.

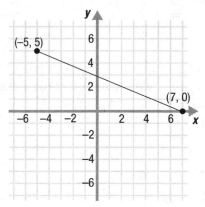

79. Find the center and the radius of the circle whose equation is $(x + 5)^2 + (y + 2)^2 = 3^2$.

80. Find the center and the radius of the circle whose equation is $(x - 10)^2 + (y - 1)^2 = 7^2$.

81. Find the center and the radius of the circle whose equation is $(x + 9)^2 + (y - 12)^2 = 6^2$.

82. Find the center and the radius of the circle whose equation is $(x - 8)^2 + (y + 2)^2 = 25$.

83. Find the center and the radius of the circle whose equation is $(x + 9)^2 + (y - 3)^2 = 121$.

84. Find the center and the radius of the circle whose equation is $(x - 3)^2 + (y + 15)^2 = 144$.

Practice Test

Take this practice test to be sure that you are prepared for the final quiz in Evaluate.

Use Figure 3.1.11 to answer questions 1–3.

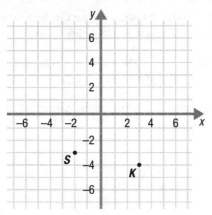

Figure 3.1.11

1. Find the coordinates of point K.

2. Plot the point P(5, 2.5).

3. In what quadrant does the point S(–2, –3) lie?

4. For selected years, average gas mileage for American cars is listed in the table below (rounded to the nearest whole number). Plot the ordered pairs (*year*, *mileage*) on the set of axes provided in Figure 3.1.12.

Year	Average Gas Mileage (mpg)
1970	14
1975	15
1980	23
1985	26
1990	27

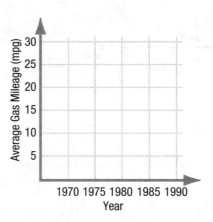

Figure 3.1.12

5. Find the rise and the run in moving from point $P_1(1, -5)$ to $P_2(7, 5)$ by drawing one vertical and one horizontal line on the grid in Figure 3.1.13.

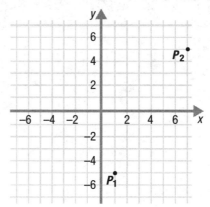

Figure 3.1.13

6. Find the rise and the run from $P_1(-7, -8)$ to $P_2(0, 4)$ by subtracting the appropriate coordinates.

7. Find the rise and the run from $P_1(-12, 7)$ to $P_2(24, 16)$ by subtracting the appropriate coordinates.

8. The average price for a gallon of gasoline is plotted in Figure 3.1.14 for selected years. Use this information to determine which five-year period had the greatest rise in gas prices.

Year	Price (cents)
1950	26.8
1955	29.1
1960	31.1
1965	31.2
1970	35.7
1975	56.7
1980	119.1
1985	111.5
1990	114.9

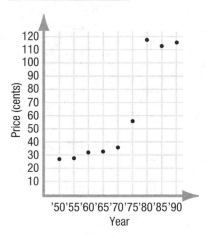

Figure 3.1.14

9. If $a = 9$ and $b = 12$, use the Pythagorean Theorem to find c, the length of the hypotenuse of the right triangle shown in Figure 3.1.15.

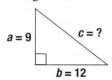

Figure 3.1.15

10. Use the Pythagorean Theorem to find the distance between the points $(-3, 1)$ and $(1, -2)$. See Figure 3.1.16.

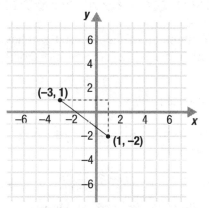

Figure 3.1.16

11. Use the distance formula to find the distance between the points $(10, 2)$ and $(-2, -7)$.

12. Find the radius and the center of the circle whose equation is below.

$$(x - 1)^2 + [y - (-5)]^2 = 2^2$$

13. A point with a negative x-coordinate and a positive y-coordinate lies in which quadrant?

Use Figure 3.1.17 to answer questions 14−16.

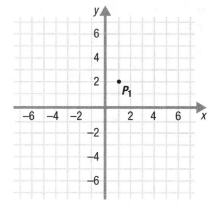

Figure 3.1.17

14. Plot a point in Quadrant III whose x-coordinate is -4.

15. Starting at the point $P_1(1, 2)$, find the coordinates of P_2 if the rise from P_1 to P_2 is 5 and the run is 1.

16. Plot a point, (x, y), where $y = x - 1$.

Cumulative Review Problems

These problems combine all of the material you have covered so far in this course. You may want to test your understanding of this material before you move on to the next topic, or you may wish to do these problems to review for a test.

1. Write in lowest terms: $\dfrac{12}{36}$

2. Evaluate the expression $2xy - 6y + 12$ when $x = -2$ and $y = 4$.

3. Simplify the expression $3(x - 7) + 2(9 - x)$.

4. Plot the points $P_1(1, 2)$ and $P_2(6, 4)$. Draw one vertical and one horizontal line to find the rise and the run from P_1 to P_2.

5. Plot the points $Q_1(-4, -3)$ and $Q_2(-1, 5)$. Draw one vertical and one horizontal line to find the rise and the run from Q_1 to Q_2.

6. Plot three points, (x, y), in Quadrant III where $x = y$. Use the grid in Figure 3.1.

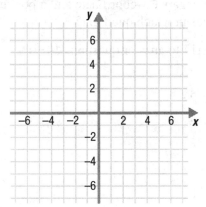

Figure 3.1

7. Seven years ago, Raoul was as old as Christine is now. If the sum of their ages is 63, how old is each person?

8. Find the rise and the run from $V_1(-54, -37)$ to $V_2(-8, 63)$ by subtracting the appropriate coordinates.

9. Solve for x: $4x + 9 < 13$. Then graph its solution on the number line below.

10. Find: $\dfrac{3}{4} + \dfrac{9}{10}$

11. Einstein's famous formula, $E = mc^2$, shows the amount of energy, E, which can be obtained from a particle of mass m. Solve this formula for c.

12. Circle the true statements.

    The equation $x + 3 = x - 7$ has no solution.

    $\dfrac{5}{6} \neq \dfrac{2}{4} + \dfrac{3}{2}$

    $5 \cdot 5 \cdot 5 = 3^5$

    $-3 < -2$

    $|-3| < |-2|$

13. Find: $7[2 - 3(5 - 4) + 1]$

14. Solve for z: $2 < z - 4 \leq 7$. Circle the number below that is not a solution.

    11

    2

    6.1

    7

15. Plot four points, (x, y), where $y = x - 3$. Use the grid in Figure 3.2.

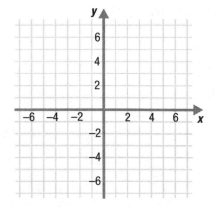

Figure 3.2

16. One number is 3 more than twice another number. If the sum of the two numbers is -33, what are the two numbers?

17. Circle the true statements.

$\left|-\dfrac{1}{2}\right| = -\left|\dfrac{1}{2}\right|$

$16 \div (-2) = (-16) \div 2$

every value of y is a solution of the equation
$4y = 8(y - 2)$

$2^3 \cdot 5^2 = 5^2 \cdot 2^3$

$\dfrac{6}{9} = \dfrac{2}{3}$

18. Write the coordinates of the point on the grid in Figure 3.3 that:

    a.   has an x-value more than -2.

    b.   has a y-value twice its x-value.

    c.   has a y-value less than 1.

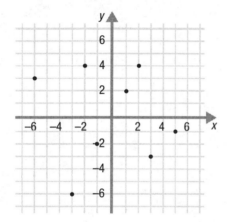

Figure 3.3

19. Find: $\dfrac{7}{12} - \dfrac{3}{8}$

20. Find the rise and the run from $T_1(-29, -31)$ to $T_2(14, 26)$ by subtracting the appropriate coordinates.

21. Solve for x: $-5 \le 8 - 3x < 2$

22. Solve for z: $\dfrac{2}{5}(4z - 1) = \dfrac{1}{10}(8z + 20)$

23. Plot the point $P(3, -5)$.

24. Plot the point $Q(-4, -6.5)$.

25. Plot the point $R(0, 6)$.

26. Shade in Quadrant I.

27. Solve for x: $7x + 3 = 38$

28. Use the fact that $R = \{1, 2, 3, 4, 5\}$ and $S = \{2, 4, 6, 8, 10\}$ to determine if each statement below is true.

    a. $2 \in R$

    b. $2 \in S$

    c. $3 \in R$

    d. $3 \in S$

29. Write the equation of the circle with radius 4 whose center is at $(2, 3)$.

30. Use the Pythagorean Theorem to find the distance between the points $(-1, -4)$ and $(4, 8)$.

31. Find: $\dfrac{18}{25} \div \dfrac{6}{5}$

32. Circle the true statements.

    a. $z = 3$ is a solution of the inequality $2z - 5 < 3$

    b. $|0| > |-5|$

    c. $0 > -5$

    d. $7^4 = 7 \cdot 7 \cdot 7 \cdot 7$

    e. $\dfrac{5}{10} = \dfrac{1}{2} = \dfrac{4}{8}$

33. Solve for y: $-3(y + 2) = 6\left(4 - \dfrac{1}{2}y\right)$

34. Use the distance formula to find the distance between the points $(-6, 3)$ and $(9, -5)$.

35. Find the radius and the center of the circle whose equation is $(x + 5)^2 + (y - 1)^2 = 49$.

36. If $R = \{1, 2, 3, 4, 5, 6, 7, 8, 9, 10\}$, $S = \{2, 4, 6, 8, 10\}$, and $T = \{1, 3, 5, 7, 9\}$, then which of the statements below are true?

    a. $S \subset R$

    b. $R \subset S$

    c. $T \subset R$

    d. $R \subset T$

    e. $S \subset T$

    f. $T \subset S$

TOPIC 4
GRAPHING LINEAR EQUATIONS AND INEQUALITIES

You have already learned how to plot points. In some cases, points lie on a straight line.

In this topic we will learn about such lines and the relationships among points which produce them.

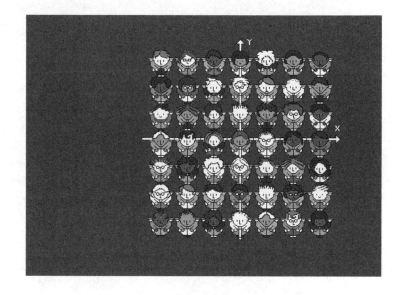

Lesson 4.1 Graphing Equations

Concept 1: Graphing Lines I
Solutions of a Linear Equation
Graphing a Linear Equation

Concept 2: Graphing Lines II
Graphing a Horizontal Line
Graphing a Vertical Line
Intercepts of a Line

Concept 3: Slope of a Line
Definition of Slope
Positive and Negative Slopes
Horizontal Lines and Vertical Lines
Using Slope to Graph a Line
Slopes of Parallel Lines
Slopes of Perpendicular Lines

Lesson 4.2 The Equation of a Line

Concept 1: Finding the Equation I
Point-Slope Form for the Equation of a Line
Standard Form for the Equation of a Line

Concept 2: Finding the Equation II
Slope-Intercept Form for the Equation of a Line
Equations of Horizontal Lines and Vertical Lines

Lesson 4.3 Graphing Inequalities

Concept 1: Linear Inequalities
Solutions of a Linear Inequality
Graphing a Linear Inequality
Another Way to Graph a Linear Inequality

LESSON 4.1
GRAPHING EQUATIONS

 Overview

You may have noticed a relationship between the number of hours you work and the amount of money you earn; and between the distance you drive and the amount of gas left in your tank.

When you are given the relationship between two quantities, a graph may help you understand the relationship. Sometimes the graph is a straight line.

In this lesson, you will learn how to graph a line. First, you will learn how to graph a line by plotting points whose coordinates satisfy the equation of the line. Then, you will learn about the slope of a line, and how to graph a line given the slope of the line and the coordinates of a single point on the line.

 Explain

Concept 1 has sections on

- **Solutions of a Linear Equation**

- **Graphing a Linear Equation**

CONCEPT 1:
GRAPHING LINES I

Solutions of a Linear Equation

Raoul and Rosa found a store that has Nut Creme and Coco Silk candy bars on sale. The price is four dollars for any six bars.

Raoul likes Nut Creme bars but Rosa likes Coco Silk bars.
They want to decide how many of each kind to buy for four dollars.

From their study of algebra, they know their choice will be a solution of the equation:

Number of Nut Creme bars + Number of Coco Silk bars = 6

$$x \qquad + \qquad y \qquad = 6$$

This is an example of a **linear equation in two variables**.

— Definition —
Linear Equation in Two Variables

A linear equation in two variables, x and y, is an equation that can be written in the form

$$Ax + By = C$$

where A, B, and C are real numbers and A and B are not both 0.

A solution of a linear equation in two variables is an ordered pair that, when substituted into the equation, results in a true statement. A solution is said to **satisfy** the equation.

A solution of the candy bar equation is
$x = 4$ and $y = 2$ since $4 + 2 = 6$.

$$x + y = 6$$
$$4 + 2 = 6$$

This solution may be written as the ordered pair $(4, 2)$.

The equation has other solutions, including $(3, 3)$ and $(1, 5)$.

$$3 + 3 = 6$$
$$1 + 5 = 6$$

Example | **4.1.1**

Determine if each ordered pair below is a solution of $2x + y = 4$.

a. $(-2, 8)$ b. $(5, 2)$

Solution $2x + y = 4$

a.   Replace x with -2 and y with 8.   Is $2(\mathbf{-2}) + \mathbf{8} = 4$?

     Simplify.   Is $4 = 4$? **Yes**

     The ordered pair $(-2, 8)$ is a solution of $2x + y = 4$.

b.   Replace x with 5 and y with 2.   Is $2(\mathbf{5}) + \mathbf{2} = 4$?

     Simplify.   Is $12 = 4$? **No**

     Since $12 \neq 4$, the ordered pair $(5, 2)$ is not a solution of $2x + y = 4$.

We can use the following procedure to find a solution of a linear equation in two variables.

— Procedure —
To Find a Solution of a Linear Equation in Two Variables

Step 1   Choose a value for one of the variables and substitute it in the equation.

Step 2   Solve the equation for the remaining variable.

Step 3   Write the numbers from Step 1 and Step 2 as an ordered pair.

Example 4.1.2

Find a solution of $2x + y = 7$.

Solution

Step 1 Choose a value for one of the variables and substitute it in the equation.

We may select any real number for x or y. $2x + y = 7$

Let's select 3 for x and substitute it into the equation. $2(\mathbf{3}) + y = 7$

Step 2 Solve the equation for the remaining variable.

Simplify . $\mathbf{6} + y = 7$

Subtract 6 from both sides. $y = 1$

Step 3 Write the numbers from Step 1 and Step 2 as an ordered pair.

A solution of the equation $2x + y = 7$ is (3, 1).

Example 4.1.3

Complete the table for the equation $-3x + y = 4$.

x	y
2	
	-8

Solution

For each ordered pair, substitute the given value in the equation. Then solve for the remaining variable.

Let $x = 2$. $-3x + y = 4$

Substitute 2 for x. $-3(\mathbf{2}) + y = 4$

Simplify. $-6 + y = 4$

Add 6 to both sides. $y = 10$

Let $y = -8$. $-3x + y = 4$

Substitute -8 for y. $-3x + (\mathbf{-8}) = 4$

Add 8 to both sides. $-3x = 12$

Divide both sides by -3. $x = -4$

The completed data table looks like this:

x	y
2	**10**
-4	-8

Graphing a Linear Equation

An equation of the form $Ax + By = C$ is called a **linear** equation because its graph is a straight **line**.

> **— Procedure —**
> **To Graph a Linear Equation Using a Table of Ordered Pairs**
>
> **Step 1** Make a table of ordered pairs that satisfy the equation.
>
> **Step 2** Plot the ordered pairs.
>
> **Step 3** Draw a line through the plotted points.

Example 4.1.4

Graph $3x + 2y = 6$.

Solution

Step 1 Make a table of ordered pairs that satisfy the equation.

Choose any values for x or y. We let x equal -1, 0, 2, and 3.

Then, substitute each value for x in the equation $3x + 2y = 6$ and solve for y.

The table of ordered pairs is shown.

x	y
-1	4.5
0	3
2	0
3	-1.5

Step 2 Plot the ordered pairs.

The points are plotted.

Step 3 Draw a line through the plotted points.

Each point on the line represents a solution of the equation $3x + 2y = 6$.

We need only two points to plot a line. However, we plot more than two points as a check against possible errors.

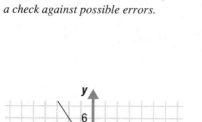

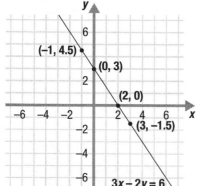

Here is a summary of this concept from *Academic Systems Algebra*.

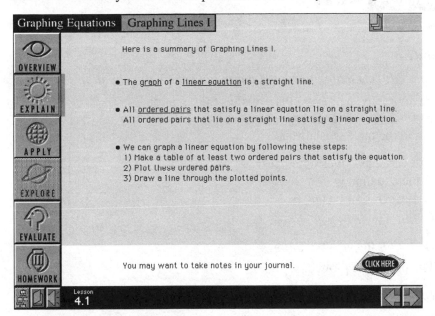

CONCEPT 2: GRAPHING LINES II

Graphing a Horizontal Line

A linear equation in two variables is an equation that can be written in the form $Ax + By = C$, where A, B, and C are real numbers and A and B are not **both** 0.

If either A or B is 0, the equation can be written with only one variable.

For example, the equation $y = -2$ is a linear equation since it can be written as $0x + 1y = -2$.

Here, A is 0, B is 1, and C is -2.

Now we will graph the equation $y = -2$.

Concept 2 has sections on

- **Graphing a Horizontal Line**
- **Graphing a Vertical Line**
- **Intercepts of a Line**

Example 4.1.5

Graph $y = -2$.

Solution

Step 1 Make a table of ordered pairs that satisfy the equation.

Each ordered pair (x, y) that satisfies the equation
$y = -2$ has y-coordinate -2.
So, in the table, y is always -2.

The variable x does not appear
in the equation $y = -2$.
So we can let x be any real
number; but y is always -2.

x	y
-5	-2
-3	-2
0	-2
3	-2

Step 2 Plot the ordered pairs.

The points are plotted.

Step 3 Draw a line through the plotted points.

Since the y-value of each ordered pair is -2, the graph is a horizontal
line two units below the x-axis.

Every point on this line represents a solution of $y = -2$.

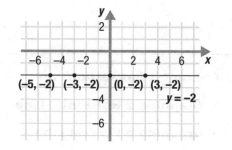

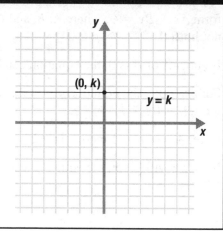

— Definition —
Graph of a Horizontal Line y = k

The graph of an equation of the
form $y = k$ is a horizontal line
through the point $(0, k)$, where k
is a constant.

Graphing a Vertical Line

The equation $x = 4$ is a linear equation since it can be written as $1x + 0y = 4$. Let's look at the graph.

Example 4.1.6

Graph $x = 4$.

Solution

Step 1 Make a table of ordered pairs that satisfy the equation.

Each ordered pair (x, y) that satisfies $x = 4$ has x-coordinate **4**. So, in the table, x is always 4.

The variable y does not appear in the equation $x = 4$. So we can let y be any real number; but x is always 4.

x	y
4	2
4	-5
4	3
4	0

Step 2 Plot the ordered pairs.

The points are plotted.

Step 3 Draw a line through the plotted points.

Since the x-value of each ordered pair is 4, the graph is a vertical line 4 units to the right of the y-axis.

Each point on this line represents a solution of $x = 4$.

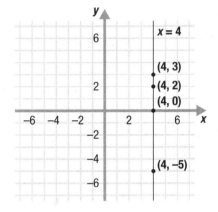

— Definition —
Graph of a Vertical Line x = k

The graph of an equation of the form $x = k$ is a vertical line through the point $(k, 0)$, where k is a constant.

Intercepts of a Line

When we graph a line, the **x-intercept** and the **y-intercept** are two points that are often easy to find and use.

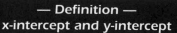

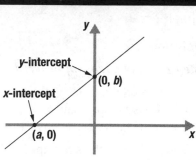

The x-intercept of a line is the point where the line crosses the x-axis. The x-intercept has the form $(a, 0)$, where a is a constant.

The y-intercept of a line is the point where the line crosses the y-axis. The y-intercept has the form $(0, b)$, where b is a constant.

In Example 4.1.4, we graphed the line $3x + 2y = 6$.

We can use the graph to find the intercepts.

The x-intercept is the point $(2, 0)$.

The y-intercept is the point $(0, 3)$.

We can use intercepts to graph a line.

Example 4.1.7

Given the equation $4x - 3y = 12$:

a. Find the x-intercept.

b. Find the y-intercept.

c. Use the intercepts to graph the line.

Solution

a. The x-intercept has the form $(a, 0)$.

To find the x-intercept, substitute 0 for y. Then solve for x.

$$4x - 3y = 12$$
$$4x - 3(0) = 12$$

Simplify.

$$4x = 12$$

Divide both sides by 4.

$$x = 3$$

The x-intercept is $(3, 0)$.

b. The *y*-intercept has the form $(0, b)$.

x	*y*	
3	0	*x-intercept*
0	−4	*y-intercept*
6	4	*check point*

To find the *y*-intercept, substitute 0 for *x*. Then solve for *y*.

$$4x - 3y = 12$$
$$4(\mathbf{0}) - 3y = 12$$

Simplify.

$$-3y = 12$$

Divide both sides by −3.

$$y = -4$$

The *y*-intercept is $(0, -4)$.

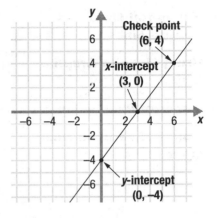

c. To graph the line $4x - 3y = 12$, plot the *x*-intercept and the *y*-intercept.

Then, draw a line through the intercepts.

As a check, it is a good idea to find a third point on the line.

For example, choose 6 for *x* in the equation $4x - 3y = 12$.

Solve for *y*. The result $y = 4$.

Since $(6, 4)$ is a solution of the equation $4x - 3y = 12$, the line should pass through the point $(6, 4)$.

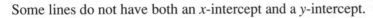

Some lines do not have both an *x*-intercept and a *y*-intercept.

- A horizontal line, other than the *x*-axis, has a *y*-intercept, but no *x*-intercept.

   For example, the horizontal line $y = 6$ has *y*-intercept $(0, 6)$, but no *x*-intercept.

- A vertical line, other than the *y*-axis, has an *x*-intercept, but no *y*-intercept.

   For example, the vertical line $x = 2$ has *x*-intercept $(2, 0)$, but no *y*-intercept.

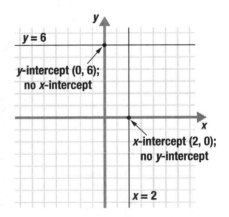

Here is a summary of this concept from *Academic Systems Algebra*.

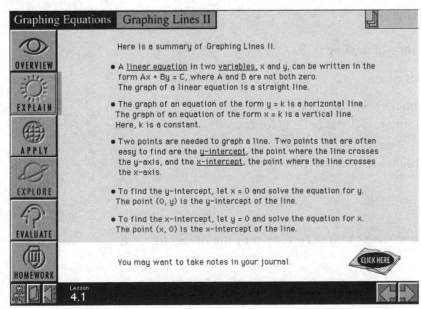

CONCEPT 3: SLOPE OF A LINE

Definition of Slope

The **slope** of a line is the ratio of the rise to the run when moving from any point on the line to any other point on the line. This ratio is a number that describes the steepness of the line.

By tradition, the letter m is used to represent the slope of a line.

— Definition —
Slope

The slope of the line between two points, (x_1, y_1) and (x_2, y_2), is given by

$$m = \frac{\text{rise}}{\text{run}} = \frac{\text{change in } y}{\text{change in } x} = \frac{y_2 - y_1}{x_2 - x_1}$$

where $x_1 \neq x_2$.

Example **4.1.8**

Find the slope of the line through the points $(-2, 1)$ and $(3, 5)$.

Solution

It does not matter which point we choose for (x_1, y_1).

For example,

let $(x_1, y_1) = (-2, 1)$ and $(x_2, y_2) = (3, 5)$.
$$m = \frac{y_2 - y_1}{x_2 - x_1}$$

Substitute the values in the slope formula.
$$= \frac{5 - 1}{3 - (-2)}$$

Simplify.
$$= \frac{4}{5}$$

The slope of the line is $\frac{4}{5}$.

To move from $(-2, 1)$ to $(3, 5)$, the ratio of rise to run is $\frac{4}{5}$.

We obtain the same slope if we choose
$(3, 5)$ for (x_1, y_1) and $(-2, 1)$ for (x_2, y_2).
$$m = \frac{y_2 - y_1}{x_2 - x_1}$$

Substitute the values in the slope formula.
$$= \frac{1 - 5}{-2 - 3}$$

Simplify.
$$= \frac{-4}{-5}$$

To move from $(3, 5)$ to $(-2, 1)$, the ratio of rise to run is $\frac{4}{5}$.

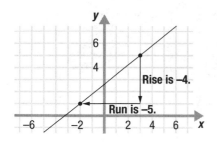

Example 4.1.9

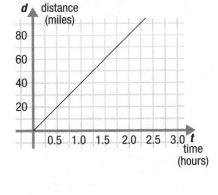

The graph shows the relationship between distance and time for a car traveling at a constant speed.

a. Find the slope of the line.

b. Interpret the meaning of the slope.

Solution

a. Choose any two points on the line, for example, (0, 0) and (2, 80).

Let $(x_1, y_1) = (0, 0)$ and $(x_2, y_2) = (2, 80)$. $\qquad m = \dfrac{y_2 - y_1}{x_2 - x_1}$

Substitute the values in the slope formula. $\qquad = \dfrac{80 \text{ miles} - 0 \text{ miles}}{2 \text{ hours} - 0 \text{ hours}}$

$\qquad = \dfrac{80 \text{ miles}}{2 \text{ hours}}$

Simplify. $\qquad = \dfrac{40 \text{ miles}}{1 \text{ hour}}$

The slope is $\dfrac{40 \text{ miles}}{1 \text{ hour}}$.

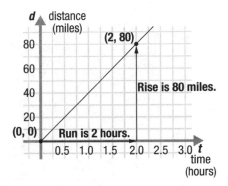

We write this as 40 miles per hour or 40 mph.

b. The slope, 40 mph, is the speed of the car.

Positive and Negative Slopes

A line with a positive slope slants upward as we move from left to right on the graph.

Each line shown has a positive slope.

To verify this, we can choose any two points on a line and find the slope.

For example, we will find the slope of line *A*.

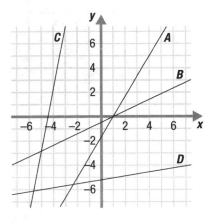

Example 4.1.10

Find the slope of line *A*.

Solution

Choose any two points on line *A*.

For example, choose $(-2, -5)$ and $(4, 5)$.

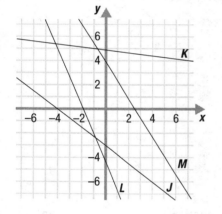

Let $(x_1, y_1) = (-2, -5)$ and $(x_2, y_2) = (4, 5)$.

$$m = \frac{y_2 - y_1}{x_2 - x_1}$$

Substitute the values in the slope formula.

$$= \frac{5 - (-5)}{4 - (-2)}$$

Simplify.

$$= \frac{10}{6}$$

Reduce.

$$= \frac{5}{3}$$

The slope of line *A* is a positive number, $\frac{5}{3}$.

Line *A* slants upward as we move from left to right on the graph, so we expected a positive slope.

A line with a negative slope slants downward as we move from left to right on the graph.

Each line shown has a negative slope.

To verify this, we can choose any two points on a line and find the slope.

For example, we will find the slope of line *J*.

Example 4.1.11

Find the slope of line *J*.

Solution

Choose any two points on line *J*. For example, choose $(-4, 0)$ and $(4, -6)$.

Let $(x_1, y_1) = (-4, 0)$ and $(x_2, y_2) = (4, -6)$.

$$m = \frac{y_2 - y_1}{x_2 - x_1}$$

Substitute the values in the slope formula.

$$= \frac{-6 - 0}{4 - (-4)}$$

Simplify.

$$= -\frac{6}{8}$$

Reduce.

$$= -\frac{3}{4}$$

The slope of line *J* is a negative number, $-\frac{3}{4}$.

Line *J* slants downward as we move from left to right on the graph, so we expected a negative slope.

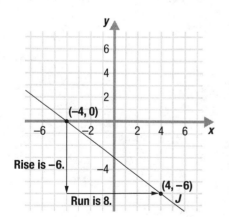

Horizontal Lines and Vertical Lines

The slope of a horizontal line is neither positive nor negative.

The slope of a vertical line is undefined. That is, a vertical line does not have a slope.

Example 4.1.12

Find the slope of the horizontal line through points $(-4, 2)$ and $(3, 2)$.

Solution

Let $(x_1, y_1) = (-4, 2)$ and $(x_2, y_2) = (3, 2)$.

$$m = \frac{y_2 - y_1}{x_2 - x_1}$$

Substitute the values in the slope formula.

$$= \frac{2 - 2}{3 - (-4)}$$

$$= \frac{0}{7}$$

Simplify.

$$= 0$$

The slope of the line is 0.

To move from one point to another on a horizontal line, the rise is 0.

So the slope of a horizontal line is 0.

Example 4.1.13

Find the slope of the vertical line that passes through $(3, -4)$ and $(3, 2)$.

Solution

Let $(x_1, y_1) = (3, -4)$ and $(x_2, y_2) = (3, 2)$.

$$m = \frac{y_2 - y_1}{x_2 - x_1}$$

Substitute the values in the slope formula.

$$= \frac{2 - (-4)}{3 - 3}$$

Simplify.

$$= \frac{6}{0}$$

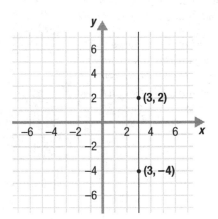

Division by 0 is undefined, so the slope of the line is undefined.

To move from one point to another on a vertical line, the run is 0. The slope of a vertical line is undefined. That is, a vertical line does not have a slope.

- **Positive slope:** Line slants upward as we move from left to right.

- **Negative slope:** Line slants downward as we move from left to right.

- **Zero slope:** A horizontal line has slope 0.

- **Undefined slope:** The slope of a vertical line is undefined.

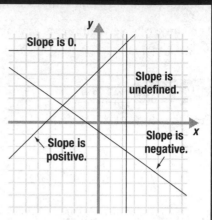

Using Slope to Graph a Line

We have graphed a line by making a table of at least two ordered pairs and plotting the ordered pairs on a Cartesian coordinate system.

If we are given only one point on a line, we can graph the line if we also know its slope.

— Procedure —
To Graph a Line Using a Point and the Slope

We "rise" in the y-direction and "run" in the x-direction.

positive rise: move up
negative rise: move down
positive run: move right
negative run: move left

Step 1 Plot any point on the line.

Step 2 From this point, rise in the *y*-direction the number of units in the numerator of the slope.

Step 3 Then run in the *x*-direction the number of units in the denominator of the slope. Plot a point at this location.

Step 4 Draw a line through the two points.

Example 4.1.14

Graph the line that passes through the point $(4, -3)$ with slope $-\frac{2}{3}$.

Solution

Step 1 Plot any point on the line.

Plot the given point $(4, -3)$.

Step 2 From this point, rise in the y-direction the number of units in the numerator of the slope.

The slope is $-\frac{2}{3}$. We can write this as $\frac{-2}{3}$. Thus, the rise is -2.

From $(4, -3)$, move down 2 units to $(4, -5)$.

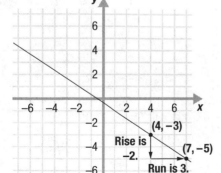

Step 3 *Then run in the x-direction the number of units in the denominator of the slope. Plot a point at this location.*

We wrote the slope as $\frac{-2}{3}$, so the run is 3.

From $(4, -5)$ move 3 units to the right to $(7, -5)$.

Place a dot at $(7, -5)$.

Step 4 *Draw a line through the two points.*

Draw the line through $(4, -3)$ and $(7, -5)$.

We could also write the slope, $-\frac{2}{3}$, as $\frac{2}{-3}$. Then, the rise is $+2$ and the run is -3.

Using that rise and run, we end up at $(1, -1)$. That point is also on the line.

Slopes of Parallel Lines

Distinct **parallel lines** never intersect.
Lines that are parallel (and not vertical) have the same slope.

Example 4.1.15

Find the slope of a line parallel to the line that passes through the points $(3, 4)$ and $(-2, -6)$.

Solution

First, find the slope of the line through the given points.

$$m = \frac{y_2 - y_1}{x_2 - x_1}$$

Let $(x_1, y_1) = (3, 4)$ and $(x_2, y_2) = (-2, -6)$.

Substitute the values in the slope formula.

$$= \frac{-6 - 4}{-2 - 3}$$

Simplify.

$$= 2$$

The slope of the line through $(3, 4)$ and $(-2, -6)$ is 2.

A line parallel to the line through $(3, 4)$ and $(-2, -6)$ has the same slope, 2.

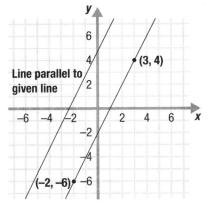

Slopes of Perpendicular Lines

Perpendicular lines intersect at a right angle.

If two nonvertical lines are perpendicular, then their slopes are negative reciprocals of each other.

That is, if the slope of one line is $\frac{a}{b}$, then the slope of any perpendicular line is $-\frac{b}{a}$.

The product of the slopes of two perpendicular lines is -1.

$$\frac{a}{b} \cdot \left(-\frac{b}{a}\right) = -1$$

To find the negative reciprocal of a fraction, switch the numerator and the denominator and change the sign.

For example, the negative reciprocal of $\frac{5}{2}$ is $-\frac{2}{5}$. The negative reciprocal of -3 is $\frac{1}{3}$.

Example 4.1.16

Find the slope of a line perpendicular to the line that passes through the points $(-4, 1)$ and $(1, -2)$.

Solution

First, find the slope of the line through the given points.

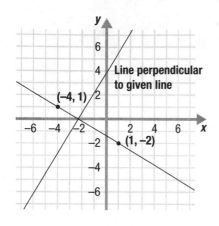

Let $(x_1, y_1) = (-4, 1)$ and $(x_2, y_2) = (1, -2)$.

$$m = \frac{y_2 - y_1}{x_2 - x_1}$$

Substitute the values in the slope formula.

$$= \frac{-2 - 1}{1 - (-4)}$$

Simplify.

$$= -\frac{3}{5}$$

The slope of the line through $(-4, 1)$ and $(1, -2)$ is $-\frac{3}{5}$.

The negative reciprocal of $-\frac{3}{5}$ is $\frac{5}{3}$.

A line perpendicular to the line through $(-4, 1)$ and $(1, -2)$ has slope $\frac{5}{3}$.

Example 4.1.17

Determine if line A is perpendicular to line B.

Solution

First, find the slope of each line.

$$m = \frac{y_2 - y_1}{x_2 - x_1}$$

For line A, we use the points $(-4, -3)$ and $(2, 4)$.

$$= \frac{4 - (-3)}{2 - (-4)}$$

The slope of line A is $\frac{7}{6}$.

$$= \frac{7}{6}$$

Next, find the slope of line B.
We use the points $(-3, 0)$ and $(5, -6)$.

$$= \frac{-6 - 0}{5 - (-3)}$$

The slope of line B is $-\frac{6}{8}$.

$$= -\frac{6}{8}$$

The slopes, $\frac{7}{6}$ and $-\frac{6}{8}$, are not negative reciprocals so the lines are not perpendicular.

Be careful! The lines do look perpendicular. But the relationship between their slopes tells us the lines are not perpendicular.

Here is a summary of this concept from *Academic Systems Algebra*.

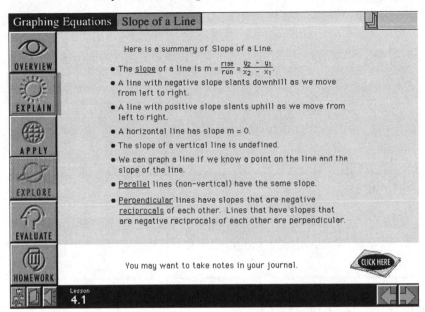

Graphing Equations | **Slope of a Line**

OVERVIEW
EXPLAIN
APPLY
EXPLORE
EVALUATE
HOMEWORK

Here is a summary of Slope of a Line.

- The <u>slope</u> of a line is $m = \dfrac{rise}{run} = \dfrac{y_2 - y_1}{x_2 - x_1}$.
- A line with negative slope slants downhill as we move from left to right.
- A line with positive slope slants uphill as we move from left to right.
- A horizontal line has slope $m = 0$.
- The slope of a vertical line is undefined.
- We can graph a line if we know a point on the line and the slope of the line.
- <u>Parallel</u> lines (non-vertical) have the same slope.
- <u>Perpendicular</u> lines have slopes that are negative <u>reciprocals</u> of each other. Lines that have slopes that are negative reciprocals of each other are perpendicular.

You may want to take notes in your journal.   CLICK HERE

Lesson
4.1

Checklist Lesson 4.1

Here is what you should know after completing this lesson.

Words and Phrases

linear equation in two variables
solution of a linear equation in two variables
satisfy
x-intercept

y-intercept
slope
parallel lines
perpendicular lines

Ideas and Procedures

❶ Solution of a Linear Equation in Two Variables
Find a solution to a linear equation in two variables.

Example 4.1.2
   Find a solution of $2x + y = 7$.

See also: Example 4.1.1, 4.1.3
            Apply 1-7

❷ Graph a Linear Equation
Construct the graph of a linear equation in two variables.

Example 4.1.4
   Graph $3x + 2y = 6$.

See also: Apply 8-28

❸ Graph a Horizontal or Vertical Line
Construct the graph of an equation of the form $y = k$ or $x = k$.

Example 4.1.6
   Graph $x = 4$.

See also: Example 4.1.5
            Apply 29-42

❹ Intercepts
Find the x-intercept and the y-intercept of a line.

Example 4.1.7
   Given the equation $4x - 3y = 12$:
   a. Find the x-intercept
   b. Find the y-intercept
   c. Use the intercepts to graph the line.

See also: Apply 43-56

❺ Slope

Write the formula for the slope of a line.

The slope of the line between two points, (x_1, y_1) and (x_2, y_2), is given by

$$m = \frac{\text{rise}}{\text{run}} = \frac{\text{change in } y}{\text{change in } x} = \frac{y_2 - y_1}{x_2 - x_1}$$

where $x_1 \neq x_2$.

Find the slope of a line.

Example 4.1.8
Find the slope of the line through the points $(-2, 1)$ and $(3, 5)$.

See also: Example 4.1.9, 4.1.10, 4.1.11, 4.1.12, 4.1.13
Apply 57-70

Graph a line given its slope and one point on the line.

Example 4.1.14
Graph the line that passes through the point $(4, -3)$ with slope $-\frac{2}{3}$.

See also: Apply 83-84

---

❻ The Slopes of Parallel and Perpendicular Lines

Find the slope of a line that is either parallel to or perpendicular to a given line.

Example 4.1.16
Find the slope of a line perpendicular to the line that passes through the points $(-4, 1)$ and $(1, -2)$.

See also: Example 4.1.15, 4.1.17
Apply 71-82

Homework Problems

Circle the homework problems assigned to you by the computer, then complete them below.

☼ Explain

Graphing Lines I

1. Which points below lie on the line described by the equation $x + y = 5$.
   (1, 4)
   (−3, 5)
   (9, 6)
   (−2, 7)
   (−8, 4)

2. Graph the equation $x + y = 3$.

3. Graph the equation $2x + y = 6$.

4. Which points below lie on the line described by the equation $x − 2y = 8$.
   (3, 2)
   (−4, 6)
   (−7, 4)
   (0, −4)
   (2, −3)

5. Graph the equation $x + 3y = 6$.

6. Graph the equation $4x + y = 12$.

7. Graph the equation $5x − 4y = 10$.

8. Graph the equation $2x − 3y = 6$.

9. Jay has decided to devote a total of 10 hours a week to his music, either playing his guitar or writing songs. If x = the number of hours he spends playing the guitar, and y = the number of hours he spends writing songs, then the equation $x + y = 10$ describes how he can split his time. Graph this equation.

10. Barbara is going to donate a total of $50 to two charities. If x = the amount she will donate to the American Heart Association and y = the amount she will donate to the American Cancer Society, then the equation $x + y = 50$ describes how she can divide her money. Graph this equation.

11. Graph the equation $\frac{2}{3}x + y = 4$.

12. Graph the equation $x − \frac{3}{5}y = −2$

Graphing Lines II

13. Complete the table below to find six ordered pairs that satisfy the equation $y = 5$.

x	y
5	
3	
0	
2	
−2	
−4	

14. Graph the equation $y = 5$.

15. Find the x- and y-intercepts of the line $x + 4y = 4$.

16. Graph the equation $x = −4$.

17. Graph the equation $y = 1$.

18. Find the x- and y-intercepts of the line $4x − 3y = 12$.

19. Graph the equation $y = −6$.

20. Graph the equation $x = 3$.

21. To change a temperature from degrees Fahrenheit to degrees Celsius, use the formula $C = \frac{5}{9}(F − 32)$. Graph this equation.

22. To change a temperature from degrees Fahrenheit to degrees Celsius, use the formula $C = \frac{5}{9}(F − 32)$. Find the F- and C-intercepts of the line described by this equation.

23. Graph the equation $x = 3.5$.

24. Find the x- and y-intercepts of the line $x − \frac{3}{4}y = 2$.

Slope of a Line

25. Find the slope of the line through the points (2, 4) and (5, 7).

26. Find the slope of the line through the points (1, 3) and (5, 3).

27. The point (1, –4) lies on a line with slope $\frac{2}{3}$. Graph this line by finding another point that lies on the line.

28. Find the slope of a line parallel to the line through the points (−1, 2) and (2, 8).

29. Find the slope of the line through the points (−4, −3) and (−4, 5).

30. The point (1, 3) lies on a line with slope 1. Graph this line by finding another point that lies on the line.

31. Find the slope of a line perpendicular to the line through the points (2, −4) and (6, 1).

32. The point (−5, 2) lies on a line that has slope $-\frac{3}{7}$. Graph this line by finding another point that lies on the line.

33. The number of eggs used by a bakery can be expressed by the equation $y = 12x$, where x is the number of cartons purchased and y is the number of eggs used. Use the point (0, 0) and the slope of the line, 12, to find another point on the line.

34. The linear equation $P = 4s$ describes the relationship between the perimeter, P, of a square and the length of each of its sides, s. If the length of the sides of a square is 0, its perimeter is 0. Use the point (0, 0) and the slope of the line, 4, to find three other points that satisfy the equation $P = 4s$.

35. Each line listed in the left column below is parallel to a line listed in the right column. Match pairs of parallel lines.

The line through (2, 5) and (−1, −2).	The line through (3, 2) and (5, 6).
A line with slope 2.	The line through (4, 5) and (1, −2).
The line through (9, −1) and (3, −4).	A line with slope $-\frac{3}{4}$.
The line through (1, 2) and (5, −1).	The line through (−1, 1) and (11, 7).

36. Each line listed in the left column below is perpendicular to a line listed in the right column. Match pairs of perpendicular lines.

The line through (12, 4) and (3, 7).	A line with slope 3.
The line through (2, 6) and (0, 8).	The line through (3, −1) and (−2, −3).
The line through (5, 6) and (7, 1).	The line through (−3, 4) and (4, 8).
The line through (−4, 10) and (0, 3).	The line through (−2, 2) and (1, 5).

Practice Problems

Here are some additional practice problems for you to try.

Graphing Lines I

1. Which points below lie on the line whose equation is $2x - y = 5$.
    (2, 1)
    (3, 1)
    (0, −5)
    (−5, 0)
    (1, −3)

2. Which points below lie on the line whose equation is $x + 3y = 6$.
    (3, 3)
    (0, 2)
    (5, 1)
    (−3, 3)
    (3, 1)

3. Which points below lie on the line whose equation is $x + 2y = 6$.
    (−2, 3)
    (1, 3)
    (0, 3)
    (6, 0)
    (−2, 4)

4. Which points below lie on the line whose equation is $3x - 2y = 12$.
    (2, −3)
    (−2, 3)
    (−2, 9)
    (4, 0)
    (0, 4)

5. Which points below lie on the line whose equation is $4x - y = 3$.
    (1, 1)
    (0, −3)
    (−1, 1)
    (2, 5)
    (3, 15)

6. Which points below lie on the line whose equation is $\frac{1}{2}x - \frac{2}{3}y = 6$.
    (2, 3)
    (4, −6)
    (0, 9)
    (12, 0)
    (−8, −15)

7. Which points below lie on the line whose equation is $\frac{1}{3}x + \frac{3}{4}y = 4$.
    (6, 4)
    (−6, 8)
    (0, 4)
    (12, 0)
    (21, −4)

8. Graph the equation $x + y = 4$.

9. Graph the equation $x + y = -5$.

10. Graph the equation $x + y = -2$.

11. Graph the equation $x - y = -1$.

12. Graph the equation $x - y = 2$.

13. Graph the equation $x - y = 3$.

14. Graph the equation $x + 3y = 6$.

15. Graph the equation $3x - y = -3$.

16. Graph the equation $2x + y = -2$.

17. Graph the equation $2x + 3y = -6$.

18. Graph the equation $3x + 5y = 15$.

19. Graph the equation $4x - 3y = 12$.

20. Graph the equation $3x + 2y = -5$.

21. Graph the equation $x - 2y = 2$.

22. Graph the equation $2x - 5y = -1$.

23. Graph the equation $\frac{2}{3}x - \frac{1}{2}y = 2$.

24. Graph the equation $\frac{3}{4}x + \frac{2}{5}y = 1$.

25. Graph the equation $\frac{1}{2}x + \frac{2}{3}y = 1$.

26. Graph the equation $\frac{1}{3}x - \frac{1}{2}y = 1$.

27. Graph the equation $\frac{1}{2}x + \frac{2}{5}y = -1$.

28. Graph the equation $\frac{1}{4}x + \frac{1}{5}y = 1$.

Graphing Lines II

29. Graph the equation $y = 5$.

30. Graph the equation $y = -6$.

31. Graph the equation $y = -3$.

32. Graph the equation $y = 1$.

33. Graph the equation $y = -3$.

34. Graph the equation $y = 4$.

35. Graph the equation $x = 5$.

36. Graph the equation $x = -4.5$.

37. Graph the equation $x = 2.5$.

38. Graph the equation $y = 0$.

39. Graph the equation $x = 0$.

40. Graph the equation $x = 6$.

41. Graph the equation $x = -5$.

42. Graph the equation $x = -1.5$.

43. Find the x- and y-intercepts of the line $x - y = 6$.

44. Find the x- and y-intercepts of the line $x + y = 5$.

45. Find the x- and y-intercepts of the line $3x + y = 9$.

46. Find the x- and y-intercepts of the line $x + 2y = 8$.

47. Find the x- and y-intercepts of the line $2x + y = 6$.

48. Find the x- and y-intercepts of the line $3x + 5y = 15$.

49. Find the x- and y-intercepts of the line $4x - 3y = 24$.

50. Find the x- and y-intercepts of the line $2x - 9y = 18$.

51. Find the x- and y-intercepts of the line $3x + 4y = 9$.

52. Find the x- and y-intercepts of the line $5x + 2y = 8$.

53. Find the x- and y-intercepts of the line $2x - 3y = 10$.

54. Find the x- and y-intercepts of the line $\frac{2}{5}x + y = 6$.

55. Find the x- and y-intercepts of the line $x + \frac{3}{4}y = 9$.

56. Find the x- and y-intercepts of the line $x - \frac{2}{3}y = 18$.

Slope of a Line

57. Find the slope of the line through the points $(1, 4)$ and $(-3, -2)$.

58. Find the slope of the line through the points $(5, 3)$ and $(-10, -3)$.

59. Find the slope of the line through the points $(2, 3)$ and $(-4, -1)$.

60. Find the slope of the line through the points $(-3, 6)$ and $(2, 5)$.

61. Find the slope of the line through the points $(-2, 7)$ and $(4, -5)$.

62. Find the slope of the line through the points $(-5, 1)$ and $(3, -7)$.

63. Find the slope of the line through the points $(7, 5)$ and $(3, 1)$.

64. Find the slope of the line through the points $(9, 5)$ and $(4, 3)$.

65. Find the slope of the line through the points $(8, 6)$ and $(1, 2)$.

66. Find the slope of the line through the points $(0, -5)$ and $(3, 0)$.

67. Find the slope of the line through the points $(0, 7)$ and $(4, 0)$.

68. Find the slope of the line through the points $(0, 3)$ and $(-7, 0)$.

69. What is the slope of a horizontal line?

70. What is the slope of a vertical line?

71. Find the slope of a line parallel to the line that passes through the points $(12, 2)$ and $(8, -3)$.

72. Find the slope of a line parallel to the line that passes through the points $(8, 7)$ and $(4, -3)$.

73. Find the slope of a line parallel to the line that passes through the points $(15, 3)$ and $(10, -2)$.

74. Find the slope of a line parallel to the line that passes through the points $(6, 2)$ and $(9, -1)$.

75. Find the slope of a line parallel to the line that passes through the points $(5, -1)$ and $(-4, 7)$.

76. Find the slope of a line parallel to the line that passes through the points $(7, -2)$ and $(-1, 4)$.

77. Find the slope of a line perpendicular to the line that passes through the points $(-1, -3)$ and $(4, 7)$.

78. Find the slope of a line perpendicular to the line that passes through the points $(5, -2)$ and $(-3, 8)$

79. Find the slope of a line perpendicular to the line that passes through the points $(-2, -3)$ and $(4, 12)$.

80. Find the slope of a line perpendicular to the line that passes through the points $(-4, 5)$ and $(2, -7)$.

81. Find the slope of a line perpendicular to the line that passes through the points $(9, 3)$ and $(-1, -2)$.

82. Find the slope of a line perpendicular to the line that passes through the points $(-3, 5)$ and $(-6, 4)$.

83. The point $(5, 1)$ lies on a line with slope $\frac{2}{5}$. Graph this line by finding another point that lies on the line.

84. The point $(3, 2)$ lies on a line with slope $-\frac{1}{3}$. Graph this line by finding another point that lies on the line.

Evaluate

Practice Test

Take this practice test to be sure that you are prepared for the final quiz in Evaluate.

1. The table below contains three points whose coordinates satisfy the equation $2x - 3y = 12$. Plot these ordered pairs then graph the line through them.

x	y
6	0
0	−4
3	−2

2. Which ordered pairs in the table below have coordinates that do not satisfy the equation $x + y = 7$.

x	y
6	1
2.7	4.3
5	−2
3	−4
12	−5
4	11
−2	9

3. Graph the equation $x + 2y = 6$.

4. Complete the table below so that the coordinates of the ordered pairs in the table satisfy the equation $\frac{2}{5}x + \frac{4}{5}y = 8$.

x	y
30	
	5
0	
−10	
	0

5. Complete the table below to find three ordered pairs whose coordinates satisfy the equation $x = -3$. Then graph the line.

x	y
	0
	5
	−4

6. Which statement(s) below are true about the equation $y = -7$.

   Its graph is a horizontal line.
   Its graph is a vertical line.
   Its graph is a line that passes through the origin.
   Its graph is none of the above.

7. Find the x- and y-intercepts of the line $4x - y = 7$.

8. Find the x- and y-intercepts of the line $5x - 3y = 15$.

9. Find the slope of the line that passes through the points $(7, -2)$ and $(4, 5)$.

10. The line $y = \frac{5}{4}x$ is shown in Figure 4.1.1. What is the slope of this line?

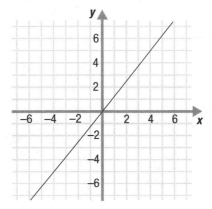

Figure 4.1.1

11. The line through the points $(-2, 3)$ and $(8, 1)$ is shown in Figure 4.1.2. What is the slope of a line that is perpendicular to this line?

12. Draw the line that passes through the point $(1, 3)$ and has slope $m = 0$.

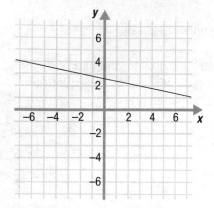

Figure 4.1.2

LESSON 4.2
THE EQUATION OF A LINE

 Overview

Suppose a chemistry student needs to measure the temperature of a chemical reaction at different times during an experiment. Or, suppose a family wants to figure out the amount of time it will take them to drive from their home to the Grand Canyon.

To better understand the relationship between time and temperature or between time and distance, these people might plot their data as points on an *xy*-plane. In each case, the points might lie on a line.

In this lesson, you will learn how to find the equation of a line when you are given a point and the slope of the line, or when you are given two points on the line. You will also learn how to find the equation of a vertical line and a horizontal line.

 Explain

Concept 1 has sections on

- **Point-Slope Form for the Equation of a Line**

- **Standard Form for the Equation of a Line**

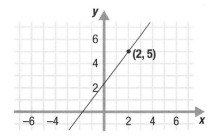

CONCEPT 1:
FINDING THE EQUATION I

Point-Slope Form for the Equation of a Line

Suppose we want to find the equation of the line that passes through the point (2, 5) with slope $\frac{4}{3}$.

Recall the formula for the slope of a line through the points (x_1, y_1) and (x_2, y_2).

$$m = \frac{y_2 - y_1}{x_2 - x_1}$$

We know the slope, m, is $\frac{4}{3}$.

We are given the coordinates of one point, (2, 5). So we substitute 2 for x_1 and 5 for y_1.

$$\frac{4}{3} = \frac{y_2 - 5}{x_2 - 2}$$

We use (x, y) to represent another point on the line.

Substitute x for x_2 and y for y_2.

$$\frac{4}{3} = \frac{y - 5}{x - 2}$$

To clear the fraction on the right side, multiply both sides by $x - 2$.

$$\frac{4}{3}(x - 2) = y - 5$$

Finally, exchange the left and right sides of the equation.

$$y - 5 = \frac{4}{3}(x - 2)$$

This equation of the line is in **point-slope form**.

It displays the coordinates of a point, (2, 5), and the slope, $\frac{4}{3}$.

We can easily write the equation of a line in point-slope form when we are given the coordinates of a point on the line and the slope of the line.

— Definition —
Point-Slope Form for the Equation of a Line

The point-slope form for the equation of a line that passes through the point (x_1, y_1) with slope m is:

$$y - y_1 = m(x - x_1)$$

Note that m, x_1, and y_1 are constants, whereas x and y are variables.

Example 4.2.1

Find the equation of the line that passes through the point (7, −4) with slope 3.

Write your answer in point-slope form.

Solution

Here is the point-slope form for the equation of a line.

$$y - y_1 = m(x - x_1)$$

The slope, m, is 3. So, replace m with 3.

$$y - y_1 = 3(x - x_1)$$

You can simplify the left side of the equation to obtain

$$y + 4 = 3(x - 7)$$

A point, (x_1, y_1), on the line is (7, −4). So, replace x_1 with 7, and replace y_1 with −4.

$$y - (-4) = 3(x - 7)$$

The equation of the line in point-slope form is $y - (-4) = 3(x - 7)$.

Example 4.2.2

Find the equation of the line that passes through the points $(-2, 7)$ and $(6, 3)$. Write your answer in point-slope form.

Solution

To find the equation in point-slope form, we first find m, the slope of the line.

Let $(x_1, y_1) = (-2, 7)$ and $(x_2, y_2) = (6, 3)$. $\quad m = \dfrac{y_2 - y_1}{x_2 - x_1}$

Substitute the values in the slope formula. $\quad = \dfrac{3 - 7}{6 - (-2)}$

Simplify. $\quad = \dfrac{-4}{8}$

Reduce. $\quad = -\dfrac{1}{2}$

The slope of the line is $-\dfrac{1}{2}$.

Now that we have the slope and a point, we can use the point-slope form to find the equation of the line. $\quad y - y_1 = m(x - x_1)$

Substitute $-\dfrac{1}{2}$ for m. $\quad y - y_1 = -\dfrac{1}{2}(x - x_1)$

We can substitute either given point for (x_1, y_1). Let's use $(6, 3)$.

If we had used the other point, $(-2, 7)$, we would have obtained:

$$y - 7 = -\tfrac{1}{2}(x + 2)$$

Therefore, substitute 6 for x_1 and 3 for y_1. $\quad y - 3 = -\dfrac{1}{2}(x - 6)$

This equation is equivalent to

$$y - 3 = -\tfrac{1}{2}(x - 6)$$

The point-slope form of the equation of the line that passes through $(-2, 7)$ and $(6, 3)$ is $y - 3 = -\dfrac{1}{2}(x - 6)$.

Standard Form for the Equation of a Line

When we wrote the equation of a line in point-slope form, the equations looked different depending on the point we chose. To show that the equations are equivalent, rewrite each equation in **standard form**.

— Definition —
Standard Form for the Equation of a Line

The standard form for the equation of a line is
$$Ax + By = C$$
Where A, B, and C are real numbers and A and B are not both zero.

To write the equation of a line in standard form, move the terms with variables to the left side and the constant term to the right side of the equation.

Example 4.2.3

In Example 4.2.2, we found the equation of the line that passes through the points $(-2, 7)$ and $(6, 3)$.

We used the point $(6, 3)$ to obtain: $y - 3 = -\frac{1}{2}(x - 6)$

If we instead use $(-2, 7)$, we obtain: $y - 7 = -\frac{1}{2}(x + 2)$

a. Write $y - 3 = -\frac{1}{2}(x - 6)$ in standard form.

b. Write $y - 7 = -\frac{1}{2}(x + 2)$ in standard form.

c. What conclusion can you draw?

Solution

In each case, we want the x-term and y-term on the left side of the equation. We want the constant term on the right side of the equation.

a. To clear the fraction, multiply both sides by 2.

$$2 \cdot (y - 3) = 2 \cdot \left[-\frac{1}{2}(x - 6)\right]$$

Simplify.

$$2y - 6 = -1(x - 6)$$

Distribute -1.

$$2y - 6 = -x + 6$$

Add x to both sides.

$$x + 2y - 6 = 6$$

Add 6 to both sides.

$$x + 2y = 12$$

b. To clear the fraction, multiply both sides by 2.

$$2 \cdot (y - 7) = 2 \cdot \left[-\frac{1}{2}(x + 2)\right]$$

Simplify.

$$2y - 14 = -1(x + 2)$$

Distribute -1.

$$2y - 14 = -x - 2$$

Add x to both sides.

$$x + 2y - 14 = -2$$

Add 14 to both sides.

$$x + 2y = 12$$

$Ax + By = C$

$x + 2y = 12$

Here, A is 1, B is 2, and C is 12.

c. In standard form, each equation is $x + 2y = 12$.

No matter which point we choose, we get the same result in standard form.

Here is a summary of this concept from *Academic Systems Algebra*.

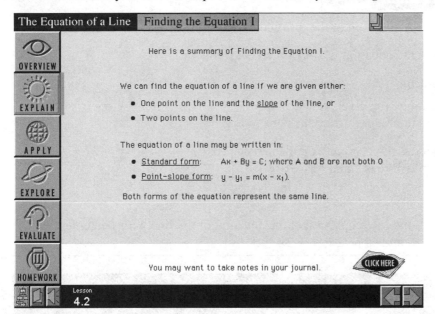

The Equation of a Line | Finding the Equation I

OVERVIEW
EXPLAIN
APPLY
EXPLORE
EVALUATE
HOMEWORK

Here is a summary of Finding the Equation I.

We can find the equation of a line if we are given either:

- One point on the line and the <u>slope</u> of the line, or
- Two points on the line.

The equation of a line may be written in:

- <u>Standard form</u>: $Ax + By = C$; where A and B are not both 0
- <u>Point-slope form</u>: $y - y_1 = m(x - x_1)$.

Both forms of the equation represent the same line.

You may want to take notes in your journal. CLICK HERE

Lesson 4.2

CONCEPT 2: FINDING THE EQUATION II

Concept 2 has sections on

- **Slope-Intercept Form for the Equation of a Line**

- **Equations of Horizontal Lines and Vertical Lines**

Slope-Intercept Form for the Equation of a Line

We have found the equation of a line in point-slope form and in standard form.

Another form for the equation of a line is the **slope-intercept form**. We can derive this from the point-slope form.

We begin with the point-slope form for the equation of a line.

$$y - y_1 = m(x - x_1)$$

Use the y-intercept, $(0, b)$, for the point (x_1, y_1). That is, substitute 0 for x_1 and b for y_1.

$$y - b = m(x - 0)$$

Simplify the right side.

$$y - b = mx$$

Add b to both sides.

$$y = mx + b$$

— Definition —
Slope-Intercept Form for the Equation of a Line

The slope-intercept form for the equation of a line with slope m and y-intercept $(0, b)$ is:

$$y = mx + b$$

Example 4.2.4

Find the equation of the line with y-intercept $(0, -6)$ and slope 2.

Write the equation in slope-intercept form.

Solution

Substitute the given values in the slope-intercept form of the equation.

$$y = mx + b$$

Both the slope, m, and the y-intercept, $(0, b)$, are given: m is 2 and b is -6.

$$y = 2x + (-6)$$

Simplify.

$$y = 2x - 6$$

The slope-intercept form of the equation of the line with y-intercept $(0, -6)$ and slope 2 is $y = 2x - 6$.

— Note —
To Write the Equation of a Line Given Two Points

Here are two ways to write the equation of a line when given two points:

Use the Point-Slope Form

Step 1 Find the slope.

Step 2 Substitute the slope, m, and the coordinates of one of the points, (x_1, y_1), in

$$y - y_1 = m(x - x_1)$$

Step 3 Simplify.

Use the Slope-Intercept Form

Step 1 Find the slope.

Step 2 Substitute the slope, m, and the coordinates of one of the points, (x, y), in

$$y = mx + b$$

Then, solve the equation for b.

Step 3 Substitute the value of m and the value b in $y = mx + b$.

Example `4.2.5`

Find the equation of the line that passes through the points $(-4, 9)$ and $(8, 0)$. Write your answer in slope-intercept form.

Solution

To find the equation in slope-intercept form, $y = mx + b$, we need to find the slope, m, and the y-coordinate, b, of the y-intercept.

Step 1 Find the slope.

$$m = \frac{y_2 - y_1}{x_2 - x_1}$$

Substitute the values in the slope formula.

$$= \frac{0 - 9}{8 - (-4)}$$

Simplify.

$$= \frac{-9}{12}$$

Reduce.

$$= -\frac{3}{4}$$

The slope, m, is $-\frac{3}{4}$.

Step 2 Substitute the slope, m, and the coordinates of one of the points, (x, y), in y = mx + b. Then solve the equation for b.

$$y = mx + b$$

The slope, m, is $-\frac{3}{4}$.

$$y = -\frac{3}{4}x + b$$

Substitute the coordinates of either point for x and y. Let's use $(8, 0)$.

$$\mathbf{0} = -\frac{3}{4}(\mathbf{8}) + b$$

Simplify.

$$0 = \mathbf{-6} + b$$

Add 6 to both sides.

$$6 = b$$

Step 3 Substitute the value of m and the value of b in y = mx + b.

Since m is $-\frac{3}{4}$ and b is 6, the equation of the line is $y = -\frac{3}{4}x + 6$.

In some cases, it is helpful to write the equation of a line in a form that is different from the given form. In the next example, this will help us find the slope and y-intercept of the line.

Example 4.2.6

Given the equation of a line: $-4x + 3y = 6$

a. Find the slope and the y-intercept.

b. Graph the line.

Solution

a. The equation $-4x + 3y = 6$ is in standard form.

Rewrite the equation in slope-intercept form, $y = mx + b$.

Then, identify the slope, m, and the y-coordinate, b, of the y-intercept $(0, b)$.

To get the equation in slope-intercept form, we solve for y. $\qquad -4x + 3y = 6$

Add $4x$ to both sides. $\qquad 3y = \mathbf{4x} + 6$

Divide both sides by 3. $\qquad y = \frac{4}{3}x + 2$

The equation is now in slope-intercept form, $y = mx + b$.

The slope is $\frac{4}{3}$ and the y-intercept is $(0, 2)$.

b. To draw the graph, first plot the y-intercept, $(0, 2)$.

The slope is $\frac{4}{3}$. So we can run 3 units and rise 4 units to get to another point on the line.

Start at $(0, 2)$. Move right 3 units (the run), then up 4 units (the rise). This gets us to $(3, 6)$. Plot this point.

Finally, connect the points with a straight line.

It is a good idea to check a third point to be sure you have not made a mistake. Choose any point on the line and substitute its coordinates in the original equation.

If you obtain a true statement, the point belongs on the line and the graph is correct.

Let's use the point $(-3, -2)$. $\qquad\qquad -4x + 3y = 6$

Substitute -3 for x and -2 for y. $\quad$ Is $-4(\mathbf{-3}) + 3(\mathbf{-2}) = 6$?

Simplify. $\qquad\qquad$ Is $\qquad\qquad 6 = 6$? **Yes**

Since $6 = 6$ is a true statement the point satisfies the equation and the graph is correct.

Here is one way to divide $3y = 4x + 6$ by 3:

$$\frac{3y}{3} = \frac{4x + 6}{3}$$

$$y = \frac{4x}{3} + \frac{6}{3}$$

$$y = \frac{4}{3}x + 2$$

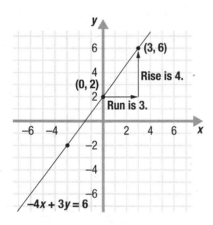

You can also verify that the graph is correct by substituting both (0, 2) and (3, 6) into $-4x + 3y = 6$.

Example 4.2.7

Find the equation of the line that is perpendicular to the line $2x - 3y = 12$ and that passes through the point $(3, -2)$. Write the equation in slope-intercept form.

Solution

First, find the slope of the given line. To do this, write the equation in slope-intercept form, $y = mx + b$.

$$2x - 3y = 12$$

Subtract $2x$ from both sides.

$$-3y = -2x + 12$$

Divide both sides by -3.

$$y = \frac{2}{3}x - 4$$

The slope of the given line is $\frac{2}{3}$.

The slope of a perpendicular line is $-\frac{3}{2}$, the negative reciprocal of $\frac{2}{3}$.

Use the point-slope form to find the equation of the line.

$$y - y_1 = m(x - x_1)$$

Using the point $(3, -2)$, substitute 3 for x_1, -2 for y_1, and $-\frac{3}{2}$ for m.

$$y - (-2) = -\frac{3}{2}(x - 3)$$

Simplify.

$$y + 2 = -\frac{3}{2}x + \frac{9}{2}$$

Subtract 2, which is equivalent to $\frac{4}{2}$, from each side.

$$y = -\frac{3}{2}x + \frac{5}{2}$$

The equation of the line that is perpendicular to the line $2x - 3y = 12$ and that passes through the point $(3, -2)$ is $y = -\frac{3}{2}x + \frac{5}{2}$.

Here is one way to divide $-3y = -2x + 12$ by -3:

$$\frac{-3y}{-3} = \frac{-2x + 12}{-3}$$

$$y = \frac{-2x}{-3} + \frac{12}{-3}$$

$$y = \frac{2}{3}x - 4$$

We could find the equation directly in slope-intercept form, $y = mx + b$.

To do this, substitute values for m, x, and y.

Then solve for b.

Finally, substitute values for m and b into $y = mx + b$.

Equations of Horizontal Lines and Vertical Lines

You have graphed horizontal lines and vertical lines. Now we will learn how to find the equations of such lines.

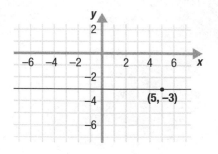

Each point on the horizontal line has y-coordinate −3. So, the equation of the line is y = −3.

Example 4.2.8

Find the equation of the horizontal line that passes through the point $(5, -3)$.

Solution

The line is horizontal. A horizontal line has slope 0, so m is 0.

We know a point and the slope, so we use the point-slope form to find the equation of the line.

$$y - y_1 = m(x - x_1)$$

Substitute -3 for y_1, 0 for m, and 5 for x_1.

$$y - (\mathbf{-3}) = \mathbf{0}(x - \mathbf{5})$$

Simplify.

$$y + 3 = 0$$

Subtract 3 from both sides.

$$y = -3$$

The equation of the horizontal line that passes through the point $(5, -3)$ is $y = -3$.

— Note —
The Equation of a Horizontal Line

The equation of a horizontal line can be written in the form

$$y = b$$

where b is a real number.

The line intersects the y-axis at the point $(0, b)$.

The slope of a vertical line is undefined. Therefore, to find the equation of a vertical line, we cannot use the point-slope formula or the slope-intercept formula.

Example 4.2.9

Find the equation of the vertical line that passes through the point $(4, 2)$.

Solution

On the vertical line through $(4, 2)$, each ordered pair has x-coordinate 4. That is, $x = 4$.

The equation of the vertical line that passes through the point $(4, 2)$ is $x = 4$.

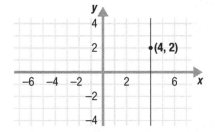

Each point on the vertical line has x-coordinate 4. So, the equation of the line is x = 4.

The equation of a vertical line can be written in the form

$$x = a$$

where a is a real number.

The line intersects the x-axis at the point $(a, 0)$.

Here is a summary of this concept from *Academic Systems Algebra*.

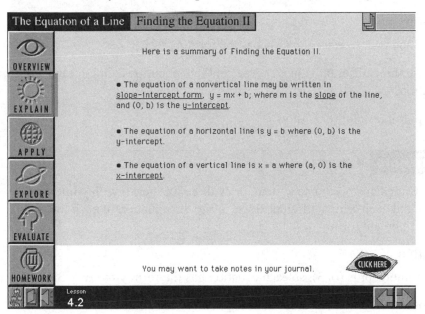

The Equation of a Line | Finding the Equation II

Here is a summary of Finding the Equation II.

• The equation of a nonvertical line may be written in slope-intercept form, $y = mx + b$; where m is the slope of the line, and $(0, b)$ is the y-intercept.

• The equation of a horizontal line is $y = b$ where $(0, b)$ is the y-intercept.

• The equation of a vertical line is $x = a$ where $(a, 0)$ is the x-intercept.

OVERVIEW
EXPLAIN
APPLY
EXPLORE
EVALUATE
HOMEWORK

You may want to take notes in your journal.

CLICK HERE

Lesson 4.2

On the computer you used the Grapher to analyze different forms of linear equations and their graphs. Here is an additional exploration.

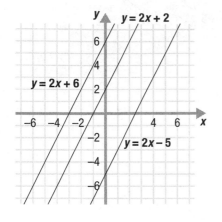

Example 4.2.10

On a Cartesian coordinate system, draw three lines each with slope 2, but each with a different y-intercept. Write the equation of each line in slope-intercept form.

Solution

The slope is 2, so each equation has the form $y = 2x + b$.

Choose three different values of b to get three equations. Graph each equation.

One possible solution is shown.

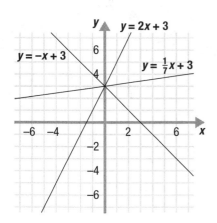

Example 4.2.11

On a Cartesian coordinate system, draw three lines each with y-intercept $(0, 3)$, but each with a different slope. Write the equation of each line in slope-intercept form.

Solution

The y-intercept is $(0, 3)$, so each equation has the form $y = mx + 3$.

Choose three different values of m to get three equations.

One possible solution is shown.

Here is a summary of this Exploration from *Academic Systems Algebra*.

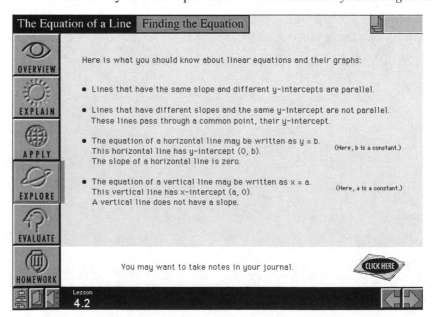

The Equation of a Line · Finding the Equation

Here is what you should know about linear equations and their graphs:

- Lines that have the same slope and different y-intercepts are parallel.

- Lines that have different slopes and the same y-intercept are not parallel. These lines pass through a common point, their y-intercept.

- The equation of a horizontal line may be written as y = b. This horizontal line has y-intercept (0, b). The slope of a horizontal line is zero. (Here, b is a constant.)

- The equation of a vertical line may be written as x = a. This vertical line has x-intercept (a, 0). A vertical line does not have a slope. (Here, a is a constant.)

You may want to take notes in your journal.

Lesson 4.2

Checklist Lesson 4.2

Here is what you should know after completing this lesson.

Words and Phrases

point-slope form
standard form

slope-intercept form

Ideas and Procedures

❶ Point-Slope Form
Write the formula for the point-slope form of the equation of a line.

$$y - y_1 = m(x - x_1)$$
where m is the slope of the line and (x_1, y_1) is a point on the line.

Find the point-slope form of the equation of a line given the slope and one point on the line, or given two points on the line.

Example 4.2.2
Find the equation of the line that passes through the points $(-2, 7)$ and $(6, 3)$. Write your answer in point-slope form.

See also: Example 4.2.1
Apply 1-10, 20-28

❷ Standard Form of the Equation of a Line
Write the formula for the standard form of the equation of a line.

$$Ax + By = C$$
where A, B, and C are real numbers and A and B are not both zero.

Find the standard form of the equation of a line given two points on the line.

Example 4.2.3a
Write $y - 3 = -\frac{1}{2}(x - 6)$ in standard form.
See also: Example 4.2.3b, c
Apply 11-28

❸ Slope-Intercept Form
Write the formula for the slope-intercept form of the equation of a line.

$$y = mx + b$$
where m is the slope of the line and $(0, b)$ is the y-intercept.

Find the slope-intercept form of the equation of a line given the slope and one point on the line, or two points on the line.

Example 4.2.4
Find the equation of the line with y-intercept $(0, -6)$ and slope 2. Write the equation in slope-intercept form.

See also: Example 4.2.5, 4.2.7
Apply 29-44

Find the slope and y-intercept of a line given the equation of the line in standard form.

Example 4.2.6
Given the equation of a line, $-4x + 3y = 6$, find the slope and the y-intercept.

See also: Apply 45-50

❹ Equations of Horizontal Lines and Vertical Lines

Find the equation of a horizontal or vertical line that passes through a given point.

Example 4.2.9

Find the equation of the vertical line that passes through the point (4, 2).

See also: Example 4.2.8
Apply 51-56

Homework

Homework Problems

Circle the homework problems assigned to you by the computer, then complete them below.

 Explain

Finding The Equation I

1. Find the equation of the line that passes through the point (4, 1) and has slope 2. Write your answer in point-slope form.

2. Find the equation of the line that passes through the points (2, 3) and (4, 7). Write your answer in point-slope form.

3. Rewrite the equation of the line below in standard form.

   $y - 2 = -3(x - 7)$

4. Find the equation of the line that passes through the point (2, 9) and has slope 4. Write your answer in point-slope form.

5. Find the equation of the line that passes through the points (6, 3) and (5, 0). Write your answer in point-slope form.

6. Rewrite the equation of the line below in standard form.

   $y + 7 = 2(x - 4)$

7. Find the equation of the line that passes through the point (8, 4) and has slope -1. Write your answer in point-slope form.

8. Find the equation of the line that passes through the points (3, 1) and (5, -2). Write your answer in standard form.

9. Alberto is rafting on a river that flows at a constant rate. After 1 hour he had gone 6 miles. Write the equation of the line that shows how fast Alberto is traveling, then use your equation to find out when he will have gone 27 miles. Let $x =$ the length of time Alberto has been rafting; let $y =$ the number of miles he has traveled.

10. Jenne set her cruise control and is driving at a constant rate. After 2 hours she has driven 128 miles. Write the equation of the line that shows how fast Jenne is driving, then use your equation to find out after how many hours she will have driven 288 miles. Let $x =$ the length of time Jenne has been driving; let $y =$ the distance she has gone.

11. Find the equation of the line that passes through the point (0, -7) and has slope $-\frac{2}{5}$. Write your answer in point-slope form and in standard form.

12. Find the equation of the line that passes through the points (3, -6) and (-4, -2). Write your answer in point-slope form and in standard form.

Finding the Equation II

13. Find the slope and the y-intercept of the line $y = 2x + 5$.

14. Find the equation of the line that passes through the point (0, 2) and has slope 3. Write your answer in slope-intercept form.

15. Find the equation of the vertical line that passes through the point (4, 3).

16. Find the slope and the y-intercept of the line $y = \frac{4}{5}x - 3$.

17. Find the equation of the line that passes through the point (0, -6) and has slope 1. Write your answer in slope-intercept form.

18. Find the equation of the horizontal line that passes through the point (1, -3).

19. Find the slope and the y-intercept of the line $7x - 4y = 2$.

20. Find the equation of the line that passes through the point (-4, 6) and has slope 2. Write your answer in slope-intercept form.

21. Dina planted a six-foot tree in her backyard which she expects to grow at the rate of 4 feet per year. Find the equation of the line that shows how tall the tree will be each year, then use your equation to find out how tall the tree will be 4 years after she plants it. Let x = the number of years since she planted the tree; let y = the height of the tree in feet.

22. A city's diving pool is being drained. If the pool is 14 feet deep and the water level goes down 3 feet every 2 hours, write an equation that shows how fast the water is being drained from the pool. Then use your equation to find out how many hours will pass before the pool is empty. Let x = the number of hours the pool has been draining; let y = the depth of the water in the pool.

23. Find the equation of the line that passes through the point $(-8, 11)$ and has slope $-\frac{7}{4}$. Write your answer in slope-intercept form and in standard form.

24. Find the equation of the line that passes through the point $(-2, 4)$ and has slope $-\frac{5}{3}$. Write your answer in slope-intercept form and in standard form.

25. Graph each of the equations below. Then write several sentences to describe the effect that changing the slope has on the graphs.

$$y = x + 1 \qquad y = 2x + 1 \qquad y = 3x + 1$$

26. Graph the line that passes through the point $(0, -4)$ and has slope 2. Then find the x-intercept of the line. Write several sentences describing the relationship of the y-intercept and the slope to the x-intercept.

27. On a grid, draw three lines through the point $(-2, 3)$:

   a. one line with slope -1

   b. one line with slope -2

   c. one line with slope -3

   Write several sentences comparing the y-intercepts of the lines.

28. Graph each of the equations below. Then write several sentences to describe the effect that changing the y-intercept has on the graphs.

$$y = 2x + 1 \qquad y = 2x + 5 \qquad y = 2x - 3$$

29. Graph the line that passes through the point $(0, 3)$ with slope $\frac{3}{2}$. Then find the x-intercept of the line. Write several sentences describing the relationship of the y-intercept and the slope to the x-intercept.

30. On a grid, draw three lines with slope 1:

   a. one line through the point $(2, 4)$

   b. one line through the point $(2, 2)$

   c. one line through the point $(2, -3)$

   Write several sentences comparing the distance between each pair of points and the distance between the y-intercepts of each pair of lines.

 **Apply**

Practice Problems

Here are some additional practice problems for you to try.

Finding the Equation I

1. Find the equation of the line that passes through the point (3, 1) and has slope $m = 2$. Write your answer in point-slope form.

2. Find the equation of the line that passes through the point (5, 2) and has slope $m = 3$. Write your answer in point-slope form.

3. Find the equation of the line that passes through the point (2, 7) and has slope $m = -3$. Write your answer in point-slope form.

4. Find the equation of the line that passes through the point (1, 6) and has slope $m = -2$. Write your answer in point-slope form.

5. Find the equation of the line that passes through the point (4, −2) and has slope $m = \frac{2}{3}$. Write your answer in point-slope form.

6. Find the equation of the line that passes through the point (2, −4) and has slope $m = -\frac{3}{5}$. Write your answer in point-slope form.

7. Find the equation of the line that passes through the point (3, −1) and has slope $m = -\frac{1}{2}$. Write your answer in point-slope form.

8. Find the equation of the line that passes through the point (−3, 1) and has slope $m = -\frac{4}{5}$. Write your answer in point-slope form.

9. Find the equation of the line that passes through the point (−5, 3) and has slope $m = \frac{3}{8}$. Write your answer in point-slope form.

10. Find the equation of the line that passes through the point (−4, 2) and has slope $m = \frac{5}{7}$. Write your answer in point-slope form.

11. Rewrite the equation $y - 2 = 3(x - 5)$ in standard form.

12. Rewrite the equation $y + 7 = 4(x - 2)$ in standard form.

13. Rewrite the equation $y + 3 = 5(x - 4)$ in standard form.

14. Rewrite the equation $y - 6 = -3(x + 4)$ in standard form.

15. Rewrite the equation $y + 2 = -5(x - 1)$ in standard form.

16. Rewrite the equation $y - 7 = -2(x + 4)$ in standard form.

17. Rewrite the equation $y - 4 = \frac{3}{4}(x - 8)$ in standard form.

18. Rewrite the equation $y + 5 = -\frac{4}{7}(x + 7)$ in standard form.

19. Rewrite the equation $y + 8 = -\frac{2}{5}(x + 5)$ in standard form.

20. Find the equation of the line that passes through the points (4, 5) and (2, 11). Write your answer in point-slope form and standard form.

21. Find the equation of the line that passes through the points (−6, 2) and (−3, −4). Write your answer in point-slope form and standard form.

22. Find the equation of the line that passes through the points (3, 2) and (1, 12). Write your answer in point-slope form and standard form.

23. Find the equation of the line that passes through the points (2, 7) and (5, 13). Write your answer in point-slope form and standard form.

24. Find the equation of the line that passes through the points (−1, 5) and (−2, 1). Write your answer in point-slope form and standard form.

25. Find the equation of the line that passes through the points $(6, 7)$ and $(3, -2)$. Write your answer in point-slope form and standard form.

26. Find the equation of the line that passes through the points $(8, 2)$ and $(1, 7)$. Write your answer in point-slope form and standard form.

27. Find the equation of the line that passes through the points $(-3, 4)$ and $(5, -2)$. Write your answer in point-slope form and standard form.

28. Find the equation of the line that passes through the points $(-4, 8)$ and $(3, 2)$. Write your answer in point-slope form and standard form.

Finding the Equation II

29. Find the equation of the line in slope-intercept form that passes through the point $(3, 1)$ and has slope $m = 4$.

30. Find the equation of the line in slope-intercept form that passes through the point $(-1, 3)$ and has slope $m = 5$.

31. Find the equation of the line in slope-intercept form that passes through the point $(4, -2)$ and has slope $m = -2$.

32. Find the equation of the line in slope-intercept form that passes through the point $(-4, 8)$ and has slope $m = 3$

33. Find the equation of the line in slope-intercept form that passes through the point $(5, -6)$ and has slope $m = -1$.

34. Find the equation of the line in slope-intercept form that passes through the point $(0, -3)$ and the point $(4, 5)$.

35. Find the equation of the line in slope-intercept form that passes through the point $(-2, 0)$ and the point $(-3, -2)$.

36. Find the equation of the line in slope-intercept form that passes through the point $(4, -3)$ and the point $(6, -2)$.

37. Find the equation of the line in slope-intercept form that passes through the point $(3, -5)$ and the point $(6, -4)$.

38. Find the equation of the line in slope-intercept form that passes through the point $(5, -3)$ and the point $(2, -1)$.

39. Find the equation of the line in slope-intercept form that passes through the point $\left(\frac{2}{5}, \frac{3}{5}\right)$ and is parallel to the line $y = 3x + 7$.

40. Find the equation of the line in slope-intercept form that passes through the point $\left(\frac{1}{4}, \frac{3}{4}\right)$ and is parallel to the line $y = -2x - 11$.

41. Find the equation of the line in slope-intercept form that passes through the point $\left(\frac{1}{2}, \frac{3}{2}\right)$ and is parallel to the line $y = 4x - 6$.

42. Find the equation of the line in slope-intercept form that passes through the point $(6, -3)$ and is perpendicular to the line $y = -3x + 10$.

43. Find the equation of the line in slope-intercept form that passes through the point $(-2, 7)$ and is perpendicular to the line $y = \frac{1}{5}x - 16$.

44. Find the equation of the line in slope-intercept form that passes through the point $(6, -2)$ and is perpendicular to the line $y = -2x + 4$.

45. Find the slope and y-intercept of the line $-3x + y = 8$.

46. Find the slope and y-intercept of the line $4x - y = -13$.

47. Find the slope and y-intercept of the line $2x - y = 4$.

48. Find the slope and y-intercept of the line $2x + 5y = 12$.

49. Find the slope and y-intercept of the line $4x - 3y = 6$.

50. Find the slope and y-intercept of the line $3x - 2y = -5$.

51. Find the equation of the vertical line that passes through the point $(7, 3)$.

52. Find the equation of the vertical line that passes through the point $(-10, -5)$.

53. Find the equation of the vertical line that passes through the point $(8, -2)$.

54. Find the equation of the horizontal line that passes through the point $(7, 0)$.

55. Find the equation of the horizontal line that passes through the point $(-2, 9)$.

56. Find the equation of the horizontal line that passes through the point $(6, -5)$.

Practice Test

Take this practice test to be sure that you are prepared for the final quiz in Evaluate.

1. Find the equation of the line that passes through the point $(2, -5)$ and has slope -2.

2. The equation of a line in point-slope form is $y - 1 = 4(x + 2)$. Find the slope of the line and the coordinates of one point that lies on the line.

3. Find the equation of the line that passes through the point $(-5, -3)$ and has slope $\frac{4}{7}$. Write your answer in standard form.

4. Find the equation of the line that passes through the points $(-6, -8)$ and $(-1, 7)$. Write your answer in standard form.

5. Find the equation of the line that passes through the point $(0, 2)$ and has slope -3. Write your answer in standard form.

6. The equation of a line in slope-intercept form is $y = 2x - 7$. Find the slope of the line and the y-intercept of the line.

7. Find the equation of the horizontal line that passes through the point $(0, -6)$.

8. The point $P(4, -3)$ is plotted in Figure 4.2.1. Plot another point Q so that the slope of the line that passes through the points P and Q is undefined.

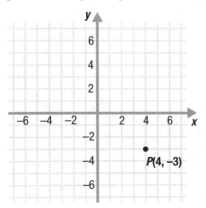

Figure 4.2.1

9. Which equations below represent a line that passes through the point $(5, 2)$.

$$y - 5 = \frac{1}{5}(x - 2) \qquad y - 2 = 3(x - 5)$$

$$y + 2 = 4(x + 5) \qquad y - 2 = \frac{3}{4}(x - 5)$$

$$y + 2 = -2(x + 5)$$

10. Find the equation of the line that passes through the point $(2, -3)$ and is parallel to the line $y = 3x + 4$. Write your answer in standard form.

11. Use the graphs of the lines A and B in Figure 4.2.2 to decide which of the following statements are true.

The slope of line A is greater than the slope of line B.

The slope of line A is less than the slope of line B.

The y-coordinate of the y-intercept of line A is less than the y-coordinate of the y-intercept of line B.

The x-coordinate of the x-intercept of line A is less than the x-coordinate of the x-intercept of line B.

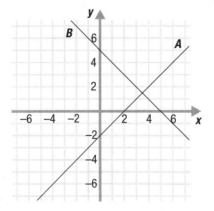

Figure 4.2.2

12. The y-intercepts of two parallel lines are $(0, -4)$ and $(0, 3)$. If the slope of each line is 2, what are the equations of the lines?

LESSON 4.3
GRAPHING INEQUALITIES

 **Overview**

Suppose you have $5.00 to spend at the grocery store and want to buy apples and oranges. Apples cost $0.50 per pound and oranges cost $1.25 per pound. You must decide how much of each you can buy for $5.00 or less.

Or, suppose you have two 100-point exams remaining in your math class and you need at least 184 more points to earn an A. What are the possible pairs of exam scores that will enable you to earn an A?

Linear inequalities can help you answer questions such as these.

 **Explain**

Concept 1 has sections on

- **Solutions of a Linear Inequality**

- **Graphing a Linear Inequality**

- **Another Way to Graph a Linear Inequality**

CONCEPT 1: LINEAR INEQUALITIES

Solutions of a Linear Inequality

Suppose we have two expressions, $2x + 3$ and $-2y + 9$.

A linear equation, such as $2x + 3 = -2y + 9$, consists of two expressions joined by an equals sign, $=$.

A **linear inequality**, such as $2x + 3 < -2y + 9$, consists of two expressions joined by an inequality symbol: $<$, $\leq$, $>$, or $\geq$.

> — Definition —
> **Linear Inequality in Two Variables**
>
> A linear inequality in two variables, x and y, is an inequality that can be written in one of the following forms:
>
> $$Ax + By < C, \quad Ax + By \leq C, \quad Ax + By > C, \quad Ax + By \geq C,$$
>
> where A, B, and C are real numbers and A and B are not both 0.

A **solution of a linear inequality in two variables** is an ordered pair, which when substituted in the inequality, results in a true statement. That is, a solution that satisfies the inequality.

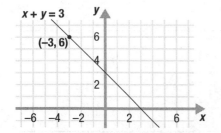

$x + y = 3$

$(-3, 6)$

A linear inequality, such $x + y < 3$, has infinitely many solutions. To identify these solutions, we often use the graph of the corresponding linear equation.

For example, consider the graph of the linear equation $x + y = 3$.

Notice that the line divides the xy-plane into three regions:

- Points *above* the line.

- Points *on* the line.

- Points *below* the line.

Points on the line, such as $(-3, 6)$, are solutions of the equation $x + y = 3$.

Points NOT on the line are solutions of one of the following inequalities:

$x + y < 3$

$x + y > 3$.

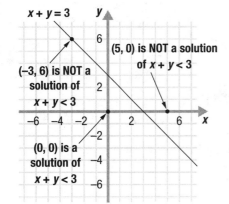

$x + y = 3$

$(-3, 6)$ is NOT a solution of $x + y < 3$

$(0, 0)$ is a solution of $x + y < 3$

$(5, 0)$ is NOT a solution of $x + y < 3$

Example 4.3.1

Determine if each ordered pair is a solution of $x + y < 3$.

a. $(0, 0)$ b. $(5, 0)$ c. $(-3, 6)$

Solution $x + y < 3$

a.   Substitute 0 for x and 0 for y.   Is $\mathbf{0 + 0} < 3$?

     Simplify.   Is $0 < 3$? **Yes**

     Since $0 < 3$ is true, the ordered pair $(0, 0)$ is a solution of $x + y < 3$.

     Notice that the point $(0, 0)$ lies *below* the line $x + y = 3$.

b.   Substitute 5 for x and 0 for y.   Is $\mathbf{5 + 0} < 3$?

     Simplify.   Is $5 < 3$? **No**

     Since $5 < 3$ is false, the ordered pair $(5, 0)$ is NOT a solution of $x + y < 3$.

     Notice that the point $(5, 0)$ lies *above* the line $x + y = 3$.

c.   Substitute -3 for x and 6 for y.   Is $\mathbf{-3 + 6} < 3$?

     Simplify.   Is $3 < 3$? **No**

     Since $3 < 3$ is false, the ordered pair $(-3, 6)$ is NOT a solution of $x + y < 3$.

     Notice that the point $(-3, 6)$ lies *on* the line $x + y = 3$.

Recall that a line divides the xy-plane into three regions: points on the line and points on either side of the line.

If a point in a region satisfies an inequality, then **every** point in that region satisfies the inequality. Likewise, if a point in a region does not satisfy an inequality then **no** point in that region satisfies the inequality.

In the previous example we found that

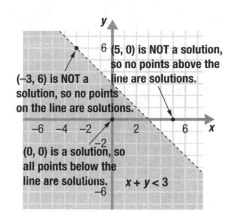

(5, 0) is NOT a solution, so no points above the line are solutions.

(−3, 6) is NOT a solution, so no points on the line are solutions.

(0, 0) is a solution, so all points below the line are solutions.

$x + y < 3$

- (0, 0) is a solution of $x + y < 3$.

    Since (0, 0) lies below the line $x + y = 3$, every point below the line is a solution of $x + y < 3$.

    To graph these solutions, shade the region below the line.

- (5, 0) is not a solution of $x + y < 3$.

    Since (5, 0) lies above the line $x + y = 3$, no point above the line is a solution of $x + y < 3$.

- (−3, 6) is not a solution of $x + y < 3$.

    Since (−3, 6) lies on the line $x + y = 3$, no point on the line is a solution of $x + y < 3$.

    To show this, we use a dotted line for $x + y = 3$.

The points (0, 0) and (5, 0) are often called test points.

A **test point** is a point that we substitute in a linear inequality to determine the region of the xy-plane that represents the solution of the inequality.

For a test point, we can use any point NOT on the line.

The solution of the inequality $x + y < 3$ is the set of all ordered pairs in the region below the line $x + y = 3$. The graph of the inequality is the shaded region. (The line is not included.)

You may want to choose a test point from each side of the line to check that you have found the region that represents the solution.

Graphing a Linear Inequality

Use the following procedure to graph a linear inequality in two variables.

— Procedure —
To Graph a Linear Inequality in Two Variables

Step 1 Graph the equation that corresponds to the given inequality.

- If the inequality symbol is $\leq$ or $\geq$, use a **solid line** to show that points on the line are solutions of the inequality.

- If the inequality symbol is $<$ or $>$, use a **dotted line** to show that points on the line are not solutions of the inequality.

Step 2 Use a test point NOT on the line to determine the region whose points satisfy the inequality.

Step 3 Shade the region whose points satisfy the inequality.

Example 4.3.2

Graph the inequality $2x - y < 4$.

Solution

Step 1 Graph the equation that corresponds to the given inequality.

Graph the equation $2x - y = 4$.

To do this, substitute 0 for y and solve for x to get the x-intercept, $(2, 0)$.

Next, substitute 0 for x and solve for y to get the y-intercept, $(0, -4)$.

Then, plot the points.

Since the inequality symbol "$<$" does **not** contain "equal to," draw a dotted line through the plotted points.

The dotted line shows that points on the line are not solutions of the inequality.

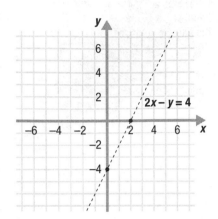

Step 2 Use a test point NOT on the line to determine the region whose points satisfy the inequality.

The point $(0, 0)$ is not on the line, so it can be used as a test point.

Substitute 0 for x and 0 for y.   Is $2(0) - 0 < 4$?

Simplify.   Is $0 < 4$? **Yes**

Since $0 < 4$ is true, the ordered pair $(0, 0)$ is a solution of the inequality $2x - y < 4$.
This means all the points in the region containing $(0, 0)$ are solutions.

Step 3 Shade the region whose points satisfy the inequality.

Shade the region that includes $(0, 0)$. This is the region above the dotted line.

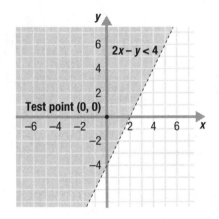

— Note —
Using (0, 0) as a Test Point

If the point $(0, 0)$ does not lie on the line, it is a good test point since it often makes the calculations easier.

Example 4.3.3

Graph the inequality $x \geq 3$.

Solution

Step 1 Graph the equation that corresponds to the given inequality.

Graph the equation $x = 3$.

The graph is a vertical line through $(3, 0)$.

Since the inequality symbol "$\geq$" contains "equal to," draw a solid line. The solid line shows that points on the line are solutions of the inequality.

A vertical line divides the xy-plane into three regions:

• *points on the line*
• *points to the right of the line*
• *points to the left of the line.*

Step 2 *Use a test point NOT on the line to determine the region whose points satisfy the inequality.*

The point $(0, 0)$ is not on the line, so it can be used as a test point.

Substitute 0 for x. The resulting statement, $0 \geq 3$, is false.

Therefore, the solutions do not lie in the region containing $(0, 0)$.

The solutions lie in the other region and on the line.

Step 3 *Shade the region whose points satisfy the inequality.*

Since the test point $(0, 0)$ does NOT satisfy $x \geq 3$,
shade the region that does NOT include $(0, 0)$.
This is the region to the right of the solid line, including the solid line.

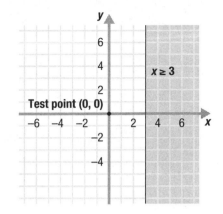

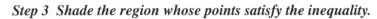

Example 4.3.4

Graph the inequality $y \geq -x$.

Solution

Step 1 *Graph the equation that corresponds to the given inequality.*

The equation $y = -x$ can be written as $y = -1x + 0$. The y-intercept is $(0, 0)$ and the slope is -1. We use this information to graph the equation.

Since the inequality symbol "$\geq$" contains "equal to," draw a solid line to show that points on the line are solutions of the inequality.

Step 2 *Use a test point NOT on the line to determine the region whose points satisfy the inequality.*

The point $(0, 0)$ is on the line, so we must select a different test point. Let's use $(2, 0)$.

In $y \geq -x$, substitute 2 for x and 0 for y. The resulting statement, $0 \geq -2$, is true.

Therefore, the solutions lie in the region that contains $(2, 0)$.

Step 3 *Shade the region whose points satisfy the inequality.*

Since the test point $(2, 0)$ satisfies $y \geq -x$,
shade the region that contains $(2, 0)$.
This is the region above the solid line, including the solid line.

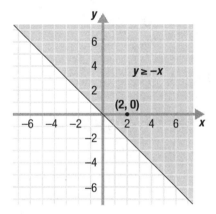

Another Way to Graph a Linear Inequality

To graph a linear inequality in x and y, you may find it helpful to first solve the inequality for y. Once that has been done, the inequality can be graphed using the following guidelines:

Inequality	Solution
$y > mx + b$	Draw a **dotted** line and shade the region **above** the line.
$y \geq mx + b$	Draw a **solid** line and shade the region **above** the line.
$y < mx + b$	Draw a **dotted** line and shade the region **below** the line.
$y \leq mx + b$	Draw a **solid** line and shade the region **below** the line.

Example 4.3.5

Graph the inequality $3x - 2y \leq -12$.

Solution

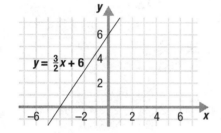

First, solve the inequality for y. $\qquad\qquad 3x - 2y \leq -12$

Subtract $3x$ from both sides. $\qquad\qquad -2y \leq -3x - 12$

Divide both sides by -2. Remember to reverse the direction of the inequality symbol. $\qquad y \geq \dfrac{3}{2}x + 6$

Next, graph the corresponding equation $y = \dfrac{3}{2}x + 6$.

The inequality has the form $y \geq mx + b$, so draw a **solid** line.

Then, shade the region **above** the line.

It is a good idea to check the shading with a test point.

Substitute $(0, 0)$ in $3x - 2y \leq -12$.

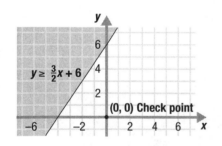

The result is $0 \leq -12$, which is false.

Since $(0, 0)$ is not a solution, the region that contains $(0, 0)$ should not be shaded. This agrees with the graph as we have drawn it.

Example 4.3.6

Suppose you have $5.00 to spend at the grocery store and you want to buy apples and oranges. Apples cost $0.50 per pound and oranges cost $1.25 per pound. How many pounds of each fruit can you buy?

Solution

The cost of the fruit can be calculated by adding the cost of the apples and the cost of the oranges. The sum must be less than or equal to $5.00.

This situation can be described with a linear inequality in two variables.

Let x represent the number of pounds of apples.

Let y represent the number of pounds of oranges.

Then, we can write the following inequality:

$$\text{cost of apples} \quad + \quad \text{cost of oranges} \quad \leq \$5.00$$

$$\frac{\$0.50}{\text{pound}} \cdot x \text{ pounds} + \frac{\$1.25}{\text{pound}} \cdot y \text{ pounds} \leq \$5.00$$

$$0.50x \quad + \quad 1.25y \quad \leq \quad 5.00$$

Step 1 Graph the equation that corresponds to the given inequality.

Graph $0.50x + 1.25y = 5.00$. We first plot the intercepts.

To find the x-intercept, let $y = 0$. $0.50x + 1.25(0) = 5.00$
                                                            $0.50x = 5.00$

The intercept is $(10, 0)$. $x = 10$

To find the y-intercept, let $x = 0$. $0.50(0) + 1.25y = 5.00$
                                                            $1.25y = 4.00$

The y-intercept is $(0, 4)$. $y = 4$

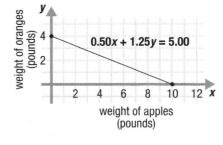

Plot the intercepts $(0, 4)$ and $(10, 0)$. Then, connect the points with a solid line. (The inequality symbol "≤" contains "equal to.")

Note that it is not possible to buy negative pounds of apples or oranges. Therefore, the graph only makes sense in Quadrant I and on the axes that border Quadrant I.

Step 2 Use a test point NOT on the line to determine the region whose points satisfy the inequality.

The point $(0, 0)$ is not on the line, so it can be used as a test point.

Substitute 0 for x and 0 for y.

The resulting statement, $0 \leq 5.00$ is true.

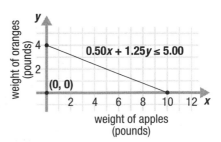

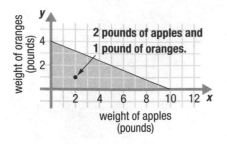

weight of oranges (pounds)

2 pounds of apples and 1 pound of oranges.

weight of apples (pounds)

Step 3 *Shade the region whose points satisfy the inequality.*

Since the test point (0, 0) satisfies $0.50x + 1.25y \leq 5.00$, shade the region that includes (0, 0).

This is the region below the solid line and includes the solid line.

Let's check the solution with a specific pair of numbers.

Suppose you decide to buy 2 pounds of apples and 1 pound of oranges. Then,

cost of apples $+$ cost of oranges $\leq$ $5.00

Is $\dfrac{\$0.50}{\text{pound}} \cdot 2 \text{ pounds} + \dfrac{\$1.25}{\text{pound}} \cdot 1 \text{ pound} \leq \$5.00$

Is $\$1.00$ $+$ $\$1.25$ $\leq \$5.00$?

Is $\$2.25$ $\leq \$5.00$? **Yes**

Therefore, one possibility is to buy 2 pounds of apples and 1 pound of oranges. In this case, you will have some money left over.

Here is a summary of this concept from *Academic Systems Algebra*.

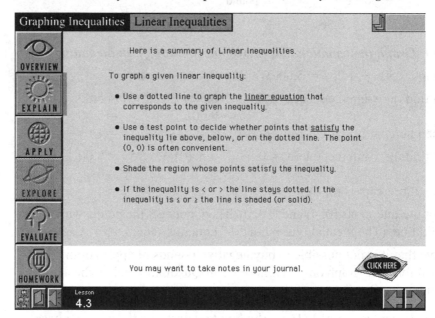

Checklist Lesson 4.3

Here is what you should know after completing this lesson.

Words and Phrases

linear inequality
solution of a linear inequality in two variables

test point

Ideas and Procedures

❶ **Solutions of a Linear Inequality**
Determine if an ordered pair is a solution of a
linear inequality.

Example 4.3.1
  Determine if each ordered pair is a solution of
  $x + y < 3$.
  a. $(0, 0)$ b. $(5, 0)$ c. $(-3, 6)$

See also: Apply 1-4

❷ **Linear Inequality**
Graph a linear inequality.

Example 4.3.2
  Graph the inequality $2x - y < 4$.

See also: Example 4.3.3, 4.3.4, 4.3.5, 4.3.6
            Apply 5-28

 **Homework**

Homework Problems

Circle the homework problems assigned to you by the computer, then complete them below.

 Explain

Linear Inequalities

1. In each row, check the boxes corresponding to the coordinates that make the statement true.

	(1, 7)	(4, 2)	(2, 5)	(0, 0)	(−6, 3)	(−4, −3)	(3, −6)
$y < 2x + 1$							
$y = 2x + 1$							
$y > 2x + 1$							

2. Graph the inequality $y \leq x + 2$.

3. Graph the inequality $x + y \geq -5$.

4. Find the coordinates of three points that satisfy the inequality $y \leq 3x - 2$.

5. Graph the inequality $y \geq \frac{2}{5}x - 2$.

6. Graph the inequality $3x - 2y > 12$.

7. In what ways do the graphs of the inequalities $x + y < 4$ and $x + y \leq 4$ differ?

8. Graph the inequality $2x > 7y$.

9. Janna has up to $5.00 to spend on snacks at a new health food store. If guava chips are $4.00 per pound and shredded coconut is $2.50 per pound, graph the inequality that represents how much of each she can buy.

10. Shobana has up to $12.00 to spend on junk food. If she can buy bulk candy for $2.25 per pound and cookies for $3.00 per pound, graph the inequality that represents how much of each she can buy.

11. Graph the inequality $5x - 4y \geq 0$.

12. In what ways do the graphs of the inequalities $2x - y > 3$ and $2x - y < 3$ differ?

 **Apply**

Practice Problems

Here are some additional practice problems for you to try.

Linear Inequalities

1. In each row, check the boxes corresponding to the coordinates that make the statement true.

	(2, −1)	(4, −2)	(−5, 2)	(3, 8)	(−3, 1)	(4, 3)	(−1, 6)
$x - y < 1$							
$x - y = 1$							
$x - y > 1$							

2. In each row, check the boxes corresponding to the coordinates that make the statement true.

	(1, −3)	(3, −4)	(−6, 2)	(2, 7)	(−2, 1)	(6, 5)	(−2, 5)
$x + y < -1$							
$x + y = -1$							
$x + y > -1$							

3. In each row, check the boxes corresponding to the coordinates that make the statement true.

	(−3, 4)	(−5, 3)	(−1, 4)	(3, 5)	(3, −8)	(5, −1)	(−4, −5)
$2x - y < 1$							
$2x - y = 1$							
$2x - y > 1$							

4. In each row, check the boxes corresponding to the coordinates that make the statement true.

	(−2, 7)	(−4, 2)	(−1, 6)	(2, 5)	(2, −5)	(4, −2)	(−1, −2)
$3x + y < 1$							
$3x + y = 1$							
$3x + y > 1$							

5. Graph the inequality $x - y > 4$.

6. Graph the inequality $x - y < -3$.

7. Graph the inequality $x - y < 5$.

8. Graph the inequality $x + y > 1$.

9. Graph the inequality $x + y < -5$.

10. Graph the inequality $x + y < -2$.

11. Graph the inequality $x + y \leq -1$.

12. Graph the inequality $x + y \geq 5$.

13. Graph the inequality $x + y \geq 1$.

14. Graph the inequality $x - y \leq -4$.

15. Graph the inequality $x - y \geq 6$.

16. Graph the inequality $x - y \geq -3$.

17. Graph the inequality $\frac{2}{3}x + y < -3$.

18. Graph the inequality $\frac{1}{4}x + y > 1$.

19. Graph the inequality $\frac{1}{2}x + y > -2$.

20. Graph the inequality $3x - y \geq 2$.

21. Graph the inequality $-4x - y \leq -3$.

22. Graph the inequality $-2x - y \leq 1$.

23. Graph the inequality $4x - 3y < 12$.

24. Graph the inequality $2x + 5y > -5$.

25. Graph the inequality $3x + 2y > 8$.

26. Graph the inequality $-3x + \frac{1}{3}y \geq -2$.

27. Graph the inequality $2x - \frac{3}{2}y \leq 3$.

28. Graph the inequality $2x - \frac{1}{2}y \leq 1$.

Practice Test

Take this practice test to be sure that you are prepared for the final quiz in Evaluate.

1. Graph the inequality $y > \frac{2}{3}x - 1$.

2. The graph of the line $x + 2y = 4$ is shown in Figure 4.3.1. Circle the point(s) below that satisfy the inequality $x + 2y \le 4$.

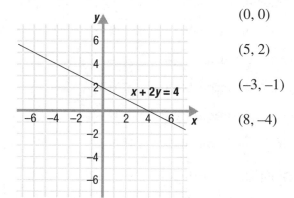

(0, 0)

(5, 2)

(−3, −1)

(8, −4)

Figure 4.3.1

3. Graph the inequality $y \le 2x - 1$.

4. Which point(s) below satisfy the linear inequality $y \le 4$.

   (23, 56)   (0, 0)

   (8, −14)   (−6, 7)

5. Which inequality below has a solution represented on the graph shown in Figure 4.3.2.

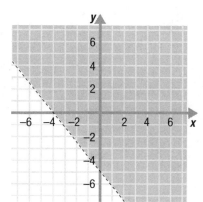

$5x + 4y > -20$

$4x - 5y < 20$

$4x + 5y > -20$

$5x - 4y < 20$

Figure 4.3.2

6. Graph the inequality $y \le 2x + 3$.

7. The graph of the equation $y = -\frac{1}{2}x - 2$ is shown in Figure 4.3.3. Which point(s) below satisfy the inequality $y \ge -\frac{1}{2}x - 2$.

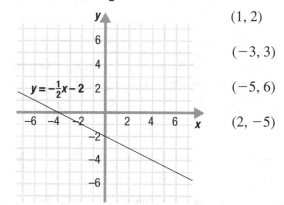

(1, 2)

(−3, 3)

(−5, 6)

(2, −5)

Figure 4.3.3

8. Which inequality below has a solution represented on the graph shown in Figure 4.3.4.

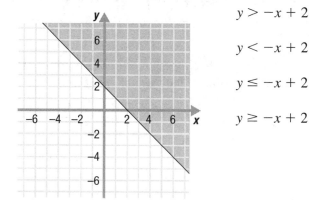

$y > -x + 2$

$y < -x + 2$

$y \le -x + 2$

$y \ge -x + 2$

Figure 4.3.4

TOPIC 4 Cumulative Activities

Cumulative Review Problems

These problems combine all of the material you have covered so far in this course. You may want to test your understanding of this material before you move on to the next topic, or you may wish to do these problems to review for a test.

1. Graph the equation $x - y = -2$.

2. Find the x- and y-intercepts of the line $2x + y = 3$.

3. Find the equation of the line through the point $(9, 4)$ with slope $\frac{5}{4}$. Write the equation in standard form.

4. Graph the line through the point $(3, 3)$ with slope 2.

5. Evaluate the expression $-5a^2b - 4a^3 + 7b^4$ when $a = 2$ and $b = -2$.

6. Find: $[3 + 2(5 - 7)^2] + 8$

7. Graph the inequality $y \geq 4x - 2$.

8a. Find the equation of the vertical line through the point $(-4, 5)$.

8b. What is the slope of this line?

8c. Find the equation of the horizontal line through the point $(-4, 5)$.

8d. What is the slope of this line?

9. Write in lowest terms: $\frac{270}{405}$

10. Graph the line $y = 4$.

11. Find: $\left| -\frac{7}{9} + \frac{5}{6} \right|$

12. The sum of three consecutive numbers is -18. What are the numbers?

13. Graph the inequality $\frac{2}{5}x + y < 2$.

14. Find the x- and y-intercepts of the line $\frac{6}{7}x - \frac{4}{7}y = 2$.

15a. Find four points whose coordinates satisfy the inequality $x + 2y < 5$.

15b. Find four points whose coordinates satisfy the inequality $x + 2y > 5$.

15c. Find four points whose coordinates satisfy the equation $x + 2y = 5$.

16. Graph the equation $3x + 4y = 12$.

17. Find: $8\frac{2}{5} - 4\frac{1}{7}$

18. Solve for x: $2x - 4 = \frac{2}{3}(-3 + x)$

19. Find: $\frac{8}{11} \div \frac{16}{55}$

20. Graph the line through the point $(-2, -5)$ with slope -1.

21. Find the equation of the line through the points $(-7, 3)$ and $(0, 4)$. Write your answer in standard form.

22. Write in lowest terms: $\frac{20}{35}$

23. Solve for y: $-5(y - 2) = \frac{2}{7}\left(6y - \frac{1}{2}\right)$

24. Graph the inequality $\frac{2}{3}x - \frac{1}{2}y < -1$.

25. Paul is 21 years older than Rita. Ten years ago, Paul was twice as old as Rita was then. How old is each of them now?

26. The surface area, S, of a sphere is $S = 4\pi r^2$, where r is the radius of the sphere. Solve this formula for r.

27. Graph the line $x = -7$.

28. Evaluate the expression $2x^2 + 4xy - 3y + 1$ when $x = -3$ and $y = 5$.

29. Solve $-3 < 2x + 1 \leq 8$ for x, then graph its solution on the number line below.

30. Find the slope of the line through the points $(3, 8)$ and $(-2, 1)$.

31. Graph the inequality $7x - 5y > 0$.

32. Write in lowest terms: $\dfrac{42}{63}$

33. Solve for y: $y + 1 = -\dfrac{1}{5}(67 + 9y)$

34. Write the equation of the line through the point $(-8, -6)$ with slope $\dfrac{9}{4}$. Write your answer in slope-intercept form.

35. Find the slope of the line perpendicular to the line through the points $(7, -3)$ and $(4, 9)$.

36. Graph the equation $\dfrac{2}{5}x + \dfrac{1}{5}y = -1$.

37. Find the equation of the line through the point $(5, -1)$ with slope 4. Write your answer in point-slope form.

38. Find the slope and y-intercept of the line $3x + 2y = 8$.

39. Find: $3\dfrac{7}{9} + 1\dfrac{2}{3}$

40. Solve $\dfrac{3}{2} < 2 - x \leq 7$ for x, then graph its solution on the number line below.

TOPIC 5
SOLVING LINEAR SYSTEMS

Many problems can be described and solved using just one linear equation. Sometimes, however, a system of two linear equations is needed to describe a situation. In that case, we are interested in the solutions that satisfy both equations.

In this topic, you will learn how to solve a linear system of equations. First you will solve by graphing, then by using algebraic methods.

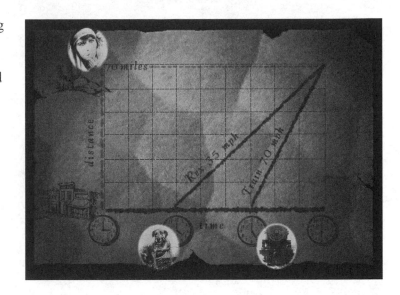

LESSON 5.1
SOLVING LINEAR SYSTEMS

 Overview

A customer wants to buy a blend of coffee for a specific price, and as the clerk you want to know how much of each type of coffee to put in the mixture.

The owner of the club where you sing sold some cheap tickets and some expensive tickets to the show last night, and you want to know how many tickets of each type were sold.

In each of these situations, you can find the answer by setting up and solving a system of two linear equations.

In this lesson, you will learn about systems of two linear equations. First, you will learn how to find the solution of such systems by graphing. Then, you will learn two algebraic methods for solving linear systems.

 Explain

Concept 1 has sections on

- **Systems of Linear Equations**

- **Solving a Linear System by Graphing**

- **Linear Systems with No Solution**

- **Linear Systems with Infinitely Many Solutions**

CONCEPT 1:
SOLUTION BY GRAPHING

Systems of Linear Equations

A **system of equations** consists of two or more equations, each of which contains at least one variable. Here are three examples:

System 1	System 2	System 3
$3x + y = -5$	$-7x + 9y = 0$	$5x - 4y = 11$
$4x - 2y = 7$	$3y = 8$	$y = 3x + 1$

Each system is called a **linear system in two variables**. This is because the graph of each equation is **linear** (that is, the graph is a straight line) and two variables are involved.

An ordered pair, (x, y), is a **solution of a linear system of equations in two variables** if the ordered pair makes each equation true. An ordered pair that is a solution is said to **satisfy** the system.

Example **5.1.1**

Determine if $(5, -2)$ is a solution of this system.

$3x - 4y = 23$ First equation
$x + y = 3$ Second equation

Solution

In each equation, replace x with 5 and y with -2. Then simplify.

First equation	Second equation
$3x - 4y = 23$	$x + y = 3$
Is $3(\mathbf{5}) - 4(\mathbf{-2}) = 23$?	Is $(\mathbf{5}) + (\mathbf{-2}) = 3$?
Is $15 + 8 = 23$?	Is $3 = 3$? **Yes**
Is $23 = 23$? **Yes**	

Since $(5, -2)$ satisfies each equation, it is a solution of the system.

The solution can be written as $x = 5$ and $y = -2$, or simply $(5, -2)$.

Solving a Linear System by Graphing

One way to find the solution of a linear system in two variables is to graph each equation on the same coordinate axes.

If the lines intersect, the point(s) of intersection is the solution of the system.

Example **5.1.2**

Graph each equation to find the solution of this system.

$3x - 2y = 8$
$y = -x + 6$

Solution

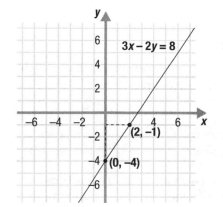

To graph each equation, first write it in slope-intercept form, $y = mx + b$.

- Let's start with the first equation. $3x - 2y = 8$

  Subtract $3x$ from both sides. $-2y = -3x + 8$

  Divide both sides by -2. $y = \dfrac{3}{2}x - 4$

  The y-intercept is $(0, -4)$.

  Plot the point $(0, -4)$.

  The slope is $\dfrac{3}{2}$. This is the ratio $\dfrac{\text{rise}}{\text{run}}$.

  To locate a second point, start at $(0, -4)$, move up 3 (the rise) and then move right 2 (the run).

  Plot the new point $(2, -1)$.

  Finally, draw the line through $(0, -4)$ and $(2, -1)$.

  Each point on this line represents a solution of $3x - 2y = 8$.

304   TOPIC 5   SOLVING LINEAR SYSTEMS

- The second equation, $y = -x + 6$, is given in the form $y = mx + b$.

  The y-intercept is $(0, 6)$. Plot the point $(0, 6)$.

  The slope is -1, which can be written as $\dfrac{-1}{1}$.

  To locate a second point, start at $(0, 6)$, move down 1 (the rise) and then move right 1 (the run).

  Plot the new point $(1, 5)$.

  Finally, draw the line through $(0, 6)$ and $(1, 5)$.

  Every point on this line represents a solution of $y = -x + 6$.

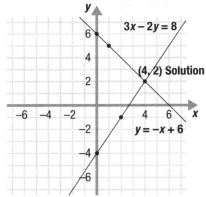

The system has one solution, (4, 2).

From the graph, it appears that the lines intersect at the point $(4, 2)$.

The point $(4, 2)$ is a solution of each equation.

Therefore, the solution of the system is $(4, 2)$.

Let's verify that $(4, 2)$ satisfies both equations.

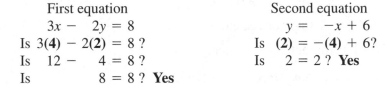

First equation	Second equation
$3x - 2y = 8$	$y = -x + 6$
Is $3(4) - 2(2) = 8$?	Is $(2) = -(4) + 6$?
Is $12 - 4 = 8$?	Is $2 = 2$? **Yes**
Is $8 = 8$? **Yes**	

Since $(4, 2)$ satisfies both equations, it is the solution of the system.

The solution can be written as $x = 4$ and $y = 2$, or simply $(4, 2)$.

A system that has at least one solution is called a **consistent system**.

Linear Systems with No Solution

A linear system has no solution if the graphs of the equations have no points in common.

That is, if the lines are parallel and distinct, the linear system does not have a solution.

Example 5.1.3

Graph each equation to find the solution of this system.

$$x - 2y = 6$$
$$-2x + 4y = 4$$

Solution

To graph each equation, first write it in slope-intercept form, $y = mx + b$.

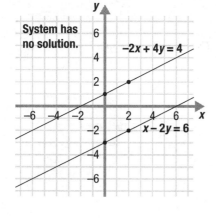

System has no solution.

- In slope-intercept form, the first equation is $y = \frac{1}{2}x - 3$.

  The y-intercept is $(0, -3)$. Plot $(0, -3)$.

  Use the slope, $\frac{1}{2}$, to plot a second point.

  Draw the line through the two points.

- In slope-intercept form, the second equation is $y = \frac{1}{2}x + 1$.

  The y-intercept is $(0, 1)$. Plot $(0, 1)$.

  Use the slope, $\frac{1}{2}$, to plot a second point.

  Draw the line through the two points.

The lines have the same slope, $\frac{1}{2}$, but different y-intercepts.

Therefore, the lines are distinct parallel lines.

Since distinct parallel lines never intersect, this system has no solution.

A system that has no solution is called an **inconsistent system**.

Linear Systems with Infinitely Many Solutions

A linear system has infinitely many solutions if the graphs of the two equations **coincide**.

That is, if the graphs are identical, the linear system has infinitely many solutions.

Example 5.1.4

Graph each equation to find the solution of this system.

$$2y + 6 = -4x$$
$$2x + y = -3$$

Solution

To graph each equation, first write it in slope-intercept form.

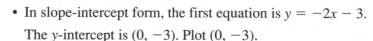

System has infinitely many solutions.

- In slope-intercept form, the first equation is $y = -2x - 3$.

  The y-intercept is $(0, -3)$. Plot $(0, -3)$.

  Use the slope, $\frac{-2}{1}$, to plot a second point.

  Draw the line through the two points.

- In slope-intercept form, the second equation is $y = -2x - 3$.

   This equation is identical to the first equation.

   Therefore, its graph is identical to that of the first equation.

      Thus, the lines coincide.

Because the lines coincide they have infinitely many points in common. Thus, the system has infinitely many solutions.

These solutions may be stated in several ways, including:

- "The set of all ordered pairs for which $2y + 6 = -4x$."
- "The set of all ordered pairs for which $2x + y = -3$."
- "The set of all ordered pairs for which $y = -2x - 3$."

If the graphs of the equations of a system are identical, as in Example 5.1.4, the equations are called **dependent**. Otherwise, the equations are called **independent**.

— Procedure —
To Solve a Linear System of Equations By Graphing

Graph each line on the same coordinate axes.

There are three possible outcomes:

- The lines intersect at exactly one point.
  See Example 5.1.2.

  The system has exactly one solution.

  The solution is the coordinates of the point of intersection.

  The system is consistent.

  The equations are independent.

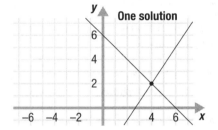

- The lines do not intersect.
  See Example 5.1.3.

  The system has no solution because the lines have no points in common.

  The system is inconsistent.

  The equations are independent.

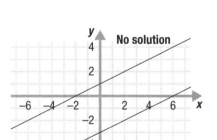

- The lines coincide.
  See Example 5.1.4.

  The system has infinitely many solutions. The solutions may be stated by writing one of the equations of the system.

  The system is consistent.

  The equations are dependent.

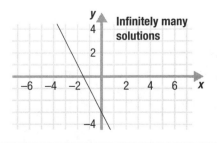

Here is a summary of this concept from *Academic Systems Algebra*.

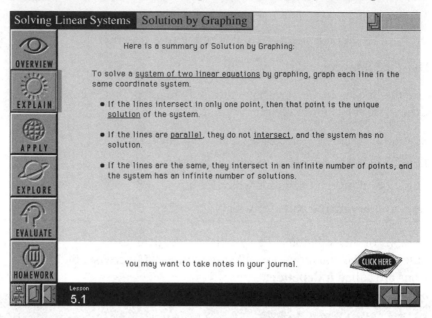

Concept 2 has sections on

- **Solving a Linear System by Substitution**

- **Solving a Linear System by Elimination**

- **Helpful Strategies When Using Elimination**

- **Special Cases of Linear Systems**

CONCEPT 2: SOLUTION BY ALGEBRA

Solving a Linear System by Substitution

Graphing is not always the best way to find the solution of a system of equations. It may be difficult to read the coordinates of the point of intersection. This is especially true when the coordinates are not integers.

Instead we can use algebraic methods to solve the system. One algebraic method for finding the solution of a linear system is the **substitution method**.

— Procedure —
To Solve a Linear System By Substitution

Step 1 Solve one equation for one of the variables in terms of the other variable.

Step 2 Substitute the expression found in Step 1 into the other equation. Then, solve for the variable.

Step 3 Substitute the value obtained in Step 2 into one of the equations containing both variables. Then, solve for the remaining variable.

Step 4 To check the solution, substitute it into each original equation. Then simplify.

Example 5.1.5

Use substitution to find the solution of this system.

$2x + y = 4$ First equation
$3x + y = 7$ Second equation

Solution

Step 1 ***Solve one equation for one of the variables in terms of the other variable.***

Either equation may be solved for either variable.

For instance, let's solve the first equation for y. $2x + y = 4$

Subtract $2x$ from both sides. $y = -2x + 4$

The equation $y = -2x + 4$ means that y and the expression $-2x + 4$ are equivalent.

It's easy to solve either equation for y. Just subtract the x-term from both sides. To solve for x, you would need to subtract and divide.

Step 2 ***Substitute the expression found in Step 1 into the other equation. Then, solve for the variable.***

$$3x + y = 7$$

Substitute $-2x + 4$ for y in the second equation. $3x + (\mathbf{-2x + 4}) = 7$

Combine like terms. $x + 4 = 7$

Subtract 4 from both sides. $x = 3$

Now we know $x = 3$.

Next, we will find y.

Step 3 ***Substitute the value obtained in Step 2 into one of the equations containing both variables. Then, solve for the remaining variable.***

We will use the equation from Step 1. $y = -2x + 4$

Substitute 3 for x. $y = -2(\mathbf{3}) + 4$

Simplify. $y = -2$

The solution of the system is $x = 3$ and $y = -2$.

The solution may also be written as $(3, -2)$.

Substituting 3 for x into either original equation would have resulted in the same value, −2, for y.

Step 4 ***To check the solution, substitute it into each original equation. Then simplify.***

Substitute $x = 3$ and $y = -2$ into both of the original equations:

First equation	Second equation
$2x + y = 4$	$3x + y = 7$
Is $2(\mathbf{3}) + (\mathbf{-2}) = 4$?	Is $3(\mathbf{3}) + (\mathbf{-2}) = 7$?
Is $6 - 2 = 4$?	Is $9 - 2 = 7$?
Is $4 = 4$? **Yes**	Is $7 = 7$? **Yes**

If we graphed the system, the lines would intersect at the point (3, −2).

Since $(3, -2)$ satisfies both equations, it is the solution of the system.

Example 5.1.6

Use substitution to find the solution of this system.

$$-3x + 4y = 17 \qquad \text{First equation}$$
$$x - 6y = -8 \qquad \text{Second equation}$$

Solution

Step 1 Solve one equation for one of the variables in terms of the other variable.

Either equation may be solved for either variable.

It's easiest to start with the second equation because it already contains the term x.

For instance, let's solve the second equation for x. $\qquad x - 6y = -8$

Add $6y$ to both sides. $\qquad\qquad\qquad\qquad\qquad x = 6y - 8$

Step 2 Substitute the expression found in Step 1 into the other equation. Then, solve for the variable.

$$-3x + 4y = 17$$

Substitute $6y - 8$ for x in the first equation. $\qquad -3(\mathbf{6y - 8}) + 4y = 17$

Remove parentheses. $\qquad\qquad\qquad\qquad\qquad -18y + 24 + 4y = 17$

Combine like terms. $\qquad\qquad\qquad\qquad\qquad\quad -14y + 24 = 17$

Subtract 24 from both sides. $\qquad\qquad\qquad\qquad\qquad -14y = -7$

Divide both sides by -14. $\qquad\qquad\qquad\qquad\qquad\qquad y = \dfrac{1}{2}$

Now we know $y = \dfrac{1}{2}$.

Next, we will find x.

Step 3 Substitute the value obtained in Step 2 into one of the equations containing both variables. Then, solve for the remaining variable.

We will use the equation from Step 1. $\qquad\qquad x = 6y - 8$

Substitute $\dfrac{1}{2}$ for y. $\qquad\qquad\qquad\qquad\qquad x = 6\left(\dfrac{1}{2}\right) - 8$

Simplify. $\qquad\qquad\qquad\qquad\qquad\qquad\qquad\quad x = -5$

The solution of the system is $\left(-5, \dfrac{1}{2}\right)$.

Step 4 To check the solution, substitute it into each original equation. Then simplify.

If we graphed the system, the lines would intersect at the point $\left(-5, \dfrac{1}{2}\right)$.

Substitute -5 for x and $\dfrac{1}{2}$ for y into each original equation.

Then simplify.

In each case, the result will be a true statement.

The details of the check are left to you.

Solving a Linear System by Elimination

A second algebraic method for finding the solution of a system of linear equations is the **elimination method**.

This method allows us to add two equations to form a new equation. Why add the two equations? In some instances this will result in a new equation that has only one variable. This new equation may then be solved to find the value of that variable.

The following example shows how to solve a linear system by elimination.

The elimination method makes use of the Addition Principle of Equality which states that you can add equivalent quantities to both sides of an equation without changing the solutions of the equation.

Example 5.1.7

Use elimination to find the solution of this system.

$$x - 3y = -17 \quad \text{First equation}$$
$$-x + 8y = 52 \quad \text{Second equation}$$

Solution

Add the two equations.

$$\begin{array}{r} x - 3y = -17 \\ -x + 8y = 52 \\ \hline 0x + 5y = 35 \end{array}$$

Simplify. The x-terms have been eliminated. $5y = 35$

To solve for y, divide both sides by 5. $y = 7$

To find the value of x, substitute 7 for y in either of the original equations. Then solve for x.

We will use the first equation. $x - 3y = -17$

Substitute 7 for y. $x - 3(\mathbf{7}) = -17$

Multiply. $x - \mathbf{21} = -17$

Add 21 to both sides. $x = 4$

The solution of the system is $(4, 7)$.

To check the solution, substitute 4 for x and 7 for y into each original equation. Then simplify.

In each case, the result will be a true statement.

The details of the check are left to you.

If we graphed the system, the line would intersect at the point (4, 7).

We could also solve this system by substitution.

In the two original equations in the previous example, the coefficients of x were opposites. Thus, when the equations were added, the x-terms were eliminated.

$$\begin{array}{r} 1x - 3y = -17 \\ -1x + 8y = 52 \\ \hline 5y = 35 \end{array}$$

When the coefficients of neither variable are opposites, we choose a variable. Then we multiply both sides of one (or both) equations by an appropriate number (or numbers) to make the coefficients of that variable opposites.

The Multiplication Principle of Equality enables us to multiply both sides of an equation by the same nonzero number without changing the solutions of the equation.

Procedure —
To Solve a Linear System By Elimination

Step 1 Eliminate one variable.

- If necessary, multiply both sides of one or both equations by an appropriate number so that the coefficients of one variable are opposites.

- Add the new equations to form a single equation in one variable.

- Solve the equation.

Step 2 Substitute the value found in Step 1 into either of the original equations and solve.

Step 3 To check the solution, substitute it into each original equation. Then simplify.

Example 5.1.8

Use elimination to find the solution of this system.

$4x + 3y = 13$ First equation
$5x - 6y = -52$ Second equation

Solution

The coefficients of the x-terms are **not** opposites.

The coefficients of the y-terms are **not** opposites.

So, adding the equations will not eliminate a variable.

However, the coefficients of y can be made opposites by multiplying both sides of the first equation by 2.

Step 1   Eliminate one variable.

Multiply both sides of the first equation by 2.

$$2(4x + 3y = 13) \rightarrow 8x + 6y = 26$$

Add the two equations.
Notice the coefficients of y,
6 and -6, are opposites.

$$\begin{aligned} 8x + 6y &= 26 \\ 5x - 6y &= -52 \\ \hline 13x + 0y &= -26 \end{aligned}$$

Simplify. The y-terms have been eliminated. $13x = -26$

Divide both sides by 13. $x = -2$

Now we know $x = -2$.

Next we will find y.

Step 2 Substitute the value found in Step 1 into either of the original equations and solve.

We will use the first equation.	$4x + 3y = 13$
Substitute -2 for x.	$4(-2) + 3y = 13$
Multiply.	$-8 + 3y = 13$
Add 8 to both sides.	$3y = 21$
Divide both sides by 3.	$y = 7$

The solution is $(-2, 7)$.

Step 3 To check the solution, substitute it into each original equation. Then simplify.

Substitute -2 for x and 7 for y into each original equation and then simplify.

In each case, the result will be a true statement. The details of the check are left to you.

In some systems it is necessary to multiply each equation by a constant so that one variable will be eliminated when the equations are added.

Example 5.1.9

Use elimination to find the solution of this system.

$3x + 4y = 18$
$17x + 6y = 52$

Solution

Step 1 Eliminate one variable.

Let's eliminate y.

- Multiply both sides of the first equation by 3 to make the y-coefficient 12.

  $3(3x + 4y = 18) \rightarrow 9x + 12y = 54$

- Multiply both sides of the second equation by -2 to make the y-coefficient -12.

  $-2(17x + 6y = 52) \rightarrow -34x - 12y = -104$

Add the two equations.

$$\begin{array}{r} 9x + 12y = 54 \\ -34x - 12y = -104 \\ \hline -25x + 0y = -50 \end{array}$$

Simplify. The y-terms have been eliminated. $-25x = -50$

Divide both sides by -25. $x = 2$

$3x + 4y = 18$
$17x + 6y = 52$

In this system, the coefficients of y are 4 and 6, respectively.
*Multiples of 4 are 4, 8, **12**,...*
*Multiples of 6 are 6, **12**, 18,...*

Notice that 12 is the least common multiple of 4 and 6. To make the coefficients of y opposites:

- *multiply both sides of the first equation by 3.*

- *multiply both sides of the second equation by -2.*

Step 2 *Substitute the value found in Step 1 into*
        either of the original equations and solve. $3x + 4y = 18$

Substitute 2 for x in the first equation. $3(2) + 4y = 18$

Multiply. $\mathbf{6} + 4y = 18$

Subtract 6 from both sides. $4y = \mathbf{12}$

Divide both sides by 4. $y = 3$

The solution is (2, 3).

Step 3 *To check the solution, substitute it into each original equation.*
        Then simplify.

Substitute 2 for x and 3 for y into each original equation. Then simplify.

In each case, the result will be a true statement.

The details of the check are left to you.

Helpful Strategies When Using Elimination

Different linear systems may require different strategies for eliminating one of the variables.

1. In some linear systems, a variable can be eliminated simply by adding the equations.

      Add the equations to eliminate y.

The solution of the system is $(-1, 5)$

$$\begin{array}{r} 4x - 3y = -19 \\ -x + 3y = 16 \\ \hline 3x + 0y = -3 \end{array}$$

      There is no need to multiply either equation by a constant.

2. In a system that contains fractions, multiply both sides of an equation by the LCD of its fractions to clear the fractions and make the system easier to work with.

LCD stands for least common denominator.

      To clear the fractions in the first equation, multiply both sides by 15, the LCD of $\frac{2}{3}$ and $\frac{1}{5}$.

$$\frac{2}{3}x + \frac{1}{5}y = 5$$
$$x - 3y = -9$$

      Multiply both sides of the first equation by 15.

$$\mathbf{15} \cdot \left(\frac{2}{3}x + \frac{1}{5}y = 5\right) \rightarrow \mathbf{10}x + \mathbf{3}y = \mathbf{75}$$

The solution of the system is (6, 5).

      Do not change the second equation.
      Add the equations to eliminate y.

$$\begin{array}{r} x - 3y = -9 \\ \hline 11x - 0y = 66 \end{array}$$

3. In some systems, only one equation needs to be multiplied by a constant.

Eliminate x.

$$5x - 7y = -33$$
$$15x + 8y = 17$$

Multiply both sides of the first equation by -3.

$$-3(5x - 7y = -33) \rightarrow -15x + 21y = 99$$

Do not change the second equation.

$$15x + 8y = 17 \qquad \underline{15x + 8y = 17}$$

Add the equations to eliminate x.

$$0x + 29y = 116 \qquad \textit{The solution of the system is } (-1, 4).$$

4. In some systems, both equations must be multiplied by a constant.

Eliminate x.

$$-2x + 11y = -28$$
$$3x - 5y = 19$$

Multiply both sides of the first equation by 3.

$$3(-2x + 11y = -28) \rightarrow -6x + 33y = -84$$

Multiply both sides of the second equation by 2.

$$2(3x - 5y = 19) \rightarrow \underline{6x - 10y = 38}$$

Add the equations to eliminate x.

$$0x + 23y = -46 \qquad \textit{The solution of the system is } (3, -2).$$

Special Cases of Linear Systems

When discussing the graphing method of solving a linear system we found there were three possible outcomes for a system of two equations in two variables:

• The lines intersect at exactly one point.

• The lines do not intersect. (They are distinct parallel lines.)

• The lines intersect at every point. (They coincide.)

We have solved the first type of system by elimination and by substitution.

We can also use these methods on the other two types of systems.

Example 5.1.10

Use elimination to find the solution of this system.

$$3x - 6y = 12$$
$$-9x + 18y = -36$$

Solution

To eliminate x, multiply the first equation by 3.

$$3(3x - 6y = 12) \rightarrow 9x - 18y = 36$$

Do not change the second equation.

$$-9x + 18y = -36 \qquad -9x + 18y = -36$$

Add the two equations.

$$0x + 0y = 0$$

Both variables are eliminated. The result is the identity $0 = 0$.

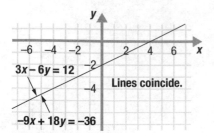

$3x - 6y = 12$

Lines coincide.

$-9x + 18y = -36$

When the result is an identity, the graphs of the equations coincide.

This system has infinitely many solutions because the lines intersect at infinitely many points.

These solutions may be stated in several ways, including:

• "The set of all ordered pairs for which $3x - 6y = 12$."

• "The set of all ordered pairs for which $-9x + 18y = -36$."

The system is consistent. (It has at least one solution.)

The equations of the system are dependent. (The graphs are identical.)

If we solve the same system by substitution, we also end up with an identity.

If we solve the same system by substitution, we also end up with an identity.

You can see this as follows:

Solve the first equation, $3x - 6y = 12$, for x:

$$3x = 6y + 12$$
$$x = 2y + 4$$

In the second equation, replace x with $2y + 4$. Then simplify.

$$-9x + 18y = -36$$
$$-9(2y + 4) + 18y = -36$$
$$-18y - 36 + 18y = -36$$
$$-36 = -36 \quad \text{An identity}$$

Example 5.1.11

Use elimination to find the solution of this system.

$$\frac{1}{2}x + \frac{1}{3}y = \frac{7}{2}$$
$$0.3x + 0.2y = -1$$

Solution

To make the equations easier to work with:

• Clear the fractions in the first equation by multiplying both sides by 6, the LCD of the fractions.

$$6\left(\frac{1}{2}x + \frac{1}{3}y = \frac{7}{2}\right) \rightarrow \quad 3x + 2y = 21$$

• Clear the decimals from the second equation by multiplying both sides by 10.

$$10(0.3x + 0.2y = -1) \rightarrow \quad 3x + 2y = -10$$

To make the x-coefficients opposites, multiply the transformed second equation by -1.
Add the equations.

$$3x + 2y = 21 \qquad 3x + 2y = 21$$
$$-1(3x + 2y = -10) \rightarrow \underline{-3x - 2y = 10}$$
$$0x + 0y = 31$$

Both variables are eliminated. The result is the false statement $0 = 31$.

When the result is a false statement, the graphs of the equations never intersect. The graph confirms that the lines are parallel and have no points in common.

This system has no solution because the lines never intersect.

The system is inconsistent. (It has no solution.)

The equations of the system are independent. (Their graphs are not identical.)

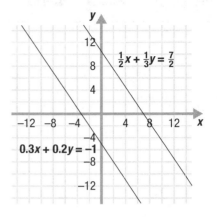

— Note —
Solving a Linear System: Special Cases

When using either substitution or elimination, if both variables are eliminated there are two possible outcomes:

- If the resulting equation is an identity, such as $5 = 5$, then the lines coincide.

  The system has infinitely many solutions.

  The solutions may be stated as the set of all points on the line.

- If the resulting equation is a false statement, such as $0 = 4$, then the lines are parallel and never intersect.

  The system has no solution.

  The system is inconsistent and the equations are independent.

Here is a summary of this concept from *Academic Systems Algebra*.

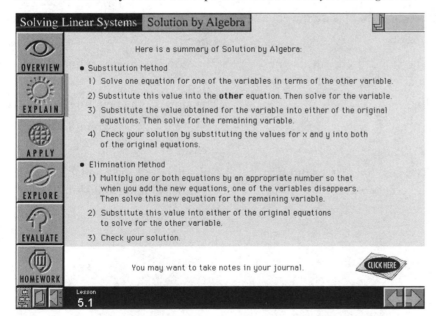

Explore

On the computer you used the Grapher to solve and analyze systems of linear inequalities. Here is an additional exploration.

Example 5.1.12

A system of two linear equations has the solution $(-2, 2)$.

The slope of one line is one-quarter the slope of the other line. If the equation of one line is $y = 2x + 6$, what are the two possible equations of the other line?

Solution

We are given the equation $y = 2x + 6$. Let's call the slope of this line m_1.

$m_1 = 2$

- **Possibility 1** Find the equation of the line through $(-2, 2)$ with slope one-quarter of m_1.

Find the slope, m_2, of the new line.

$m_2 = \frac{1}{4}m_1 = \frac{1}{4} \cdot 2 = \frac{1}{2}$

We are given that this second line passes through the point $(-2, 2)$.

We can use the point-slope formula to determine the equation of the line.

$y - y_1 = m(x - x_1)$

Substitute **2** for y_1, $\frac{1}{2}$ for m, and -2 for x_1.

$y - 2 = \frac{1}{2}(x - (-2))$

Solve for y.

$y = \frac{1}{2}x + 3$

Let's check to be sure the equation satisfies the given conditions.

Condition	*Check*
• The slope of one line is one-quarter the slope of the other line.	• The slope of the given line, $y = 2x + 6$, is 2. The slope of the new line, $y = \frac{1}{2}x + 3$, is $\frac{1}{2}$, which is one-quarter of 2. ✓
• The new line passes through the point $(-2, 2)$.	• Substitute -2 for x and 2 for y in the new equation and simplify. $y = \frac{1}{2}x + 3$ Is $2 = \frac{1}{2}(-2) + 3$? Is $2 = 2$? **Yes** ✓

- **Possibility 2** Find the equation of the line through $(-2, 2)$ with slope 4 times m_1, the slope of the given line.

In this case, the slope of the given line, $y = 2x + 6$, is one-quarter that of the new line.

Let's call the slope of this new line m_3. $m_1 = \frac{1}{4}m_3$

Substitute **2** for m_1. $2 = \frac{1}{4}m_3$

Multiply both sides by 4. $8 = m_3$

Now, we know the slope of the new line is 8. Also, the line passes through $(-2, 2)$.

To find the equation of the new line, we use the point-slope formula as in Possibility 1. $y - y_1 = m(x - x_1)$

Substitute **2** for y_1, 8 for m, **−2** for x_1. $y - 2 = \mathbf{8}(x - (\mathbf{-2}))$

Solve for y. $y = 8x + 18$

We leave it to you to check that this equation satisfies the given conditions.

Here is a summary of this Exploration from *Academic Systems Algebra.*

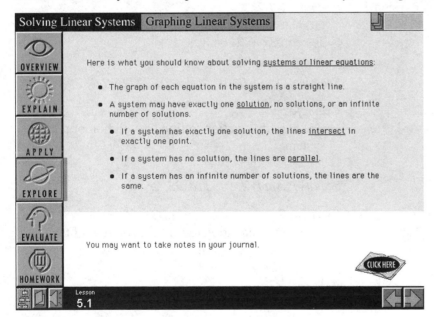

Solving Linear Systems | Graphing Linear Systems

OVERVIEW

EXPLAIN

APPLY

EXPLORE

EVALUATE

HOMEWORK

Here is what you should know about solving <u>systems of linear equations</u>:

- The graph of each equation in the system is a straight line.
- A system may have exactly one <u>solution</u>, no solutions, or an infinite number of solutions.
  - If a system has exactly one solution, the lines <u>intersect</u> in exactly one point.
  - If a system has no solution, the lines are <u>parallel</u>.
  - If a system has an infinite number of solutions, the lines are the same.

You may want to take notes in your journal.

CLICK HERE

Lesson 5.1

Checklist Lesson 5.1

Here is what you should know after completing this lesson.

Words and Phrases

system of equations
linear system in two variables
linear
solution of a linear system of equations in two variables
satisfy
consistent system

inconsistent system
coincide
dependent
independent
substitution method
elimination method

Ideas and Procedures

❶ Solution of a Linear System

Determine if an ordered pair is the solution of a linear system.

Example 5.1.1
   Determine if (5, –2) is a solution of this system:
   $3x - 4y = 23$
   $x + y = 3$

See also: Apply 1-5

❷ Graphing Method

Use the graphing method to solve a linear system.

Example 5.1.2
   Graph each equation to find the solution of this system: $3x - 2y = 8$
                                   $y = -x + 6$

See also: Apply 6-10, 14-16, 20-22, 26-28

When solving a linear system by graphing, recognize that the system has no solution.

Example 5.1.3
   Graph each equation to find the solution of this system: $x - 2y = 6$
                   $-2x + 4y = 4$

See also: Apply 11, 13, 18, 23, 25

When solving a linear system by graphing, recognize that the system has infinitely many solutions.

Example 5.1.4
   Graph each equation to find the solution of this system: $2y + 6 = -4x$
                         $2x + y = -3$

See also: Apply 12, 17, 19, 24

❸ Substitution Method

Use the substitution method to solve a system of linear equations algebraically.

Example 5.1.6
   Use substitution to find the solution of this system:
   $-3x + 4y = 17$
   $x - 6y = -8$

See also: Example 5.1.5
                Apply 29-40

❹ Elimination Method

Use the elimination method to solve a system of linear equations algebraically.

Example 5.1.9
   Use elimination to find the solution of this system:
   $$3x + 4y = 18$$
   $$17x + 6y = 52$$

See also: Example 5.1.7, 5.1.8
               Apply 43-54

❺ Linear Systems with Infinitely Many Solutions

When solving a linear system algebraically, recognize that the system has infinitely many solutions.

Example 5.1.10
   Use elimination to find the solution of this system:
   $$3x - 6y = 12$$
   $$-9x + 18y = -36$$

See also: Apply 41, 56

❻ Linear Systems with No Solution

When solving a linear system algebraically, recognize that the system has no solution.

Example 5.1.11
   Use elimination to find the solution of this system:
   $$\frac{1}{2}x + \frac{1}{3}y = \frac{7}{2}$$
   $$0.3x + 0.2y = -1$$

See also: Apply 42, 55

Homework

Homework Problems

Circle the homework problems assigned to you by the computer, then complete them below.

☀ Explain

Solution By Graphing

Use Figure 5.1.1 to answer questions 1 through 3.

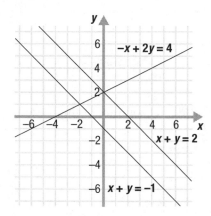

Figure 5.1.1

1. Which two lines form a system that has a solution of $(-2, 1)$?

2. Which two lines form a system that has no solution?

3. Which two lines form a system that has a solution of $(0, 2)$?

4. The ordered pair $(-2, -5)$ is a solution of which system of equations?

$$\begin{array}{ll} x - y = 7 & 4x + y = 6 \\ 3x + 2y = -11 & x - 2y = 8 \end{array}$$

$$\begin{array}{ll} 2x - y = 1 & x - 3y = 9 \\ x + y = -7 & 2x + y = -1 \end{array}$$

Use Figure 5.1.2 to answer questions 5 through 8.

5. Which two lines form a system that has a solution of $(1, 6)$?

6. Which two lines form a system that has a solution of $(-4, 1)$?

7. Which two lines form a system that has no solution?

8. What is the solution of the system of equations $x + 2y = -2$ and $3x + y = 9$?

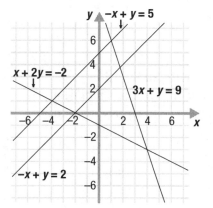

Figure 5.1.2

9. Raymond weighs 180 pounds and wants to lose some weight before his high school reunion. He figures he can lose 2 pounds a week if he sticks to a strict diet. If his reunion is in 14 weeks and he really sticks to his diet, will he be able to get down to his goal weight of 150 pounds? If so, how long will it take him? If not, how much longer will he have to stay on his diet? Graph the system to help you answer the questions.
$$y = 180 - 2x$$
$$y = 150$$

10. Katelyn has $50 in her bank account and saves $10 per week. Caesar has $200 in his bank account and withdraws $20 per week. When will Katelyn and Caesar have the same amount of money and how much will each have? Graph the system to help you answer the question.
$$y = 50 + 10x$$
$$y = 200 - 20x$$

Use Figure 5.1.3 to answer questions 11 and 12.

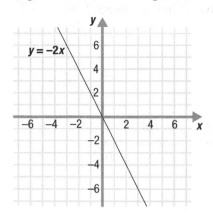

Figure 5.1.3

11. Draw a line on the grid in Figure 5.1.3 so that the system of equations has no solution.

12. Draw a line on the grid in Figure 5.1.3 so that the system of equations has one solution at the point $(2, -4)$.

Solution by Algebra

13. Use the substitution method to solve this system:
$$x + 2y = 4$$
$$2x + 3y = 7$$

14. Use the elimination method to solve this system:
$$x + y = 7$$
$$x - y = 1$$

15. Use the elimination method to solve this system:
$$4x - y = -8$$
$$3x + 2y = 5$$

16. Use the substitution method to solve this system:
$$4x + y = 14$$
$$3x + 5y = -15$$

17. Use the substitution method to solve this system:
$$2x + y = 5$$
$$6x + 3y = 15$$

18. Use the elimination method to solve this system:
$$x + 7y = 31$$
$$x - 9y = -1$$

19. Use the elimination method to solve this system:
$$3x + y = 5$$
$$6x + 2y = 9$$

20. Use the substitution method to solve this system:
$$3x + y = 6$$
$$6x + 2y = 10$$

21. When renting a compact car, you have a choice of paying a flat rate of $25 per day with unlimited mileage or you can pay $15 per day and 20¢ per mile. How many miles can you drive before the cost of paying for mileage is the same as getting unlimited mileage? Use the substitution method or the elimination method to solve the system below to get the answer.
$$y = 25$$
$$y = 15 + 0.20x$$

22. The monthly rate for phone service can be paid for in one of two ways. One choice is to pay a measured rate of $4.45 per month and $0.03 a minute for each local call. The other choice is to pay a flat rate of $8.35 per month. How many minutes of local calls can you make before the cost for measured rate service is the same as the cost for flat rate service? Use the substitution method or the elimination method to solve the system below to get the answer.
$$y = 4.45 + 0.03x$$
$$y = 8.35$$

23. Solve this system:
$$x - 4y = -31$$
$$3x + 2y = 5$$

24. Solve this system:
$$12x - 3y = 132$$
$$6x + 5y = 14$$

 Explore

25. A system of two linear equations has the solution $(2, 4)$. The slope of one of the lines is twice the slope of the other line. If the equation of one of the lines is $y = 3x - 2$, what are the two possible equations of the other line?

26. Which of the following systems of equations have no solutions?
$$x - y = 7$$
$$3x - y = 9$$

$$x + y = 3$$
$$2y = -2x + 9$$

$$2x - 3y = 5$$
$$x = 2y + 1$$

$$x + y = 3$$
$$2x - 5y = 6$$

27. Find the vertices of the triangle formed by the lines whose equations are shown below.

$$y = x + 4 \qquad y = -2x + 4 \qquad \frac{1}{2}x + y = -5$$

28. A system of two linear equations has the solution $(0, -2)$. The slope of one of the lines is three times the slope of the other line. If the equation of one of the lines is $y = 3x - 2$, what are the two possible equations of the other line?

29. Which of the following systems of equations have exactly one solution in Quadrant II?

$$\begin{array}{ll} y = x + 3 & 3x + 2y = 6 \\ x + y = -1 & x + 4y = -2 \end{array}$$

$$\begin{array}{ll} y = x + 2 & x + y = -6 \\ y = -\dfrac{1}{2}x - 4 & 3x + y = -12 \end{array}$$

30. Find the vertices of the triangle formed by the lines whose equations are shown below.

$$y = -2x + 3 \qquad 2y - 5x = 10 \qquad 5y = 2x - 15$$

 **Apply**

Practice Problems

Here are some additional practice problems for you to try.

Solution by Graphing

1. Which two lines form a system whose solution is (2, 1)?

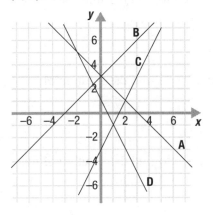

2. Which two lines form a system whose solution is (1, −2)?

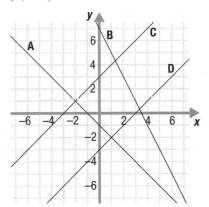

3. Which two lines form a system whose solution is (−3, 3)?

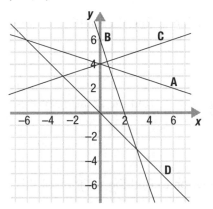

4. Which two lines form a system that has no solution?

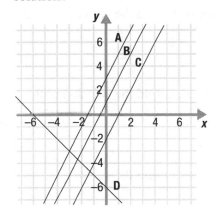

5. Which two lines form a system that has no solution?

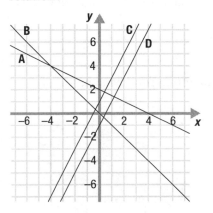

6. Graph each equation to find the solution of this system:
$$x - 4y = 8$$
$$2x + y = -2$$

7. Graph each equation to find the solution of this system:
$$2x + y = 4$$
$$3x - 4y = 6$$

8. Graph each equation to find the solution of this system:
$$x + y = 3$$
$$2x - y = 3$$

9. Graph each equation to find the solution of this system:
$$x + 3y = -6$$
$$x - 3y = 0$$

10. Graph each equation to find the solution of this system:
$$x - y = -4$$
$$x + 2y = -1$$

11. Graph each equation to find the solution of this system:
$$3x - 2y = -6$$
$$-6x + 4y = 9$$

12. Graph each equation to find the solution of this system:
$$4x - y = 8$$
$$-8x + 2y = -16$$

13. Graph each equation to find the solution of this system:
$$2x - y = 4$$
$$-4x + 2y = 6$$

14. Graph each equation to find the solution of this system:
$$x - y = 4$$
$$2x + 3y = -2$$

15. Graph each equation to find the solution of this system:
$$2x + y = -6$$
$$3x - y = 1$$

16. Graph each equation to find the solution of this system:
$$x + y = 2$$
$$2x + 3y = 8$$

17. Graph each equation to find the solution of this system:
$$x + 2y = 4$$
$$-2x - 4y = -8$$

18. Graph each equation to find the solution of this system:
$$-2x + 3y = -6$$
$$6x - 9y = -18$$

19. Graph each equation to find the solution of this system:
$$x - 3y = 6$$
$$-2x + 6y = -12$$

20. Graph each equation to find the solution of this system:
$$x + y = 4$$
$$2x - y = 5$$

21. Graph each equation to find the solution of this system:
$$x + y = 4$$
$$5x - 2y = -1$$

22. Graph each equation to find the solution of this system:
$$2x + 2y = 8$$
$$x - 3y = 8$$

23. Draw a line on the grid below so that the system of equations has no solution.

24. Draw a line on the grid below so that the system of equations has an infinite number of solutions.

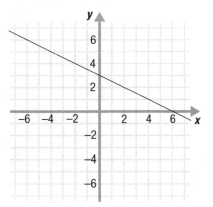

25. Draw a line on the grid below so that the system of equations has no solution.

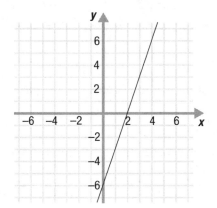

26. Draw a line on the grid below so that the system of equations has one solution at the point (1, 2).

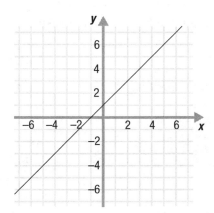

27. Draw a line on the grid below so that the system of equations has one solution at the point $(-4, 3)$.

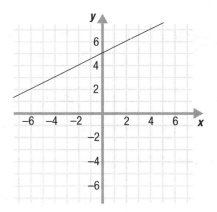

28. Draw a line on the grid below so that the system of equations has one solution at the point $(3, -2)$.

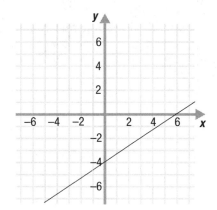

Solution by Algebra

29. Use the substitution method to solve this system:
$$x - 2y = -1$$
$$x + y = 5$$

30. Use the substitution method to solve this system:
$$x - y = 4$$
$$3x + y = 4$$

31. Use the substitution method to solve this system:
$$2x + y = -1$$
$$x - y = 7$$

32. Use the substitution method to solve this system:
$$4x - 3y = -7$$
$$x + 2y = 12$$

33. Use the substitution method to solve this system:
$$3x + 5y = 1$$
$$4x - y = 9$$

34. Use the substitution method to solve this system:
$$3x - 7y = 4$$
$$2x + y = -3$$

35. Use the substitution method to solve this system:
$$4x + y = 7$$
$$x + 2y = 2$$

36. Use the substitution method to solve this system:
$$4x - 2y = 7$$
$$4x + y = -2$$

37. Use the substitution method to solve this system:
$$5x + y = 1$$
$$x - 3y = 2$$

38. Use the substitution method to solve this system:
$$-3x + 2y = 8$$
$$x + 2y = -6$$

39. Use the substitution method to solve this system:
$$4x - 3y = -2$$
$$-3x + y = 6$$

40. Use the substitution method to solve this system:
$$2x - 3y = 1$$
$$-4x + y = 7$$

41. Use the substitution method to solve this system:
$$3x - y = 5$$
$$-6x + 2y = -10$$

42. Use the substitution method to solve this system:
$$x + 5y = 5$$
$$3x + 15y = 11$$

43. Use the elimination method to solve this system:
$$x - y = 3$$
$$x + y = 5$$

44. Use the elimination method to solve this system:
$$x + y = 3$$
$$-x + y = 7$$

45. Use the elimination method to solve this system:
$$x + y = 10$$
$$x - y = 2$$

46. Use the elimination method to solve this system:
$$x - 2y = -4$$
$$x + y = 2$$

47. Use the elimination method to solve this system:
$$3x - y = 7$$
$$x + y = 5$$

48. Use the elimination method to solve this system:
$$x + 2y = 8$$
$$x - y = -1$$

49. Use the elimination method to solve this system:
$$3x - 2y = 4$$
$$-6x + 3y = -15$$

50. Use the elimination method to solve this system:
$$4x - 5y = 12$$
$$6x + 10y = 18$$

51. Use the elimination method to solve this system:
$$5x - 8y = 10$$
$$3x + 4y = 6$$

52. Use the elimination method to solve this system:
$$2x - 2y = -1$$
$$3x + 3y = 2$$

53. Use the elimination method to solve this system:
$$-3x + 2y = 3$$
$$4x + 3y = -2$$

54. Use the elimination method to solve this system:
$$2x + 2y = -1$$
$$5x - 5y = 1$$

55. Use the elimination method to solve this system:
$$3x - 2y = 5$$
$$-9x + 6y = 12$$

56. Use the elimination method to solve this system:
$$2x - 7y = 0$$
$$6x - 21y = 0$$

Evaluate

Practice Test

Take this practice test to be sure that you are prepared for the final quiz in Evaluate.

1. The graph of the linear system below is shown in Figure 5.1.4. Find the solution of the system.
$$-x + \ y = -2$$
$$3x - 2y = \ \ \ 8$$

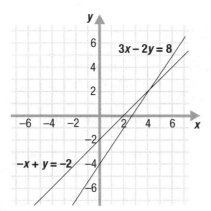

Figure 5.1.4

2. The graph of the linear system below is shown in Figure 5.1.5. Find the solution of the system.
$$y = 2x + 13$$
$$x + 2y = 6$$

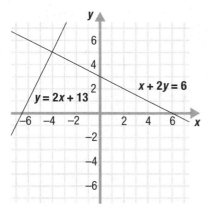

Figure 5.1.5

3. The graph of the linear system below is shown in Figure 5.1.6.
$$x + 2y = -12$$
$$-3x + \ y = \ \ \ 1$$

Circle the statements that are true.
   The system has a solution at the point $(-2, -5)$.
   The system has only one solution but it is not shown on the graph.
   The system has no solution.
   The system has an infinite number of solutions.

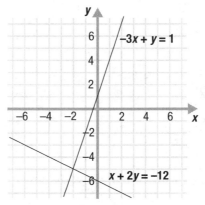

Figure 5.1.6

4. The graph of the linear system below is shown in Figure 5.1.7. Find the solution of the system.
$$2x - 5y = 10$$
$$4x + 5y = 20$$

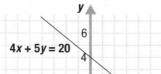
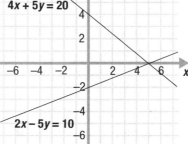

Figure 5.1.7

5. One of the equations in a linear system is $2x + 3y = 6$. Its graph is shown in Figure 5.1.8. If the solution of the system is $(-6, 6)$, which of the following could be the other equation in the system?

$$5x - y = 7$$
$$3x + 4y = 6$$
$$x + 3y = -11$$
$$2x - 4y = 1$$

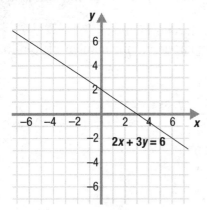

Figure 5.1.8

6. The graph of the linear system below is shown in Figure 5.1.9.

$$3x + 2y = 8$$
$$x - 4y = 12$$

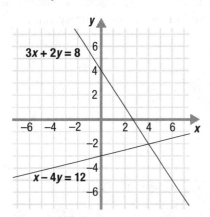

Figure 5.1.9

Which other line passes through the solution of the system?

$$4x - y = 12$$
$$-2x + y = -5$$
$$3x - 3y = 7$$
$$x + y = 2$$

7. Find the solution of this system:
$$x = -1$$
$$y = 4$$

8. The solution of the following linear system is $(-2, -3)$.
$$5x - 3y = -1$$
$$2x + 7y = -25$$

If the first equation is multiplied by 7 and the second equation is multiplied by 3, the result is this system:
$$35x - 21y = -7$$
$$6x + 21y = -75$$

Which of the following statements are true?
   The system has an infinite number of solutions.
   The system has no solution.
   The system has only one solution, the point $(-2, -3)$.
   The system has only one solution, the point $(-14, -9)$.

9. Use substitution to solve this linear system:
$$3x - 5y = 11$$
$$2x + y = 29$$

10. Use substitution to solve this linear system:
$$x - 3y = -3$$
$$2x + y = 22$$

11. Use the elimination method to solve this linear system:
$$2x + y = 4$$
$$5x - 2y = 1$$

12. Solve this linear system:
$$7x - 6y = 27$$
$$4x - 5y = 17$$

LESSON 5.2
PROBLEM SOLVING

 Overview

Many real-world situations can be modeled by systems of linear equations.

For example, suppose you want to replace the fluid in your car's radiator and need to make a mixture of antifreeze and water that has a specific concentration which will protect the radiator fluid from freezing.

In this lesson, you will learn to write and and solve a system of linear equations to solve this problem and others like it.

 Explain

Concept 1 has sections on

- **A General Procedure for Solving Word Problems Using Linear Systems**

- **Number Problems**

- **Interest Problems**

- **Mixture Problems**

- **Money Problems**

CONCEPT 1: USING LINEAR SYSTEMS

A General Procedure for Solving Word Problems Using Linear Systems

Many word problems have the same basic structure and so may be solved using the general procedure described below.

> **— Procedure —**
> **To Solve a Word Problem Using a Linear System**
>
> **Step 1** List the quantities to be found. Use English phrases.
> **Step 2** Represent these quantities algebraically.
> **Step 3** Write a linear system of equations that describes the problem.
> **Step 4** Solve the system.
> **Step 5** Check that the numbers satisfy the original problem.

Number Problems

Studying **number problems** will help you develop and practice the skills you will need to solve real-world applications.

Example 5.2.1

The sum of two numbers is 32. The difference between twice the larger number and three times the smaller number is 39. What are the numbers?

Solution

Step 1 List the quantities to be found. Use English phrases.

A larger number and a smaller number.

Step 2 Represent these quantities algebraically.

Let L represent the larger number. L = larger number

Let S represent the smaller number. S = smaller number

Step 3 Write a linear system of equations that describes the problem.

The problem states "The sum of two numbers is 32."

$$\left(\begin{array}{c}\text{larger}\\\text{number}\end{array}\right) + \left(\begin{array}{c}\text{smaller}\\\text{number}\end{array}\right) = 32$$

Substitute the variables from Step 2. $L + S = 32$

The problem states "The difference between twice the larger number and three times the smaller number is 39."

$$2 \cdot \left(\begin{array}{c}\text{larger}\\\text{number}\end{array}\right) - 3 \cdot \left(\begin{array}{c}\text{smaller}\\\text{number}\end{array}\right) = 39$$

Substitute the variables from Step 2. $2L - 3S = 39$

Step 4 Solve the system.

We'll use elimination to solve this system.

$$\begin{array}{rcr} L + S = & & 32 \\ 2L - 3S = & & 39 \end{array}$$

Multiply the first equation by -2.
Do not change the second equation.
Add the equations.

$$\begin{array}{rcr} -2L - 2S = & & -64 \\ \underline{2L - 3S = } & & \underline{39} \\ 0L - 5S = & & -25 \end{array}$$

Divide both sides by -5. $S = \mathbf{5}$

To find L, substitute 5 for S in the first equation, $L + S = 32$. $L + 5 = 32$

Subtract 5 from both sides. $L = \mathbf{27}$

The larger number, L, is **27**. The smaller number, S, is **5**.

Step 5 Check that the numbers satisfy the original problem.

Condition	Check
• "The sum of two numbers is 32."	• $27 + 5 = 32$. ✓
• "The difference between twice the larger number and three times the smaller number is 39."	• Twice 27 is 54. Three times 5 is 15. The difference between 54 and 15 is $54 - 15 = 39$. ✓

Interest Problems

If you borrow money to pay for college or to buy a house, eventually you will have to pay it back, plus interest. The **simple interest formula** is often used to calculate the interest on a loan.

— Formula —
Simple Interest Formula

The simple interest on a loan is

$$i = prt$$

where

i represents the **interest**, the amount paid to borrow the money.

p represents the **principal**, the amount borrowed.

r represents the annual interest **rate**, expressed as a decimal.

t represents the **time** (in years) the money was borrowed.

$r = \dfrac{interest\ paid\ on\ \$100\ for\ one\ year}{\$100}$

For example, suppose you borrow $1500 to pay for college. Let's say the bank charges you an annual rate of 8% and you pay back the money in 1 year.

The simple interest formula can be used to calculate the interest on the loan.

$$i = prt$$

Substitute $1500 for p, 0.08 per year for r, and 1 year for t.

$$= \$1500 \cdot \frac{0.08}{\cancel{year}} \cdot 1\ \cancel{year}$$

$$= \$120$$

$r = 8\% = \dfrac{8}{100} = 0.08$

This means you pay $8 interest for every $100 borrowed per year. This can be written as:

$$\frac{\frac{\$8}{\$100}}{1\ year} = \frac{0.08}{year}$$

Therefore, at the end of the year you owe the original $1500 plus $120 in interest for a grand total of $1620.

Example 5.2.2

Manuel owed a total of $4200 on his two credit cards for one year. He paid a total of $706 in interest. If the annual rate on one card was 14% and the annual rate on the other card was 18%, how much did he owe on each card?

Solution

Step 1 List the quantities to be found. Use English phrases.

The principal owed on the card that charges 14%.

The principal owed on the card that charges 18%.

Step 2 Represent these quantities algebraically.

Let x represent the principal owed on the card that charges 14%.

x = principal on 14% card

Let y represent the principal owed on the card that charges 18%.

y = principal on 18% card

Step 3 Write a linear system of equations that describes the problem.

Manuel owed a total of $4200.

$$\left(\begin{array}{c}\text{principle on}\\ \text{14\% card}\end{array}\right) + \left(\begin{array}{c}\text{principle on}\\ \text{18\% card}\end{array}\right) = 4200$$

Substitute the variables from Step 2.

This is the first equation. $x \quad + \quad y \quad = 4200$

Calculate the interest on x dollars at 14% for 1 year.

$$i = prt$$
$$= x \cdot (0.14) \cdot (1)$$
$$= 0.14x$$

Likewise, calculate the interest on y dollars at 18% for 1 year.

$$i = y \cdot (0.18) \cdot (1)$$
$$= 0.18y$$

Manuel paid a total of $706 in interest.

$$\left(\begin{array}{c}\text{interest on}\\ \text{14\% card}\end{array}\right) + \left(\begin{array}{c}\text{interest on}\\ \text{18\% card}\end{array}\right) = 706$$

Substitute the expressions for interest.

If you want to remove the decimals in $0.14x + 0.18y = 706$, multiply each side by 100.

This is the second equation. $0.14x \quad + \quad 0.18 \quad = 706$

Step 4 Solve the system.

We'll use substitution to solve this system. $x + y = 4200$

$0.14x + 0.18y = 706$

Solve the first equation for x by subtracting y from both sides. $x = 4200 - y$

In the second equation, substitute $4200 - y$ for x.	$0.14(\mathbf{4200 - y}) + 0.18y = 706$ ✓
Distribute 0.14 to remove the parentheses.	$\mathbf{588 - 0.14y} + 0.18y = 706$
Combine like terms.	$588 \mathbf{+ 0.04y} = 706$
Subtract 588 from both sides.	$0.04y = \mathbf{118}$
Divide both sides by 0.04.	$y = \mathbf{2950}$

To find x, substitute $\mathbf{2950}$ for y in the transformed first equation, $x = 4200 - y$.	$x = 4200 - \mathbf{2950}$
Subtract.	$x = \mathbf{1250}$

The amount owed on the 14% card, x, is **$1250**.

The amount owed on the 18% card, y, is **$2950**.

Step 5 Check that the numbers satisfy the original problem.

Condition	*Check*
• Manuel owed a total of $4200.	• He owed $2950 on one card and $1250 on the other. $2950 + 1250 = 4200$. ✓
• He paid a total of $706 in interest.	• He owed $1250 on the 14% card. The interest on that card is $0.14 \cdot 1250 = 175$. He owed $2950 on the 18% card. The interest on that card is $0.18 \cdot 2950 = 531$. The interest owed on both cards is $175 + 531 = 706$. ✓

Mixture Problems

Some **mixture problems** involve concentrations given in the form of a percent.

For example, suppose you have 300 ounces of 2% milk.

The 2% label means that the milk contains 2% butterfat.

Since 2% is a shorthand way of writing $\frac{2}{100}$,

2% butterfat means $\frac{2 \text{ ounces butterfat}}{100 \text{ ounces milk}}$.

The amount of butterfat in 300 ounces of 2% milk can be calculated by multiplying the concentration, 2%, by the amount of milk, 300 ounces.

$$\text{amount of butterfat} = \frac{2 \text{ ounces butterfat}}{100 \text{ ounces milk}} \cdot 300 \text{ ounces milk}$$

$$= 6 \text{ ounces butterfat}$$

Therefore, there are 6 ounces of butterfat in 300 ounces of 2% milk.

If you have x quarts of a solution that is 25% antifreeze, then the amount of antifreeze in the solution may be calculated by multiplying the concentration, 25%, by the amount of solution, x quarts.

$$\text{amount of antifreeze} = \frac{25 \text{ quarts antifreeze}}{100 \text{ quarts solution}} \cdot x \text{ quarts solution}$$

$$= 0.25x \text{ quarts antifreeze}$$

Example 5.2.3

Wei has a solution that is 25% antifreeze and a solution that is 65% antifreeze. How much of each should he use to obtain 12 liters of solution that is 50% antifreeze?

Solution

Step 1 List the quantities to be found. Use English phrases.

The amount (in liters) of the 25% solution.

The amount (in liters) of the 65% solution.

Step 2 Represent these quantities algebraically.

Let x represent the amount of the 25% solution.　　　x = amount of 25% solution

Let y represent the amount of the 65% solution.　　　y = amount of 65% solution

Step 3 Write a linear system of equations that describes the problem.

The total amount of solution needed is 12 liters.　　　$\left(\begin{matrix} \text{amount of} \\ \text{25\% solution} \end{matrix} \right) + \left(\begin{matrix} \text{amount of} \\ \text{65\% solution} \end{matrix} \right) = 12$

Substitute the variables from Step 2.

This is the first equation.　　　$x \quad + \quad y \quad = 12$

Express the amount of antifreeze in x liters of a 25% solution. $0.25x$ liters

Express the amount of antifreeze in y liters of a 65% solution. $0.65y$ liters

Calculate the amount of antifreeze in 12 liters of a 50% solution. $0.50 \cdot 12 = 6$ liters

---

The sum of the amounts of antifreeze in the original solutions must equal the amount of antifreeze in the new solution.

$$\begin{pmatrix} \text{amount of} \\ \text{antifreeze in} \\ \text{25\% solution} \end{pmatrix} + \begin{pmatrix} \text{amount of} \\ \text{antifreeze in} \\ \text{65\% solution} \end{pmatrix} = \begin{pmatrix} \text{amount of} \\ \text{antifreeze} \\ \text{in 50\%} \\ \text{solution} \end{pmatrix}$$

Substitute the expressions from above.

This is the second equation. $\mathbf{0.25x} \quad + \quad \mathbf{0.65y} \quad = 6$

Step 4 Solve the system.

We'll use substitution to solve this system.

$$x + y = 12$$
$$0.25x + 0.65y = 6$$

Solve the first equation for x by subtracting y from both sides. $x = 12 - y$

In the second equation, substitute $12 - y$ for x. $0.25(\mathbf{12 - y}) + 0.65y = 6$

Distribute 0.25 to remove the parentheses. $\mathbf{3 - 0.25y} + 0.65y = 6$

Solve for y. (We leave the details for you.) $y = \mathbf{7.5}$

To find x, substitute 7.5 for y in the transformed first equation, $x = 12 - y$. $x = 12 - \mathbf{7.5}$

Subtract. $x = \mathbf{4.5}$

The amount of 25% solution, x, is **4.5** liters.

The amount of 65% solution, y, is **7.5** liters.

Step 5 Check that the numbers satisfy the original problem.

Condition	*Check*
• The total amount of solution is 12 liters.	• There are 7.5 liters of the 65% solution. There are 4.5 liters of the 25% solution. 7.5 liters + 4.5 liters = 12 liters. ✓

- The 12 liters of solution contains 50% antifreeze.

- 12 liters of a 50% solution should contain $0.50 \cdot 12 = 6$ liters of antifreeze.

  7.5 liters of a 65% solution contains $0.65 \cdot 7.5 = 4.875$ liters of antifreeze.

  4.5 liters of a 25% solution contains $0.25 \cdot 4.5 = 1.125$ liters of antifreeze.

  4.875 liters $+$ 1.125 liters $= 6$ liters. ✓

In some mixture problems, we must calculate the costs of various items.

For example, suppose you wish to purchase 12 gallons of diesel fuel that sells for $1.25 per gallon. To calculate the cost of the fuel multiply the price per gallon by the number of gallons you wish to buy.

$$\text{cost} = \left(\begin{array}{c}\text{price per} \\ \text{gallons}\end{array}\right) \cdot \left(\begin{array}{c}\text{number} \\ \text{of gallons}\end{array}\right)$$

Therefore, the cost of 12 gallons of fuel is $15.00

$$= \frac{\$1.25}{\cancel{\text{gallon}}} \cdot 12 \; \cancel{\text{gallons}}$$

$$= \$15.00$$

Likewise, if you have c pounds of Colombian coffee that sells for $9.00 per pound, the cost of the coffee may be calculated by multiplying the price per pound by the number of pounds.

$$\text{cost} = \left(\begin{array}{c}\text{price per} \\ \text{pound}\end{array}\right) \cdot \left(\begin{array}{c}\text{number} \\ \text{of pounds}\end{array}\right)$$

Therefore, the cost of c pounds of Colombian coffee is $9c$ dollars.

$$= \frac{\$9.00}{\cancel{\text{pound}}} \cdot c \; \cancel{\text{pounds}}$$

$$= \$9.00c$$

$$= 9c \text{ dollars}$$

Example 5.2.4

The owner of a coffee shop has 16 pounds of Brazilian coffee that sells for $7.75 per pound. How many pounds of Colombian coffee, which sells for $9.00 per pound, should she add to obtain a blend that will sell for $8.50 per pound?

Solution

Step 1 List the quantities to be found. Use English phrases.

The number of pounds of Colombian coffee.

Step 2 Represent these quantities algebraically.

Let c represent the number of pounds of Colombian coffee.

c = pounds of Colombian coffee

Even though the problem only asks for one quantity, there is another unknown that we have to take into account. That is the total number of pounds of the coffee mix.

Therefore, let t represent the total pounds of the coffee mix.

t = total pounds of coffee mix

Step 3 Write a linear system of equations that describes the problem.

Add the two amounts of coffee to get the total amount of coffee in the mix.

$$\begin{pmatrix} \text{amount of} \\ \text{Brazilian} \\ \text{coffee} \end{pmatrix} + \begin{pmatrix} \text{amount of} \\ \text{Colombian} \\ \text{coffee} \end{pmatrix} = \begin{pmatrix} \text{total amount} \\ \text{of coffee} \end{pmatrix}$$

Substitute the variables from Step 2.

This is the first equation. $\mathbf{16 \quad + \quad c \quad = t}$

Calculate the cost in dollars, of the Brazilian coffee.

$$\frac{\$7.75}{\text{pound}} \cdot 16 \; \text{pounds} = \$124.00$$

Express the cost in dollars, of the Colombian coffee.

$$\frac{\$9.00}{\text{pound}} \cdot c \; \text{pounds} = \$9.00c = 9c \; \text{dollars}$$

Express the cost in dollars, of the coffee mix.

$$\frac{\$8.50}{1 \; \text{pound}} \cdot \frac{t \; \text{pounds}}{1} = \$8.50t = 8.5t \; \text{dollars}$$

Since she adds the two types of coffee to form a mix, the cost of the mix must equal the sum of the costs of the Brazilian and Colombian coffees.

$$\begin{pmatrix} \text{cost of} \\ \text{Brazilian} \\ \text{coffee} \end{pmatrix} + \begin{pmatrix} \text{cost of} \\ \text{Colombian} \\ \text{coffee} \end{pmatrix} = \begin{pmatrix} \text{cost of} \\ \text{mix} \end{pmatrix}$$

Substitute the values for each term.

This is the second equation. $\mathbf{124 \quad + \quad 9c \quad = 8.5t}$

Step 4 Solve the system.

We'll use substitution to solve the system.

$$16 + c = t$$
$$124 + 9c = 8.5t$$

The first equation is already solved for t.

Substitute $16 + c$ for t in the second equation. $124 + 9c = 8.5(\mathbf{16 + c})$

Solve for c. (We leave the details for you.) $c = \mathbf{24}$

The amount of Colombian coffee needed, c, is **24** pounds.

Step 5 Check that the numbers satisfy the original problem.

We leave the check to you.

Money Problems

Money problems are similar to mixture problems except that they involve mixing different denominations of coins or bills.

Example 5.2.5

Mohammed decides to hold a garage sale. In his change box he has a total of 56 nickels and dimes worth \$4.40. How many of each type of coin does he have?

Solution

Step 1 List the quantities to be found. Use English phrases.

The number of nickels.

The number of dimes.

Step 2 Represent these quantities algebraically.

Let n represent the number of nickels. n = number of nickels

Let d represent the number of dimes. d = number of dimes

Step 3 Write a linear system of equations that describes the problem.

Add the two quantities of coins to get the total number of coins in the box.

$$\binom{\text{number}}{\text{of nickels}} + \binom{\text{number}}{\text{of dimes}} = \binom{\text{number}}{\text{of coins}}$$

Substitute the variables from Step 2.

This is the first equation. $n \quad + \quad d \quad = 56$

Express the dollar value of the nickels. $\dfrac{\$0.05}{\text{nickel}} \cdot n \text{ nickels} = \$0.05n$

Express the dollar value of the dimes. $\dfrac{\$0.10}{\text{dime}} \cdot d \text{ dimes} = \$0.10d$

Add the dollar value of the nickels and the dollar value of the dimes to get the total value of the coins.

$$\binom{\boldsymbol{value}\text{ of}}{\text{nickels}} + \binom{\boldsymbol{value}\text{ of}}{\text{dimes}} = \binom{\boldsymbol{value}}{\text{of coins}}$$

$$\mathbf{0.05n \quad + \quad 0.10d \quad = 4.40}$$

Step 4 Solve the system.

We'll use elimination to solve this system.

$$n + d = 56$$
$$0.05n + 0.10d = 4.40$$

Multiply the first equation by -0.05.	$-0.05n + -0.05d = -2.80$
Do not change the second equation.	$\underline{0.05n + 0.10d = 4.40}$
Add the equations.	$0.00n + 0.05d = 1.60$
Simplify.	$0.05d = 1.6$
Divide both sides by 0.05.	$d = 32$

Substitute 32 for d in the first equation, $n + d = 56$.	$n + \mathbf{32} = 56$
Subtract **32** from both sides.	$n = 24$

There are 24 nickels and 32 dimes.

Step 5 Check that the numbers satisfy the original problem.

We leave the check to you.

Here is a summary of this concept from *Academic Systems Algebra*.

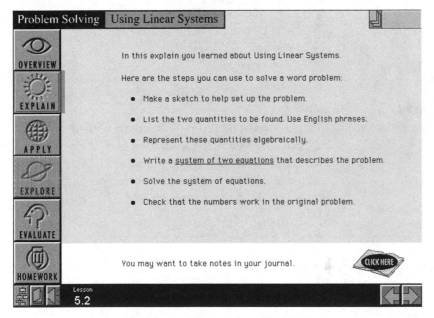

Checklist Lesson 5.2

Here is what you should know after completing this lesson.

Words and Phrases

number problems
simple interest formula
interest
principal

rate
mixture problems
money problems

Ideas and Procedures

❶ Number Problems

Solve word problems that involve relationships between numbers.

Example 5.2.1
    The sum of two numbers is 32. The difference between twice the larger number and three times the smaller number is 39. What are the numbers?

See also: Apply 1-4

❷ Simple Interest Formula

State the simple interest formula.

$i = prt$
    where i = interest
        p = principal
        r = rate
        t = time

❸ Interest Problems

Use the simple interest formula to solve word problems that involve investing or borrowing money.

Example 5.2.2
    Manuel owed a total of $4200 on his two credit cards for one year. He paid a total of $706 in interest. If the annual rate on one card was 14% and the annual rate on the other card was 18%, how much did he owe on each card?

See also: Apply 5-10

❹ Mixture Problems

Solve word problems that involve solutions of different concentrations of ingredients with different prices.

Example 5.2.3
    Wei has a solution that is 25% antifreeze and a solution that is 65% antifreeze. How much of each should he use to obtain 12 liters of a solution that is 50% antifreeze?

See also: Example 5.2.4
        Apply 17-28

❺ Money Problems

Solve word problems that involve different denominations of coins or bills.

Example 5.2.5
    Mohammed decides to hold a garage sale. In his change box he has a total of 56 nickels and dimes worth $4.40. How many of each type of coin does he have?

See also: Apply 11-16

Homework

Homework Problems

Circle the homework problems assigned to you by the computer, then complete them below.

 Explain

Word Problems

1. The difference between two numbers is 9. The sum of twice the larger number and three times the smaller number is 33. Find the two numbers.

2. Last year Wanda divided $12,400 between a savings account and a mutual fund. The savings account paid 4% in interest and the mutual fund paid 8% in interest. If she earned a total of $896 in interest, how was her money split between the two accounts?

3. Jae-Hun is the manager of a movie theater. For one show he sold 540 tickets and collected a total of $2935. If he sold adult tickets for $6.50 and student tickets for $4.00, how many of each did he sell?

4. Midori emptied out a token machine in the arcade in which she works and collected $278 in one dollar and five dollar bills. If she had a total of 114 bills, how many five dollar bills did she collect?

5. Josef wants to earn $63.75 in interest this year. He has $1400 to split between his checking account, which pays $2\frac{1}{2}$% interest, and his savings account, which pays 5% interest. How should Josef divide his money?

6. The sum of two numbers is 15. The sum of the larger number and twice the smaller number is -1. What are the two numbers?

7. Vladimir collected $16.35 in dimes and quarters from a vending machine. If he had a total of 87 coins, how many quarters did he get?

8. Cara is making punch for a party. She wants to combine a 20% real fruit juice drink with a 100% real fruit juice drink to get 16 cups of a mixture that is 80% real fruit juice. How much of each type of drink should she use?

9. The difference between two numbers is 7. The sum of half the larger number and twice the smaller number is 51. What are the two numbers?

10. Harry owed $5568 on his two credit cards last year on which he paid a total of $1015.68 in interest. If the rate charged by one card was 21% and the rate charged by the other card was 15%, how much did he owe on each card?

11. Marina mixed almonds and walnuts to take on her camping trip. Almonds cost $3.00 per pound and walnuts cost $4.20 per pound. If she ended up with three pounds of a mixture that cost $3.36 per pound, how many pounds of each kind of nut did she use?

12. Abebe has $6.65 in nickels and dimes. If he has a total of 99 coins, how many of each does he have?

Apply

Practice Problems

Here are some additional practice problems for you to try.

Word Problems

1. The sum of two numbers is 367. The difference between the two numbers is 29. What are the numbers?

2. The sum of two numbers is 245. The difference between the two numbers is 19. What are the numbers?

3. The sum of two numbers is 135. One-fourth the larger number is equal to two times the smaller number. What are the numbers?

4. The difference between two numbers is 23. One-third the larger number plus three times the smaller number is 81. What are the numbers?

5. Sophia has a total of $2475 in two different savings accounts. Last year, one savings account paid 3% interest and the other account paid 6.5% interest. If she earned $116.25 in interest for the year, how was her money divided between the two accounts?

6. Samuel has a total of $1639 in two different savings accounts. Last year, one savings account paid 2% interest and the other account paid 5.5% interest. If he earned $59.59 in interest for the year, how was his money divided between the two accounts?

7. Roderick has invested a total of $3500 in two mutual funds. Last year, one of the mutual funds earned a 12% dividend and the other fund earned a 9.5% dividend. If he earned $377.20 in dividends for the year, how was his money divided between the two funds?

8. The Heaths are paying off two car loans. One loan charges 5% interest per year. The other loan charges 8% interest per year. They owe $2400 more on the 5% loan than they do on the other. Last year they paid a total of $710.20 interest. How much do they owe on each loan?

9. Hollis is paying off two student loans. One loan charges 7% interest per year. The other loan charges 9% interest per year. He owes $1500 more on the 7% loan than he does on the other. Last year he paid a total of $617 interest. How much does he owe on each loan?

10. Stacey is paying off two student loans. One loan charges 6% interest per year. The other loan charges 10% interest per year. She owes $2000 more on the 6% loan than she does on the other. Last year she paid a total of $815 interest. How much does she owe on each loan?

11. Sally has a total of 40 quarters and dimes worth $6.55. How many of each does she have?

12. Phylicia has a total of 60 five dollar bills and twenty dollar bills worth $525. How many of each does she have?

13. Saul has a total of 65 dimes and nickels worth $4.15. How many of each does he have?

14. Reese has $225 in ten dollar bills and five dollar bills. The number of five dollar bills is 15 more than the number of ten dollar bills. How many of each does he have?

15. Lena has $31.05 in dimes and quarters. The number of dimes is one-fifth the number of quarters. How many of each does she have?

16. Zack has $20.25 in nickels and quarters. The number of nickels is 33 less than the number of quarters. How many of each does he have?

17. Zoe has a solution that is 75% sulfuric acid and a solution that is 25% sulfuric acid. How much of each should she use to to obtain 400 ml of a solution that is 45% sulfuric acid?

18. Coltin has a solution that is 55% isopropyl alcohol and a solution that is 20% isopropyl alcohol. How much of each should he use to obtain 250 ml of a solution that is 41% isopropyl alcohol?

19. Dory has a solution that is 65% boric acid and a solution that is 15% boric acid. How much of each should she use to obtain 300 ml of a solution that is 35% boric acid?

20. Phil has 30 ounces of a 60% sulfuric acid solution. How many ounces of 15% sulfuric acid solution should he add to obtain a solution that is 40% sulfuric acid?

21. Kayla has 25 ounces of a 75% boric acid solution. How many ounces of 35% boric acid solution should she add to obtain a solution that is 60% boric acid?

22. Dion has 20 ounces of a 70% salt solution. How many ounces of 45% salt solution should he add to obtain a solution that is 55% salt?

23. Tasha wants 25 pounds of a nut mix that she can sell for $5.00 per pound. If she has cashews that sell for $6.50 per pound and pistachio nuts that sell for $4.00 per pound, how much of each should she use?

24. Aaron wants 30 pounds of a coffee blend that he can sell for $7.00 per pound. If he has coffee that sells for $6.00 per pound and coffee that sells for $7.50 per pound, how much of each should he use?

25. Tanya wants to make 20 pounds of a snack mix that she can sell for $2.44 per pound. If she has chocolate covered raisins that sell for $2.80 per pound and peanuts that sell for $2.00 per pound, how much of each should she use?

26. Casey has 15 pounds of cashews that sell for $5.25 per pound. If peanuts sell for $2.50 per pound, how many pounds of peanuts should he add to the cashews to obtain a mixture that will sell for $3.75 per pound?

27. Lena has 16 pounds of coffee that sells for $6.50 per pound. If she has a second coffee that sells for $8.00 per pound, how many pounds of the second coffee should be added to the first coffee to obtain a blend that will sell for $7.00 per pound?

28. Horatio has 12 pounds of carob coated peanuts that sell for $3.60 per pound. If sunflower seeds sell for $1.80 per pound, how many pounds of sunflower seeds should he add to the carob coated peanuts to obtain a snack mix that will sell for $2.80 per pound?

Evaluate

Practice Test

Take this practice test to be sure that you are prepared for the final quiz in Evaluate.

1. The sum of two numbers is 25. When twice the larger number is subtracted from four times the smaller number, the result is 4. What are the two numbers?

2. Sunil has 19 five dollar and ten dollar bills worth a total of $150. How many of each does she have?

3. Last year a small college accepted 363 students out of the 1340 people that applied. If the college accepted 30% of the female applicants and 25% of the male applicants, how many women applied?

4. The local coffee shop combines two kinds of beans to make a blended mixture of beans. If Ethiopian Harrar beans cost $7.25 per pound, and Arabian Mocha beans cost $13.70 per pound, how many pounds of each should be used to make 3 pounds of a blend that costs $10.26 per pound?

5. In 7 years Deac will be twice as old as Irina. Four years ago he was three times as old as Irina was then. How old are each of them now?

6. Admission to a skating rink is $4.25 for children and $7.50 for adults. If one evening the skating rink collected $930 and 150 people were admitted, how many children went skating?

7. Nobutaka needs 200 ml of 6% HCl. If he has solutions of 5% HCl and 9% HCl, how many milliliters of each should he mix together?

8. Alexis had $2375 to invest last year. She put some of her money in a savings account that paid 4% interest and the rest of her money in a mutual fund that paid 11% interest. If she earned $168.50 in interest, how did she divide her money between the two accounts?

LESSON 5.3
SYSTEMS OF INEQUALITIES

 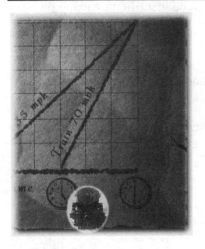

Overview

A system of linear inequalities is useful for solving a problem that involves more than one condition or constraint.

For example, suppose Keisha wants to spend at least twice as much time studying as she spends working at her job. However, she doesn't want to spend more than a total of 30 hours per week studying and working.

In this lesson, you will learn how to solve systems of linear inequalities, including the system that represents Keisha's situation.

Explain

Concept 1 has a section on

- **Solving a System of Linear Inequalities**

CONCEPT 1:
SOLVING LINEAR SYSTEMS

Solving a System of Linear Inequalities

The **solution of a system of linear inequalities in two variables** is the set of ordered pairs that satisfy all the inequalities of the system. The solution can be found by graphing each inequality and noting where the graphs overlap.

— Procedure —
To Solve a System of Two Linear Inequalities in Two Variables

Step 1 Solve the first inequality for y. Then graph the inequality.

Step 2 Solve the second inequality for y. Then graph the inequality.

Step 3 Shade the region where the two graphs overlap.

The solution is the set of all ordered pairs in the shaded region.

To graph each inequality, first write its corresponding equation in slope-intercept form, $y = mx + b$.

When graphing each inequality, use either a solid line or a dotted line, as follows:

- If the original inequality symbol is $\leq$ or $\geq$, use a **solid line** to show that points on the line are solutions of the inequality.

- If the original inequality symbol is $<$ or $>$, use a **dotted line** to show that points on the line are not solutions of the inequality.

The region that satisfies each inequality can be identified by using the following guidelines:

Inequality	Solution
$y > mx + b$	Draw a **dotted** line and shade the region **above** the line.
$y \geq mx + b$	Draw a **solid** line and shade the region **above** the line.
$y < mx + b$	Draw a **dotted** line and shade the region **below** the line.
$y \leq mx + b$	Draw a **solid** line and shade the region **below** the line.

Before you use these guidelines, be sure that each inequality has been solved for y. That is, be sure that y is by itself on the left side of each inequality.

Example 5.3.1

Graph the system of inequalities.

$$y \leq -\frac{3}{2}x + 6$$

$$y + 2 > x$$

Solution

Step 1 Solve the first inequality for y. Then graph the inequality.

To graph the inequality $y \leq -\dfrac{3}{2}x + 6$,

first graph the equation $y = -\dfrac{3}{2}x + 6$.

- The y-intercept is $(0, 6)$. Plot $(0, 6)$.

- The slope is $-\dfrac{3}{2}$. To find a second point on the line, start at $(0, 6)$ and move down 3 and right 2 to the point $(2, 3)$. Plot $(2, 3)$.

For the inequality $y \leq -\dfrac{3}{2}x + 6$, the inequality symbol is "$\leq$". This stands for "is ***less than*** or ***equal to***."

- To represent "***equal to***," draw a ***solid*** line through $(0, 6)$ and $(2, 3)$.
- To represent "***less than***," shade the region ***below*** the line.

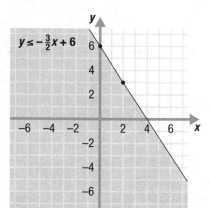

If you use the slope to plot several more points, it will be easier to draw the line.

Step 2 *Solve the second inequality for y. Then graph the inequality.*

To solve for y, subtract 2 from both sides of $y + 2 > x$.

The result is $y > x - 2$.

To graph $y > x - 2$, first graph the equation $y = x - 2$.

- The y-intercept is $(0, -2)$. Plot $(0, -2)$.

- The slope is $1 = \dfrac{1}{1}$. To find a second point on the line, start at $(0, -2)$ and move up 1 and right 1 to the point $(1, -1)$. Plot $(1, -1)$.

For the inequality $y > x - 2$, the inequality symbol is ">". This stands for "is ***greater than***."

- Since the inequality symbol ">" does ***not*** contain "equal to," draw a ***dotted*** line through $(0, -2)$ and $(1, -1)$.

- To represent "***greater than***," shade the region ***above*** the line.

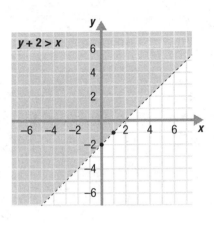

Step 3 *Shade the region where the two graphs overlap.*

The solution is the region where the graphs overlap. This region contains the points that satisfy both inequalities.

As a check, choose a point in the solution region. For example, choose $(0, 0)$.

To confirm that $(0, 0)$ is a solution of the system, substitute **0** for x and **0** for y in each original inequalities and simplify.

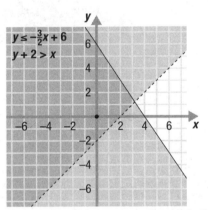

First inequality	***Second inequality***
$y \le -\dfrac{3}{2}x + 6$	$y + 2 > x$
Is $0 \le -\dfrac{3}{2}(0) + 6$?	Is $0 + 2 > 0$?
Is $0 \le 6$? **Yes**	Is $2 > 0$? **Yes**

The solution of the system is the set of all points in the dark shaded region, including the points on the line $y = -\dfrac{3}{2}x + 6$.

Since $(0, 0)$ satisfies each inequality, it is a solution of the system.

Example 5.3.2

Graph the system of inequalities.

$$x \le 0$$
$$x - 2y > 2$$

Solution

Step 1 *Solve the first inequality for y. Then graph the inequality.*

The first inequality does not contain the variable y.

To graph the first inequality, $x \le 0$, first graph the corresponding equation, $x = 0$.

- This is a vertical line that passes through the x-axis at the point $(0, 0)$; it is the y-axis.

For the inequality $x \le 0$, the inequality symbol is "$\le$". This stands for "is ***less than*** or ***equal to***."

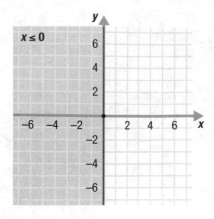

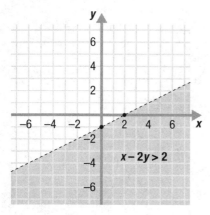

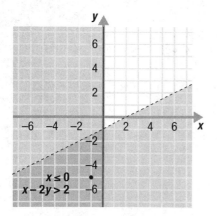

The solution of the system is the dark shaded region.

- To represent "*equal to*," draw a *solid* line along the y-axis.
- To represent "*less than*," shade the region to the *left* of the line. Each point in that region has an x-coordinate less than 0.

Step 2 Solve the second inequality for y. Then graph the inequality.

To solve $x - 2y > 2$ for y, do the following:

Subtract x from both sides. $\qquad\qquad -2y > -x + 2$

Divide both sides by -2. Be sure to reverse the inequality symbol because you are dividing by a negative number. $\dfrac{-2y}{-2} < \dfrac{-1x}{-2} + \dfrac{2}{-2}$

Simplify. $\qquad\qquad\qquad\qquad\qquad y < \dfrac{1}{2}x - 1$

To graph $y < \dfrac{1}{2}x - 1$, first graph the equation $y = \dfrac{1}{2}x - 1$.

- The y-intercept is $(0, -1)$. Plot $(0, -1)$.
- The slope is $\dfrac{1}{2}$. To find a second point on the line, start at $(0, -1)$ and move up 1 and right 2 to the point $(2, 0)$. Plot $(2, 0)$.
- Since the inequality symbol "$<$" does *not* contain "equal to," draw a *dotted* line through $(0, -1)$ and $(2, 0)$.
- To represent "*less than*," shade the region *below* the line.

Step 3 Shade the region where the two graphs overlap.

The solution is the region where the graphs overlap.

As a check, choose a point in the solution region. For example, choose $(-1, -5)$.

To confirm that $(-1, -5)$ is a solution of the system, substitute -1 for x and -5 for y in each of the original inequalities and simplify.

First inequality	*Second inequality*
$x \leq 0$	$x - 2y > 2$
Is $-1 \leq 0$? **Yes**	Is $-1 - 2(-5) > 2$?
	Is $\quad -1 + 10 > 2$?
	Is $\qquad\quad 9 > 2$? **Yes**

Since $(-1, -5)$ satisfies each inequality, it is a solution of the system.

Example 5.3.3

Graph the system of inequalities. $2x + y \leq -4$
$$6x + 3y > 0$$

Solution

Step 1 Solve the first inequality for y. Then graph the inequality.

To solve $2x + y \leq -4$ for y, subtract $2x$ from both sides.
The result is $y \leq -2x - 4$.

To graph $y \leq -2x - 4$, first graph the equation $y = -2x - 4$.

- Plot the y-intercept $(0, -4)$. Then use the slope, $-2 = -\dfrac{2}{1}$ to plot a second point at $(1, -6)$.

For the inequality $y \leq -2x - 4$, the inequality symbol is "$\leq$". This stands for "is *less than* or *equal to*."

- To represent "*equal to*," draw a *solid* line through $(0, -4)$ and $(1, -6)$.

- To represent "*less than*," shade the region *below* the line.

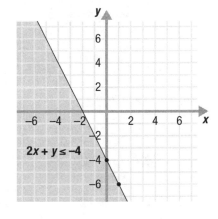

Step 2 Solve the second inequality for y. Then graph the inequality.

To solve $6x + 3y > 0$ for y, do the following:

Subtract $6x$ from both sides. $3y > -6x + 0$

Divide both sides by 3. $y > -2x + 0$

To graph $y > -2x + 0$, first graph the equation $y = -2x + 0$.

- Plot the y-intercept $(0, 0)$. Then use the slope, $-2 = \dfrac{-2}{1}$, to plot a second point at $(1, -2)$.

For the inequality $y > -2x$, the inequality symbol is "$>$". This stands for "*is greater than*."

- Since the inequality symbol "$>$" does *not* contain "equal to," draw a *dotted* line through $(0, 0)$ and $(1, -2)$.

- To represent "*greater than*," shade the region *above* the line.

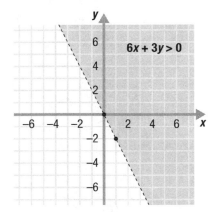

Step 3 Shade the region where the two graphs overlap.

The shaded regions do not overlap.

So the system of inequalities has no solution.

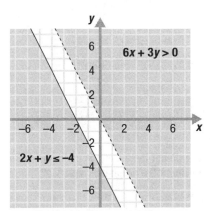

The system has no solution.

Example 5.3.4

Graph the system of inequalities. $y \le x + 5$
                                      $y < x - 3$

Solution

Step 1 Solve the first inequality for y. Then graph.

The graph of $y \le x + 5$ is shown.

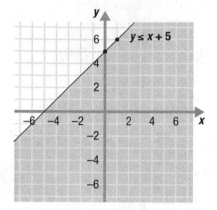

Step 2 Solve the second inequality for y. Then graph.

The graph of $y < x - 3$ is shown.

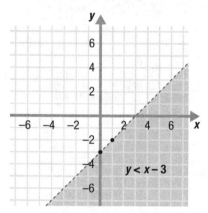

Step 3 Shade the region where the two graphs overlap.

The solution is the region below the line $y = x - 3$ since it is where the graphs overlap.

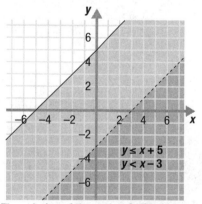

The solution of the system is the dark region where the graph overlaps.

Example 5.3.5

Keisha wants to spend at least twice as much time studying as she spends working at her job. However, she doesn't want to spend more than a total of 30 hours per week studying and working. Write a system of two linear inequalities that represents Keisha's options. Then, graph the system. Finally, give several possible solutions to Keisha's problem.

Solution

Step 1 List the quantities to be found. Use English phrases.

The number of hours Keisha spends studying.

The number of hours Keisha spends working.

Step 2 Represent these quantities algebraically.

Let x represent the number of hours $x =$ hours studying
Keisha spends studying.

Let y represent the number of hours $y =$ hours working
Keisha spends working.

Step 3 Write a system of inequalities that describes the problem.

She wants to spend at least twice as much time studying as working. $\left(\dfrac{\text{hours}}{\text{studying}}\right) \geq 2 \cdot \left(\dfrac{\text{hours}}{\text{working}}\right)$ *We used the symbol "$\geq$" to represent the words "at least."*

Substitute the variables from Step 2. $\mathbf{x \geq 2y}$

She doesn't want to spend more than a total of 30 hours per week studying and working. $\left(\dfrac{\text{hours}}{\text{studying}}\right) + \left(\dfrac{\text{hours}}{\text{working}}\right) \leq 30$ *We used the symbol "$\leq$" to represent the words "not more than."*

Substitute variables from Step 2. $\mathbf{x \;\; + \;\; y \;\; \leq 30}$

There are two more constraints that are not explicitly mentioned in the statement of the problem.

Keisha may not study a negative number of hours. $\mathbf{x \geq 0}$

Keisha may not work a negative number of hours. $\mathbf{y \geq 0}$

Step 4 Solve the system.

The system has four inequalities:

$x \geq 2y$ Solve for y. The result is $\dfrac{x}{2} \geq y$ or $y \leq \dfrac{1}{2}x$.

The solution is the region that contains the points on and below the line $y = \dfrac{1}{2}x$.

$x + y \leq 30$ Solve for y. The result is $y \leq -x + 30$.

The solution is the region that contains the points on and below the line $y = -x + 30$.

$x \geq 0$ This represents the region on and to the right of the vertical line through $(0, 0)$.

$y \geq 0$ This represents the region on and above the horizontal line through $(0, 0)$.

The solution of the system is the region where all four regions overlap.

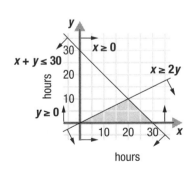

Step 5 Check that the numbers satisfy the original problem.

Any point in the shaded region is a solution of Keisha's problem. Let's check two points inside the shaded regions:

- (20, 10) She studies 20 hours and works 10 hours.

  This checks since $20 \geq 2 \cdot 10$, and $20 + 10 \leq 30$. ✓

- (15, 5) She studies 15 hours and works 5 hours. In this case, she has some time left over for doing other things.

  This checks since $15 \geq 2 \cdot 5$, and $15 + 5 \leq 30$. ✓

Now let's look at two points outside of the shaded region. These points are not solutions of Keisha's problem.

- (25, 10) She studies 25 hours and works 10 hours.

  This does not check. The first constraint, that she studies for twice as many hours as she works, is met. That is, $25 \geq 2 \cdot 10$ is true.

  However, the second constraint, that she spend no more than 30 hours studying and working is not true. That is, $25 + 10 \leq 30$ is false. This is consistent with the graph since (25, 10) lies outside the shaded region.

- (15, −5) She studies 15 hours and works −5 hours.

  This checks with the two constraints given in the problem: $15 \geq 2 \cdot (-5)$ and $15 + (-5) \leq 30$.

However, it is not possible to work −5 hours. Therefore, (15, −5) is not a solution. (That is why we included the constraint $y \geq 0$.)
Note that (15, −5) lies outside the shaded region.

Here is a summary of this concept from *Academic Systems Algebra*.

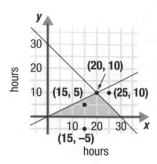

$x = hours\ studying$
$y = hours\ working$
$x \geq 2y$
$x + y \leq 30$
$x \geq 0$
$y \geq 0$

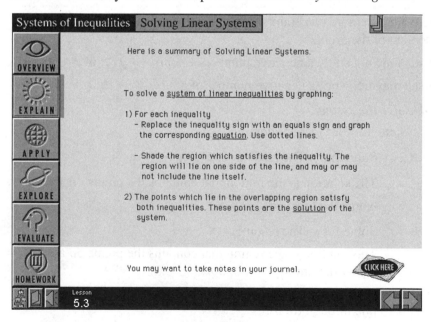

 **Explore**

On the computer you used the Grapher to solve and analyze systems of linear inequalities. Here is an additional exploration.

Example **5.3.6**

Given the following system of linear inequalities:

$x > -5$
$x \leq 3$
$y < 4$
$y \geq -2$

a. Graph the system.

b. Find the coordinates of three points that satisfy all four inequalities.

c. Find the points of intersection of each pair of corresponding lines.

d. Find the area of the region whose points are the solution of the system.

Solution

a. Graph each inequality and shade the region where the graphs overlap.

b. Each point in the shaded region is a solution of the system.
   For example, $(0, 0)$, $(-2, 1)$, and $(-4, 1)$ each satisfy the system.

c. The points of intersection are the corners of a rectangle.
   The points are $(3, 4)$, $(-5, 4)$, $(-5, -2)$, and $(3, -2)$.
   (Note: Only one corner $(3, -2)$, is also a solution of the system.)

d. To find the area of a rectangle, multiply its length by its width.
   The length of the rectangle is 8 units; the width is 6 units.
   The area is length · width = 8 units · 6 units = 48 square units.

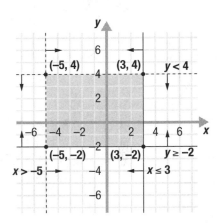

Here is a summary of this explore from *Academic Systems Algebra.*

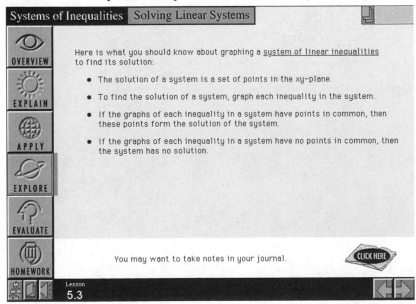

Checklist Lesson 5.3

Here is what you should know after completing this lesson.

Words and Phrases

solution of a system of linear inequalities in two variables

Ideas and Procedures

❶ **Solving a System of Linear Inequalities**
Graph a system of linear inequalities to find its solution.

Example 5.3.2
    Graph the system of inequalities: $x \leq 0$
                                        $x - 2y > 2$

See also: Examples 5.3.1, 5.3.3, 5.3.4, 5.3.5
            Apply 1-28

Homework Problems

Circle the homework problems assigned to you by the computer, then complete them below.

 Explain

Solving Linear Systems

1. Graph the system of inequalities below. Use the grid in Figure 5.3.1. Then write the coordinates of the plotted points that are solutions of this system.

   $x + 2y < 3$
   $2x - 3y \geq 12$

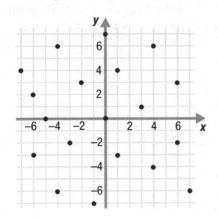

Figure 5.3.1

2. Graph the system of inequalities below to find its solution.

   $y \geq x - 4$
   $x + 2y < 6$

3. Graph the system of inequalities below to find its solution.

   $x \leq 5$
   $y > \frac{2}{3}x - 1$

4. Graph the system of inequalities below to find its solution.

   $y > 3x + 4$
   $2y < 3x + 8$

5. Graph the system of inequalities below to find its solution.

   $y \geq \frac{3}{4}x + 5$
   $y \geq \frac{3}{4}x - 1$

6. Graph the system of inequalities below to find its solution.

   $4x + y < -11$
   $3x - 8y \leq 2$

7. Graph the system of inequalities below to find its solution.

   $y < 6$
   $x > -\frac{7}{2}$

8. Graph the system of inequalities below to find its solution.

   $y \geq -\frac{5}{3}x + 1$
   $y \geq -\frac{5}{3}x - 4$

9. Conchita is moving out of her rental house and needs to clean it up. Because she is so busy, she won't have more than 10 hours to spend cleaning. She wants to spend at least as much time cleaning the inside of the house as she spends picking up the yard. Let x equal the number of hours Conchita spends picking up the yard; let y equal the number of hours she spends cleaning the house. Write a system of two linear inequalities that represents Conchita's cleaning options. Then graph the system.

10. Aki is trying to decide how to divide her exercise time between running and swimming. She wants to spend at least three times as much time swimming as she spends running, but she doesn't want to spend more than 9 hours per week swimming. Let x equal the number of hours per week Aki spends running; let y equal the number of hours per week she spends swimming. Write a system of two linear inequalities that represents Aki's exercise options. Then graph the system.

11. Graph the system of inequalities below to find its solution.
    $$x \leq 1$$
    $$x \geq -3$$

12. Graph the system of inequalities below to find its solution.
    $$y \leq x + 4$$
    $$x + 5y \geq -16$$
    $$2x + y \leq 4$$

 Explore

13. Graph the system of inequalities below. Find the points of intersection of each pair of lines.
    $$x \geq 0$$
    $$3y \geq 5x - 15$$
    $$5x + 3y \leq 15$$

14. Graph the system of inequalities below. Then find the coordinates of four points that satisfy both inequalities in the system.
    $$y \leq 7$$
    $$y \geq -2$$

15. Graph the system of inequalities below. Find the points of intersection of each pair of lines and the area of the region whose points are the solution of the system.
    $$x \geq 0$$
    $$y \geq 0$$
    $$x \leq 3$$
    $$y \leq 5$$

16. Graph the system of inequalities below. If the direction of both inequality signs are reversed, what region contains the points that are the solution of the new system?
    $$2y < x + 4$$
    $$2x + y < 7$$

17. Graph the system of inequalities below. Then find the coordinates of four points that satisfy both inequalities in the system.
    $$2x + y \geq -6$$
    $$y \leq x + 4$$

18. Graph the system of inequalities below. Find the points of intersection of each pair of lines and the area of the region whose points are the solution of the system.
    $$y \geq x - 4$$
    $$x + y \geq -4$$
    $$2y \leq x + 10$$
    $$x + 2y \leq 10$$

Apply

Practice Problems

Here are some additional practice problems for you to try.

Solving Linear Systems

1. Graph the system of inequalities below.
    $y > x + 3$
    $y < -x - 2$

2. Graph the system of inequalities below.
    $y \geq x + 1$
    $y \leq -x + 4$

3. Graph the system of inequalities below.
    $y > x - 2$
    $y < -2x + 3$

4. Graph the system of inequalities below.
    $y < x - 2$
    $y < -2x + 3$

5. Graph the system of inequalities below.
    $y \leq 3x - 1$
    $y \leq -x + 3$

6. Graph the system of inequalities below.
    $y < x - 1$
    $y < -3x + 2$

7. Graph the system of inequalities below.
    $x + y \geq 4$
    $x - y < -2$

8. Graph the system of inequalities below.
    $x - y > -4$
    $x + y \leq -5$

9. Graph the system of inequalities below.
    $x + y \leq 6$
    $x - y > 2$

10. Graph the system of inequalities below.
    $y > x + 5$
    $y \leq -3x + 2$

11. Graph the system of inequalities below.
    $y \leq -x - 4$
    $y < 2x + 5$

12. Graph the system of inequalities below.
    $y \geq x - 3$
    $y < -2x - 3$

13. Graph the system of inequalities below.
    $y > \frac{3}{2}x + 3$
    $y \leq \frac{1}{2}x - 2$

14. Graph the system of inequalities below.
    $y \geq \frac{1}{4}x + 4$
    $y \leq \frac{1}{4}x - 3$

15. Graph the system of inequalities below.
    $y \leq -\frac{4}{3}x + 2$
    $y > \frac{1}{3}x + 5$

16. Graph the system of inequalities below.
    $x + y > 3$
    $2x - y \leq 2$

17. Graph the system of inequalities below.
    $3x + y \geq 4$
    $x - y < 1$

18. Graph the system of inequalities below.
    $x - y \geq 3$
    $2x + y \geq 1$

19. Graph the system of inequalities below.
    $y > \frac{3}{4}x + 1$
    $y \leq -\frac{1}{3}x - 2$

20. Graph the system of inequalities below.
    $y > \frac{1}{4}x + 5$
    $y \leq -\frac{3}{2}x + 1$

21. Graph the system of inequalities below.
    $y > \frac{3}{5}x + 2$
    $y < -\frac{2}{3}x - 1$

22. Graph the system of inequalities below.
$y > 3$
$y < 3x - 4$

23. Graph the system of inequalities below.
$x \geq -1$
$y \geq 2x + 5$

24. Graph the system of inequalities below.
$y < -2$
$y \leq -2x - 1$

25. Graph the system of inequalities below.
$y > x$
$y \leq 3$

26. Graph the system of inequalities below.
$y < -x$
$x > -2$

27. Graph the system of inequalities below.
$y > 3x + 1$
$y < 3x - 4$

28. Graph the system of inequalities below.
$y \geq -2x - 3$
$y \leq -2x + 4$

Evaluate

Practice Test

Take this practice test to be sure that you are prepared for the final quiz in Evaluate.

1. Graph the system of inequalities below. Use the grid in Figure 5.3.2. Then write the coordinates of the plotted points that are solutions of this system.

$$y < \frac{2}{3}x + 1$$
$$x + y \geq -6$$

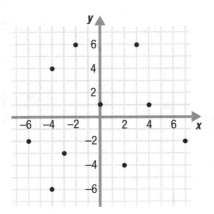

Figure 5.3.2

2. Graph the system of inequalities below to find its solution.
$$x + 2y \leq 4$$
$$y > 3$$

3. Graph the system of inequalities below. Use the grid in Figure 5.3.3. Then write the coordinates of the plotted points that are **not** solutions of either inequality in this system.
$$2x - 5y < 15$$
$$3x + 4y \leq -5$$

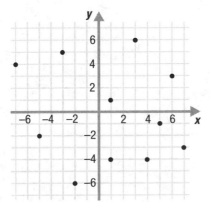

Figure 5.3.3

4. Graph the system of inequalities below to find its solution.
$$y \leq x + 3$$
$$y \geq x - 4$$

5. Graph the system of inequalities below to find its solution.
$$x \leq 2$$
$$y \geq -3$$
$$2y \leq 3x + 2$$

6. Graph the system of inequalities below. Use the grid in Figure 5.3.4. Then write the coordinates of the plotted points that are solutions of this system.

$$y \geq 0$$
$$x \geq -6$$
$$y \leq -\frac{1}{2}x + 2$$

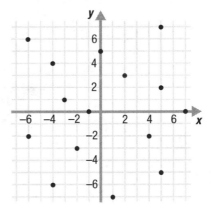

Figure 5.3.4

7. The system of inequalities below is graphed in Figure 5.3.5. If the direction of the first inequality sign is reversed, outline the region(s) that contains the points that are the solution of the new system.

$$2x + y < 4$$
$$x + 2y > -4$$

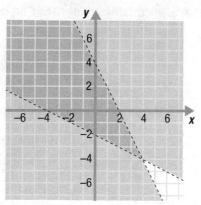

Figure 5.3.5

8. Graph the system of inequalities below. Then write the coordinates of a point that satisfies the first two inequalities but not the third inequality.

$$x \geq 0$$
$$2x - y \leq 6$$
$$y \leq x$$

TOPIC 5 Cumulative Activities

Cumulative Review Problems

These problems combine all of the material you have covered so far in this course. You may want to test your understanding of this material before you move on to the next topic, or you may wish to do these problems to review for a test.

1. Evaluate the expression $3x^3 - 7x^2y + 8y^2 + 2$ when $x = 3$ and $y = 6$.

2. a. Find the GCF of 75, 84, and 180.

   b. Find the LCM of 75, 84, and 180.

3. The sum of two numbers is 53. The difference of these numbers is 15. What are the two numbers?

4. Write the equation of the line through the point (4, 1) with slope 1:

   a. in point-slope form.

   b. in slope-intercept form.

   c. in standard form.

5. Solve this system:
   $x + y = 4$
   $x - y = 7$

6. Solve $-4 \le 3 + 4x < 5$ for x, then graph its solution on the number line below.

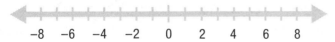

7. Find the slope of the line through the points (0, 5) and (8, –3).

8. Solve $5x = 3(x - 2) - x$ for x.

9. Graph the system of inequalities below to find its solution.
   $y \le 2x + 3$
   $y \ge 2x - 4$

10. Reduce to lowest terms: $\dfrac{3080}{5390}$

11. Solve this system:
    $x + 2y = -2$
    $3x - 7y = 33$

12. The point (–2, –6) lies on a line with slope 3. Graph this line by finding another point that lies on the line.

13. Find the slope of the line that is perpendicular to the line $4x - 9y = 5$.

14. Graph the system of inequalities below to find its solution.
    $y \ge 2x - 4$
    $y \le \ x + 2$

15. a. Find the GCF of 168, 231, and 315.

    b. Find the LCM of 168, 231, and 315.

16. Write the equation of the line through the point (2, –5) with slope –3:

    a. in point-slope form.

    b. in slope-intercept form.

    c. in standard form.

17. Solve: $3y + 5 = 9 - 2y$ for y.

18. Last year Keith split $4,500 between his savings account, which paid 4% in interest, and his checking account, which paid 1.5% in interest. If he earned a total of $143.25 in interest, how was his money divided between the two accounts?

19. Solve this system:
    $4x + 5y = 12$
    $5x + 4y = -3$

20. Graph the system of inequalities below to find its solution.
    $3y < 2x + 12$
    $x - 5y \ge -6$

21. Evaluate the expression $11a^2 - b + 6ab$ when $a = 4$ and $b = 12$.

Use Figure 5.1 to answer questions 22 through 25.

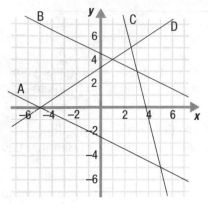

Figure 5.1

22. Which two lines form a system that has a solution of $(5, -5)$?

23. Which two lines form a system that has a solution of $(1, 4)$?

24. Which two lines form a system that has a solution of $(-5, 0)$?

25. Which two lines form a system that has no solution?

26. Find the slope of the line through the points $(-19, 12)$ and $(23, -11)$.

27. Find: $\dfrac{6}{7} - \dfrac{5}{6}$

28. Solve $\dfrac{2}{13}\left(\dfrac{9}{2}x + 5\right) = \dfrac{7}{13}\left(\dfrac{1}{2} + x\right) + 1$ for x.

29. Solve this system:
$$11x - 7y = -19$$
$$17x + 14y = -23$$

30. Graph this system of inequalities to find its solution.
$$x < -1$$
$$y \geq -3$$

31. Solve $2 < 10 - 9y < 4$ for y, then graph its solution on the number line below.

32. Write the equation of the line through the point $(-8, -7)$ with slope $\dfrac{6}{5}$:

    a. in point-slope form.

    b. in slope-intercept form.

    c. in standard form.

33. Brad emptied the money from a newspaper vending machine that accepted only dimes and quarters and got 181 coins worth a total of $31.30. How many dimes did he collect?

34. Find: $\dfrac{6}{35} \div \dfrac{8}{21}$

35. Solve $8y + 7 = 1 - 3y$ for y.

36. Solve this system:
$$9x + y = 58$$
$$\dfrac{1}{2}x + 8y = 35$$

37. Find the slope of the line $6x - 5y = 8$.

TOPIC 6
EXPONENTS AND POLYNOMIALS

Just as exponential notation is useful in writing numbers with repeating factors, such as 49, it is also helpful for writing algebraic expressions such as x^6, $x^2y^3 + 5y$, and $x^2 + 2x - 5$. These expressions are called polynomials.

In this topic, you will learn more about exponents and polynomials, concepts which will help you to understand everything from population growth to the legends of ancient kings.

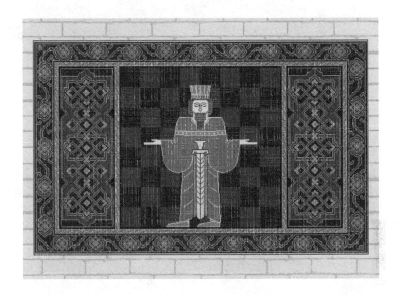

Lesson 6.1 Exponents

Concept 1: Properties of Exponents
Exponential Notation
Multiplication Property
Division Property
Power of a Power Property
Power of a Product Property
Power of a Quotient Property
Zero Power Property
Using Several Properties of Exponents

Lesson 6.2 Polynomial Operations I

Concept 1: Adding and Subtracting Polynomials
Definitions
Degree of a Polynomial
Writing Terms in Descending Order
Evaluating a Polynomial
Adding Polynomials
Subtracting Polynomials

Concept 2: Multiplying and Dividing Polynomials
Multiplying a Monomial by a Monomial
Multiplying a Polynomial by a Monomial
Dividing a Monomial by a Monomial
Dividing a Polynomial by a Monomial

Lesson 6.3 Polynomial Operations II

Concept 1: Multiplying Binomials
Using the "FOIL" Method to Multiply Two Binomials
Using Patterns to Multiply Two Binomials

Concept 2: Multiplying and Dividing Polynomials
Multiplying Polynomials with Two or More Terms
Multiplying More Than Two Polynomials
Dividing a Polynomial by a Polynomial

LESSON 6.1
EXPONENTS

Overview

Rosa plans to invest $1000 in an Individual Retirement Account (IRA). She can invest in bonds that offer a return of 7% annually, or a riskier stock fund that is expected to return 10% annually.

Rosa would like to know how much her money can grow in 30 years. Exponents can help her answer this question.

In this lesson, you will study exponents and their properties.

Explain

Concept 1 has sections on

- **Exponential Notation**

- **Multiplication Property**

- **Division Property**

- **Power of a Power Property**

- **Power of a Product Property**

- **Power of a Quotient Property**

- **Zero Power Property**

- **Using Several Properties of Exponents**

CONCEPT 1: PROPERTIES OF EXPONENTS

Exponential Notation

Exponents are used to indicate repeated multiplication of the same number.

For example, we use **exponential notation** to write:

$$5 \cdot 5 \cdot 5 \cdot 5 = 5^4$$

5^4 is read "five to the fourth power."

In the expression 5^4:

- The **base**, 5, is the repeated factor.

- The **exponent**, 4, indicates the number of times the base appears as a factor. An exponent is also called a **power**.

$$\text{Base} \longrightarrow 5^{\overset{\displaystyle \text{Exponent}}{4}} = \underbrace{5 \cdot 5 \cdot 5 \cdot 5}_{4 \text{ factors}} = \underset{\text{Product}}{625}$$

Example 6.1.1

Find: 2^3

Solution

The base is 2 and the exponent is 3.

$$2^3 = \underbrace{2 \cdot 2 \cdot 2}_{3 \text{ factors}} = 8$$

Example 6.1.2

Rewrite using exponential notation: $10 \cdot 10 \cdot 10 \cdot 10 \cdot 10 \cdot 10$

Solution

There are six factors. Each is 10. Therefore, the base is 10 and the exponent is 6.

$$\underbrace{10 \cdot 10 \cdot 10 \cdot 10 \cdot 10 \cdot 10}_{6 \text{ factors}} = 10^6$$

Exponents have several properties. We will use these properties to simplify expressions.

In the properties that follow, each variable represents a real number.

Multiplication Property

> — Property —
> **Multiplication Property of Exponents**
>
> **English** To multiply two exponential expressions with the same base, add their exponents. The base stays the same.
>
> **Algebra** $x^m \cdot x^n = x^{m+n}$
> (Here, m and n are positive integers.)
>
> **Example** $5^4 \cdot 5^2 = 5^{4+2} = 5^6$

Example 6.1.3

a. Use the Multiplication Property of Exponents to simplify $2^3 \cdot 2^4$.

b. Use the definition of exponential notation to justify your answer.

Solution

Remember to add the exponents, but leave the bases alone. That is, $2^3 \cdot 2^4 = 2^{3+4} = 2^7$, not 4^7.

a. The operation is multiplication and the bases are the same. Therefore, add the exponents and use 2 as the base.

$$2^3 \cdot 2^4 = 2^{3+4} = 2^7$$

Note the difference between $2^3 \cdot 2^4$ and $2^3 + 2^4$.

$2^3 \cdot 2^4 = 2^{3+4} = 2^7 = 128$
$2^3 + 2^4 = 8 + 16 = 24$

b. Rewrite the product to show the factors. Then simplify.

$$2^3 \cdot 2^4 = \underbrace{(2 \cdot 2 \cdot 2)}_{3 \text{ factors}} \cdot \underbrace{(2 \cdot 2 \cdot 2 \cdot 2)}_{4 \text{ factors}} = \underbrace{2 \cdot 2 \cdot 2 \cdot 2 \cdot 2 \cdot 2 \cdot 2}_{7 \text{ factors}} = 2^7$$

— Caution —
Negative Bases

A negative sign is part of the base only when the negative sign is inside the parentheses that enclose the base.

For example, consider the following cases:

In $(-3)^2$, the base is -3.

$(-3)^2 = (-3) \cdot (-3) = +9$

In -3^2, the base is 3.

You can think of -3^2 as the "opposite" of 3^2.

$-3^2 = -(3 \cdot 3) = -9$

Example 6.1.4

If possible, use the Multiplication Property of Exponents to simplify each expression:

a. $(-2)^2 \cdot (-2)^4$ b. $-2^2 \cdot 2^4$ c. $-2^2 \cdot (-2)^4$

Solution

a. In $(-2)^2 \cdot (-2)^4$, the base is -2.

$$(-2)^2 \cdot (-2)^4 = (-2)^{2+4}$$
$$= (-2)^6$$
$$= 64$$

b. In $-2^2 \cdot 2^4$, the base is 2. We may think of $-2^2 \cdot 2^4$ as the opposite of $2^2 \cdot 2^4$.

$$-2^2 \cdot 2^4 = -(2^2) \cdot (2^4)$$
$$= -(2^{2+4})$$
$$= -(2^6)$$
$$= -64$$

c. In $-2^2 \cdot (-2)^4$, the base of the first factor, -2^2, is 2.

The base of the second factor, $(-2)^4$, is -2.

The bases are **not** the same, so we cannot use the Multiplication Property of Exponents.

However, we can still evaluate the expression. $-2^2 \cdot (-2)^4 = -4 \cdot 16 = -64$

We can extend the Multiplication Property of Exponents to multiply more than two factors.

Example 6.1.5

Find: $8^4 \cdot 8 \cdot 8^5$. Leave your answer in exponential notation.

Solution

The bases are the same, so we can use the Multiplication Property of Exponents.

Note: $8 = 8^1$ $8^4 \cdot 8 \cdot 8^5 = 8^4 \cdot 8^1 \cdot 8^5 = 8^{4+1+5} = 8^{10}$

We left 8^{10} in exponential form. To evaluate 8^{10}, use the "y^x" key on a scientific calculator or the "^" key on a graphing calculator.

$8^{10} = 1,073,741,824$

Example 6.1.6

Find: $x^7 \cdot x^3 \cdot x^5$

Solution

The operation is multiplication and
the bases are the same.
Therefore, add the exponents and
use x as the base.

$$x^7 \cdot x^3 \cdot x^5 = x^{7+3+5} = x^{15}$$

Division Property

— Property —
Division Property of Exponents

English To divide two exponential expressions with the same base:
Compare the exponents.
- If the greater exponent is in the numerator, write the base in the numerator.
- If the greater base is in the denominator, write the base in the denominator.

Then subtract the smaller exponent from the greater.
Use the result as the new exponent.

Algebra

$\dfrac{x^m}{x^n} = x^{m-n}$ for $m > n$ and $x \neq 0$.

$\dfrac{x^m}{x^n} = \dfrac{1}{x^{n-m}}$ for $m < n$ and $x \neq 0$.

(Here, m and n are positive integers.)

Example

$\dfrac{2^5}{2^3} = 2^{5-3} = 2^2$

$\dfrac{2^3}{2^5} = \dfrac{1}{2^{5-3}} = \dfrac{1}{2^2}$

Example 6.1.7

Since $3 < 4$, we use the form $\dfrac{x^m}{x^n} = \dfrac{1}{x^{n-m}}$.

a. Use the Division Property of Exponents to find $\dfrac{5^3}{5^4}$.

b. Use the definition of exponential notation to justify your answer.

Solution

a. The bases are the same,
so subtract the exponents.

$$\frac{5^3}{5^4} = \frac{1}{5^{4-3}} = \frac{1}{5}$$

b. Rewrite the numerator and
denominator to show the factors.

$$\frac{5^3}{5^4} = \frac{5 \cdot 5 \cdot 5}{5 \cdot 5 \cdot 5 \cdot 5}$$

Cancel the common factors.

$$= \frac{\overset{1}{\cancel{5}} \cdot \overset{1}{\cancel{5}} \cdot \overset{1}{\cancel{5}}}{\underset{1}{\cancel{5}} \cdot \underset{1}{\cancel{5}} \cdot \underset{1}{\cancel{5}} \cdot 5} = \frac{1}{5}$$

Example 6.1.8

Find: $7^9 \div 7^6$. Leave your answer in exponential notation.

Solution

The operation is division and the bases are the same. Therefore, subtract the exponents and use 7 as the base.

$$7^9 \div 7^6 = \frac{7^9}{7^6} = 7^{9-6} = 7^3$$

Since $9 > 6$, we use the form $\frac{x^m}{x^n} = x^{m-n}$.

Example 6.1.9

Find: $w^8 \div w^{13}$

Solution

The operation is division and the bases are the same. Therefore, subtract the exponents and use w as the base.

$$w^8 \div w^{13} = \frac{w^8}{w^{13}} = \frac{1}{w^{13-8}} = \frac{1}{w^5}$$

Since $8 < 13$, we use the form $\frac{x^m}{x^n} = \frac{1}{x^{n-m}}$.

Power of a Power Property

— Property —
Power of a Power Property of Exponents

English To raise a power to a power, multiply the exponents.

Algebra $(x^m)^n = x^{mn}$
(Here, m and n are positive integers.)

Example $(7^2)^4 = 7^{2 \cdot 4} = 7^8$

Example 6.1.10

a. Use the Power of a Power Property of Exponents to simplify $(5^2)^3$.

b. Use the definition of exponential notation to justify your answer.

Solution

a. To raise a power to a power, multiply the exponents.

$$(5^2)^3 = 5^{2 \cdot 3} = 5^6$$

b. Rewrite each power to show the factors. Then simplify.

$$(5^2)^3 = \underbrace{(5^2) \cdot (5^2) \cdot (5^2)}_{\textbf{3} \text{ factors}} = \underbrace{(5 \cdot 5) \cdot (5 \cdot 5) \cdot (5 \cdot 5)}_{\textbf{6} \text{ factors}} = 5^6$$

Example 6.1.11

Simplify: $(y^5)^3$

Solution

To simplify a power of a power, multiply the exponents.

$$(y^5)^3 = y^{5 \cdot 3} = y^{15}$$

Power of a Product Property

— Property —
Power of a Product Property of Exponents

English To raise a product to a power, you can first raise each factor to the power. Then multiply.

Algebra $(xy)^n = x^n y^n$ *(Here, n is a positive integer.)*

Example $(2x)^3 = 2^3 x^3 = 8x^3$

Example 6.1.12

a. Use the Power of a Product Property of Exponents to simplify $(3y)^2$.

b. Use the definition of exponential notation to justify your answer.

Solution

a. Raise each factor to the power 2.
$$(3y)^2 = 3^2 y^2 = 9y^2$$

b. Rewrite the power to show the factors. Then simplify.
$$\begin{aligned}
(3y)^2 &= (3y) \cdot (3y) \\
&= 3 \cdot 3 \cdot y \cdot y \\
&= 3^2 y^2 \\
&= 9y^2
\end{aligned}$$

Example 6.1.13

Simplify: $(2^3 \cdot w^5)^4$

Solution

Use the Power of a Product Property of Exponents to raise each factor inside the parentheses to the power 4.

$$(2^3 \cdot w^5)^4 = (2^3)^4 (w^5)^4$$

Use the Power of a Power Property of Exponents.

$$= (2^{3 \cdot 4})(w^{5 \cdot 4})$$

Simplify.

$$= 2^{12} w^{20}$$

We left 2^{12} in exponential form. To evaluate 2^{12}, use the "y^x" key on a scientific calculator or the "^" key on a graphing calculator.

$$2^{12} = 4096$$

Power of a Quotient Property

> **— Property —**
> **Power of a Quotient Property of Exponents**
>
> **English** To raise a quotient to a power, you can first raise the numerator and denominator each to the power. Then divide.
>
> **Algebra** $\left(\dfrac{x}{y}\right)^n = \dfrac{x^n}{y^n}, y \neq 0$
>
> (Here, n is a positive integer.)
>
> **Example** $\left(\dfrac{2}{x}\right)^4 = \dfrac{2^4}{x^4} = \dfrac{16}{x^4}$

Example 6.1.14

a. Use the Power of a Quotient Property of Exponents to simplify $\left(\dfrac{2}{5}\right)^3$.

b. Use the definition of exponential notation to justify your answer.

Solution

a. Raise the numerator to the power 3.
Raise the denominator to the power 3.

$$\left(\frac{2}{5}\right)^3 = \frac{2^3}{5^3} = \frac{8}{125}$$

b. Rewrite the power to show the factors.
Then simplify.

$$\left(\frac{2}{5}\right)^3 = \underbrace{\left(\frac{2}{5}\right) \cdot \left(\frac{2}{5}\right) \cdot \left(\frac{2}{5}\right)}_{\textbf{3 factors}} = \frac{2 \cdot 2 \cdot 2}{5 \cdot 5 \cdot 5} = \frac{2^3}{5^3} = \frac{8}{125}$$

Zero Power Property

> **— Property —**
> **Zero Power Property**
>
> **English** Any real number, except zero, raised to the power 0 is 1.
>
> **Algebra** $x^0 = 1, x \neq 0$
>
> **Example** $17^0 = 1$

Here's a way to understand why 17^0 is 1.

Suppose we write 0 as $2 - 2$.
Then, $17^0 = 17^{2-2}$.

By the Division Property of Exponents, $17^{2-2} = \dfrac{17^2}{17^2} = \dfrac{\overset{1}{\cancel{17}} \cdot \overset{1}{\cancel{17}}}{\underset{1}{\cancel{17}} \cdot \underset{1}{\cancel{17}}} = 1$.

Since $17^0 = 17^{2-2}$ and $17^{2-2} = 1$, we have $17^0 = 1$.

This same reasoning applies no matter what power or nonzero base we choose.

$$\frac{x^n}{x^n} = x^{n-n} = x^0$$

$$\frac{x^n}{x^n} = 1$$

Therefore, $x^0 = 1$ for $x \neq 0$.

Example 6.1.15

a. Use the Zero Power Property to simplify 5^0.

b. Justify your answer.

Solution

a. Any real number, except zero, raised to the power 0 is 1.

$$5^0 = 1$$

b. Suppose we have $\dfrac{5^3}{5^3}$.

We can simplify this using the Division Property of Exponents.

$$\frac{5^3}{5^3} = 5^{3-3} = 5^0$$

But if we reduce the fraction $\dfrac{5^3}{5^3}$, the result is 1.

$$\frac{5^3}{5^3} = \frac{\overset{1}{\cancel{5}} \cdot \overset{1}{\cancel{5}} \cdot \overset{1}{\cancel{5}}}{\underset{1}{\cancel{5}} \cdot \underset{1}{\cancel{5}} \cdot \underset{1}{\cancel{5}}} = 1$$

Since $\dfrac{5^3}{5^3}$ is equivalent to both 5^0 and 1, we conclude $5^0 = 1$.

Example 6.1.16

Find each of the following. (Assume each variable represents a nonzero real number).

a. $(-7)^0$ b. $\dfrac{w^0}{4}$ c. $(12x^4y^5)^0$ d. $-2y^0$ e. 0^0

Solution

In each case, we apply the Zero Power Property: any nonzero real number raised to the zero power is 1.

a. The base is the real number -7.

$$(-7)^0 = 1$$

b. The base, w, represents a nonzero real number.

$$\frac{w^0}{4} = \frac{1}{4}$$

c. The base, $12x^4y^5$, represents a nonzero real number.

$$(12x^4y^5)^0 = 1$$

d. Only y is raised to the power 0.

$$-2y^0 = -2 \cdot 1 = -2$$

e. In the Zero Power Property, the base cannot be 0.

$$0^0 \text{ is undefined}$$

Using Several Properties of Exponents

To simplify an exponential expression, we may need to use several properties of exponents.

Example 6.1.17

Find: $\left(\dfrac{2^5 \cdot x^4}{2^8}\right)^3$

Solution

First, we simplify the expression inside the parentheses.

$$\left(\frac{2^5 \cdot x^4}{2^8}\right)^3$$

To combine the powers of 2, subtract exponents. (Division Property of Exponents)

$$= \left(\frac{x^4}{2^3}\right)^3$$

Since 5 < 8, we use the form $\dfrac{x^m}{x^n} = \dfrac{1}{x^{n-m}}$.

Raise the numerator and the denominator each to the power 3. (Power of a Quotient Property of Exponents)

$$= \frac{(x^4)^3}{(2^3)^3}$$

Multiply exponents: $4 \cdot 3 = 12$ and $3 \cdot 3 = 9$. (Power of a Power Property of Exponents)

$$= \frac{x^{4 \cdot 3}}{2^{3 \cdot 3}}$$

$$= \frac{x^{12}}{2^9}$$

Example 6.1.18

Find: $\dfrac{(x^3 \cdot x^5 y^4)^3}{(y^4)^2}$

Solution

First, we simplify the expression inside the parentheses in the numerator.

$$\frac{(x^3 \cdot x^5 y^4)^3}{(y^4)^2}$$

To combine the powers of x, add their exponents. (Multiplication Property of Exponents)

$$= \frac{(x^8 y^4)^3}{(y^4)^2}$$

In the numerator, raise each factor to the power 3. (Power of a Product Property of Exponents)

$$= \frac{(x^8)^3(y^4)^3}{(y^4)^2}$$

Multiply exponents: $8 \cdot 3 = 24$ and $4 \cdot 3 = 12$ and $4 \cdot 2 = 8$. (Power of a Power Property of Exponents).

$$= \frac{x^{24}y^{12}}{y^8}$$

To combine the powers of y, subtract their exponents. (Division Property of Exponents)

$$= x^{24}y^4$$

Since 12 > 8, we use the form $\dfrac{x^m}{x^n} = x^{m-n}$.

Example 6.1.19

Find: $\dfrac{2x^2(3y^4)^2}{6xy^5}$

Solution

Raise each factor inside the parentheses to the power 2. (Power of a Product Property of Exponents)	$\dfrac{2x^2(3y^4)^2}{6xy^5}$ $= \dfrac{2x^2(3)^2(y^4)^2}{6xy^5}$
To simplify $(y^4)^2$, multiply exponents: $4 \cdot 2 = 8$. (Power of a Power Property of Exponents)	$= \dfrac{2x^2 3^2 y^8}{6xy^5}$
Multiply the constants: $2 \cdot 3^2 = 2 \cdot 9 = 18$	$= \dfrac{18x^2 y^8}{6xy^5}$
Divide 18 by 6. To combine the powers of x, subtract their exponents. To combine the powers of y, subtract their exponents. (Division Property of Exponents)	$= 3xy^3$

Real world problems often involve exponents. For example, the following formula may be used to calculate the value of an investment after a certain number of years.

$$A = P(1 + r)^t$$

where A is the value of the investment,
   P is the original principal invested,
   r is the annual rate of return, and
   t is the number of years the money is invested.

Example 6.1.20

Rosa plans to invest $1000 in an Individual Retirement Account (IRA). She can invest in a bond fund that averages a 7% annual return, or in a riskier stock fund that is expected to have a 10% annual return.

a. Determine the value of the bond fund after 30 years.

b. Determine the projected value of the stock fund after 30 years.

c. Compare the returns on the two investments.

Solution

For each investment, the principal,
P, is $1000. The time, t, is 30 years.

$$A = P(1 + r)^t$$

a. For the bond fund, the annual rate
    of return is 7%. So, $r = 0.07$.
    In the formula, substitute 1000 for P,
    0.07 for r, and 30 for t.

    $$A = \mathbf{1000}(1 + \mathbf{0.07})^{\mathbf{30}}$$

    Add 1 and 0.07.

    $$= 1000(\mathbf{1.07})^{30}$$

    On a calculator, use the "y^x" key
    or the "^" key to approximate 1.07^{30}.

    $$\approx 1000(\mathbf{7.612255043})$$

    Multiply and round to the nearest
    hundredth (cent).

    $$\approx \$7{,}612.26$$

    To get a better estimate, we waited until the end of the problem to round the answer.

    After 30 years, the bond fund will be worth $7,612.26.

b. For the stock fund, the projected annual
    rate of return is 10%. So $r = 0.10$.
    In the formula, substitute 1000 for P,
    0.10 for r, and 30 for t.

    $$A = \mathbf{1000}(1 + \mathbf{0.10})^{\mathbf{30}}$$

    Add 1 and 0.10.

    $$= 1000(\mathbf{1.10})^{30}$$

    On a calculator, use the "y^x" key or
    the "^" key to approximate 1.10^{30}.

    $$\approx 1000(\mathbf{17.44940227})$$

    Multiply and round to the nearest
    hundredth (cent).

    $$\approx \$17{,}449.40$$

    After 30 years, the stock fund should be worth $17,449.40.

c. The bond fund would grow to almost 8 times its original value.

    The stock fund would grow to over 17 times its original value.

    The stock fund, which is riskier than the bond fund, is projected to be
    worth more than twice as much as the bond fund in 30 years.

Here is a summary of this concept from *Academic Systems Algebra.*

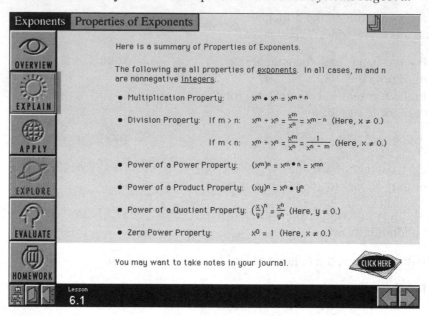

Exponents | Properties of Exponents

Here is a summary of Properties of Exponents.

The following are all properties of <u>exponents</u>. In all cases, m and n are nonnegative <u>integers</u>.

- Multiplication Property: $x^m \cdot x^n = x^{m+n}$

- Division Property: If m > n: $x^m \div x^n = \dfrac{x^m}{x^n} = x^{m-n}$ (Here, x ≠ 0.)

  If m < n: $x^m \div x^n = \dfrac{x^m}{x^n} = \dfrac{1}{x^{n-m}}$ (Here, x ≠ 0.)

- Power of a Power Property: $(x^m)^n = x^{m \cdot n} = x^{mn}$

- Power of a Product Property: $(xy)^n = x^n \cdot y^n$

- Power of a Quotient Property: $\left(\dfrac{x}{y}\right)^n = \dfrac{x^n}{y^n}$ (Here, y ≠ 0.)

- Zero Power Property: $x^0 = 1$ (Here, x ≠ 0.)

You may want to take notes in your journal.   CLICK HERE

Lesson
6.1

OVERVIEW
EXPLAIN
APPLY
EXPLORE
EVALUATE
HOMEWORK

Checklist Lesson 6.1

Here is what you should know after completing this lesson.

Words and Phrases

exponential notation
base

exponent
power

Ideas and Procedures

❶ **Exponential Notation**
Given an expression written in exponential notation, identify the base, identify the exponent, and evaluate the expression.

Example 6.1.1
   Find: 2^3
See also: Example 6.1.2

❷ **Properties of Exponents**
Use the following properties of exponents to simplify an expression:
   Multiplication Property of Exponents
   Division Property of Exponents
   Power of a Power Property of Exponents
   Power of a Product Property of Exponents
   Power of a Quotient Property of Exponents
   Zero Power Property

Example 6.1.18

   Find: $\dfrac{(x^3 \cdot x^5 y^4)^3}{(y^4)^2}$

See also: Example 6.1.3-6.1.17, 6.1.19, 6.1.20
      Apply 1-28

Homework Problems

Circle the homework problems assigned to you by the computer, then complete them below.

☀ Explain

Properties of Exponents

Use the appropriate properties of exponents to simplify the expressions in questions 1 through 12. (Keep your answers in exponential form where possible.)

1. Find:

    a. $3^2 \cdot 3^5$ b. $5^2 \cdot 5^5$

    c. $7^2 \cdot 7^5$

2. Find:

    a. $\dfrac{3^9}{3^5}$ b. $\dfrac{3^5}{3^9}$

    c. $\dfrac{3^9}{3^9}$

3. Find:

    a. $(7^3)^2$ b. $(7^2)^3$

4. Find:

    a. $(5 \cdot x)^3$ b. $(3 \cdot y)^2$

    c. $(a^2 \cdot b)^4$

5. Find:

    a. $\left(\dfrac{x^3 \cdot x^5}{x^4}\right)^2$ b. $\left(\dfrac{a^{12} \cdot a^6}{a^9 \cdot a^7}\right)^4$

    c. $\left(\dfrac{b^6 \cdot b^5}{b^3 \cdot b^8}\right)^3$ d. $\dfrac{2^3 \cdot x^5}{2^5 \cdot x^2}$

6. Find:

    a. $(a^2 \cdot a^3)^2 + (a^2 \cdot a^3)^2$

    b. $\dfrac{y^4 \cdot 3y^2}{y^8}$

    c. $x^4 \cdot x^9 \cdot x \cdot y^5 \cdot y^{11}$

7. Find:

    a. $(b^3)^2 \cdot (b^4)^3$

    b. $\dfrac{y^6}{y^{17}} \cdot (y^5)^2 \cdot (y^3)^4$

    c. $\dfrac{a^4 \cdot b^6}{a^{11} \cdot b^3}$

8. Find:

    a. $\dfrac{(xy)^4}{y^9 \cdot x^7}$ b. $\dfrac{(3b)^6}{(3b^2)^4}$

9. As animals grow, they get taller faster than they get stronger. In general, this proportion of increase in height to increase in strength can be written as $\dfrac{x^2}{x^3}$. Simplify this fraction.

10. An animal is proportionally stronger the smaller it is. If a person is 200 times as tall as an ant, figure out how much stronger a person is, pound for pound, by simplifying the expression $\dfrac{200^2}{200^3}$.

11. Find:

    a. $\left(\dfrac{4xy^2z}{5x^2yz^3}\right)^0$ b. $\dfrac{y^7 \cdot y}{y^9 \cdot y^2}$

    c. $\left(\dfrac{b^3 \cdot b^5}{b^6 \cdot b^3}\right)^4$ d. $-2x^0 + 5y^0$

12. Find:

    a. $\left(\dfrac{(x^3 \cdot x^4)^2}{x^7}\right)^5$ b. $\dfrac{(4a^2)^0 - 3b^0}{2}$

    c. $\left(\dfrac{(3x \cdot 3x^2)^2}{3^{11} \cdot x^7}\right)^3$ d. $\left(\dfrac{b^8}{(b^2 \cdot b^7)}\right)^4$

 **Apply**

Practice Problems

Here are some additional practice problems for you to try.

Properties of Exponents

1. Find: $7^5 \cdot 7^3$. Leave your answer in exponential notation.

2. Find: $6^3 \cdot 6^4$. Leave your answer in exponential notation.

3. Find: $b^{12} \cdot b^3$

4. Find: $c^9 \cdot c^4$

5. Find: $a^6 \cdot a^5$

6. Find: $5^7 \div 5^3$. Leave your answer in exponential notation.

7. Find: $9^{10} \div 9^4$. Leave your answer in exponential notation.

8. Find: $\dfrac{m^{10}}{m^4}$

9. Find: $\dfrac{n^{20}}{n^{15}}$

10. Find: $\dfrac{b^{12}}{b^5}$

11. Find: $(5^3)^4$. Leave your answer in exponential notation.

12. Find: $(8^2)^5$. Leave your answer in exponential notation.

13. Find: $(13^5)^6$. Leave your answer in exponential notation.

14. Find: $(y^8)^3$

15. Find: $(z^{12})^4$

16. Find: $(x^9)^4$

17. Find: $(3 \cdot a)^4$

18. Find: $(4 \cdot b)^2$

19. Find: $(2 \cdot y)^3$

20. Find: $\dfrac{a^6 b^5}{a^8 b^2}$

21. Find: $\dfrac{m^7 n^4}{m^3 n^{10}}$

22. Find: $\dfrac{x^3 y^7 z^{12}}{x y^8 z^5}$

23. Find: 5^0

24. Find: 348^0

25. Find: x^0

26. Find: $5^1 + (4z)^0$

27. Find: $a^0 - (xyz)^0 + 3^1$

28. Find: $2^1 - (3x)^0 + y^0$

Practice Test

Take this practice test to be sure that you are prepared for the final quiz in Evaluate.

1. Rewrite each expression below. Keep your answer in exponential form where possible.

   a. $11 \cdot 11 \cdot 11 \cdot 11$

   b. $3 \cdot 3 \cdot y \cdot y \cdot y \cdot y \cdot y$

   c. $5^{12} \cdot 5^8 \cdot 5^{23}$

   d. $x^7 \cdot y \cdot y^{19} \cdot x^{14} \cdot y^6$

   e. $7^8 \cdot b^5 \cdot b^8 \cdot 7^{10} \cdot b$

2. Rewrite each expression below in simplest form using exponents.

   a. $\dfrac{2 \cdot 2 \cdot 2 \cdot 2 \cdot 2 \cdot 2}{2 \cdot 2 \cdot 2}$

   b. $\dfrac{b^{20}}{b^{14}}$

   c. $\dfrac{3^{12} \cdot x^7}{3^9 \cdot x^{16}}$

   d. $\dfrac{y^{17}}{y^{14} \cdot y^3 \cdot y^4}$

3. Circle the expressions below that simplify to $\dfrac{x^3}{y^5}$.

   $\dfrac{x^6 y^2}{x^3 y^7}$ $\qquad$ $\dfrac{y^{11} x^5}{y^2 x^4}$

   $\dfrac{x y^9}{x^6 y^4}$ $\qquad$ $\dfrac{x^7 y}{x^4 y^6}$

4. Circle the expressions below that simplify to $5y$.

   $(31 x^8)^0 \cdot 5y$

   $-(-5y)^0$

   $\dfrac{5 y^2}{y}$

   $\dfrac{(5y)^2}{5y}$

   $\dfrac{5 \cdot 5 \cdot 5 \cdot y \cdot y \cdot y \cdot y}{5 \cdot 5 \cdot y \cdot y}$

5. Simplify each expression below.

   a. $(b^4 \cdot b^2)^8$

   b. $(3^5 \cdot a^6)^2$

   c. $(2^9 \cdot x^4 \cdot y^6)^{11}$

6. Simplify each expression below.

   a. $\left(\dfrac{5 y^{10}}{3 x^8}\right)^4$

   b. $\left(\dfrac{7 a^3 b^4}{5 a^2}\right)^6$

7. Calculate the value of each expression below.

   a. $(4x)^0 - 2y^0$

   b. $(5 x y^2 \cdot 4 x^3)^0$

   c. $-2 x^0 - y^0$

   d. $\dfrac{(4x)^0}{2} + \dfrac{3 x^0}{2} + \dfrac{-2 x^0}{2}$

8. Rewrite each expression below using a single exponent.

   a. $\left(\dfrac{a^4 \cdot a^5}{a \cdot a^3}\right)^7$

   b. $\left(\dfrac{a \cdot a^3}{a^4 \cdot a^5}\right)^7$

LESSON 6.2
POLYNOMIAL OPERATIONS I

 Overview

In business, people use algebra everyday to find unknown quantities.

For example, a manufacturer may use algebra to determine a product's selling price in order to maximize the company's profit. A landscape architect may be interested in finding a formula for the area of a patio deck.

To find these quantities, you need to be able to add, subtract, multiply, and divide polynomials.

 Explain

Concept 1 has sections on

- **Definitions**
- **Degree of a Polynomial**
- **Writing Terms in Descending Order**
- **Evaluating a Polynomial**
- **Adding Polynomials**
- **Subtracting Polynomials**

CONCEPT 1: ADDING AND SUBTRACTING POLYNOMIALS

Definitions

A **monomial** is an algebraic expression that contains exactly one term. The term may be a constant, or the product of a constant and one or more variables. The exponent of any variable must be a nonnegative integer (that is, a whole number).

The following are monomials:

$$12 \qquad x^2 \qquad -5wy^3 \qquad \frac{1}{2}gt^2 \qquad 4.35T$$

A monomial in one variable, x, can be written in the form ax^r, where a is any real number and r is a nonnegative integer.

The following are **not** monomials:

$\dfrac{2}{x^3}$ The denominator contains a variable with a positive exponent. So the term *cannot* be written in the form ax^r where r is a nonnegative integer.

$\sqrt[3]{x^2}$ There is a squared variable under a cube root symbol. So the term cannot be written in the form ax^r where r is a nonnegative integer.

A **polynomial** is the sum of one or more monomials.
Here are some examples:

$$2x^3 - 5x + 2 \qquad x + 2 \qquad 5 \qquad 3xy^2 - 7x + 5y - 1$$

A polynomial with one, two, or three terms has a special name.

Name	Number of terms	Examples
monomial	1	$x, \ 5y, \ 3xy^3, \ 5$
binomial	2	$x + 1, \ 2x^2 - 3, \ 5xy^3 + 4x^3y^2$
trinomial	3	$x^2 + 2x + 1, \ 3x^2y^3 - xy + 5$

A polynomial with 4 terms is called a "four term polynomial."
A polynomial with 5 terms is called a "five term polynomial," and so on.

Example 6.2.1

Determine if each expression is a polynomial.

a. $-4w^3$ b. $\dfrac{24}{x^2} - 3x$ c. $\sqrt{x^3} + 2$ d. $x + 2$

Solution

a.   The expression is a polynomial.
It has one term, so it is a monomial.
The term has the form aw^r, where $a = -4$ and $r = 3$.

b.   The expression is *not* a polynomial.
The term $\dfrac{24}{x^2}$ cannot be written in the form ax^r where r is a nonnegative integer.

c.   The expression is *not* a polynomial.
The term $\sqrt{x^3}$ cannot be written in the form ax^r where r is a nonnegative integer.

Remember:
$x^0 = 1$, for $x \neq 0$
$x^1 = x$

d.   The expression is a polynomial.
It has two terms, so it is a binomial.
Each term can be written in the form ax^r:

$$x + 2$$

$$\mathbf{1x^1 + 2x^0}$$

Degree of a Polynomial

The **degree of a term** of a polynomial is the sum of the exponents of the variables in that term.

For example, consider this trinomial: $\qquad 6x^3y^2 + xy^2 + 3^5x^4.$

The degree of the first term is 5.
$$6x^3y^2$$
$$\text{degree} = 3 + 2 = 5$$

The degree of the second term is 3.
$$xy^2 = x^1y^2$$
$$\text{degree} = 1 + 2 = 3$$

The degree of the last term is 4.
In 3^5, the exponent does not contribute to the degree because the base, 3, is not a variable.
$$3^5x^4$$
$$\text{degree} = 4$$

The **degree of a polynomial** is equal to the degree of the term with the highest degree.

In this polynomial, the term with the highest degree has degree 5.
So this polynomial has degree 5.

degree **5**   degree **3**   degree **4**
$$6x^3y^2 + x^1y^2 + 3^5x^4$$
The polynomial has degree **5**.

Writing Terms in Descending Order

The terms of a polynomial in one variable are usually arranged by degree, in descending order, when read from left to right.

For example, this polynomial contains one variable, x.
$$x^3 + 7x^2 - 4x + 2$$

The terms of the polynomial are arranged by degree in descending order.
$$x^3 + 7x^2 - 4x^1 + 2x^0$$

degree 3   degree 2   degree 1   degree 0

Example 6.2.2

Arrange the terms of this polynomial in descending order and determine the degree of the polynomial: $7x^3 - 8 + 2x - x^4$

Solution

Write -8 as $-8x^0$. Write $2x$ as $2x^1$.

$$= 7x^3 - 8x^0 + 2x^1 - x^4$$

Arrange the terms by degree in descending order (4, 3, 1, 0).

$$= -x^4 + 7x^3 + 2x^1 - 8x^0$$

The last two terms may be written without exponents.

$$= -x^4 + 7x^3 + 2x - 8$$

The term of highest degree is $-x^4$. The degree of $-x^4$ is 4. So, the degree of this polynomial is 4.

Evaluating a Polynomial

To **evaluate a polynomial**, we replace each variable with the given number, then simplify.

Example 6.2.3

Evaluate this polynomial when $w = -3$ and $y = 2$: $6w^2 + 4wy - y^4 + 5$

Solution

Substitute -3 for w and 2 for y.

$$6(-3)^2 + 4(-3)(2) - (2)^4 + 5$$

First, do the calculations with the exponents.

$$= 6(9) \quad + 4(-3)(2) - 16 \quad + 5$$

Multiply.

$$= 54 \quad\quad - 24 \quad\quad - 16 \ + 5$$

Add and subtract.

$$= 19$$

Adding Polynomials

To add polynomials, combine like terms.
Recall that like terms are terms that have the same variables raised to the same power. That is, like terms have the same variables with the same exponents.

Like terms

$3x, \ -12x$

$-8xy^2, \ 5.6xy^2$

$24, \ -11$

$4xy, \ 6yx$

NOT like terms

$7x, \ -5xy$ The variables do not match.

$3x^2y^3, \ -2x^3y^2$ The powers of x do not match.
                         The powers of y do not match.

Example 6.2.4

Find: $(5x^3 - 13x^2 - 7) + (16x^3 + 8x^2 - x + 15)$

Solution	$(5x^3 - 13x^2 - 7) + (16x^3 + 8x^2 - x + 15)$
Remove the parentheses.	$= 5x^3 - 13x^2 - 7 + 16x^3 + 8x^2 - x + 15$
Write like terms next to each other.	$= 5x^3 + 16x^3 - 13x^2 + 8x^2 - x - 7 + 15$
Combine like terms.	$= 21x^3 - 5x^2 - x + 8$

We can also place one polynomial beneath the other and add like terms.

$$\begin{array}{r} 5x^3 - 13x^2 \quad\ - 7 \\ + 16x^3 + 8x^2 - x + 15 \\ \hline 21x^3 - 5x^2 - x + 8 \end{array}$$

Example 6.2.5

Find the sum of $(3z^3 + 2zy^2 - 6y^3)$ and $(15z^3 - 5zy^2 + 4z^2)$.

Solution

Write the sum.	$(3z^3 + 2zy^2 - 6y^3) + (15z^3 - 5zy^2 + 4z^2)$
Remove the parentheses.	$= 3z^3 + 2zy^2 - 6y^3 \ + \ 15z^3 - 5zy^2 + 4z^2$
Write like terms next to each other.	$= 3z^3 + 15z^3 + 2zy^2 - 5zy^2 - 6y^3 + 4z^2$
Combine like terms.	$= 18z^3 - 3zy^2 - 6y^3 + 4z^2$

We can also place one polynomial beneath the other and add like terms.

$$\begin{array}{r} 3z^3 + 2zy^2 - 6y^3 \\ + 15z^3 - 5zy^2 \qquad\quad + 4z^2 \\ \hline 18z^3 - 3zy^2 - 6y^3 + 4z^2 \end{array}$$

Subtracting Polynomials

To subtract one polynomial from another, add the first polynomial to the opposite of the polynomial being subtracted.

To find the opposite of a polynomial, multiply each term by -1.

For example:

The opposite of $5x^2$ is $-5x^2$.
The opposite of $-2x + 7$ is $2x - 7$.

Here's a way to find the opposite of a polynomial:

Change the sign of each term.

Example 6.2.6

Find: $(-18w^2 + w - 32) - (40 - 13w^2)$

Solution	$(-18w^2 + w - 32) - (40 - 13w^2)$
Change the subtraction to addition of the opposite.	$= (-18w^2 + w - 32) + (-1)(40 - 13w^2)$
Remove the parentheses.	$= -18w^2 + w - 32 - 40 + 13w^2$
Write like terms next to each other.	$= -18w^2 + 13w^2 + w - 32 - 40$
Combine like terms.	$= -5w^2 + w - 72$

So, $(-18w^2 + w - 32) - (40 - 13w^2) = -5w^2 + w - 72$.

We can also place one polynomial beneath the other and subtract like terms.

$$\begin{array}{r} -18w^2 + w - 32 \\ - (-13w^2 \qquad + 40) \\ \hline \end{array}$$

To do the subtraction, we change the sign of each term being subtracted, then add.

$$\begin{array}{r} -18w^2 + w - 32 \\ + (+13w^2 \qquad - 40) \\ \hline -5w^2 + w - 72 \end{array}$$

Example 6.2.7

Subtract $(15z^2 - 5yz^2 + 4y^3)$ from $(6y^3 - 10z^3 + 2yz^2)$.

Solution

Be careful! "Subtract A from B" means B − A. The order is important.

Write the difference. $\qquad (6y^3 - 10z^3 + 2yz^2) - (15z^2 - 5yz^2 + 4y^3)$

Change the subtraction to addition of the opposite.

$$= (6y^3 - 10z^3 + 2yz^2) + (-1)(15z^2 - 5yz^2 + 4y^3)$$

Remove the parentheses.

$$= 6y^3 - 10z^3 + 2yz^2 - 15z^2 + 5yz^2 - 4y^3$$

Write like terms next to each other.

$$= 6y^3 - 4y^3 - 10z^3 + 2yz^2 + 5yz^2 - 15z^2$$

Combine like terms. $\quad = 2y^3 - 10z^3 + 7yz^2 - 15z^2$

Here is a summary of this concept from *Academic Systems Algebra*.

We can also place one polynomial beneath the other and subtract like terms.

$$6y^3 - 10z^3 + 2yz^2$$
$$\underline{- (4y^3 \qquad - 5yz^2 + 15z^2)}$$

To do the subtraction, we change the sign of each term being subtracted, then add.

$$6y^3 - 10z^3 + 2yz^2$$
$$\underline{+ (-4y^3 \qquad + 5yz^2 - 15z^2)}$$
$$2y^3 - 10z^3 + 10yz^2 - 15z^2$$

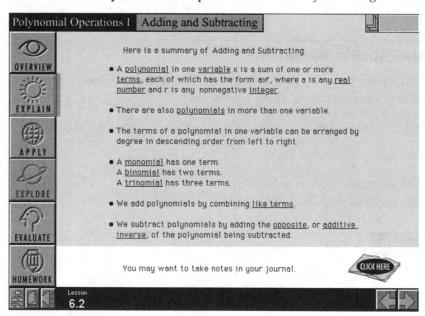

Polynomial Operations I — Adding and Subtracting

OVERVIEW
EXPLAIN
APPLY
EXPLORE
EVALUATE
HOMEWORK

Here is a summary of Adding and Subtracting.

- A polynomial in one variable x is a sum of one or more terms, each of which has the form ax^r, where a is any real number and r is any nonnegative integer.

- There are also polynomials in more than one variable.

- The terms of a polynomial in one variable can be arranged by degree in descending order from left to right.

- A monomial has one term.
  A binomial has two terms.
  A trinomial has three terms.

- We add polynomials by combining like terms.

- We subtract polynomials by adding the opposite, or additive inverse, of the polynomial being subtracted.

You may want to take notes in your journal. CLICK HERE

Lesson 6.2

CONCEPT 2: MULTIPLYING AND DIVIDING POLYNOMIALS

Concept 2 has sections on

- **Multiplying a Monomial by a Monomial**

- **Multiplying a Polynomial by a Monomial**

- **Dividing a Monomial by a Monomial**

- **Dividing a Polynomial by a Monomial**

Multiplying a Monomial By a Monomial

To find the product of two monomials, multiply the coefficients. Then, use the Multiplication Property of Exponents to combine variable factors that have the same base.

Example 6.2.8

Find: $7m^3n^4 \cdot 6mn^2$

Solution

Write the coefficients next to each other. Write the factors with base m next to each other, and write the factors with base n next to each other.

$$7m^3n^4 \cdot 6mn^2$$
$$= (7 \cdot 6)(m^3 \cdot m^1)(n^4 \cdot n^2)$$

Use the Multiplication Property of Exponents.

$$= (7 \cdot 6)(m^{3+1}n^{4+2})$$

Simplify.

$$= 42m^4n^6$$

Multiplication Property of Exponents:
$$x^m \cdot x^n = x^{m+n}$$

Example 6.2.9

Find: $\frac{1}{3}w^3x^7y \cdot 6w^2y^5$

Solution

Write the coefficients next to each other. Write the factors with base w next to each other, and write the factors with base y next to each other.

$$\frac{1}{3}w^3x^7y \cdot 6w^2y^5$$
$$= \left(\frac{1}{3} \cdot 6\right)(w^3 \cdot w^2)(x^7)(y^1 \cdot y^5)$$

Use the Multiplication Property of Exponents.

$$= \left(\frac{1}{3} \cdot 6\right)(w^{3+2})(x^7)(y^{1+5})$$

Simplify.

$$= 2w^5x^7y^6$$

Example 6.2.10

Find: $(-5x^3y)(3x^5)(2xy^5)$

Solution

Write the coefficients next to each other.

$(-5x^3y)(3x^5)(2xy^5)$

Write the factors with base x next to each other and write the factors with base y next to each other.

$= (-5 \cdot 3 \cdot 2)(x^3 \cdot x^5 \cdot x^1)(y^1 \cdot y^5)$

Use the Multiplication Property of Exponents.

$= (-5 \cdot 3 \cdot 2)(x^{3+5+1})(y^{1+5})$

Simplify.

$= -30x^9y^6$

Multiplying a Polynomial By a Monomial

To multiply a monomial by a polynomial with more than one term, use the Distributive Property to distribute the monomial to each term in the polynomial.

Example 6.2.11

Find: $-8w^3y(4w^2y^5 - w^4)$

Solution

$-8w^3y(4w^2y^5 - w^4)$

Multiply each term in the polynomial by the monomial, $-8w^3y$.

$= (-8w^3y)(4w^2y^5) - (-8w^3y)(w^4)$

Within each term, write the coefficients next to each other. Write the factors with base w next to each other and write the factors with base y next to each other.

$= (-8 \cdot 4)(w^3 \cdot w^2)(y \cdot y^5) - (-8)(w^3 \cdot w^4)(y)$

Use the Multiplication Property of Exponents.

$= (-8 \cdot 4)(w^{3+2}y^{1+5}) - (-8)(w^{3+4}y)$

Simplify.

$= \quad -32w^5y^6 \quad + \quad 8w^7y$

Example 6.2.12

Find: $5x^4(3x^2y^2 - 2xy^2 + x^3y)$

Solution
$$5x^4(3x^2y^2 - 2xy^2 + x^3y)$$

Multiply each term in the polynomial by the monomial, $5x^4$.

$$= (\mathbf{5x^4})(3x^2y^2) - (\mathbf{5x^4})(2xy^2) + (\mathbf{5x^4})(x^3y)$$

Within each term, write the coefficients next to each other. Write the factors with base x next to each other and write the factors with base y next to each other.

$$= (5 \cdot 3)(x^4x^2y^2) - (5 \cdot 2)(x^4x^1y^2) + (5 \cdot 1)(x^4x^3y)$$

Use the Multiplication Property of Exponents.

$$= (5 \cdot 3)(x^{\mathbf{4+2}}y^2) - (5 \cdot 2)(x^{\mathbf{4+1}}y^2) + (5 \cdot 1)(x^{\mathbf{4+3}}y)$$

Simplify.
$$= \quad 15x^6y^2 \quad - \quad 10x^5y^2 \quad + \quad 5x^7y$$

Dividing a Monomial By a Monomial

To divide a monomial by a monomial, use the Division Property of Exponents. (Assume that any variable in the denominator is not equal to zero.)

Division Property of Exponents

$$\frac{x^m}{x^n} = x^{m-n} \text{ for } m > n \text{ and } x \neq 0$$

$$\frac{x^m}{x^n} = \frac{1}{x^{n-m}} \text{ for } m < n \text{ and } x \neq 0$$

Example 6.2.13

Find: $-36w^5xy^3 \div 9w^2y^7$

Solution
$$-36w^5xy^3 \div 9w^2y^7$$

Rewrite the problem using a division bar.
$$= \frac{-36w^5xy^3}{9w^2y^7}$$

Cancel the common factor, 9, in the numerator and denominator.
$$= \frac{-\mathbf{4}w^5xy^3}{w^2y^7}$$

Use the Division Property of Exponents.
$$= \frac{-4w^{5-2}x}{y^{7-3}}$$

Simplify.
$$= \frac{-4w^3x}{y^4}$$

Dividing a Polynomial By a Monomial

When you added fractions, you learned: $\dfrac{a}{c} + \dfrac{b}{c} = \dfrac{a+b}{c}$, where $c \neq 0$

If we exchange the expressions on either side of the equals sign, we have: $\dfrac{a+b}{c} = \dfrac{a}{c} + \dfrac{b}{c}$

We will use this property to divide a polynomial by a monomial. To divide a polynomial by a monomial, divide each term of the polynomial by the monomial.

Example 6.2.14

Find: $(27w^5x^3y^2 - 12w^3x^2y) \div 3w^2xy$

Solution $\hspace{3cm} (27w^5x^3y^2 - 12w^3x^2y) \div 3w^2xy$

Rewrite the problem using a division bar.

$$= \frac{27w^5x^3y^2 - 12w^3x^2y}{3w^2xy}$$

Divide each term of the polynomial by the monomial.

$$= \frac{27w^5x^3y^2}{3w^2xy} - \frac{12w^3x^2y}{3w^2xy}$$

Cancel the common factor, 3, in each fraction.

$$= \frac{9w^5x^3y^2}{w^2xy} - \frac{4w^3x^2y}{w^2xy}$$

Use the Division Property of Exponents.

$$= \frac{9w^{5-2}x^{3-1}y^{2-1}}{1} - \frac{4w^{3-2}x^{2-1}y^{1-1}}{1}$$

Note that $y^{1-1} = y^0 = 1$.

$$= 9w^3x^2y - 4wx$$

Example 6.2.15

A landscape architect is designing a patio. She wants to estimate the cost of the patio for various widths and lengths.

a. Construct an expression for the area of the patio in terms of x and y.

b. If the brick she will use costs $4.50 per square foot, find the cost of the brick for a patio that is 10 feet wide by 40 feet long.

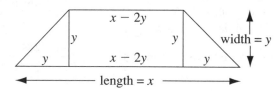

Solution

a. The patio is made up of two triangles and a rectangle.
    Recall two formulas from geometry:

Area of a rectangle = length · width   Area = lw

Area of a triangle = $\frac{1}{2}$(base)(height)   Area = $\frac{1}{2}bh$

Express the area of each triangle   Area = $\frac{1}{2}bh$
in terms of y.

Each triangle has base y $= \frac{1}{2}(y)(y)$
and height y.

$= \frac{1}{2}y^2$

Express the area of the rectangle   Area = lw
in terms of x and y.

The rectangle has length $(x - 2y)$ $= (x - 2y)y$
and width y. $= xy - 2y^2$

The area of the patio is the
sum of the areas of the two   Area = $\begin{array}{c}\text{area of}\\\text{triangle}\end{array}$ + $\begin{array}{c}\text{area of}\\\text{rectangle}\end{array}$ + $\begin{array}{c}\text{area of}\\\text{triangle}\end{array}$
triangles and the rectangle.

Substitute the expressions for area. $= \frac{1}{2}y^2 \quad + xy - 2y^2 + \frac{1}{2}y^2$

Simplify. $= xy - y^2$

Therefore, the area of the patio in terms of x and y is $xy - y^2$.

b. The length of the base of the patio is x. This is 40 feet.
    The width of the patio, y, is 10 feet.

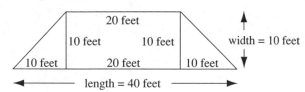

In the formula for the area of   Area = $xy - y^2$
the patio, substitute 40 feet $=$ **(40 feet)(10 feet)** $-$ **(10 feet)**^{2}
for x and 10 feet for y. $=$ 300 feet^2

The cost of the patio is the   Cost = $\dfrac{\$4.50}{1 \text{ foot}^2} \cdot 300 \text{ feet}^2$
price per square foot times
the number of square feet. $= \$1350$

The bricks for the patio will cost \$1350.

Here is a summary of this concept from *Academic Systems Algebra*.

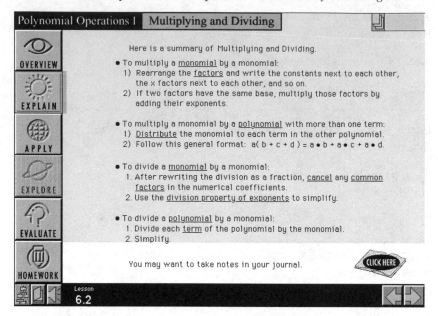

| Polynomial Operations I | Multiplying and Dividing |

Here is a summary of Multiplying and Dividing.

- To multiply a <u>monomial</u> by a monomial:
  1) Rearrange the <u>factors</u> and write the constants next to each other, the x factors next to each other, and so on.
  2) If two factors have the same base, multiply those factors by adding their exponents.

- To multiply a monomial by a <u>polynomial</u> with more than one term:
  1) <u>Distribute</u> the monomial to each term in the other polynomial.
  2) Follow this general format: $a(b + c + d) = a \bullet b + a \bullet c + a \bullet d$.

- To divide a <u>monomial</u> by a monomial:
  1. After rewriting the division as a fraction, <u>cancel</u> any <u>common factors</u> in the numerical coefficients.
  2. Use the <u>division property of exponents</u> to simplify.

- To divide a <u>polynomial</u> by a monomial:
  1. Divide each <u>term</u> of the polynomial by the monomial.
  2. Simplify.

You may want to take notes in your journal.

CLICK HERE

Lesson 6.2

Checklist Lesson 6.2

Here is what you should know after completing this lesson.

Words and Phrases

monomial
polynomial
binomial
trinomial

degree of a term
degree of a polynomial
evaluate a polynomial

Ideas and Procedures

❶ Definition of a Polynomial
Determine whether a given expression is a polynomial.

Example 6.2.1b
    Determine if $\dfrac{24}{x^2} - 3x$ is a polynomial.

See also: Example 6.2.1a, c, d
              Apply 1-4

❷ Degree of a Polynomial
Arrange the terms of a polynomial in descending order by degree and determine the degree of the polynomial.

Example 6.2.2
    Arrange the terms of this polynomial in descending order and determine the degree of the polynomial:
    $7x^3 - 8 + 2x - x^4$

See also: Apply 5-7

❸ Evaluate a Polynomial
Evaluate a polynomial when given a specific value for each variable.

Example 6.2.3
    Evaluate this polynomial when $w = -3$ and $y = 2$:
    $6w^2 - 4wy - y^4 + 5$

See also: Apply 8-13

❹ Add Polynomials
Find the sum of polynomials.

Example 6.2.5
    Find the sum of $(3z^3 + 2zy^2 - 6y^3)$ and $(15z^3 - 5zy^2 + 4z^2)$.

See also: Example 6.2.4
              Apply 14-22

❺ Subtract Polynomials
Find the difference of polynomials.

Example 6.2.7
    Subtract $(15z^2 - 5yz^2 + 4y^3)$ from $(6y^3 - 10z^3 + 2yz^2)$.

See also: Example 6.2.6
              Apply 23-28

❻ Multiply Monomials
Find the product of monomials.

Example 6.2.10
   Find: $(-5x^3y)(3x^5)(2xy^5)$

See also: Example 6.2.8, 6.2.9
   Apply 29-35

❼ Multiply a Monomial by a Polynomial
Find the product of a monomial and a polynomial.

Example 6.2.12
   Find: $5x^4(3x^2y^2 - 2xy^2 + x^3y)$

See also: Example 6.2.11
   Apply 36-41

❽ Divide a Monomial by a Monomial
Find the quotient of two monomials.

Example 6.2.13
   Find: $-36w^5xy^3 \div 9w^2y^7$

See also: Apply 42-50

❾ Divide a Polynomial by a Monomial
Find the quotient of a polynomial divided by a monomial.

Example 6.2.14
   Find: $(27w^5x^3y^2 - 12w^3x^2y) \div 3w^2xy$

See also: Example 6.2.15
   Apply 51-56

Homework

Homework Problems

Circle the homework problems assigned to you by the computer, then complete them below.

 Explain

Adding and Subtracting Polynomials

1. Circle the algebraic expression that is a polynomial.

   $3\frac{1}{4}y^3 + \sqrt{3y^2 - 5}$

   $3\frac{1}{4}y^3 + 3y^2 - 5$

   $\frac{1}{4y^3} + 3y^2 - 5$

2. Write m beside the monomial, b beside the binomial, and t beside the trinomial.

   _____ $34x + x^2 + z$

   _____ wxy^3z^2

   _____ $pn^2 - 13n^3$

3. Given the polynomial $3y - 2y^3 - 4y^5 + 2$:

   a. write the terms in descending order.

   b. find the degree of each term.

   c. find the degree of the polynomial.

4. Find:
   $(-3w - 12w^3 + 2) + (15w - 2w^3 + 4w^5 - 3)$

5. Find: $(2v^3 + 6v^2 + 2) - (5v + v^3 + 4v^7 - 3)$

6. Evaluate $\frac{1}{4}xy + 3y^2 - 5x^3$ when $x = 2$ and $y = 4$.

7. Find: $(-s^2t + s^3t^3 + 4st^2 - 27) +$
   $\qquad (3st^2 + 2st - 8s^3t^3 - 13t + 36)$

8. Find: $(12x^3y + 9x^2y^2 + 6xy - y + 7) -$
   $\qquad (7xy - x + y - 11x^3y + 3x^2y^2 - 4)$

9. Angelina works at a pet store. Today, she is cleaning three fish tanks. These polynomials describe the volumes of the tanks:

   Tank 1: xy^2

   Tank 2: $x^2y - 2y^3 + 4xy^2 + 3$

   Tank 3: $x^2y + 5xy^2 + 6y^3$

   Write a polynomial that describes the total volume of the three tanks.
   Hint: Add the polynomials.

   volume = _____

10. Angelina has three fish tanks to clean. These polynomials describe their volumes.

    Tank 1: xy^2

    Tank 2: $x^2y - 2y^3 + 4xy^2 + 3$

    Tank 3: $x^2y + 5xy^2 + 6y^3$

    What is the total volume of the fish tanks if $x = 3$ feet and $y = 1.5$ feet?

    volume = _____ cubic feet

11. Find: $(w^2yz + 3w^3 - 2wyz^2 + 4wyz) -$
    $(4wy^2z - 3w^2yz + 2wyz^2) + (2wyz + 3)$

12. Find: $(tu^2v - 4t^2u^2v + 9t^3uv + 3tv) +$
    $(3t^2u^2 + 2tv - t^3) - (4t^2u^2v + 3tv + 2tu^2v)$
    $- (6t^3uv + 2tv)$

Multiplying and Dividing Polynomials

13. Find: $xyz \cdot x^2y^2z^2$

14. Find: $3p^2r \cdot 2p^3qr$

15. Find: $-6t^3u^2v^{11} \cdot \frac{1}{2}tu^2v^4$

16. Find: $3y(2x^3 + 3x^2y)$

17. Find: $5p^2r^3(2pr + p^2r^2)$

18. Find: $t^3uv^4(2tu - 3uv + 4tv + 5)$

19. Write $12w^7x^3y^2z^6 \div 4w^2x^2y^3z^6$ as a fraction and simplify.

20. Write $(36x^3y^3 + 15x^2y^5) \div 9x^2y$ as a fraction and simplify.

21. Find: $15a^7b^4d^2 \div 10a^4b^9c^3d$

22. Tony is an algebra student. This is how he answered a question on a test:
$(2t^8u^3 - 4t^4u^9 + 6t^{12}u^6) \div 2t^4u^3 =$
$t^2u - 2tu^3 + 3t^3u^2$

Is his answer right or wrong? Why? Circle the most appropriate response.

The answer is right.

The answer is wrong. Tony divided the exponents rather than adding them.
The correct answer is
$t^{12}u^6 - t^8u^{12} + t^{16}u^9$.

The answer is wrong. The terms need to be ordered by degree. The correct answer is $3t^3u^2 + t^2u - 2tu^3$.

The answer is wrong. Tony divided the exponents rather than subtracting them.
The correct answer is
$t^4 - 2u^6 + 3t^8u^3$.

The answer is wrong. Tony shouldn't have canceled the numerical coefficients.
The correct answer is
$2t^2u - 4tu^3 + 6t^3u^2$.

23. Find: $(16x^2y^4 + 20x^3y^5) \div 12xy^2$

24. Find: $(20t^5u^{11} + 5t^3u^5 + 30tu^6v^5) \div 10t^4u^5$

 **Apply**

Practice Problems

Here are some additional practice problems for you to try.

Adding and Subtracting Polynomials

1. Circle the algebraic expressions below that are polynomials.

   $2xy + 5xz$

   $\dfrac{2}{3x} + 6x$

   $9y^2 + 13yz - 8z^2$

   $\sqrt{24x^5}$

   $\dfrac{15a^3}{5a^8}$

2. Circle the algebraic expressions below that are polynomials.

   $8xy + \dfrac{3}{y}$

   $\sqrt{17x^3}$

   $3w - 7wz - 1$

   $7x^2 - 13x + 8y^2$

   $\dfrac{12x^2}{3x^3}$

3. Identify each polynomial below as a monomial, a binomial, or a trinomial.

   a. $17x + 24z$

   b. $13ab^2 - 5$

   c. $m - n + 10$

   d. $42a^2b^4c$

   e. $73 + 65x - 21y$

4. Identify each polynomial below as a monomial, a binomial, or a trinomial.

   a. $25 - 6xyz - 4x$

   b. $2xyz^3$

   c. $x + y - 1$

   d. $36 - 3xyz$

   e. $32x^2y$

5. Find the degree of the polynomial $8a^3b^5 - 11a^2b^3 + 7b^6$.

6. Find the degree of the polynomial $12m^4n^7 - 16m^{12}$.

7. Find the degree of the polynomial $7x^3y^2z + 3x^2y^3z^4 + 6z^7$.

8. Evaluate $2x^2 - 8x + 11$ when $x = -1$.

9. Evaluate $x^3 + 3x^2 - x + 1$ when $x = -2$.

10. Evaluate $2x^2 - 5x + 8$ when $x = 3$.

11. Evaluate $x^2y + xy^2$ when $x = 2$ and $y = -3$.

12. Evaluate $5mn + 4mn^2 + 8m - n$ when $m = 4$ and $n = -2$.

13. Evaluate $3uv - 6u^2v + 2u - v + 4$ when $u = 2$ and $v = -4$.

14. Find: $(3x^2 + 7x) + (x^2 - 5)$

15. Find: $(5x^2 + 4x - 8) + (x^2 + 7x)$

16. Find: $(6a^2 + 8a - 10) + (-3a^2 - 2a + 7)$

17. Find: $(12m^2n^3 + 7m^2n^2 - 14mn) + (3m^2n^3 - 5m^2n^2 + 7mn)$

18. Find: $(10x^4y^3 - 9x^2y^3 + 6xy^2 - x) + (28x^4y^3 + 14x^2y^3 + 3xy^2 + x)$

19. Find: $(13a^3b^2 + 6a^2b - 5ab^3 + b) + (2a^3b^2 - 2a^2b + 4ab^3 - b)$

20. Find: $(11u^5v^4w^3 + 6u^3v^2w) + (6u^5v^4w^3 - 11u^3v^2w)$

21. Find: $(7xy^2z^3 - 19x^2yz^2 + 26x^3y^3z) + (13xy^2z^3 - 11x^2yz^2 - 16x^3y^3z)$

22. Find: $(9a^4b^2c - 3a^2b^3c + 5abc) + (2abc - 6a^4b^2c - 2) + (3a^2b^3c + 5)$

23. Find: $(5x^3 + 7x) - (x^3 + 8)$

24. Find: $(9a^2 + 7ab + 14b) - (3a^2 - 7b)$

25. Find: $(2y^2 + 6xy + 3y) - (y^2 - y)$

26. Find: $(8x^3 + 9x^2 + 17) - (5x^3 - 3x^2 + 15)$

27. Find: $(9a^5b^3 + 8a^4b - 6b) -$
$\quad (-2a^5b^3 + 12a^4b + 3b)$

28. Find: $(7x^4y^2 - 3x^2y + 5x) - (9x^4y^2 + 3x^2y - 2x)$

Multiplying and Dividing Polynomials

29. Find: $3y^4 \cdot 5y$

30. Find: $5x^3 \cdot 2x$

31. Find: $-5a^5 \cdot 9a^4$

32. Find: $-3x^3 \cdot 12x^4$

33. Find: $4x^3y^5 \cdot 7xy^3$

34. Find: $-7a^5b^6c^3 \cdot 8ab^3c$

35. Find: $-3w^2x^3y^2z \cdot 2x^2yz^2$

36. Find: $4y^3(3y^2 + 5y - 10)$

37. Find: $-2a^3b^2(3a^4b^5 - 5ab^3 + 6a)$

38. Find: $2xy^3(2x^6 - 5x^4 + y^2)$

39. Find: $5a^2b^2(4a^2 + 2a^2b - 7ab^2 - 3b)$

40. Find: $-4mn^3(-3m^2n + 12mn^2 - 6m + 7n^2)$

41. Find: $4x^3y^3(3x^3 - 7xy^2 + 2xy - y)$

42. Find: $\dfrac{9x^3y}{3x^2}$

43. Find: $\dfrac{20a^5b^6}{4a^3b}$

44. Find: $\dfrac{12x^4y^6}{3x^2y}$

45. Find: $\dfrac{32a^7b^9c}{12a^5b^6c^2}$

46. Find: $\dfrac{15m^6n^{10}}{10n^4p^3}$

47. Find: $\dfrac{24x^6y^2z^7}{16wx^3z^2}$

48. Find: $\dfrac{27a^4b^3c^{12}d}{15ac^7d^3}$

49. Find: $\dfrac{42mn^6p^3q^4}{28m^2nq^5}$

50. Find: $\dfrac{36w^2x^3y^7z}{21w^5y^2z^2}$

51. Find: $\dfrac{32a^3 + 24a^5}{8a^2}$

52. Find: $\dfrac{21m^2 + 18mn^3}{3mn}$

53. Find: $\dfrac{14x + 8x^4y^2}{2xy}$

54. Find: $\dfrac{24a^2b^2c^3 - 4ab^4c^5}{16abc^3}$

55. Find: $\dfrac{32x^2y^3z^4 - 8x^5yz^7}{16x^3y^3z^4}$

56. Find: $\dfrac{32r^4st^2 - 3r^2st^5}{12r^3s^2t}$

Evaluate

Practice Test

Take this practice test to be sure that you are prepared for the final quiz in Evaluate.

1. Circle the expressions that are polynomials.

   $-\sqrt{325}$

   $\dfrac{2}{5}p^3r - 3p^2q + \sqrt{2r}$

   $t^2 - s + 5$

   $\dfrac{5}{7}c^{15} + \dfrac{3}{14}c^{11} - 3\pi$

   $m^5n^4o^3p^2r$

   $x^2 + 3xy - \dfrac{2}{3x} + y^2$

2. Write m beside the monomial(s), b beside the binomial(s), and t beside the trinomial(s).

   a. ____ w^5x^4

   b. ____ $2x^2 - 36$

   c. ____ $\dfrac{1}{3}x^{17} + \dfrac{2}{3}x^{12} - \dfrac{1}{3}$

   d. ____ 27

   e. ____ $27x^3 - 2x^2y^3$

   f. ____ $x^2 + 3xy - \dfrac{2}{3}y^2$

3. Given the polynomial $3w^3 - 13w^2 + 7w^5 + 8w^8 - 2$, write the terms in descending order by degree.

4. Find:

   a. $(5x^3y - 8x^2y^2 + 3xy - y^3 + 13) + (-2xy + 6 + y^2 - 4y^3 - 2x^3y)$

   b. $(5x^3y - 8x^2y^2 + 3xy - y^3 + 13) - (-2xy + 6 + y^2 - 4y^3 - 2x^3y)$

5. Find: $x^3y^2w \cdot x^5yw^4$

6. Find: $n^2p^3(3n + 2n^3p^2 - 35p^4)$

7. Find: $21x^5y^2z^7 \div 14xyz$

8. Find: $(15t^3u^2v - 5t^5uv^2) \div 10tuv^2$

LESSON 6.3
POLYNOMIAL OPERATIONS II

 ## Overview

Polynomials can be used to solve many types of problems, such as finding the revenue, costs, and profit in a small business.

An automobile company might use polynomials to find the average cost of manufacturing an air bag. A structural engineer might use a polynomial to find the wind force on a large building.

In this lesson, you will find the products of binomials, and will multiply and divide polynomials that have two or more terms.

 ## Explain

Concept 1 has sections on

- **Using the "FOIL" Method to Multiply Two Binomials**

- **Using Patterns to Multiply Two Binomials**

CONCEPT 1: MULTIPLYING BINOMIALS

Using the "FOIL" Method to Multiply Two Binomials

To multiply a binomial by a binomial, we use the Distributive Property twice.

For example, let's multiply $(a + b)(c + d)$.

Distribute $(c + d)$ to both a and b.

$$(a + b)(c + d) = a(c + d) + b(c + d)$$

Distribute both a and b to each term in $(c + d)$.

$$= ac + ad + bc + bd$$

Notice that each term in $(a + b)$ has been multiplied by each term in $(c + d)$.

This picture may help you remember how to use the FOIL method. The arcs form a "face."

To remember how to multiply two binomials, we use the word **FOIL**. FOIL stands for **First, Outer, Inner, Last**.

- The product of the **First** terms is ***ac***.

- The product of the **Outer** terms is ***ad***.

- The product of the **Inner** terms is ***bc***.

- The product of the **Last** terms is ***bd***.

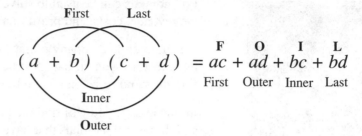

$$ (a + b)\ (c + d) = ac + ad + bc + bd $$

First Outer Inner Last

Example 6.3.1

Find: $(x - 2)(x + 5)$

Solution

| | **F** | **O** | **I** | **L** |

Use FOIL. $(x - 2)(x + 5) = (x)(x) + (x)(5) + (-2)(x) + (-2)(5)$

Simplify each product. $= x^2 + 5x - 2x - 10$

Combine like terms. $= x^2 + \mathbf{3x} - 10$

So, $(x - 2)(x + 5) = x^2 + 3x - 10$.

Example 6.3.2

Find: $(3w - 7)(9w - 5)$

Solution

Use FOIL.   **F**   **O**   **I**   **L**

$(3w - 7)(9w - 5) = (3w)(9w) + (3w)(-5) + (-7)(9w) + (-7)(-5)$

Simplify each product. $= 27w^2 - 15w - 63w + 35$

Combine like terms. $= 27w^2 - \mathbf{78w} + 35$

So, $(3w - 7)(9w - 5) = 27w^2 - 78w + 35$.

Using Patterns To Multiply Two Binomials

We can use FOIL to find the product of any two binomials. Sometimes we can find certain binomial products more quickly by recognizing patterns.

For example, let's first use FOIL to find $(a + b)^2$.

Use the definition of exponential notation to write $(a + b)^2$ as the product of two binomials. $\qquad$ $(a + b)^2 = (a + b)(a + b)$

Use FOIL. $\qquad$ $= a^2 + ab + ba + b^2$

Combine like terms. $\qquad$ $= a^2 + 2ab + b^2$

Note that $(a + b)^2$ is not equal to $a^2 + b^2$. Don't forget the middle term, 2ab.

Thus, $(a + b)^2 = a^2 + 2ab + b^2$.

We obtain a similar pattern when we square a binomial that is a difference rather than a sum.

— Formula —
Square of a Binomial

Let a and b represent any real numbers.

$(a + b)^2 = a^2 + 2ab + b^2$

$(a - b)^2 = a^2 - 2ab + b^2$

When a binomial is squared, the resulting trinomial is called a **perfect square trinomial**.

For example, both $a^2 + 2ab + b^2$ and $a^2 - 2ab + b^2$ are perfect square trinomials.

When we refer to integers, a perfect square is an integer that is the square of another integer:

9 is a perfect square because it is the result of squaring 3.

A similar situation exists for variables:

a^2 is a perfect square because it is the result of squaring a.

$64n^2$ is a perfect square because it is the result of squaring 8n.

Example 6.3.3

Find: $(6y^2 + 5)^2$

Solution

The expression $(6y^2 + 5)^2$ is in the form $(a + b)^2$.
So, we can use the formula for the square of a binomial. $\qquad$ $(a + b)^2 = a^2 + 2ab + b^2$

Substitute $6y^2$ for a and 5 for b. $\qquad$ $(\mathbf{6y^2 + 5}) = (\mathbf{6y^2})^2 + 2(\mathbf{6y^2})(\mathbf{5}) + (\mathbf{5})^2$

Simplify. $\qquad$ $= 36y^4 + 60y^2 + 25$

So, $(6y^2 + 5)^2 = 36y^4 + 60y^2 + 25$

Note that $(6y^2 + 5)^2 \neq (6y^2)^2 + (5)^2$. Don't forget the middle term, $60y^2$.

Example 6.3.4

Find: $(3w - 7y)(3w - 7y)$

Solution

Since $(3w - 7y)(3w - 7y) = (3w - 7y)^2$, we can use the shortcut for the square of a binomial.

$$(a - b)^2 = a^2 - 2ab + b^2$$

Substitute $3w$ for a and $7y$ for b.

$$(3w - 7y)^2 = (3w)^2 - 2(3w)(7y) + (7y)^2$$

Simplify.

$$= 9w^2 - 42wy + 49y^2$$

So, $(3w - 7y)(3w - 7y) = 9w^2 - 42wy + 49y^2$

Note that $(3w^2 - 7y)^2 \neq (3w^2)^2 - (7y)^2$. Don't forget the middle term, $-42wy^2$.

Example 6.3.5

	x	$+$	6
x	Region I		Region II
$+$			
6	Region III		Region IV

This large square is divided into four regions. The length of each side of the large square is $x + 6$ units.

a. Find the area of the large square.

b. Find the area of each region in the large square.

c. Explain how the area of the four regions is related to the area of the large square.

Solution

a. The large square has area = length · width.
This is $(x + 6)(x + 6)$, or $(x + 6)^2$.
This is in the form $(a + b)^2$, so we use the shortcut.

$$(a + b)^2 = a^2 + 2ab + b^2$$

Substitute x for a and 6 for b.

$$(x + 6)^2 = (x)^2 + 2(x)(6) + (6)^2$$

Simplify.

$$= x^2 + 12x + 36$$

We could also use FOIL to find $(x + 6)^2$.

$$(x + 6)(x + 6) = x^2 + 6x + 6x + 36$$
$$= x^2 + 12x + 36$$

Therefore, the area of the large square is $x^2 + 12x + 36$.

b. Each region is a rectangle with area = length · width.

Region I:	Region II:	Region III:	Region IV:
$x \cdot x = x^2$	$x \cdot 6 = 6x$	$x \cdot 6 = 6x$	$6 \cdot 6 = 36$

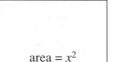

c. The sum of the areas of the four regions is: $x^2 + 6x + 6x + 36$
   We combine like terms and obtain the area
   of the large square: $= x^2 + 12x + 36$

We obtain another useful pattern when we multiply the sum and difference of the same two terms.

F   O   I   L

For example, let's use FOIL $(a + b)(a - b) = a^2 - ab + ba - b^2$
to find $(a + b)(a - b)$.

When we combine like terms, $= a^2 - b^2$
the middle terms cancel out.

The expression $a^2 - b^2$ is called the **difference of two squares** because the operation is subtraction and each term is a square.

The pattern tells us that the product of conjugates always results in the difference of two perfect squares.

The following pairs of binomials are examples of conjugates:

$a + b$ and $a - b$
$x - y$ and $x + y$
$w + 2$ and $w - 2$
$k - 5$ and $k + 5$

— Formula —
The Product of the Sum and Difference of the Same Two Terms

Let a and b represent any real numbers.
$$(a + b)(a - b) = a^2 - b^2$$

Example 6.3.6

Find: $(m + 8n)(m - 8n)$

Solution

The expression $(m + 8n)(m - 8n)$
is in the form $(a + b)(a - b)$. So we
can use the shortcut: $(a + b)(a - b) = a^2 - b^2$

Substitute m for a and $8n$ for b. $(\boldsymbol{m} + \boldsymbol{8n})(\boldsymbol{m} - \boldsymbol{8n}) = (\boldsymbol{m})^2 - (\boldsymbol{8n})^2$

Simplify. $= m^2 - 64n^2$

So, $(m + 8n)(m - 8n) = m^2 - 64n^2$.

Here is a summary of this concept from *Academic Systems Algebra*.

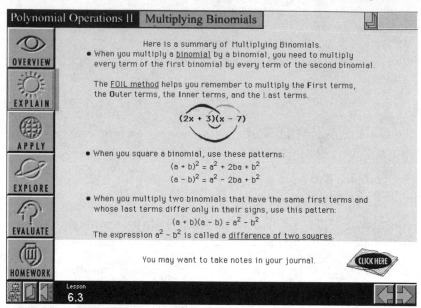

Polynomial Operations II Multiplying Binomials

OVERVIEW
EXPLAIN
APPLY
EXPLORE
EVALUATE
HOMEWORK

Here is a summary of Multiplying Binomials.
• When you multiply a binomial by a binomial, you need to multiply every term of the first binomial by every term of the second binomial.

The FOIL method helps you remember to multiply the First terms, the Outer terms, the Inner terms, and the Last terms.

(2x + 3)(x – 7)

• When you square a binomial, use these patterns:
$(a + b)^2 = a^2 + 2ba + b^2$
$(a – b)^2 = a^2 – 2ba + b^2$

• When you multiply two binomials that have the same first terms and whose last terms differ only in their signs, use this pattern:
$(a + b)(a – b) = a^2 – b^2$
The expression $a^2 – b^2$ is called a difference of two squares.

You may want to take notes in your journal.   CLICK HERE

Lesson
6.3

CONCEPT 2: MULTIPLYING AND DIVIDING POLYNOMIALS

Multiplying Polynomials with Two or More Terms

We can use the Distributive Property to multiply two polynomials where at least one of the polynomials has two or more terms.

For example, suppose we wish to find the product $(a + b)(c + d + e)$.

Distribute $(c + d + e)$ to both a and b.

$$(a + b)(c + d + e) = a(c + d + e) + b(c + d + e)$$

Distribute both a and b to each term in $(c + d + e)$.

$$= ac + ad + ae + bc + bd + be$$

Notice that each term in the first polynomial is multiplied by each term in the second polynomial. That is, a is multiplied by c, d, and e. Also, b is multiplied by c, d, and e.

This suggests a general procedure for multiplying any two polynomials.

— Procedure —
Multiplying Polynomials with Two or More Terms
Step 1 Multiply each term in the first polynomial by each term in the second polynomial.
Step 2 Simplify.

Example 6.3.7

Find: $(3x - 4)(x^3 - 5x + 8)$

Solution

Step 1 Multiply each term in the first polynomial by each term in the second polynomial.

Multiply $3x$ by x^3, $-5x$, and 8. Then multiply -4 by x^3, $-5x$, and 8.

$(3x - 4)(x^3 - 5x + 8)$
$= (3x)(x^3) + (3x)(-5x) + (3x)(8) + (-4)(x^3) + (-4)(-5x) + (-4)(8)$
$= \quad 3x^4 \quad - \quad 15x^2 \quad + \quad 24x \quad - \quad 4x^3 \quad + \quad 20x \quad - \quad 32$

Step 2 Simplify.

Combine like terms and write the terms in descending order.
$= 3x^4 - 4x^3 - 15x^2 + 44x - 32$

So, $(3x - 4)(x^3 - 5x + 8) = 3x^4 - 4x^3 - 15x^2 + 44x - 32$.

Multiplying More Than Two Polynomials

To find the product of more than two polynomials, use the same procedure as you would for multiplying more than two whole numbers.

For example, to find $2 \cdot 3 \cdot 4$, multiply any pair of factors.

For example, first multiply $2 \cdot 3$: $\mathbf{2} \cdot \mathbf{3} \cdot 4 = (\mathbf{2} \cdot \mathbf{3}) \cdot 4$

Then, multiply $6 \cdot 4$ to get the final product.
$= \mathbf{6} \cdot 4$
$= 24$

Because multiplication is commutative, the order in which you multiply the factors does not matter.
$\mathbf{2} \cdot 3 \cdot \mathbf{4} = (\mathbf{2} \cdot \mathbf{4}) \cdot 3 = \mathbf{8} \cdot 3 = 24$

$2 \cdot \mathbf{3} \cdot \mathbf{4} = (\mathbf{3} \cdot \mathbf{4}) \cdot 2 = \mathbf{12} \cdot 2 = 24$

Example 6.3.8

Find: $(2x + 1)(2x - 1)(x + 3)^2$

Solution

The first two binomials, $(2x + 1)$ and $(2x - 1)$, are respectively, the sum and the difference of two terms. Therefore, their product is the difference of two squares.

$$(2x + 1)(2x - 1)(x + 3)^2 = [(2x)^2 - (1)^2](x + 3)^2$$
$$= (4x^2 - 1)(x + 3)^2$$

The second binomial, $(x + 3)^2$ is the square of a binomial. Therefore, use the shortcut for the square of a binomial.

$$= (4x^2 - 1)[(x)^2 + 2(x)(3) + (3)^2]$$

Simplify.

$$= (4x^2 - 1)(x^2 + 6x + 9)$$

Multiply each term in the binomial by each term in the trinomial.

$$= (4x^2)(x^2) + (4x^2)(6x) + (4x^2)(9) + (-1)(x^2) + (-1)(6x) + (-1)(9)$$

Simplify.

$$= 4x^4 + 24x^3 + 36x^2 - x^2 - 6x - 9$$

Combine like terms.

$$= 4x^4 + 24x^3 + 35x^2 - 6x - 9$$

Example 6.3.9

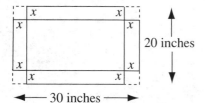

20 inches

30 inches

To make a box with an open top, Sue cuts a square from each corner of a 20 inch by 30 inch sheet of cardboard. Then, she folds up the sides to form the box.

Let x represent the length of the side of the square cut from each corner of the box.

a. Write a polynomial that represents the volume of the box.

b. Find the volume of the box if a 5 inch square is removed from each corner of the cardboard.

Solution

a. Use the formula for the volume of a box.

Volume = (length)(width)(height)

The length of the box is 30 inches minus $2x$, the length of the two squares that were cut out.

$30 - 2x$ = length of box

The width of the box is 20 inches minus $2x$, the length of the two squares that were cut out.

$20 - 2x$ = width of box

The height of the box is x, the length of the square that was cut out.

x = height of box

Substitute the expressions into the formula for the volume of the box.

Volume = (length)(width)(height)
= $(30 - 2x)(20 - 2x)(x)$

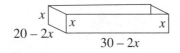

To find the product of the three factors, first use FOIL to multiply the binomials.

Write the products.　　**F**　　　　**O**　　　　**I**　　　　**L**

$(30 - 2x)(20 - 2x) = (30)(20) + (30)(-2x) + (-2x)(20) + (-2x)(-2x)$

Simplify.　　　　= 　600　　−　　60x　　−　　40x　　+　　$4x^2$

Combine like terms and write in descending order.

= 　$4x^2$　　−　　　100x　　　　+　　600

Finally, multiply $4x^2 - 100x + 600$ by x.

Volume = $(4x^2 - 100x + 600)(x)$

= $4x^3 - 100x^2 + 600x$

Therefore, the volume of the box is $4x^3 - 100x^2 + 600x$.

b. If Sue removes a 5 inch square, we can calculate the volume of the box by substituting 5 for x in the expression for volume.

Volume = $4x^3 - 100x^2 + 600x$

= $4(\mathbf{5})^3 - 100(\mathbf{5})^2 + 600(\mathbf{5})$

Simplify.

= 1000 inches^3

Thus, if a 5 inch square is removed from each corner, the resulting box will have volume 1000 cubic inches.

The volume can also be found by substituting 5 for x in the original expression

$(30 - 2x)(20 - 2x)(x).$

Dividing a Polynomial by a Polynomial

To divide a polynomial with more than one term by another polynomial with more than one term, we use **polynomial long division**.

This procedure is similar to one you may have used to divide whole numbers in arithmetic.

— Procedure —
To Divide a Polynomial by a Polynomial

Step 1 Write the problem in long division form. Arrange the terms of each polynomial in descending powers. If a term is missing, add a term of the form $0x^r$, where r is the degree of the missing term.

Step 2 Divide the first term of the dividend by the first term of the divisor.

Step 3 Multiply the divisor by the term you found in Step 2.

Step 4 Subtract the expression you found in Step 3 from the dividend.

Step 5 Bring down the next term from the dividend.

Step 6 Repeat Steps 2 through 5 until the degree of the remainder is less than the degree of the divisor.

Step 7 Write the quotient. The quotient is the expression that appears above the division symbol plus the fraction, $\frac{remainder}{divisor}$, if one exists.

Example 6.3.10

Use long division to find $(6x^3 + 7x^2 + 4x - 2) \div (2x + 1)$

Solution   **Algebra**

Step 1 Write the problem in long division form.

The terms of each polynomial are in descending order.

$$2x + 1 \overline{)6x^3 + 7x^2 + 4x - 2}$$

Step 2 *Divide the first term of the dividend by the first term of the divisor.*

Divide $6x^3$ by $2x$ to get $3x^2$.
Write $3x^2$ in the quotient line above $7x^2$, the x^2-term of the dividend.

$$\begin{array}{r} 3x^2 \\ 2x+1{\overline{\smash{)}6x^3 + 7x^2 + 4x - 2}} \end{array}$$

Here's a long division problem from arithmetic to help you see the similarities between the algebra and the arithmetic.

$$\begin{array}{r} 2 \\ 21{\overline{\smash{)}4853}} \end{array}$$

Step 3 *Multiply the divisor by the term you found in Step 2.*

Multiply $(2x + 1)$ by $3x^2$ to get $6x^3 + 3x^2$.

$$\begin{array}{r} 3x^2 \\ 2x+1{\overline{\smash{)}6x^3 + 7x^2 + 4x - 2}} \\ \mathbf{6x^3 + 3x^2} \end{array}$$

$$\begin{array}{r} 2 \\ 21{\overline{\smash{)}4853}} \\ 42 \end{array}$$

Step 4 *Subtract the expression you found in Step 3 from the dividend.*

Subtract $(6x^3 + 3x^2)$ from $(6x^3 + 7x^2)$.
The result is $4x^2$.

$$\begin{array}{r} 3x^2 \\ 2x+1{\overline{\smash{)}6x^3 + 7x^2 + 4x - 2}} \\ -(6x^3 + 3x^2) \\ \hline \mathbf{4x^2} \end{array}$$

$$\begin{array}{r} 2 \\ 21{\overline{\smash{)}4853}} \\ 42 \\ \hline 6 \end{array}$$

Step 5 *Bring down the next term from the dividend.*

Write $+ 4x$ to the right of $4x^2$.

$$\begin{array}{r} 3x^2 \\ 2x+1{\overline{\smash{)}6x^3 + 7x^2 + 4x - 2}} \\ -(6x^3 + 3x^2) \\ \hline 4x^2 + \mathbf{4x} \end{array}$$

$$\begin{array}{r} 2 \\ 21{\overline{\smash{)}4853}} \\ 42 \\ \hline 65 \end{array}$$

Step 6 *Repeat Steps 2 through 5 until the degree of the remainder is less than the degree of the divisor.*

Divide $4x^2$ by $2x$ to get $2x$.
Write $2x$ in the quotient line.

$$\begin{array}{r} 3x^2 + \mathbf{2x} \\ 2x+1{\overline{\smash{)}6x^3 + 7x^2 + 4x - 2}} \\ -(6x^3 + 3x^2) \\ \hline 4x^2 + 4x \\ -(\mathbf{4x^2 + 2x}) \\ \hline 2x - 2 \end{array}$$

$$\begin{array}{r} 23 \\ 21{\overline{\smash{)}4853}} \\ 42 \\ \hline 65 \\ 63 \\ \hline 23 \end{array}$$

Multiply $(2x + 1)$ by $2x$ to get $4x^2 + 2x$.
Subtract $(4x^2 + 2x)$ from $(4x^2 + 4x)$.
The result is $2x$.

Write -2 to the right of $2x$.

Divide $2x$ by $2x$ to get 1.
Write $+1$ in the quotient line.

$$\begin{array}{r} 3x^2 + 2x + \mathbf{1} \\ 2x+1{\overline{\smash{)}6x^3 + 7x^2 + 4x - 2}} \\ -(6x^3 + 3x^2) \\ \hline 4x^2 + 4x \\ -(4x^2 + 2x) \\ \hline 2x - 2 \\ -(\mathbf{2x + 1}) \\ \hline \mathbf{-3} \end{array}$$

$$\begin{array}{r} 231 \\ 21{\overline{\smash{)}4853}} \\ 42 \\ \hline 65 \\ 63 \\ \hline 23 \\ 21 \\ \hline 2 \end{array}$$

Multiply $(2x + 1)$ by 1 to get $2x + 1$.
Subtract $(2x + 1)$ from $(2x - 2)$.
The result is -3.

The degree of the remainder, -3, is less than the degree of the divisor, $2x + 1$. So we stop.

Step 7 *Write the quotient.*

The quotient is: $3x^2 + 2x + 1 + \dfrac{-3}{2x + 1}$.

Quotient is $231\frac{2}{21}$

Example 6.3.11

Use long division to find $(8x^3 - 1) \div (2x - 1)$.

Solution

Step 1 Write the problem in long division form.

The x^2- and x-terms are missing. So, insert the terms $0x^2$ and $0x$ as place holders.

$$2x - 1\overline{)8x^3 + 0x^2 + 0x - 1}$$

Step 2 Divide the first term of the dividend by the first term of the divisor.

Divide $8x^3$ by $2x$ to get $4x^2$. Write $4x^2$ in the quotient line above $0x^2$, the x^2-term of the dividend.

$$\begin{array}{r} 4x^2 \\ 2x - 1\overline{)8x^3 + 0x^2 + 0x - 1} \end{array}$$

Step 3 Multiply the divisor by the term you found in Step 2.

Multiply $(2x - 1)$ by $4x^2$ to get $8x^3 - 4x^2$.

$$\begin{array}{r} 4x^2 \\ 2x - 1\overline{)8x^3 + 0x^2 + 0x - 1} \\ 8x^3 - 4x^2 \end{array}$$

Step 4 Subtract the expression you found in Step 3 from the dividend.

Subtract $(8x^3 - 4x^2)$ from $(8x^3 + 0x^2)$. The result is $4x^2$.

$$\begin{array}{r} 4x^2 \\ 2x - 1\overline{)8x^3 + 0x^2 + 0x - 1} \\ -(8x^3 - 4x^2) \\ \hline 4x^2 \end{array}$$

Step 5 Bring down the next term from the dividend.

Write $+0x$ to the right of $4x^2$.

$$\begin{array}{r} 4x^2 \\ 2x - 1\overline{)8x^3 + 0x^2 + 0x - 1} \\ -(8x^3 - 4x^2) \\ \hline 4x^2 + 0x \end{array}$$

Step 6 Repeat Steps 2 through 5 until the degree of the remainder is less than the degree of the divisor.

Divide $4x^2$ by $2x$ to get $2x$. Write $+2x$ in the quotient line.

$$\begin{array}{r} 4x^2 + 2x \\ 2x - 1\overline{)8x^3 + 0x^2 + 0x - 1} \\ \underline{8x^3 - 4x^2} \\ 4x^2 + 0x \\ -(4x^2 - 2x) \\ \hline 2x - 1 \end{array}$$

Multiply $(2x - 1)$ by $2x$ to get $4x^2 - 2x$. Subtract $(4x^2 - 2x)$ from $(4x^2 + 0x)$. The result is $2x$. Write -1 to the right of $2x$.

Divide $2x$ by $2x$ to get 1.
Write $+1$ in the quotient line.

$$
\begin{array}{r}
4x^2 + 2x + \mathbf{1} \\
2x - 1\overline{)8x^3 + 0x^2 + 0x - 1} \\
\underline{8x^3 - 4x^2} \\
4x^2 + 0x \\
\underline{-(4x^2 - 2x)} \\
\mathbf{2x - 1} \\
\underline{\mathbf{-(2x - 1)}} \\
\mathbf{0}
\end{array}
$$

Multiply $(2x - 1)$ by 1 to get $2x - 1$.
Subtract $(2x - 1)$ from $(2x - 1)$.
The result is 0.

Step 7 Write the quotient.

The remainder is 0, so the quotient is $4x^2 + 2x + 1$.

To check our answer, we multiply the quotient, $4x^2 + 2x + 1$, by the divisor, $2x - 1$. The product should be the dividend, $8x^3 - 1$.

Is
$$(2x - 1)(4x^2 + 2x + 1) = 8x^3 - 1?$$

Is $(\mathbf{2x})(4x^2) + (\mathbf{2x})(2x) + (\mathbf{2x})(1) + (\mathbf{-1})(4x^2) + (\mathbf{-1})(2x) + (\mathbf{-1})(1) = 8x^3 - 1$?

Is $\quad 8x^3 \;+\; 4x^2 \;+\; 2x \;-\; 4x^2 \;-\; 2x \;-\; 1 \;= 8x^3 - 1$?

Is
$$8x^3 - 1 = 8x^3 - 1? \textbf{ Yes}$$

Since the product is the same as the dividend, our answer is correct.

Here is a summary of this concept from *Academic Systems Algebra.*

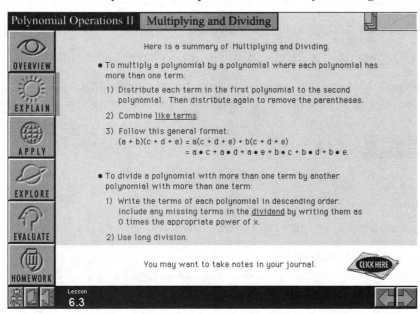

On the computer, you found products of two binomial factors.
In particular, you found patterns such as a perfect square trinomial and the difference of two squares.

Here is an exploration with another type of pattern. This pattern is based on Pascal's Triangle.

As you work through the examples, refer to this diagram.

$(a + b)^0 =$ 1 Row 1

$(a + b)^1 =$ $1a \quad + \quad 1b$ Row 2

$(a + b)^2 =$ $1a^2 \quad + \quad 2ab \quad + \quad 1b^2$ Row 3

$(a + b)^3 =$ $1a^3 \quad + \quad 3a^2b \quad + \quad 3ab^2 \quad + \quad 1b^3$ Row 4

$(a + b)^4 =$ $1a^4 + \quad 4a^3b \quad + \quad 6a^2b^2 \quad + \quad 4ab^3 \quad + \quad 1b^4$ Row 5

Notice the patterns in the triangle.

In each row the exponent of *a decreases* by 1 as you move from left to right. The exponent of *b increases* by 1 as you move from left to right.

For each term in a row, the sum of the exponents is the same. The sum is one less than the row number.

Also notice the patterns in the coefficients of the terms.

- The terms on the far left and far right always have coefficient 1.

- To find the coefficient of a term inside the triangle, add the coefficients of the two adjacent terms in the row directly above it.

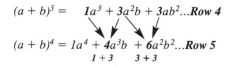

$(a + b)^3 = \quad 1a^3 + 3a^2b + 3ab^2 ...Row \ 4$

$(a + b)^4 = 1a^4 + 4a^3b + 6a^2b^2 ...Row \ 5$
           $1 + 3$ $3 + 3$

Example 6.3.12

Use Pascal's Triangle to find $(a + b)^5$.

Solution

Using the patterns, we can write the expansion of $(a + b)^5$.

First, we fill in the exponents:

$1a^5b^0 + \_\_a^4b^1 + \_\_a^3b^2 + \_\_a^2b^3 + \_\_a^1b^4 + 1a^0b^5$

Next, we use the coefficients for the expansion of $(a + b)^4$ to find the coefficients of $(a + b)^5$.

$1a^4 \quad + \quad 4a^3b^2 \quad + \quad 6a^2b^2 + \quad 4ab^3 \quad + \quad 1b^4$

$1a^5 \quad + \quad 5a^4b^1 \quad + \quad 10a^3b^2 + \quad 10a^2b^3 + \quad 5ab^4 \quad + \quad 1b^5$

So, the expansion of $(a + b)^5$ is:

$$a^5 + 5a^4b + 10a^3b^2 + 10a^2b^3 + 5ab^4 + b^5$$

Example 6.3.13

Use Pascal's Triangle to find $(3x + 2y)^4$.

Solution This corresponds to the fourth row of the triangle.

Fourth row of the triangle:
$$(a + b)^4 = 1a^4 + 4a^3b + 6a^2b^2 + 4ab^3 + 1b^4$$

Substitute $3x$ for a and $2y$ for b:
$$(3x + 2y)^4 = 1(3x)^4 + 4(3x)^3(2y) + 6(3x)^2(2y)^2 + 4(3x)(2y)^3 + 1(2y)^4$$

Simplify. $\quad = 81x^4 + 216x^3y + 216x^2y^2 + 96xy^3 + 16y^4$

Thus, $(3x + 2y)^4 = 81x + 216x^3y + 216x^2y^2 + 96xy^3 + 16y^4$.

Here is a summary of this Exploration from *Academic Systems Algebra*.

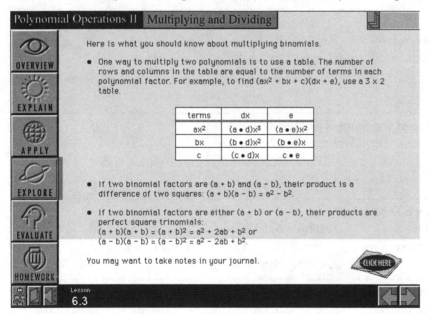

Checklist Lesson 6.3

Here is what you should know after completing this lesson.

Words and Phrases

FOIL

perfect square trinomial

difference of two squares

polynomial long division

Ideas and Procedures

❶ **FOIL**

Use FOIL (First, Outer, Inner, Last) to find the product of two binomials.

Example 6.3.2

Find: $(3w - 7)(9w - 5)$

See also: Example 6.3.1

Apply 1-9

❷ **Square of a Binomial**

Use the product for the Square of a Binomial to find the product of two identical binomials.

Example 6.3.3

Find: $(6y^2 + 5)^2$

See also: Example 6.3.4, 6.3.5

Apply 10-20

❸ **The Product of the Sum and Difference of the Same Two Terms**

Find the product of the sum and difference of the same two terms.

Example 6.3.6

Find: $(m + 8n)(m - 8n)$

See also: Apply 21-28

❹ **Multiply Polynomials with Two or More Terms**

Find the product of two polynomials when at least one of the polynomials has two or more terms.

Example 6.3.7

Find: $(3x - 4)(x^3 - 5x + 8)$

See also: Apply 29-42

❺ **Multiplying More Than Two Polynomials**

Find the product of more than two polynomials.

Example 6.3.8

Find: $(2x + 1)(2x - 1)(x + 3)^2$

See also: Example 6.3.9

❻ **Divide a Polynomial by a Polynomial**

Use polynomial long division to divide a polynomial by a polynomial.

Example 6.3.10

Use long division to find

$(6x^3 + 7x^2 + 4x - 2) \div (2x + 1)$

See also: Example 6.3.11

Apply 43-56

Homework

Homework Problems

Circle the homework problems assigned to you by the computer, then complete them below.

Explain

Multiplying Binomials

1. Given $(2p + 3)(p - p^2)$, find the:

   First terms: _____ and _____

   Outer terms: _____ and _____

   Inner terms: _____ and _____

   Last terms: _____ and _____

2. Which pattern could you use to find each of the products (a) - (f) below? Write the appropriate pattern number next to each polynomial.

   I. $(a + b)^2 = a^2 + 2ba + b^2$

   II. $(a - b)^2 = a^2 - 2ba + b^2$

   III. $(a + b)(a - b) = a^2 - b^2$

   a. ___ $(2x + 5y)^2$

   b. ___ $(2x + 5y)(2x - 5y)$

   c. ___ $(3t - 2)^2$

   d. ___ $(3t + 2)^2$

   e. ___ $(3t - 2)(3t - 2)$

   f. ___ $(2x^2 - 5y^3)^2$

3. Given $(2s^3 + 5)^2$ and the pattern $(a + b)^2 = a^2 + 2ba + b^2$:

   a. What would you replace a with in the pattern?

   _____

   b. What would you replace b with? _____

4. Use a pattern to find: $(3s + 5)^2$

5. Use the FOIL method to find: $(4x - 2y)(3x + 6)$

6. Use a pattern to find: $(3t + 4u)(3t - 4u)$

7. Use patterns to find these products:

   a. $(3x^2 - 2)(3x^2 + 2)$ c. $(3x^2 + 2)(3x^2 + 2)$

   b. $(3x^2 - 2)(3x^2 - 2)$

8. Find: $(5x^3 + 3y^2)^2$

9. A fish tank broke at the pet store where Angelina works, and part of the store was flooded. Since Angelina lost her measuring tape, she used a stick and her handspan to figure out the approximate size of the flooded area. If s equals the length of the stick and h equals the width of her handspan, these are the measurements:

   length of flooded space $= 13s + 2h$

   width of flooded space $= 13s - 2h$

   area of flooded space $= (13s + 2h)(13s - 2h)$

   Simplify the equation for the area by multiplying the binomials.

10. The owner of the pet store where Angelina works wants to replace the tile covering the entire floor, not just the flooded area. If the length of the entire floor is $250s - 3h$ and the width is $98s + h$, what is the area of the floor in terms of s and h? Hint: area $=$ length $\cdot$ width.

11. Find: $(13x^2y^2 - 10x^3)(7x^2y^2 - 6x^3)$

12. Find:

   a. $\left(\frac{1}{2}x^3 - \frac{2}{3}y^5\right)\left(\frac{1}{2}x^3 - \frac{2}{3}y^5\right)$

   b. $\left(\frac{1}{2}x^3 - \frac{2}{3}y^5\right)\left(\frac{1}{2}x^3 + \frac{2}{3}y^5\right)$

   c. $\left(\frac{1}{2}x^3 + \frac{2}{3}y^5\right)\left(\frac{1}{2}x^3 + \frac{2}{3}y^5\right)$

Multiplying and Dividing Polynomials

13. Find: $(x + 2)(3x + 4xy + 1)$

14. Find: $(p^2 + 2r + 2)(3r^4 - 2p^4)$

15. Find: $(x + y + 1)(x - y)$

16. Find: $(2t + u)(t + 2u - 1)$

17. Angelina is cleaning the windows of the guinea pig case at the pet store where she works. The surface area of the outside of the windows can be described as follows:

surface area $= 2(x + 3)(x - 2) + 2(x - 2)(x - 3)$

Simplify this equation by multiplying the polynomials.

18. The pet store where Angelina works sells an exercise arena for guinea pigs, consisting of two spheres connected by a tube. The volume of the exercise arena can be described by this equation:

volume $= 4\pi r^3 + 3\pi(r^2 + 2r + 4)(r + 2) +$
$\pi r(r - 5)(r - 5)$

Simplify the equation by multiplying the polynomials.

19. Find:
$(12x^3 - 2x^2 - 7x)\left(4x^2 - \dfrac{10}{3}x - \dfrac{1}{3} + \dfrac{7}{12x^3 - 2x^2 - 7x}\right)$

20. Find: $\left(\dfrac{1}{3}t^2 + \dfrac{2}{3}v^3\right)\left(\dfrac{1}{3}t^2 + \dfrac{2}{3}v^3\right)\left(\dfrac{1}{3}t^2 + \dfrac{2}{3}v^3\right)$

21. Find: $(3x^2 + 2x - 1) \div (x + 3)$

22. Here is how Tony answered a question on his algebra test.
$(12x^3 - 17x^2 + 3) \div (3x - 2) = 4x^2 - 3x - 2$ remainder -1.

Is his answer right or wrong? Why? Circle the most appropriate response.

His answer is right.

His answer is wrong. When doing the long division, he sometimes added negative terms rather than subtracting them. The right answer is $4x^2 + 2x - 1$.

His answer is wrong. He did not include missing terms in the quotient. The right answer is $0x^3 + 4x^2 - 3x - 2$ remainder -1.

His answer is wrong. He did not put the remainder over the dividend. The right answer is $4x^2 - 3x - 2 + \dfrac{-1}{3x - 2}$.

23. Find: $(15x^3 + x^2 + 5) \div (x + 3)$

24. Find: $(4y^3 + 5y + 3) \div (2y + 1)$

Explore

25. Find: $(3a - 1)(3a + 1)$

26. Use the table below to find a general form for multiplying two polynomials:
$(ax^2 + bx + c)(dx - e)$

terms	dx	$-e$
ax^2		
bx		
c		

$(ax^2 + bx + c)(dx - e) =$

27. Use the table below to find the general form for a difference of two squares: $(a + b)(a - b)$. Then use this pattern to find $(2x + 3y)(2x - 3y)$.

terms	a	$-b$
a		
b		

$(a + b)(a - b) =$
$(2x + 3y)(2x - 3y) =$

28. Find: $(x^2 + 3y)^2$

29. Use the table below to find the general form for a perfect square trinomial: $(a - b)(a - b)$. Then use the pattern to find $(2t^3 - 4u^2)(2t^3 - 4u^2)$.

terms	a	$-b$
a		
$-b$		

$(a - b)(a - b) =$
$(2t^3 - 4u^2)(2t^3 - 4u^2) =$

30. Use the table below to find the general form for a perfect square trinomial: $(a + b)(a + b)$. Then use this general form to find $(x^2 + 3y)(x^2 + 3y)$.

terms	a	b
a		
b		

$(a + b)(a + b) =$
$(x^2 + 3y)(x^2 + 3y) =$

 **Apply**

Practice Problems

Here are some additional practice problems for you to try.

Multiplying Binomials

1. Find: $(a + 2)(a + 5)$

2. Find: $(m - 3)(m - 7)$

3. Find: $(x - 4)(x - 11)$

4. Find: $(3b + 2)(b - 6)$

5. Find: $(5y - 8)(y + 3)$

6. Find: $(6t + 1)(t - 7)$

7. Find: $(4a + 3b)(2a + 5b)$

8. Find: $(3m - 4n)(7m + 2n)$

9. Find: $(6y + 5x)(3y - x)$

10. Find: $(p + 9)(p + 9)$

11. Find: $(x + 3)(x + 3)$

12. Find: $(3z + 2)(3z + 2)$

13. Find: $(5q + 3)(5q + 3)$

14. Find: $(4x + 1)(4x + 1)$

15. Find: $(z - 5)(z - 5)$

16. Find: $(m - 11)(m - 11)$

17. Find: $(t - 6)(t - 6)$

18. Find: $(3x - 2y)(3x - 2y)$

19. Find: $(4a - 7c)(4a - 7c)$

20. Find: $(5r - 8s)(5r - 8s)$

21. Find: $(5m + n)(5m - n)$

22. Find: $(a + 7b)(a - 7b)$

23. Find: $(2x + y)(2x - y)$

24. Find: $(3y + 8)(3y - 8)$

25. Find: $(5x + 3)(5x - 3)$

26. Find: $(m + 12n)(m - 12n)$

27. Find: $(2a + 7b)(2a - 7b)$

28. Find: $(x + 7y)(x - 7y)$

Multiplying and Dividing Polynomials

29. Find: $(4a - 3b)(2a - 7b)$

30. Find: $(3x + 5)(y + 8)$

31. Find: $(6m - 5n)(3m + 4n)$

32. Find: $(8y + 3z)(2y - 9z)$

33. Find: $(7x - 4)(2y + 3)$

34. Find: $(a + 2b)(a^2 + 6a - 3b)$

35. Find: $(3mn - n)(m^2 - 3n + 4m)$

36. Find: $(2xy - y)(x^2 + 5y - 6x)$

37. Find: $(3ab + 4b)(7a^2 + 3b - 4a)$

38. Find: $(7uv - 3v)(2u^2 - 5v + 8u)$

39. Find: $(5xy + 2y)(2x^2 - 6y + 3x)$

40. Find: $(3a^2 - 4b^2)(2a^3 + 5a^2b - 11ab - b)$

41. Find: $(5m^2n + 3n)(4m^3 - 3m^2n + 8mn^2 - 3n^2)$

42. Find: $(7x^2y + 2y)(3x^3 - 6x^2y + 8xy + y)$

43. Find: $(x^3 + x^2 - 13x + 14) \div (x - 2)$

44. Find: $(x^3 + 11x^2 + 22x - 24) \div (x + 4)$

45. Find: $(x^3 + 10x^2 + 23x + 6) \div (x + 3)$

46. Find: $(x^3 + 7x^2 - 36) \div (x + 6)$

47. Find: $(x^3 - 26x + 5) \div (x - 5)$

48. Find: $(3x^3 + 17x^2 - 58x + 40) \div (3x - 4)$

49. Find: $(4x^3 + 4x^2 - 13x + 5) \div (2x + 5)$

50. Find: $(2x^3 + 7x^2 - x - 2) \div (2x + 1)$

51. Find: $(4x^3 + 7x^2 - 14x + 6) \div (4x - 1)$

52. Find: $(2x^3 - 9x^2 + 12x - 8) \div (2x + 3)$

53. Find: $(3x^3 + 14x^2 + 11x - 8) \div (3x + 2)$

54. Find: $(6x^3 - 7x^2 - 34x + 35) \div (2x - 5)$

55. Find: $(10x^3 - 26x^2 - 7x + 2) \div (5x + 2)$

56. Find: $(8x^3 - 18x^2 + 25x - 12) \div (4x - 3)$

Practice Test

Take this practice test to be sure that you are prepared for the final quiz in Evaluate.

1. Use the FOIL method to find:
   $(2x^2 + 3xy)(3x^3y - 2)$

2. Use a pattern to find: $(2x - 3y)^2$

3. Find: $(2x + 3y)^2$

4. Use a pattern to find: $(2x - 3y)(2x + 3y)$

5. Find: $(3x - 2)(5x^2 + 8x - 2)$

6. Find: $(3p^2 + 4r^4 - 5)(3r^4 - 6p^2 + 2)$

7. Find: $(6t^2 + 5t + 1) \div (2t + 1)$

8. Find: $(8x^3 + 6x - 2) \div (4x + 2)$

9. a. Find: $(a^3 - a^5)(a + a^2)$

   b. What is the degree of the resulting polynomial?

10. Find: $(5y^4 - 2y^2 + y)(3y^2 - y + 2)$

11. Use the table in Figure 6.3.1 to find:
    $(2x^3 - 3x + 7)(5x^4 + 8)$

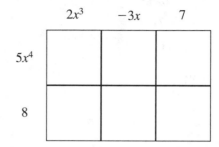

Figure 6.3.1

12. Use the table in Figure 6.3.2 to find:
    $(5x^4 - 7x^3 + 7x^2 - 8x)(x^2 + 1)$

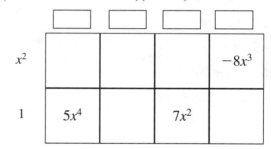

Figure 6.3.2

TOPIC 6 Cumulative Activities

Cumulative Review Problems

These problems combine all of the material you have covered so far in this course. You may want to test your understanding of this material before you move on to the next topic, or you may wish to do these problems to review for a test.

1. Find:

    a. $2^7 \cdot 2^9$ b. $\dfrac{x^{12}}{x^5}$ c. $(a^5 b^2)^4$

2. Solve $-3 \le 6 + 2y < 4$ for y, then graph its solution on the number line below.

    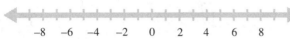

3. Find the equation of the line through the point $(3, 7)$ with slope $-\dfrac{2}{7}$:

    a. in point-slope form.   c. in standard form.

    b. in slope-intercept form.

4. Solve this system:

    $x + 2y = 5$
    $x - 2y = -13$

5. The difference of two numbers is -32. The sum of three times the smaller number and twice the larger number is 134. What are the two numbers?

6. Circle the true statements.

    The GCF of two numbers that have no factors in common is 1.

    $\dfrac{2}{9} - \dfrac{1}{5} = \dfrac{1}{4}$

    The LCM of 4 and 8 is 4.

    $3^2(4 + 2) = 9(4 + 2)$

    $\dfrac{1}{2} + \dfrac{1}{3} = \dfrac{5}{6}$

7. Write the equation of the line through the point $(20, -9)$ with slope $-\dfrac{8}{5}$:

    a. in point-slope form.   c. in standard form.

    b. in slope-intercept form.

8. Graph the system of inequalities below to find its solution.

    $2x + y \ge 3$
    $x - y < 4$

9. Find:

    a. 3^0 b. -3^0 c. $(-3)^0$

10. Graph the inequality $4x + y \le 6$.

11. Find: $15x^3 y^8 z^5 \div 10xy^4 z^{11}$

12. Lisa emptied a vending machine and got a total of 279 quarters and dimes worth $57.30. How many quarters did she get?

13. Find the slope and y-intercept of the line $4x - y = 7$.

14. Evaluate the expression $3x^2 - 4xy + 2y$ when $x = 3$ and $y = -5$.

15. Solve $-6 < 4 + 2x < -2$ for x.

16. Find:

    a. $-5x^0 + y^2$ c. $b^4 \cdot b^2 \cdot b \cdot b^6$

    b. $\left(\dfrac{a^3 \cdot b^7 \cdot c}{b^4 \cdot c^2}\right)^3$

17. Circle the true statements.

    $4(3 - 5) = 4 \cdot 3 - 5$

    $\dfrac{26}{117} = \dfrac{2}{9}$

    The LCM of 72 and 108 is 36.

    The GCF of 72 and 108 is 36.

    $\dfrac{4}{7} - \dfrac{2}{3} = -\dfrac{2}{4}$

18. Write the equation of the line through the point $(5, 2)$ with slope $-\dfrac{7}{3}$:

    a. in point-slope form.   c. in standard form.

    b. in slope-intercept form.

19. Graph the line $y = 6$.

20. Find: $(11p^2 - 3pr - 6r)(3p - 9r)$

21. Solve this system:

$4x + 5y = -9$
$6x + 5y = -6$

22. Find the equation of the line that is parallel to the line $x + 3y = 4$ and passes through the point $(2, 2)$.

23. Find the equation of the line that is perpendicular to the line $x + 3y = 4$ and passes through the point $(2, 2)$.

24. Graph the system of inequalities below to find its solution.

$y < 2x + 3$
$4x - y \geq 1$

25. Find the slope of the line perpendicular to the line through the points $(8, 9)$ and $(6, -4)$.

26. Find: $(x^3 + 5x^2 + x - 10) \div (x + 2)$

27. Solve $2y + 5 = 4\left(\frac{1}{2}y + 2\right)$ for y.

28. Find: $3xy(x^2y - 4)$

Use Figure 6.1 to answer questions 29, 30, and 31.

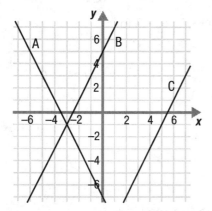

Figure 6.1

29. Which two lines form a system that has a solution of $(-3, -1)$?

30. Which two lines form a system that has no solution?

31. Which two lines form a system that has a solution that is not shown on the grid?

32. Find:

a. $(x^2yz^3)^4$ b. $\dfrac{x^5y^3}{xy^6}$ c. $(x^5)^9$

33. Evaluate the expression $-7a^4 + 3ab^2 + b - 4$ when $a = -2$ and $b = 5$.

34. Find the slope of the line through the points $(9, -4)$ and $(2, 7)$.

35. Graph the system of inequalities below to find its solution.

$9x - 4y < 20$
$9x - 4y \leq 8$

36. Graph the inequality $\frac{5}{2}x - y \geq 2$.

37. Last year Manuel split $2565 between his savings account, which paid 5% in interest, and his checking account, which paid 3.5% in interest. If he earned a total of $113.49 in interest, how did he split his money between the two accounts?

38. Graph the inequality $\frac{2}{3}x - \frac{1}{3}y \geq 2$.

39. Next to each polynomial below, write whether it is a monomial, a binomial, or a trinomial.

a. $2 + x$

b. $8ab^3 - 9abc + 1$

c. $3x^7yz^5$

d. $a^5b^2c^3d - 103a^7cd^4$

e. 10

f. $a + 7b - 4c$

40. Solve $-8\left(1 - \frac{1}{2}x\right) = 4(x - 2)$ for x.

41. Find: $(4a^2b + 3a - 9b) + (7a + 2b - 8a^2b)$

42. The perimeter of a square is the same as the perimeter of a regular hexagon. If each side of the square is 7 feet longer than each side of the hexagon, what is the perimeter of each figure?

TOPIC 7
FACTORING

You have seen that it is useful to write a whole number as a product of prime numbers. This is called finding the prime factorization of the number.

Similarly, it is often useful to write a polynomial as a product of other polynomials. This is called factoring the polynomial.

In this topic, you will learn how to factor a variety of polynomials.

$$x^3 + 3x^2y + 3xy^2 + y^3$$

Lesson 7.1 Factoring Polynomials I

Concept 1: Greatest Common Factor
  Definition of Factoring a Polynomial
  Finding the GCF of a Set of Monomials
  Factoring a Polynomial by Finding the GCF

Concept 2: Grouping
  Factoring a Polynomial Whose GCF is a Binomial
  Factoring by Grouping

Lesson 7.2 Factoring Polynomials II

Concept 1: Trinomials I
  Factoring a Trinomial of the Form $x^2 + bx + c$
  Factoring a Trinomial of the Form $x^2 + bxy + cy^2$

Concept 2: Trinomials II
  Factoring a Trinomial of the Form $ax^2 + bx + c$ by Trial and Error
  Factoring a Trinomial of the Form $ax^2 + bx + c$ by Grouping
  Solving an Equation of the Form $ax^2 + bx + c = 0$ by Factoring

Lesson 7.3 Factoring by Patterns

Concept 1: Recognizing Patterns
  Factoring a Perfect Square Trinomial
  Factoring a Difference of Two Squares
  Factoring a Sum or Difference of Two Cubes
  A General Strategy for Factoring

LESSON 7.1
FACTORING POLYNOMIALS I

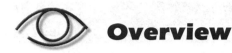 **Overview**

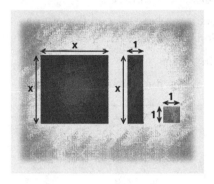

You have learned how to multiply polynomials. Now you will learn how to factor them. When you factor a polynomial, you write it as the product of other polynomials. Factoring is useful for simplifying expressions and for solving equations.

In this lesson, you will learn two factoring methods: how to factor out the greatest common factor (GCF) and how to factor by grouping.

 Explain

Concept 1 has sections on

- **Definition of Factoring a Polynomial**

- **Finding the GCF of a Set of Monomials**

- **Factoring a Polynomial by Finding the GCF**

You can think of factoring as a way to "undo" multiplication.

CONCEPT 1: GREATEST COMMON FACTOR

Definition of Factoring a Polynomial

To **factor** means to write a quantity or an expression as a product.

To factor a whole number, such as 12, we write it as a product of whole numbers. For example:

$$12 = 2 \cdot 6$$
$$12 = 2 \cdot 2 \cdot 3$$

To **factor a polynomial**, such as $x^2 + 5x$, means to write it as a product of polynomials: $x^2 + 5x = x(x + 5)$.

We say $x(x + 5)$ is the factorization of $x^2 + 5x$.

Multiply	*Factor*
$3 \cdot 5 = 15$	$15 = 3 \cdot 5$
$2 \cdot 3 \cdot 3 = 18$	$18 = 2 \cdot 3 \cdot 3$
$5x(6x + 7) = 30x^2 + 35x$	$30x^2 + 35x = 5x(6x + 7)$
$(w + 6)(w - 5) = w^2 + w - 30$	$w^2 + w - 30 = (w + 6)(w - 5)$

Finding the GCF of a Set of Monomials

Recall that the greatest common factor (GCF) of a set of numbers is the greatest number that is a factor of all the numbers in the set.

— Procedure —
To Find the Greatest Common Factor (GCF) of a Set of Numbers

Step 1 Write the prime factorization of each number.

Step 2 List each common prime factor the LEAST number of times it appears in any factorization.

Step 3 Multiply the prime factors in the list.

If two numbers have no common prime factor, then their GCF is 1.

Example 7.1.1

Find the GCF of -36, 72, and -90.

Solution

Step 1 Write the prime factorization of each number.

Prime factorization applies to natural numbers, so first write each negative number as -1 times its opposite.

$$-36 = -1 \cdot 36$$
$$-90 = -1 \cdot 90$$

A factor tree may be helpful in finding the prime factorizations.

$$-36 = -1 \cdot 2 \cdot 2 \cdot 3 \cdot 3$$
$$72 = 2 \cdot 2 \cdot 2 \cdot 3 \cdot 3$$
$$-90 = -1 \cdot 2 \cdot 3 \cdot 3 \cdot 5$$

Note that 5 is not a common factor since it is not a factor of 36 or 72.

Step 2 List each common prime factor the LEAST number of times it appears in any factorization.

$$-36 = -1 \cdot \boxed{2} \cdot 2 \cdot \boxed{3} \cdot \boxed{3}$$
$$72 = \boxed{2} \cdot 2 \cdot 2 \cdot \boxed{3} \cdot \boxed{3}$$
$$-90 = -1 \cdot \boxed{2} \cdot \boxed{3} \cdot \boxed{3} \cdot 5$$

The common prime factors are 2 and 3.

The least number of times that 2 appears in a factorization is once. So, 2 appears once in the list.

The least number of times that 3 appears in a factorization is twice. So, 3 appears twice in the list.

Here is the list: 2, 3, 3

Step 3 Multiply the prime factors in the list. $\quad 2 \cdot 3 \cdot 3 = \mathbf{18}$

Thus, the GCF of $-36, 72,$ and -90 is **18**.

To see that 18 is a common factor of
$-36, 72,$ and -90, we write each as a
product using 18 as one of the factors.

$$-36 = 18 \cdot (-2)$$
$$72 = 18 \cdot 4$$
$$-90 = 18 \cdot (-5)$$

We can use a similar procedure to find the GCF of a set of monomials that contain variables.

— Procedure —
To Find the Greatest Common Factor (GCF) of a Set of Monomials

Step 1 Write the factorization of each monomial.

Step 2 List each common factor the LEAST number of times it appears in any factorization.

Step 3 Multiply the factors in the list.

If two monomials have no common factors, other than 1, then their GCF is 1.

Example 7.1.2

Find the GCF of $15w^2y$, $24w^3y^2$, and $-30w^2xy$.

Solution

Step 1 Write the factorization of each monomial.

$$15w^2y = \mathbf{3} \cdot 5 \cdot \mathbf{w} \cdot \mathbf{w} \cdot \mathbf{y}$$
$$24w^3y^2 = 2 \cdot 2 \cdot 2 \cdot \mathbf{3} \cdot \mathbf{w} \cdot \mathbf{w} \cdot w \cdot \mathbf{y} \cdot y$$
$$-30w^2xy = -1 \cdot 2 \cdot \mathbf{3} \cdot 5 \cdot \mathbf{w} \cdot \mathbf{w} \cdot x \cdot \mathbf{y}$$

Step 2 List each common factor the LEAST number of times it appears in any factorization.

The common factors are 3, w, and y.

The least number of times that 3 appears in a factorization is once.
So, 3 appears once in the list.

The least number of times that w appears in a factorization is twice.
So, w appears twice in the list.

The least number of times that y appears in a factorization is once.
So, y appears once in the list.

Here is the list: $\qquad$ 3, w, w, y

Step 3 Multiply the factors in the list. $3 \cdot w \cdot w \cdot y = 3w^2y$

Thus, the GCF of $15w^2y$, $24w^3y^2$, and $-30w^2xy$ is $3w^2y$.

To see that $3w^2y$ is a common factor of $15w^2y$, $24w^3y^2$, and $-30w^2xy$ we write each as a product using $3w^2y$ as one of the factors.

$$15w^2y = \mathbf{3w^2y} \cdot 5$$
$$24w^3y^2 = \mathbf{3w^2y} \cdot 8wy$$
$$-30w^2xy = \mathbf{3w^2y} \cdot (-10x)$$

Factoring a Polynomial by Finding the GCF

To factor a polynomial such as $6wx^2 + 18wxy + 3wx + 9wy$, we may need to use several factoring techniques.

The first step is to factor out the GCF of the monomial terms.

— Procedure —
To Factor Out the GCF of a Polynomials

Step 1 Identify the terms of the polynomial.

Step 2 Factor each term.

Step 3 Find the GCF of the terms.

Step 4 Rewrite each term using the GCF.

Step 5 Factor out the GCF.

If there is no factor (other than 1) common to each term, the GCF is 1.

To check the factorization, multiply the factors.

Example 7.1.3

Factor: $6x^2 + 8xy^2 - 2x$

Solution

Step 1 Identify the terms of the polynomial. $6x^2, 8xy^2, -2x$

Step 2 Factor each term.

$$6x^2 = \mathbf{2} \cdot 3 \cdot \mathbf{x} \cdot x$$
$$8xy^2 = \mathbf{2} \cdot 2 \cdot 2 \cdot \mathbf{x} \cdot y \cdot y$$
$$-2x = -1 \cdot \mathbf{2} \cdot \mathbf{x}$$

Step 3 Find the GCF of the terms.

In the lists, the common factors are 2 and x.

The greatest common factor (GCF) is $2 \cdot x = 2x$.

Step 4 Rewrite each term using the GCF.

To help keep the signs straight, write the subtraction of $2x$ as the addition of $-2x$.

$$6x^2 + 8xy^2 - 2x$$
$$= 6x^2 + 8xy^2 + (-2x)$$

Rewrite each term using $\mathbf{2x}$ as a factor.

$$= \mathbf{2x} \cdot 3x + \mathbf{2x} \cdot 4y^2 + \mathbf{2x} \cdot (-1)$$

Step 5 Factor out the GCF.

Factor out $2x$. $= 2x(3x + 4y^2 - 1)$

Thus, $6x^2 + 8xy^2 - 2x = 2x(3x + 4y^2 - 1)$

Once you have factored out the GCF, the terms in parentheses should have no common factors other than 1 or −1.

We can multiply to check the factorization. We use the distributive property.

Is $2x(3x + 4y^2 - 1) = 6x^2 + 8xy^2 - 2x$?

Is $\mathbf{2x} \cdot 3x + \mathbf{2x} \cdot 4y^2 + \mathbf{2x} \cdot (-1) = 6x^2 + 8xy^2 - 2x$?

Is $6x^2 \ + \ 8xy^2 \ - \ 2x \ = 6x^2 + 8xy^2 - 2x$? **Yes**

Example 7.1.4

Factor: $9wxy^3 - 21w^2y^4 + 12w^3xy^2$

Solution

Step 1 Identify the terms of the polynomial. $9wxy^3, -21w^2y^4, 12w^3xy^2$

Step 2 Factor each term. $9wxy^3 = \mathbf{3} \cdot 3 \cdot \mathbf{w} \cdot x \cdot \mathbf{y} \cdot \mathbf{y} \cdot y$

$-21w^2y^4 = -1 \cdot \mathbf{3} \cdot 7 \cdot \mathbf{w} \cdot w \cdot \mathbf{y} \cdot \mathbf{y} \cdot y \cdot y$

$12w^3xy^2 = 2 \cdot 2 \cdot \mathbf{3} \cdot \mathbf{w} \cdot w \cdot w \cdot x \cdot \mathbf{y} \cdot \mathbf{y}$

Step 3 Find the GCF of the terms.

In the lists, the common factors are 3, w, y, and y.

The GCF is $3 \cdot w \cdot y \cdot y = 3wy^2$.

Step 4 Rewrite each term using the GCF.

To help keep the signs $9wxy^3 \ - \ 21w^2y^4 \ + \ 12w^3xy^2$
straight, write the
subtraction of $21w^2y^4$
as addition of $-21w^2y^4$. $= \ 9wxy^3 \ + \ (-21w^2y^4) \ + \ 12w^3xy^2$

Rewrite each term
using $\mathbf{3wy^2}$ as a factor. $= \mathbf{3wy^2} \cdot 3xy + \mathbf{3wy^2} \cdot (-7wy^2) + \mathbf{3wy^2} \cdot 4w^2x$

Step 5 Factor out the GCF.

Factor $3wy^2$. $= 3wy^2(3xy - 7wy^2 + 4w^2x)$

Thus, $9wxy^3 - 21w^2y^4 + 12w^3xy^2 = 3wy^2(3xy - 7wy^2 + 4w^2x)$

You can multiply to check the factorization. We leave the check to you.

Another way to decide which terms belong inside the parentheses is to ask:

"$3wy^2$ times what gives $9wxy^3$?"
        Answer: $3xy$

"$3wy^2$ times what gives $-21w^2y^4$?"
        Answer: $-7wy^2$

"$3wy^2$ times what gives $12w^3xy^2$?"
        Answer: $4w^2x$

Typically, we do not write 1 or −1 as a part of a common factor. They are factors of every polynomial and explicitly writing them usually serves no purpose.

However, factoring out −1 is sometimes helpful.

Example 7.1.5

Rewrite $5 - x$ as a product by factoring out -1.

Solution

Identify the terms of the polynomial.	5 and $-x$

Rewrite each term using -1 as a factor.
$$5 = \mathbf{-1} \cdot -5$$
$$-x = \mathbf{-1} \cdot x$$

We can write:
$$5 \quad - \quad x$$
$$= (\mathbf{-1}) \cdot (-5) + (\mathbf{-1}) \cdot x$$

Factor out -1.
$$= \mathbf{-1}(-5 + x)$$

We usually write terms with variables first. So, we use the Commutative Property of Addition to rearrange the terms inside the parentheses.
$$= -1(x - 5)$$

So we can write $5 - x$ as $-1(x - 5)$.

We multiply to check the factorization.

Is $\quad\quad\quad\quad -1(x - 5) = 5 - x$?

Is $\quad -1 \cdot x + (-1) \cdot (-5) = 5 - x$?

Is $\quad\quad\quad\quad\quad -x + 5 = 5 - x$? **Yes**

Example 7.1.6

Factor: $-6x^4y^2 - 30x^2y^3 - 2x^2y$

Solution

Step 1 Identify the terms of the polynomial. $-6x^4y^2, -30x^2y^3, -2x^2y$

Step 2 Factor each term.

Each term has a negative coefficient. So, we include -1 as a factor of each term.
$$-6x^4y^2 = \mathbf{-1} \cdot \mathbf{2} \cdot 3 \cdot \mathbf{x} \cdot \mathbf{x} \cdot x \cdot x \cdot \mathbf{y} \cdot y$$
$$-30x^2y^3 = \mathbf{-1} \cdot \mathbf{2} \cdot 3 \cdot 5 \cdot \mathbf{x} \cdot \mathbf{x} \cdot \mathbf{y} \cdot y \cdot y$$
$$-2x^2y = \mathbf{-1} \cdot \mathbf{2} \cdot \mathbf{x} \cdot \mathbf{x} \cdot \mathbf{y}$$

Step 3 Find the GCF of the terms.

In the lists, the common factors are -1, 2, x, x, and y.
So, a common factor of each term is:
$$-1 \cdot 2 \cdot x \cdot x \cdot y = -2x^2y$$

Step 4 Rewrite each term using the GCF.

To avoid an error with the signs, write each subtraction as an addition of the opposite.

$$-6x^4y^2 \quad - \quad 30x^2y^3 \quad - \quad 2x^2y$$
$$= \quad -6x^4y^2 \quad + \quad (-30x^2y^3) \quad + \quad (-2x^2y)$$

Rewrite each term using $-2x^2y$ as a factor.

$$= -2x^2y \cdot 3x^2y + (-2x^2y) \cdot 15y^2 + (-2x^2y) \cdot 1$$

Step 5 Factor out the GCF.

Factor out $-2x^2y$. $\quad = -2x^2y(3x^2y + 15y^2 + 1)$

Thus, $-6x^4y^2 - 30x^2y^3 - 2x^2y = -2x^2y(3x^2y + 15y^2 + 1)$

You can multiply to check the factorization. We leave the check to you.

Note that the third term, $-2x^2y$, is the common factor. So we write that term as $-2x^2y \cdot 1$.

We can also factor the polynomial using $+2x^2y$ as the common factor. Then we have:
$$-6x^4y^2 - 30x^2y^3 - 2x^2y$$
$$= 2x^2y(-3x^2y - 15y^2 - 1)$$

Here is a summary of this concept from *Academic Systems Algebra.*

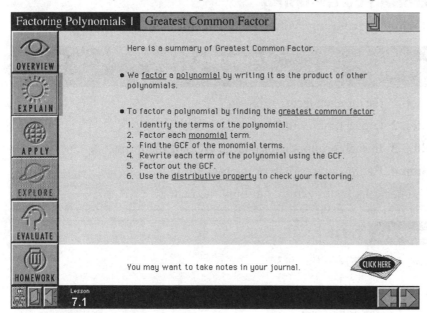

CONCEPT 2: GROUPING

Concept 2 has sections on

- **Factoring a Polynomial Whose GCF is a Binomial**

- **Factoring by Grouping**

Factoring a Polynomial Whose GCF is a Binomial

You have already seen how to factor a polynomial when the GCF of the terms is a monomial.

In this example, we factor out the monomial $2x$.

$$10x^2 + 8x$$
$$= 2x \cdot 5x + 2x \cdot 4$$
$$= 2x(5x + 4)$$

We can also factor a polynomial when the GCF of its terms is a binomial.

Here, the binomial $(x + 7)$ is a factor of each term.

$$= 5x(x + 7) + 4(x + 7)$$

So we factor out $(x + 7)$.

$$= (x + 7)(5x + 4)$$

Example 7.1.7

Factor: $2m(6n - 5) - 7(6n - 5)$

Solution

The GCF of the terms is the binomial $(6n - 5)$.

$$2m(6n - 5) - 7(6n - 5)$$

Factor out the GCF.

$$= (6n - 5)(2m - 7)$$

Factoring by Grouping

Factoring by grouping is often used to factor a four-term polynomial.

> **— Procedure —**
> **To Factor a Polynomial by Grouping**
>
> **Step 1** Factor each term.
>
> **Step 2** Group terms with common factors.
>
> **Step 3** In each group, factor out the GCF of the terms.
>
> **Step 4** Factor out the GCF of the polynomial.
>
> To check the factorization, multiply the factors.

Example 7.1.8

Factor: $5wx + 20x + 9w + 36$

Solution

Step 1 Factor each term.

$$5wx \quad + \quad 20x \quad + \quad 9w \quad + \quad 36$$
$$= 5 \cdot w \cdot x + 2 \cdot 2 \cdot 5 \cdot x + 3 \cdot 3 \cdot w + 2 \cdot 2 \cdot 3 \cdot 3$$

Step 2 Group terms with common factors.

There are several ways to form the groups. Typically, we group the first two terms and the last two terms, provided at least one of the groups has a common factor other than 1 or −1.

$$= (5 \cdot w \cdot x + 2 \cdot 2 \cdot 5 \cdot x) + (3 \cdot 3 \cdot w + 2 \cdot 2 \cdot 3 \cdot 3)$$

The terms in the first group have common factors 5 and x.

The terms in the second group have common factors 3 and 3.

$$= (5 \cdot w \cdot \boldsymbol{x} + 2 \cdot 2 \cdot \boldsymbol{5} \cdot \boldsymbol{x}) + (\boldsymbol{3} \cdot \boldsymbol{3} \cdot w + 2 \cdot 2 \cdot \boldsymbol{3} \cdot \boldsymbol{3})$$

Step 3 In each group, factor out the GCF of the terms.

Factor $5 \cdot x$ out of the first group and $3 \cdot 3$ out of the second group.

$$= \mathbf{5 \cdot x}(w + 2 \cdot 2) + \mathbf{3 \cdot 3}(w + 2 \cdot 2)$$
$$= 5x(w + 4) + 9(w + 4)$$

Step 4 Factor out the GCF of the polynomial.

Factor out the binomial $(w + 4)$.

$$= (w + 4)(5x + 9)$$

Thus, $5wx + 20x + 9w + 36 = (w + 4)(5x + 9)$

We can multiply to check the factorization.

Is $\qquad (w + 4)(5x + 9) = 5wx + 20x + 9w + 36$?

Is $\quad 5wx + 9w + 20x + 36 = 5wx + 20x + 9w + 36$? **Yes**

Example 7.1.9

Factor: $20w^2 - 21y + 12w - 35wy$

Solution

To avoid an error with the signs, write each subtraction as an addition of the opposite.

$$20w^2 \quad - \quad 21y \quad + \quad 12w \quad - \quad 35wy$$
$$= \quad 20w^2 \quad + \quad (-21y) \quad + \quad 12w \quad + \quad (-35wy)$$

Step 1 Factor each term.

$$= 2 \cdot 2 \cdot 5 \cdot w \cdot w + (-3 \cdot 7 \cdot y) + 2 \cdot 2 \cdot 3 \cdot w + (-5 \cdot 7 \cdot w \cdot y)$$

Step 2 Group terms with common factors.

The first and third terms have common factors 2, 2, and w. Therefore, group those terms together.

The second and fourth terms have common factors 7 and y. Therefore, group those terms together.

$$= [\mathbf{2 \cdot 2} \cdot 5 \cdot \mathbf{w} \cdot w + \mathbf{2 \cdot 2} \cdot 3 \cdot \mathbf{w}] + [(-3 \cdot \mathbf{7} \cdot \mathbf{y}) + (-5 \cdot \mathbf{7} \cdot w \cdot \mathbf{y})]$$

Step 3 In each group, factor out the GCF of the terms.

In the first group, factor out $2 \cdot 2 \cdot w$.

$$= \quad [2 \cdot 2 \cdot w(5 \cdot w + 3)] \quad + [(-3 \cdot 7 \cdot y) + (-5 \cdot 7 \cdot w \cdot y)]$$

Simplify.

$$= \quad [4w(5w + 3)] \quad + [(-3 \cdot 7 \cdot y) + (-5 \cdot 7 \cdot w \cdot y)]$$

In the second group, the common factor is $7y$. However, both terms are negative. Factor out $-7y$, rather than $+7y$, so the terms of the binomial have the same sign as the binomial in the first group.

$$= \quad [4w(5w + 3)] \quad + \quad [-7y(3 + 5w)]$$

In the second group, write $3 + 5w$ as $5w + 3$ to match the binomial in the first group.

$$= \quad [4w(5w + 3)] \quad + \quad [-7y(5w + 3)]$$

Step 4 Factor out the GCF of the polynomial.

Factor out the binomial $(5w + 3)$.

$$= (5w + 3)(4w - 7y)$$

We have factored the given polynomial as follows:
$$20w^2 - 21y + 12w - 35wy = (5w + 3)(4w - 7y)$$

You can multiply to check the factorization. We leave the check to you.

Example 7.1.10

Factor: $6wx^2 + 18wxy + 3wx + 9wy$

Solution

Step 1 Factor each term.

$$6wx^2 \quad + \quad 18wxy \quad + \quad 3wx \quad + \quad 9wy$$

Each term of the polynomial has $3w$ as a factor.

$$= 2 \cdot 3 \cdot w \cdot x \cdot x + 2 \cdot 3 \cdot 3 \cdot w \cdot x \cdot y + 3 \cdot w \cdot x + 3 \cdot 3 \cdot w \cdot y$$

So before we group, we factor out $3w$.

$$= \quad 3w[2 \cdot x \cdot x + \quad 2 \cdot 3 \cdot x \cdot y \quad + \quad x \quad + \quad 3 \cdot y]$$

Step 2 Group terms with common factors.

Within the brackets, 2 and x are factors of the first and second terms. Therefore, group those terms together.

$$= 3w[(2 \cdot x \cdot x + 2 \cdot 3 \cdot x \cdot y) + (1 \cdot x + 1 \cdot 3 \cdot y)]$$

Within the brackets, the third and fourth terms have no common factor except 1. Therefore, group the third and fourth terms together and write each with factor 1.

Step 3 In each group, factor out the GCF of the terms.

In the first group, factor out $2 \cdot x$.

In the second group, factor out 1. $= 3w[\mathbf{2} \cdot \mathbf{x}(x + 3 \cdot y) + \mathbf{1}(x + 3 \cdot y)]$

Step 4 Factor out the GCF of the polynomial.

Factor out $(x + 3y)$. $= 3w[(\mathbf{x} + \mathbf{3y})(2x + 1)]$

We can multiply to check the factorization.

Is $3w[(x + 3y)(2x + 1)] = 6wx^2 + 18wxy + 3wx + 9wy$?

Is $3w[2x^2 + x + 6xy + 3y] = 6wx^2 + 18wxy + 3wx + 9wy$?

Is $6wx^2 + 3wx + 18wxy + 9wy = 6wx^2 + 18wxy + 3wx + 9wy$? **Yes**

Here is a summary of this concept from *Academic Systems Algebra*.

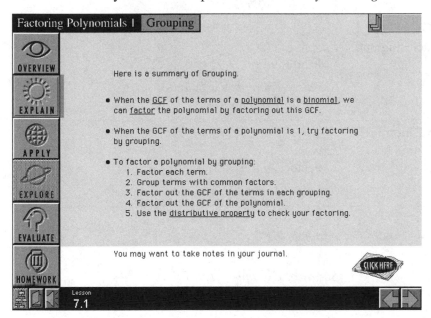

Checklist Lesson 7.1

Here is what you should know after completing this lesson.

Words and Phrases

factor
factor a polynomial

factoring by grouping

Ideas and Procedures

❶ Greatest Common Factor (GCF)
Find the GCF of a set of monomials.

Example 7.1.2
　　Find the GCF of $15w^2y$, $24w^3y^2$, and $-20w^2xy$.

See also: Example 7.1.1
　　　　　Apply 3-7

❷ Factor a Polynomial by Finding the GCF
Rewrite a polynomial as a product by factoring out the GCF.

Example 7.1.4
　　Factor: $9wxy^3 - 21x^2y^4 + 12w^3xy^2$

See also: Example 7.1.3, 7.1.5, 7.1.6
　　　　　Apply 8-28

❸ Factor a Polynomial Whose GCF is a Binomial
Factor a polynomial whose GCF is a binomial.

Example 7.1.7
　　Factor: $2m(6n - 5) - 7(6n - 5)$

See also: Apply 29-38

❹ Factor by Grouping
Factor a polynomial by grouping the terms, and then factor each group.

Example 7.1.8
　　Factor: $5wx + 20x + 9w + 36$

See also: Example 7.1.9, 7.1.10
　　　　　Apply 39-56

Homework Problems

Circle the homework problems assigned to you by the computer, then complete them below.

Explain

Greatest Common Factor

1. Circle the expressions below that are monomials.

   $x^2 + 2$ $xy^2 + y^2x$

   x^3yz^2 x

2. Circle the expressions below that are **not** monomials.

   xzy^8 $\dfrac{4}{x}$

   $\dfrac{13x}{12}$ $x^2z + zy^2$

3. Find the GCF of $12x^3y$ and $6xy^2$.

4. Find the GCF of $3xyz^3$, z, and $16yz$.

5. Factor: $x^2y + 6y^2$

6. Factor: $3x^2 + 9xy^3 - 12xy$

7. Factor: $4a^2b - 4ab^2$

8. Factor: $3x^4yz + 3xyz + 9yz$

9. Factor: $6xy^3 - 4x^2y^2 + 2xy$

10. Factor: $16a^3b^2 + 20a^2b^4 - 8a^3b^3$

11. Factor: $17x^2y^2z^2 + 68x^{10}y^{32}z + 153x^9y^4z^{12}$

12. Factor: $x^2 + xy + xz$

Factoring by Grouping

13. Find the binomial GCF: $(x^5 + y) + 6x^2(x^5 + y)$

14. Factor: $(x^5 + y) + 6x^2(x^5 + y)$

15. Find the binomial GCF:
    $(3x + y)(xy + yz) + x^2y(xy + yz) + z^3(xy + yz)$

16. Factor:
    $(3x + y)(xy + yz) + x^2y(xy + yz) + z^3(xy + yz)$

17. Factor: $a^3 - a^2b + ab^2 - b^3$

18. Factor: $3x^2 - 3xy + 3xy^3z^4 - 3y^4z^4$

19. Factor: $x^5y + zx + x^4y^2 + yz + x^4yz + z^2$

20. Factor: $15m^3 + 21m^2n + 10mn + 14n^2$

21. Factor: $x^2z + 3x^2 + y^2z + 3y^2$

22. Factor: $x^3 + x^2y + x^2z + 3x + 3z + 3y$

23. Factor: $3x + yz + xz + 3y$

24. Factor: $x^2 - 3x + 2$
    (Hint: rewrite the polynomial as $x^2 - x - 2x + 2$)

 **Apply**

Practice Problems

Here are some additional practice problems for you to try.

Greatest Common Factor

1. Circle the expressions below that are monomials.

   $8m^3n$ $\qquad$ $7y - 2y^2 + 14$ $\qquad$ $x - y$

   23 $\qquad$ $\dfrac{3}{z}$

2. Circle the expressions below that are monomials.

   $3x + 4x^2 - 7$ $\qquad$ 17 $\qquad$ $5xyz^3$

   $y + z$ $\qquad$ $\dfrac{1}{x}$

3. Find the GCF of $12a^3b$ and $16ab^4$.

4. Find the GCF of $18m^3n^5$ and $24m^4n^3$.

5. Find the GCF of $10xy^4$, and $15x^3y^2$.

6. Find the GCF of $9xy^2z^3$, $24x^5y^3z^6$, and $18x^3yz^4$.

7. Find the GCF of $6abc^4$, $12ac^3$, and $9a^5b^4c^2$.

8. Factor: $5a^3b + 10b$

9. Factor: $16mn^4 + 8m$

10. Factor: $6xy^2 + 12x$

11. Factor: $6x^4y^3 + 14xy$

12. Factor: $24mn - 16m^6n^2$

13. Factor: $8a^3b^2 - 10ab$

14. Factor: $24a^3b^4 + 42a^6b^5$

15. Factor: $36y^7z^8 - 45y^3z^5$

16. Factor: $25x^5y^7 + 35x^2y^4$

17. Factor: $4mn + 10mn^3 - 18m^4n$

18. Factor: $6xy + 9x^3y - 15xy^2$

19. Factor: $8a^3b^4 - 12ab + 20a^3b$

20. Factor: $15a^3b^4c^7 + 25a^5b^3c^2$

21. Factor: $32p^7q^3r^4 - 40p^5q^5r$

22. Factor: $24x^2y^5z^8 - 32x^4y^6z^4$

23. Factor: $9xy^2z^3 - 15x^3y^5z^4 + 21x^4y^2z^5$

24. Factor: $10h^4j^3k^6 + 25h^3j^2k - 40hj^5k^2$

25. Factor: $20a^3b^5c^2 + 12a^4b^2c^3 - 8a^2bc^3$

26. Factor: $20x^2y^4 + 10x^5y^3 - 18x^3y^4 + 12xy^3$

27. Factor:
    $6a^3b^5c^2 - 9a^4b^4c^3 + 18a^2b^3c^2 - 21a^6b^2c^3$

28. Factor:
    $18x^2y^4z^3 - 16x^5y^3z + 6x^4y^2z^3 - 10x^3y^4z^2$

Factoring by Grouping

29. Factor: $x(z + 3) + y(z + 3)$

30. Factor: $a(b - 2) + c(b - 2)$

31. Factor: $a(3b - 4) + 9(3b - 4)$

32. Factor: $z(2w + 3) - 12(2w + 3)$

33. Factor: $8m(3n^3 - 4) + 17(3n^3 - 4)$

34. Factor: $12b(2c^4 + 5) - 23(2c^4 + 5)$

35. Factor: $7x(2x^2 + 3) - 11(2x^2 + 3)$

36. Factor: $a(3a - b) - b(3a - b)$

37. Factor: $m(5m + 2n) - 3n(5m + 2n)$

38. Factor: $y(2x + y) + x(2x + y)$

39. Factor: $xw + xz + yw + yz$

40. Factor: $mp - mq + np - nq$

41. Factor: $ac + ad - bc - bd$

42. Factor: $8a^2 + 4a + 10a + 5$

43. Factor: $4a^2 + 2a - 14a - 7$

44. Factor: $6x^2 - 2x + 12x - 4$

45. Factor: $12a^2 + 18a + 10ab + 15b$

46. Factor: $21m^2 - 14m + 24mn - 16n$

47. Factor: $15x^2 + 35x + 6xy + 14y$

48. Factor: $3u^2 + 6u + uv + 2v$

49. Factor: $8z^2 - 2z + 4zw - w$

50. Factor: $2x^2 + 4x - xy - 2y$

51. Factor: $12a^2 - 10b - 15ab + 8a$

52. Factor: $8m^2 + 21n + 12m + 14mn$

53. Factor: $18x^2 - 10y - 15xy + 12x$

54. Factor: $16uv^2 + 10vw + 25w + 40uv$

55. Factor: $12pr^2 - 16rs - 20s + 15pr$

56. Factor: $20ab^2 + 15bc - 6c - 8ab$

 **Evaluate**

Practice Test

Take this practice test to be sure that you are prepared for the final quiz in Evaluate.

1. Find the GCF of $6xz$, $3xy$, and $2x$.

2. Find the GCF of $16xyz$, $x^2y^2z^2$, and $4x^3y^2z$.

3. Factor: $3x^2y - 3xy^2$

4. Factor: $3xy^3 - 6xy^2 + 3x^3y^4$

5. Factor: $13(x^2 + 4) + 6y(x^2 + 4)$

6. Factor: $17x^2(3xyz + 4z) - 3yz(3xyz + 4z)$

7. Factor: $39rs - 13s + 9r - 3$

8. Factor: $12wz - 44z + 18w - 66$

LESSON 7.2
FACTORING POLYNOMIALS II

 Overview

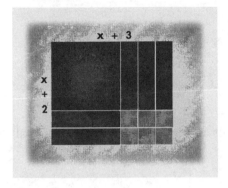

You have learned how to factor some polynomials by finding the greatest common factor (GCF) and by grouping.

In this lesson, you will learn techniques for factoring a trinomial such as $x^2 + x - 30$ or $15x^2 - 16x + 4$. Then, you will see how to use factoring to solve certain types of equations.

 Explain

Concept 1 has sections on

- **Factoring a Trinomial of the Form $x^2 + bx + c$**

- **Factoring a Trinomial of the Form $x^2 + bxy + cy^2$**

CONCEPT 1:
TRINOMIALS I

Factoring a Trinomial of the Form $x^2 + bx + c$

The product of two binomials can be a trinomial.

For example, let's multiply $(x + 7)$ by $(x + 3)$.

	F	O	I	L

Use FOIL. $(x + 7)(x + 3) = x \cdot x + x \cdot 3 + 7 \cdot x + 7 \cdot 3$

Simplify each term. $= x^2 + 3x + 7x + 21$

Combine like terms. $= x^2 + 10x + 21$

Notice the relationship between the trinomial $x^2 + 10x + 21$ and the binomials $(x + 7)$ and $(x + 3)$:

- The first term of the trinomial, x^2, is the product of x and x, the first term of each binomial.

$$(x + 7) \qquad (x + 3)$$
$$= x \cdot x + (7 + 3)x + 7 \cdot 3$$

- The coefficient of the middle term of the trinomial is 10, the sum of 3 and 7, the constants in the binomials.

$$= x^2 + 10x + 21$$

- The last term of the trinomial is 21, is the product of 3 and 7, the constants in the binomials.

This relationship holds in general.

That is, if the product of two binomials $(x + r)$ and $(x + s)$ is a trinomial of the form $x^2 + bx + c$:

- c is the product of r and s.

- b is the sum of r and s.

We use this to factor trinomials of the form $x^2 + bx + c$.

This procedure is called the **product-sum method** of factoring because we seek two integers whose product is c and whose sum is b.

— Procedure —
To Factor $x^2 + bx + c$ (Product-Sum Method)

Step 1 Find two integers whose product is c and whose sum is b.

Step 2 Use the integers from Step 1 as the constants, r and s, in the binomial factors $(x + r)$ and $(x + s)$.

To check the factorization, multiply the binomial factors.

Example 7.2.1

Factor: $x^2 + 3x + 2$

Solution

This trinomial has the form $x^2 + bx + c$ where $b = 3$ and $c = 2$.

Step 1 Find two integers whose product is c and whose sum is b.

Since c is 2, list pairs of integers whose product is 2.
Then, find the sum of each pair of integers.

Product	Sum
$1 \cdot 2$	3
$(-1) \cdot (-2)$	-3

The first product, $1 \cdot 2$, gives the required sum, 3.

Step 2 ***Use the integers from Step 1 as the constants, r and s, in the binomial factors (x + r) and (x + s).***

The result is:
$$x^2 + 3x + 2 = (x + 1)(x + 2).$$

We multiply to check the factorization.

Is $(x + 1)(x + 2) = x^2 + 3x + 2$?

Is $x^2 + 2x + 1x + 2 = x^2 + 3x + 2$?

Is $x^2 + 3x + 2 = x^2 + 3x + 2$? **Yes**

Multiplication is commutative, so the factorization may also be written:
  (x + 2)(x + 1).

Example 7.2.2

Factor: $x^2 - 7x + 12$

Solution

This trinomial has the form $x^2 + bx + c$ where $b = -7$ and $c = 12$.

Step 1 ***Find two integers whose product is c and whose sum is b.***

Since c is 12, list pairs of integers whose product is 12. Then, find the sum of each pair of integers.

Product	Sum
1 · 12	13
2 · 6	8
3 · 4	7
−1 · (−12)	−13
−2 · (−6)	−8
−3 · (−4)	−7

The last possibility, $-3 \cdot (-4)$, gives the required sum, -7.

The product, c = 12, is positive, so both integers are positive or both are negative.

Since we also know the sum, b = −7, is negative, we can conclude that both integers are negative.

Step 2 ***Use the integers from Step 1 as the constants, r and s, in the binomial factors (x + r) and (x + s).***

The result is:
$$x^2 - 7x + 12 = (x - 3)(x - 4).$$

You can multiply to check the factorization. We leave the check to you.

So we did not have to try the positive integers.

Example **7.2.3**

Factor: $x^2 + x - 30$

Solution

This trinomial has the form $x^2 + bx + c$ where $b = 1$ and $c = -30$.

Step 1 Find two integers whose product is c and whose sum is b.

These are the eight integer pairs with product −30:

$-1, \quad 30$
$-2, \quad 15$
$-3, \quad 10$
$-5, \quad 6$
$1, -30$
$2, -15$
$3, -10$
$5, -6$

Only one pair, −5 and 6, gives the required sum, 1.

There are eight possible integer pairs whose product is -30.

To reduce the list, think about the signs of 1 and -30.

- Since the product, $c = -30$, is negative, one factor must be positive and the other negative.

- Also, the sum, $b = 1$, is positive. So the integer with the greater absolute value must be positive. We need only list pairs of integers whose sum is positive.

Product	Sum
$-1 \cdot 30$	29
$-2 \cdot 15$	13
$-3 \cdot 10$	7
$-5 \cdot 6$	1

The last possibility, $-5 \cdot 6$, gives the required sum, 1.

Step 2 Use the integers from Step 1 as the constants, r and s, in the binomial factors (x + r) and (x + s).

The result is:
$$x^2 + x - 30 = (x - 5)(x + 6).$$

You can multiply to check the factorization. We leave the check to you.

Example **7.2.4**

Factor: $x^2 + 2x + 4$

Solution

This trinomial has the form $x^2 + bx + c$ where $b = 2$ and $c = 4$.

Step 1 Find two integers whose product is c and whose sum is b.

- Since the product, $c = 4$, is positive, both integers must have the same sign.

- Also the sum, $b = 2$, is positive. So both integers must be positive.

Product	Sum
$1 \cdot 4$	5
$2 \cdot 2$	4

These are the only possibilities, and neither gives the required sum, 2.

It is possible to factor $x^2 + 2x + 4$ using numbers other than integers, but that is

Since there are no two integers with product 4 and sum 2, the trinomial $x^2 + 2x + 4$ cannot be factored as $(x + r)(x + s)$ where r and s are integers.

Example 7.2.5

Factor: $x^2 - 9$

Solution

First we write the binomial $x^2 - 9$ in the form $x^2 + bx + c$.

To do this, we insert a middle term, $0x$.

The equivalent trinomial is $x^2 + 0x - 9$.

Now, we see that $b = 0$ and $c = -9$.

Step 1 Find two integers whose product is c and whose sum is b.

- Since the product, $c = -9$, is negative, one factor must be positive and the other negative.

- Since the sum is $b = 0$, the integers must be opposites.

There is only one possibility.

Product	Sum
$-3 \cdot 3$	0

These are the three integer pairs with product -9:

$1, -9$
$-1, \quad 9$
$-3, \quad 3$

Only one pair, -3 and 3, gives the required sum, 0.

Step 2 Use the integers from Step 1 as the constants, r and s, in the binomial factors (x + r) and (x + s).

The result is:
$$x^2 - 9 = (x - 3)(x + 3).$$

You can multiply to check the factorization. We leave the check to you.

Recall that the product of $(x - 3)$ and $(x + 3)$ is the difference of two squares, in this case $x^2 - 9$.

Example 7.2.6

Factor: $3x^2 - 6x - 9$

Solution

This trinomial does not have the form $x^2 + bx + c$ because the coefficient of x^2 is not 1. However, the terms of this trinomial have a GCF of 3.

$$3x^2 - 6x - 9$$

Factor out the common factor, 3.

$$= 3(x^2 - 2x - 3)$$

Now, the trinomial has the form $x^2 + bx + c$ where $b = -2$ and $c = -3$.

Step 1 Find two integers whose product is c and whose sum is b.

- Since the product, $c = -3$, is negative, one integer must be positive and the other negative.

- Also, the sum, $b = -2$, is negative. So the integer with the greater absolute value must be negative.

There is only one possibility.

Product	Sum
$1 \cdot -3$	-2

These are the two integer pairs with product -3:

$1, -3$
$-1, 3$

Only one pair, 1 and -3, gives the required sum, -2.

Step 2 Use the integers from Step 1 as the constants, r and s, in the binomial factors (x + r) and (x + s).

The factorization of $x^2 - 2x - 3$ is $(x + 1)(x - 3)$.

But don't forget the factor 3 that we factored out of the original trinomial.

The factorization of $3x^2 - 2x - 3$ is:

$3x^2 - 2x - 3 = 3(x + 1)(x - 3)$.

Factoring A Trinomial of the Form x² + bxy + cy²

A trinomial of the form $x^2 + bxy + cy^2$ contains two variables, x and y. Notice that the middle term has factor y and the last term has factor of y^2.

To factor $x^2 + bxy + cy^2$, we may follow the same procedure we used for $x^2 + bx + c$. However, we include the variable y in the second term of each binomial factor.

Example 7.2.7

Factor: $x^2 - 5xy + 6y^2$

Solution

This binomial has the form $x^2 + bxy + cy^2$ where $b = -5$ and $c = 6$.

Step 1 Find two integers whose product is c and whose sum is b.

- Since the product, $c = 6$, is positive, the integers must have the same sign.

- Also, the sum, $b = -5$, is negative. So the integers must both be negative.

Product	Sum
$-1 \cdot -6$	-7
$-2 \cdot -3$	-5

The last possibility, $-2 \cdot (-3)$, gives the required sum, -5.

Step 2 Use the integers from Step 1 as the constants, r and s, in the binomial factors (x + ry) and (x + sy).

The result is:

$x^2 - 5xy + 6y^2 = (x - 2y)(x - 3y)$.

Note that each binomial has y in its second term.

We can multiply to check the factorization.

Is $\qquad\qquad\qquad\qquad (x - 2y)(x - 3y) = x^2 - 5xy + 6y^2$?

Is $x \cdot x + x \cdot (-3y) + (-2y) \cdot x + (-2y) \cdot (-3y) = x^2 - 5xy + 6y^2$?

Is $\quad x^2 \;+\; (-3xy) \;+\; (-2xy) \;+\; \qquad 6y^2 \qquad = x^2 - 5xy + 6y^2$?

Is $\quad x^2 \;-\; \qquad\qquad 5xy \qquad\qquad +\qquad 6y^2 \qquad = x^2 - 5xy + 6y^2$? **Yes**

Example 7.2.8

Factor: $x^2 - 5x + 6y^2$

Solution

This trinomial does not have the form $x^2 + bxy + cy^2$ because there is no factor y in the middle term. This trinomial cannot be factored using integers.

Here is a summary of this concept from *Academic Systems Algebra*.

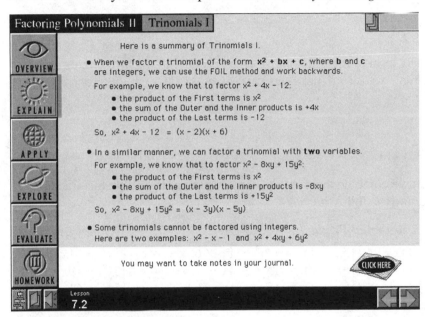

CONCEPT 2: TRINOMIALS II

Factoring a Trinomial of the Form $ax^2 + bx + c$ by Trial and Error

To factor a trinomial of the form $x^2 + bx + c$, we look for two integers whose product is c and whose sum is b. This product-sum process works because the coefficient of the x^2-term is 1.

Factoring a trinomial of the form $ax^2 + bx + c$, where $a \neq 1$, is a bit more involved.

For example, we'll try to factor $15x^2 - 16x + 4$ as a product of binomials. Then we'll use the FOIL method to check each product.

Concept 2 has sections on

- **Factoring a Trinomial of the Form $ax^2 + bx + c$ by Trial and Error**

- **Factoring a Trinomial of the Form $ax^2 + bx + c$ by Grouping**

- **Solving an Equation of the Form $ax^2 + bx + c = 0$ by Factoring**

Example 7.2.9

Factor: $15x^2 - 16x + 4$

Solution

The first term of the trinomial, $15x^2$, is the product of the first term of each binomial. So ask, "What times what gives in $15x^2$?" Here are four possibilities.

$$1x \cdot 15x$$
$$(-1x) \cdot (-15x)$$
$$3x \cdot 5x$$
$$(-3x) \cdot (-5x)$$

The last term of the trinomial, 4, is the product of the last term of each binomial. So ask, "What times what gives 4?" Here are four possibilities.

$$1 \cdot 4$$
$$(-1) \cdot (-4)$$
$$2 \cdot 2$$
$$(-2) \cdot (-2)$$

When we combine these results, we have several possible factorizations, including the following:

Binomial Product	FOIL	Simplified
$(1x + 4)(15x + 1)$ =	$15x^2 + 1x + 60x + 4$ =	$15x^2 + 61x + 4$
$(1x - 1)(15x - 4)$ =	$15x^2 - 4x - 15x + 4$ =	$15x^2 - 19x + 4$
$(1x - 4)(15x - 1)$ =	$15x^2 - 1x - 60x + 4$ =	$15x^2 - 61x + 4$
$(1x + 2)(15x + 2)$ =	$15x^2 + 2x + 30x + 4$ =	$15x^2 + 32x + 4$
$(1x - 2)(15x - 2)$ =	$15x^2 - 2x - 30x + 4$ =	$15x^2 - 32x + 4$
$(-1x - 1)(-15x - 4)$ =	$15x^2 + 4x + 15x + 4$ =	$15x^2 + 19x + 4$
$(-1x - 4)(-15x - 1)$ =	$15x^2 + 1x + 60x + 4$ =	$15x^2 + 61x + 4$
$(-1x - 2)(-15x - 2)$ =	$15x^2 + 2x + 30x + 4$ =	$15x^2 + 32x + 4$
$(3x + 4)(5x + 1)$ =	$15x^2 + 3x + 20x + 4$ =	$15x^2 + 23x + 4$
$(3x - 1)(5x - 4)$ =	$15x^2 - 12x - 5x + 4$ =	$15x^2 - 17x + 4$
$(3x - 4)(5x - 1)$ =	$15x^2 - 3x - 20x + 4$ =	$15x^2 - 23x + 4$
$(3x + 2)(5x + 2)$ =	$15x^2 + 6x + 10x + 4$ =	$15x^2 + 16x + 4$
$(3x - 2)(5x - 2)$ =	$15x^2 - 6x - 10x + 4$ =	$15x^2 - 16x + 4$
$(-3x - 1)(-5x - 4)$ =	$15x^2 + 12x + 5x + 4$ =	$15x^2 + 17x + 4$
$(-3x - 4)(-5x - 1)$ =	$15x^2 + 3x + 20x + 4$ =	$15x^2 + 23x + 4$
$(-3x - 2)(-5x - 2)$ =	$15x^2 + 6x + 10x + 4$ =	$15x^2 + 16x + 4$

Only one product, $(3x - 2)(5x - 2)$, results in the given trinomial $15x^2 - 16x + 4$.

Thus, $15x^2 - 16x + 4 = (3x - 2)(5x - 2)$.

To arrive at the factorization, we used the **trial and error method** because we made educated guesses about the factors and then multiplied to see which one was correct.

When there are so many possibilities, a factoring method based on factoring by grouping is often useful.

Factoring a Trinomial of the Form $ax^2 + bx + c$ by Grouping

In this method, we rewrite the middle term of the trinomial using two terms. Then we factor by grouping.

For example, we'll use this method to factor $15x^2 - 16x + 4$.

$$15x^2 - \quad 16x \quad + 4$$

Write the middle term, $-16x$, as $-10x - 6x$.

$$= 15x^2 - 10x - 6x + 4$$

Group the first two terms and group the last two terms.

$$= (15x^2 - 10x) + (-6x + 4)$$

Factor $5x$ out of the first group; factor -2 out the second group.

$$= 5x(3x - 2) \quad + (-2)(3x - 2)$$

Finally, factor out $(3x - 2)$.

$$= (3x - 2)(5x - 2)$$

The key to this method is knowing how to rewrite the middle term of the trinomial. The following procedure describes a way to do this.

— Procedure —
To Factor $ax^2 + bx + c$ by Grouping

Step 1 Factor out common factors (other than 1 or −1).

Step 2 List the values of a, b, and c.
Then find two integers whose product is ac and whose sum is b. If no two such integers exist then the trinomial is not factorable over the integers.

Step 3 Replace the middle term, bx, with a sum or difference using the two integers found in Step 2.

Step 4 Factor by grouping.

To check the factorization, multiply the binomial factors.

This method also works when $a = 1$. However, in those cases The Product-Sum method requires fewer steps.

Example 7.2.10

Factor: $6x^2 + 7x + 2$

Solution

Step 1 Factor out common factors (other than 1 or −1).

There are no common factors other than 1 and −1.

Step 2 List the values of a, b, and c. Then find two integers whose product is ac and whose sum is b.

$6x^2 + 7x + 2$ has the form $ax^2 + bx + c$ where $a = 6$, $b = 7$, and $c = 2$.

The product ac is $6 \cdot 2 = 12$.

Thus, find two integers whose product, ac, is 12 and whose sum, b, is 7.

• Since their product is positive, the integers must have the same sign.

• Since their sum is also positive, the integers must both be positive.

Here are the possibilities:

Product	Sum
$1 \cdot 12$	13
$2 \cdot 6$	8
$3 \cdot 4$	7

The integers 3 and 4 satisfy the requirements that their product is 12 and their sum is 7.

Step 3 Replace the middle term, bx, with a sum or difference using the two integers found in Step 2.

$$6x^2 + 7x + 2$$

Replace $7x$ with $3x + 4x$.

$$= 6x^2 + 3x + 4x + 2$$

We replaced 7x with 3x + 4x.

If we switch 3x and 4x, we can still group and factor:

$= 6x^2 + 4x + 3x + 2$
$= (6x^2 + 4x) + (3x + 2)$
$= 2x(3x + 2) + 1(3x + 2)$
$= (3x + 2)(2x + 1)$

Step 4 Factor by grouping.

Group the first pair of terms and group the second pair of terms.

$$= (6x^2 + 3x) + (4x + 2)$$

Factor $3x$ out of the first group; factor 2 out of the second group.

$$= 3x(2x + 1) + 2(2x + 1)$$

Factor out the common factor $(2x + 1)$.

$$= (2x + 1)(3x + 2)$$

The result is:

$$6x^2 + 7x + 2 = (2x + 1)(3x + 2).$$

You can multiply to check the factorization. We leave the check to you.

Example 7.2.11

Factor: $32x^2 - 20x - 3$

Solution

Step 1 Factor out common factors (other than 1 or −1).

There are no common factors other than 1 and −1.

Step 2 List the values of a, b, and c. Then find two integers whose product is ac and whose sum is b.

$32x^2 - 20x - 3$ has the form $ax^2 + bx + c$
where $a = 32$, $b = -20$, and $c = -3$.

The product ac is $32 \cdot (-3) = -96$. Thus, find two integers whose product, ac, is -96 and whose sum, b, is -20.

- Since their product is negative, the integers must have different signs.

- Also, their sum is negative, so the integer with the greater absolute value must be negative.

Here are some of the possibilities:

Product	Sum
$1 \cdot (-96)$	-95
$2 \cdot (-48)$	-46
$3 \cdot (-32)$	-29
$4 \cdot (-24)$	-20

Since 4 and −24 have product −96 and sum −20, we do not need to consider any other pairs of integers.

Step 3 Replace the middle term, bx, with a sum or difference using the two integers found in Step 2. $32x^2 - \quad 20x \quad - 3$

Replace $-20x$ with $4x - 24x$. $= 32x^2 + \mathbf{4x - 24x} - 3$

Step 4 Factor by grouping.

Group the first pair of terms and group the second pair of terms. $= (32x^2 + 4x) + (-24x - 3)$

Factor $4x$ out of the first group; factor -3 out of the second group. $= \mathbf{4x}(8x + 1) + (\mathbf{-3})(8x + 1)$

Factor out the common factor, $(8x + 1)$. $= (\mathbf{8x + 1})(4x - 3)$

The result is:
$$32x^2 - 20x - 3 = (8x + 1)(4x - 3).$$

We replaced $-20x$ with $4x - 24x$. If we switch $4x$ and $-24x$, we can still group and factor:
$$= 32x^2 - 24x + 4x - 3$$
$$= (32x^2 - 24x) + (4x - 3)$$
$$= 8x(4x - 3) + 1(4x - 3)$$
$$= (4x - 3)(8x + 1)$$

Example 7.2.12

Factor: $2x^2 + 4x + 3$

Solution

Step 1 Factor out common factors (other than 1 or −1).

There are no common factors other than 1 and −1.

Step 2 List the values of a, b, and c. Then find two integers whose product is ac and whose sum is b.

$2x^2 + 4x + 3$ has the form $ax^2 + bx + c$ where $a = 2$, $b = 4$, and $c = 3$.

The product ac is $2 \cdot 3 = 6$.

Thus, find two integers whose product, ac, is 6 and whose sum, b, is 4.

• Since their product is positive, the integers must have the same sign.

• Since their sum is also positive, the integers must both be positive.

Here are the possibilities:

Product	Sum
$1 \cdot (6)$	7
$2 \cdot (3)$	5

This approach tells us directly when the trinomial is not factorable.

That's a major advantage of this method.

Neither possibility has the required sum, 4.

Since there are no two integers whose product is 6 and whose sum is 4, we conclude that $2x^2 + 4x + 3$ is not factorable over the integers.

Example 7.2.13

Factor: $2x^2 - 8x - 10$

Solution

Step 1 Factor out common factors (other than 1 or −1).

Factor out the common factor of 2. $\qquad\qquad 2x^2 - 8x - 10$

The trinomial has the form $x^2 + bx + c$. $\qquad = 2(x^2 - 4x - 5)$

Since the coefficient of the x^2-term is 1, we can factor the trinomial by the product-sum method.

That is, we find two integers whose
product is −5 and whose sum is −4.
The integers are −5 and 1. $\qquad\qquad = 2(x - 5)(x + 1)$

The result is:
$$2x^2 - 8x - 10 = 2(x - 5)(x + 1).$$

You can multiply to check the factorization. We leave the check to you.

Solving an Equation of the Form $ax^2 + bx + c = 0$ by Factoring

The number 0 has several special properties, including this one:

*   The product of 0 and any number is 0. For example, $2 \cdot 0 = 0$.

Conversely, if the product of two real numbers is 0, then one or both must be 0. This statement is known as the **Zero Product Property**.

— Property —
Zero Product Property

English If the product of two numbers is 0, then one or both of the numbers is 0.

Algebra If a and b are real numbers, and if $a \cdot b = 0$, then $a = 0$ or $b = 0$ or both a and b are equal to 0.

Example If $(x + 2)(x + 3) = 0$, then $x + 2 = 0$ or $x + 3 = 0$.

The Zero Product Property is useful for solving certain types of equations.

Example 7.2.14

Solve: $(x - 3)(x + 5) = 0$

Solution

The product of $(x - 3)$ and $(x + 5)$ is zero. $(x - 3)(x + 5) = 0$

Use the Zero Product Property to write two separate equations. $x - 3 = 0$ or $x + 5 = 0$

Solve each equation. $x = 3$ or $x = -5$

Thus, the original equation has two solutions: 3 and -5

The solutions may be checked by substituting each value of x into the original equation and simplifying.

Check $x = 3$.	**Check $x = -5$.**
$(x - 3)(x + 5) = 0$	$(x - 3)(x + 5) = 0$
Is $(\mathbf{3} - 3)(\mathbf{3} + 5) = 0$?	Is $(\mathbf{-5} - 3)(\mathbf{-5} + 5) = 0$?
Is $\qquad (0)(8) = 0$?	Is $\qquad (-8)(0) = 0$?
Is $\qquad\qquad 0 = 0$? **Yes**	Is $\qquad\qquad 0 = 0$? **Yes**

— Definition —
Quadratic Equation

A **quadratic equation** is an equation that can be written in the form

$$ax^2 + bx + c = 0,$$

where a, b, and c are real numbers and $a \neq 0$.

A quadratic equation written in this form is said to be in **standard form**.

Now we will rewrite this equation. $(x - 3)(x + 5) = 0$

We multiply the binomials. $x^2 + 5x - 3x - 15 = 0$

We combine like terms. $x^2 + 2x - 15 = 0$

This quadratic equation is written in standard form.

Notice that the terms on the left side of $ax^2 + bx + c = 0$ are arranged in descending order by degree. The right side of the equation is zero.

Quadratic equations are also called **second-degree equations** because the degree of the polynomial, $ax^2 + bx + c$, is 2.

We will use the Zero Product Property to solve some quadratic equations by factoring.

— Procedure —
To Solve a Quadratic Equation By Factoring

Step 1 Write the quadratic equation in the form $ax^2 + bx + c = 0$.

Step 2 Factor the polynomial.

Step 3 Use the Zero Product Property.

Step 4 Solve each equation.

Step 5 Check each answer.

Example 7.2.15

Solve: $x^2 - 7x + 10 = 0$

Solution

Step 1 Write the quadratic equation in the form $ax^2 + bx + c = 0$.

The equation is given in standard form. $x^2 - 7x + 10 = 0$

Step 2 Factor the polynomial.
Find two integers whose product is 10 and
whose sum is -7. They are -5 and -2. $(x - 5)(x - 2) = 0$

Step 3 Use the Zero Product Property.

Set each factor equal to 0. $x - 5 = 0$ or $x - 2 = 0$

Step 4 Solve each equation.

There are two solutions. $x = 5$ or $x = 2$

Step 5 Check each answer.

Check $x = 5$

$x^2 - 7x + 10 = 0$

Is $(5)^2 - 7(5) + 10 = 0$?

Is $25 - 35 + 10 = 0$?

Is $0 = 0$? **Yes**

Check $x = 2$

$x^2 - 7x + 10 = 0$

Is $(2)^2 - 7(2) + 10 = 0$?

Is $4 - 14 + 10 = 0$?

Is $0 = 0$? **Yes**

Example 7.2.16

Solve: $3x^2 - 9x = 120$

Solution

Step 1 Write the quadratic equation in the form $ax^2 + bx + c = 0$.

Subtract 120 from both sides.

$3x^2 - 9x = 120$

$3x^2 - 9x - 120 = 0$

Step 2 Factor the polynomial.

Factor out the GCF, 3.

$3(x^2 - 3x - 40) = 0$

To factor the trinomial, find two integers whose product is -40 and whose sum is -3. They are -8 and 5.

$3(x - 8)(x + 5) = 0$

Step 3 Use the Zero Product Property.

Set each binomial factor equal to 0.

$x - 8 = 0$ or $x + 5 = 0$

Step 4 Solve each equation.

There are two solutions.

$x = 8$ or $x = -5$

Step 5 Check each answer.

We leave the check to you.

*When we used the Zero Product Property, you may wonder why we did not set the factor 3 equal to 0. Of course, 3 is **not** equal to 0.*

Furthermore, the product
  $3(x - 8)(x + 5)$
is 0 because either $(x - 8)$ is 0 or $(x + 5)$ is 0.

*The constant 3 does **not** make the product 0.*

Example 7.2.17

Solve: $6 = (x - 4)(x + 1)$

Solution

Step 1 *Write the quadratic equation in the form $ax^2 + bx + c = 0$.* $6 = (x - 4)(x + 1)$

Multiply the binomials on the right side.
Then simplify. $6 = x^2 - 3x - 4$

Subtract 6 from both sides. $0 = x^2 - 3x - 10$

Step 2 *Factor the polynomial.*

Find two integers whose product is -10
and whose sum is -3. They are -5 and 2. $0 = (x - 5)(x + 2)$

Step 3 *Use the Zero Product Property.*

Set each factor equal to 0. $x - 5 = 0$ or $x + 2 = 0$

Step 4 *Solve each equation.*

$x = 5$ or $x = -2$

Step 5 *Check each answer.*

We leave the check to you.

We can also write a quadratic equation with 0 on the left side:

That is, $0 = ax^2 + bx + c$ is a quadratic equation.

Here is a summary of this concept from *Academic Systems Algebra*.

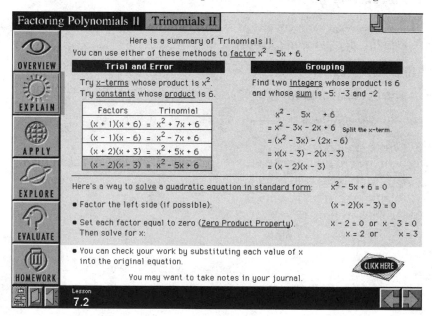

Explore

On the computer, you used overlapping circles to find the GCF of a collection of monomials. You also used a table to factor polynomials. Here are two additional examples.

Example 7.2.18

Complete the diagram to find the GCF of polynomials A, B, and C.

Solution

Factor each polynomial.

$$12x^2y = 2 \cdot 2 \cdot 3 \cdot x \cdot x \cdot y$$

$$18xy^3 = 2 \cdot 3 \cdot 3 \cdot x \cdot y \cdot y \cdot y$$

$$10xy = 2 \cdot 5 \cdot x \cdot y$$

For each polynomial, write the factors in the corresponding circle.

Since 3 is a factor of A and B only, write 3 where the circles for A and B overlap.

Since 2, x, and y are factors of A, B, and C, write 2, x, and y in the region where all three circles overlap.

The common factors lie in the region where all three circles overlap.

The factors in that region are 2, x, and y.

Therefore, the GCF of the polynomials is $2 \cdot x \cdot y = 2xy$.

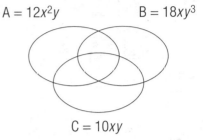

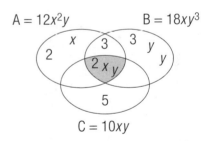

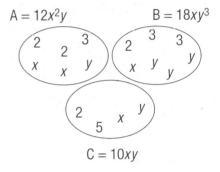

Example 7.2.19

Complete the table.

Then, write the polynomial and its factorization.

Solution

Multiply $3x$ by 5 to get $15x$.

Write this term in the upper right box.

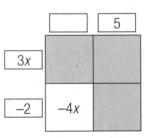

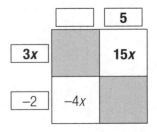

	2x	5
3x		15x
−2	−4x	

Ask yourself, "The term $-4x$ is the product of -2 and what?" The answer is $2x$.

Therefore, write $2x$ above the upper left box.

	2x	5
3x	6x²	15x
−2	−4x	−10

Multiply $3x$ by $2x$ to get $6x^2$. Write this term in the upper left box.

Likewise, multiply -2 by 5 to get -10. Write this term in the lower right box.

The sum of the terms in the boxes is
$$6x^2 + 15x - 4x - 10 = 6x^2 + 11x - 10.$$

The terms outside of the large square represent the two binomials, $(2x + 5)$ and $(3x - 2)$, that are the factors of the trinomial. That is, $6x^2 + 11x - 10 = (2x + 5)(3x - 2)$.

Here is a summary of this Exploration from *Academic Systems Algebra.*

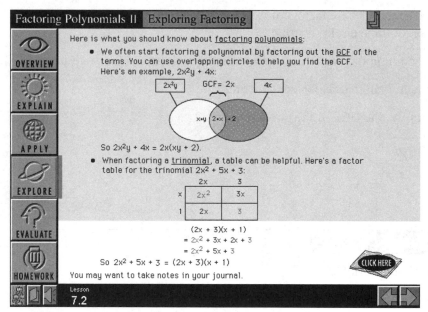

Checklist Lesson 7.2

Here is what you should know after completing this lesson.

Words and Phrases

product-sum method
trial and error method
Zero Product Property

quadratic equation
standard form (of a quadratic equation)
second-degree equation

Ideas and Procedures

❶ Factor a Trinomial of the Form $x^2 + bx + c$
Use the product-sum method to factor a trinomial of the form $x^2 + bx + c$.

Example 7.2.3
  Factor: $x^2 + x - 30$

See also: Example 7.2.1, 7.2.2, 7.2.4, 7.2.5, 7.2.6
    Apply 1-28

❷ Factor a Trinomial of the Form $x^2 + bxy + cy^2$
Use the product-sum method to factor a trinomial of the form $x^2 + bxy + cy^2$.

Example 7.2.7
  Factor: $x^2 - 5xy + 6y^2$

See also: Example 7.2.8

❸ Factor Trinomials of the Form $ax^2 + bx + c$
Use trial and error or the grouping method to factor a trinomial of the form $ax^2 + bx + c$.

Example 7.2.10
  Factor: $6x^2 + 7x + 2$

See also: Example 7.2.9, 7.2.11, 7.2.12, 7.2.13
    Apply 29-50

❹ Factor a Trinomial of the Form $ax^2 + bxy + cy^2$
Use trial and error or the grouping method to factor a trinomial of the form $ax^2 + bxy + cy^2$.

See: Apply 51-56

❺ Solve an Equation of the Form $ax^2 + bx + c = 0$
Use factoring to solve an equation that can be written in the form $ax^2 + bx + c = 0$.

Example 7.2.16
  Solve: $3x^2 - 9x = 120$

See also: Example 7.2.14, 7.2.15, 7.2.17
    Apply 57-62

Homework

Homework Problems

Circle the homework problems assigned to you by the computer, then complete them below.

 Explain

Trinomials I

1. Factor: $x^2 + 7x + 12$

2. Factor: $y^2 + 9y + 18$

3. Factor: $x^2 + 12x + 35$

4. Factor: $z^2 + 10z + 16$

5. Factor: $x^2 - 5x - 24$

6. Factor: $a^2 - 15a - 16$

7. Factor: $x^2 - x - 6$

8. Factor: $x^2 + 10x - 11$

9. Factor: $x^2 - 4x - 21$

10. Factor: $y^2 + 3y - 40$

11. Factor: $x^2 + 35x - 36$

12. Factor: $a^2 - 9a + 14$

Trinomials II

13. Factor: $2x^2 + 11x + 5$

14. Factor: $3x^2 + 13x + 4$

15. Factor: $4y^2 - 8y - 21$

16. Factor: $3z^2 - 17z + 20$

17. Factor: $15a^2 - 30a + 15$

18. Solve for x by factoring: $6x^2 = 63 - 13x$

19. Solve for x by factoring: $25x^2 + 5x = 2$

20. Factor: $4x^2 - 12x + 9$

21. Factor: $13x^2 + 37x + 22$

22. Factor: $x^2 - a^2$

23. Factor: $x^2 + 2xy + y^2$

24. Factor: $x^4 - 2ax^2 + a^2$

Explore

25. Circle the monomial(s) below that might appear in the factorization of $3x^3y^2 + 2x^2y - 3xy$

$3x^2y \qquad 2x^2y \qquad xy \qquad 3x$

26. If the GCF of the terms of a polynomial is $4x^2y^3$, which of the monomials below could be terms in the polynomial?

$4xy^3 \qquad 8x^3y^4 \quad 4x^2y^3 \quad 4x^2$

27. Factor this polynomial using overlapping circles:
$\frac{x^2y}{2} - \frac{2y}{4}$

28. A trinomial with a missing constant term has been partially factored in the table below. Complete the table and write the polynomial and its factorization.

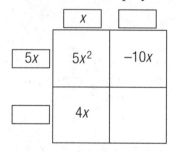

29. Complete the diagram below to find the GCF of the polynomials A, B, and C.

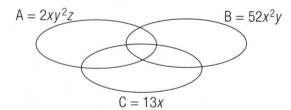

30. Factor this polynomial using overlapping circles:
$\frac{1}{2}x^2y^2 + \frac{3}{2}x^3y^3 - 3x^2y$

 **Apply**

Practice Problems

Here are some additional practice problems for you to try.

Trinomials I

1. Factor: $x^2 + 5x + 4$

2. Factor: $x^2 + 6x + 5$

3. Factor: $x^2 + 15x + 14$

4. Factor: $x^2 + 11x + 10$

5. Factor: $x^2 + 8x + 15$

6. Factor: $x^2 + 9x + 18$

7. Factor: $x^2 + 7x + 12$

8. Factor: $x^2 - 13x + 30$

9. Factor: $x^2 - 8x + 12$

10. Factor: $x^2 - 7x + 10$

11. Factor: $x^2 - 15x + 44$

12. Factor: $x^2 - 11x + 30$

13. Factor: $x^2 - 10x + 21$

14. Factor: $x^2 - 6x - 27$

15. Factor: $x^2 - 7x - 30$

16. Factor: $x^2 - 5x - 14$

17. Factor: $x^2 + 4x - 21$

18. Factor: $x^2 + 10x - 24$

19. Factor: $x^2 + 5x - 36$

20. Factor: $x^2 + 2x - 15$

21. Factor: $x^2 - 7x - 18$

22. Factor: $x^2 + 9x - 36$

23. Factor: $x^2 - 4x - 21$

24. Factor: $x^2 + 10x + 24$

25. Factor: $x^2 - 2x - 63$

26. Factor: $x^2 + 9x - 22$

27. Factor: $x^2 - 7x - 60$

28. Factor: $x^2 - 6x - 91$

Trinomials II

29. Factor: $2x^2 + 7x + 5$

30. Factor: $2x^2 + 9x + 9$

31. Factor: $3x^2 - 19x - 14$

32. Factor: $2x^2 - 3x - 20$

33. Factor: $2x^2 - x - 28$

34. Factor: $3x^2 + 16x - 35$

35. Factor: $2x^2 + 5x - 12$

36. Factor: $2x^2 + 9x - 5$

37. Factor: $2x^2 + 13x + 15$

38. Factor: $2x^2 + 15x + 28$

39. Factor: $3x^2 + 11x + 6$

40. Factor: $12x^2 - 7x + 1$

41. Factor: $10x^2 - 9x + 2$

42. Factor: $6x^2 - 5x + 1$

43. Factor: $6x^2 - 11x - 10$

44. Factor: $9x^2 - 18x - 7$

45. Factor: $8x^2 - 2x - 3$

46. Factor: $6x^2 + 13x - 28$

47. Factor: $9x^2 - 3x - 20$

48. Factor: $4x^2 - 4x - 15$

49. Factor: $36x^2 + 13x + 1$

50. Factor: $30x^2 + 11x + 1$

51. Factor: $5x^2 + 14xy - 3y^2$

52. Factor: $4x^2 - 7xy - 2y^2$

53. Factor: $3x^2 - 5xy - 2y^2$

54. Factor: $6x^2 + xy - 12y^2$

55. Factor: $9x^2 - 3xy - 2y^2$

56. Factor: $4x^2 - 4xy - 3y^2$

57. Solve: $(x - 6)(x + 2) = 0$

58. Solve: $x^2 + x - 6 = 0$

59. Solve: $x^2 - 13x = -40$

60. Solve: $x^2 = 9$

61. Solve: $0 = 2x^2 + 3x - 5$

62. Solve: $11x = 6x^2 + 3$

Practice Test

Take this practice test to be sure that you are prepared for the final quiz in Evaluate.

1. Factor: $x^2 - 10x + 24$

2. Circle the statement(s) below that are true.

    $x^2 + 2x - 1 = (x - 1)(x - 1)$

    $x^2 + 2x - 1 = (x + 2)(x - 1)$

    $x^2 + 2x - 1 = (x - 1)(x + 1)$

    $x^2 + 2x - 1 = (x + 1)(x + 1)$

    $x^2 + 2x - 1$ cannot be factored using integers

3. Factor: $t^2 - 16t - 17$

4. Factor: $r^2 + 10rt + 25t^2$

5. Factor: $5x^2 + 8x - 4$

6. Factor: $27v^2 - 57v + 28$

7. Factor: $4x^2 + 57x + 108$

8. Solve for x by factoring: $7x^2 - 5x - 12 = 0$

9. The overlapping circles contain the factors of three monomials, A, B, and C.

    Circle the true statements below.

    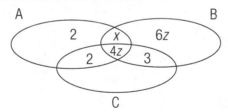

    Two factors of C are z and 2.

    $B = 72xz$

    The GCF of A and B is x.

    The GCF of A, B, and C is $4z$.

10. The overlapping circles contain the factors of two binomials, A and B. Their GCF is $(3u + 4v)$. What are A and B?

    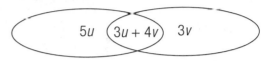

11. The polynomial $14xy + 21y - 6x^2 - 9x$ can be grouped as two binomials: $(14xy - 6x^2) + (21y - 9x)$. Find the GCF of the two binomials by factoring the polynomial using the overlapping circles below.

    $14xy - 6x^2$ $21y - 9x$

    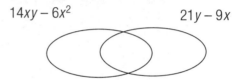

12. Finish factoring the trinomial $6x^2 - 7xy - 3y^2$ using the table below.

    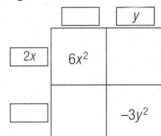

LESSON 7.3
FACTORING BY PATTERNS

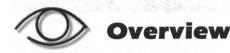 **Overview**

It is natural for people to look for patterns in their everyday lives. By observing patterns, you can often find ways to accomplish tasks more efficiently.

For example, by observing traffic patterns at different times of day, you can choose a route to work or school that will take the least amount of time.

In algebra, you can use patterns to factor some polynomials more quickly.

In this lesson, you will learn how to recognize and use patterns for factoring polynomials.

 Explain

Concept 1 has sections on

- **Factoring a Perfect Square Trinomial**

- **Factoring a Difference of Two Squares**

- **Factoring a Sum or Difference of Two Cubes**

- **A General Strategy for Factoring**

CONCEPT 1: RECOGNIZING PATTERNS

Factoring a Perfect Square Trinomial

Let's see what happens when we expand $(a + b)^2$.

First, we use the definition of exponential notation to write $(a + b)^2$ as the product of two binomials.

Next, we multiply the binomials.

Finally, we simplify and combine like terms.

$$(a + b)^2$$
$$= (a + b)(a + b)$$
$$= a^2 + ab + ba + b^2$$
$$= a^2 + 2ab + b^2$$

The expression $a^2 + 2ab + b^2$ is a **perfect square trinomial**. This means it is the result of squaring a binomial.

Note the structure of the three terms in the perfect square trinomial:

- The first term, a^2, is a perfect square.

- The last term, b^2, is a perfect square.

- The middle term, $2ab$, is twice the product of a and b.

When we recognize this pattern, we can immediately factor the trinomial as the square of a binomial.

A similar pattern holds when the middle term is subtracted rather than added.

— Pattern —
To Factor a Perfect Square Trinomial

$$a^2 + 2ab + b^2 = (a + b)(a + b) = (a + b)^2$$
$$a^2 - 2ab + b^2 = (a - b)(a - b) = (a - b)^2$$

Here is a useful procedure to follow when factoring by patterns.

— Procedure —
To Factor by Patterns

Step 1 Decide if the given polynomial fits a pattern.

Step 2 Identify a and b. Then substitute in the pattern and simplify.

To check the factorization, multiply the factors.

Example 7.3.1

Factor: $4x^2 + 4x + 1$

Solution

Step 1 Decide if the given polynomial fits a pattern.

The first term, $4x^2$, is a perfect square, $(2x)^2$.

The last term, 1, is a perfect square, $(1)^2$.

The middle term, $4x$, is twice the product of $2x$ and 1.

Therefore, $4x^2 + 4x + 1$ is a perfect square trinomial.

Step 2 Identify a and b. Then substitute in the pattern and simplify.

In the factoring pattern for a perfect square trinomial, substitute $2x$ for a and 1 for b.

$$a^2 + 2ab + b^2 = (a + b)(a + b)$$

$$(2x)^2 + 2(2x)(1) + (1)^2 = (2x + 1)(2x + 1)$$

The result is:
$$4x^2 + 4x + 1 = (2x + 1)(2x + 1).$$

This can also be written: $4x^2 + 4x + 1 = (2x + 1)^2$.

To check the factorization, we multiply.

Is $(2x + 1)(2x + 1) = 4x^2 + 4x + 1$?

Is $4x^2 + 2x + 2x + 1 = 4x^2 + 4x + 1$?

Is $4x^2 + \quad 4x \quad + 1 = 4x^2 + 4x + 1$? **Yes**

Example | **7.3.2**

Factor: $25y^2 - 40y + 16$

Solution

Step 1 Decide if the given polynomial fits a pattern.

The first term, $25y^2$, is a perfect square, $(5y)^2$.

The last term, 16, is a perfect square, $(4)^2$.

The middle term, $-40y$, is the opposite of twice the product of $5y$ and 4.

Therefore, $25y^2 - 40y + 16$ is a perfect square trinomial.

Step 2 Identify a and b. Then substitute in the pattern and simplify.

In the factoring pattern for a perfect square trinomial, substitute $5y$ for a and 4 for b.

$$a^2 - 2ab + b^2 = (a - b)(a - b)$$

$$(5y)^2 - 2(5y)(4) + (4)^2 = (5y - 4)(5y - 4)$$

The result is:

$$25y^2 - 40y + 16 = (5y - 4)(5y - 4).$$

This can also be written: $25y^2 - 40y + 16 = (5y - 4)^2$.

You can multiply to check the factorization. We leave the check to you.

Factoring a Difference of Two Squares

To find another factoring pattern, we first multiply $(a + b)$ by $(a - b)$.

$$(a + b)(a - b)$$

Multiply the binomials.

$$= a^2 - ab + ba - b^2$$

When we combine like terms, the two middle terms add to zero.

$$= a^2 - b^2$$

The result is $a^2 - b^2$, the **difference of two squares**.

Note the structure of the two terms in a difference of two squares:

- The first term, a^2, is a perfect square.

- The last term, b^2, is a perfect square.

- The terms are subtracted.

When we recognize this pattern, we can immediately factor the binomial using the following relationship.

— Pattern —
To Factor the Difference of Two Squares

$$a^2 - b^2 = (a + b)(a - b)$$

Example 7.3.3

Factor: $m^2 - 121$

Solution

Step 1 Decide if the given polynomial fits a pattern.

The first term, m^2, is a perfect square, $(m)^2$.

The last term, 121, is a perfect square, $(11)^2$.

The terms are subtracted.

Therefore, $m^2 - 121$ is a difference of two squares.

Step 2 Identify a and b. Then substitute in the pattern and simplify.

In the factoring pattern for a difference of two squares, substitute m for a and 11 for b.

$$a^2 - b^2 = (a + b)(a - b)$$

$$(m)^2 - (11)^2 = (m + 11)(m - 11)$$

The result is:
$$m^2 - 121 = (m + 11)(m - 11).$$

You can multiply to check the factorization. We leave the check to you.

Be careful!

The binomial $m^2 + 121$ is not a difference of two squares because the terms are added rather than subtracted.

The binomial $m^2 + 121$ cannot be factored over the integers.

Example 7.3.4

Factor: $16w^2 - 49y^2$

Solution

Step 1 Decide if the given polynomial fits a pattern.

The first term, $16w^2$, is a perfect square, $(4w)^2$.

The last term, $49y^2$, is a perfect square, $(7y)^2$.

The terms are subtracted.

Therefore, $16w^2 - 49y^2$ is a difference of two squares.

Step 2 Identify a and b. Then substitute in the pattern and simplify.

In the factoring pattern for a difference of two squares, substitute $4w$ for a and $7y$ for b.

$$a^2 - b^2 = (a + b)(a - b)$$

$$(4w)^2 - (7y)^2 = (4w + 7y)(4w - 7y)$$

The result is:
$$16w^2 - 49y^2 = (4w + 7y)(4w - 7y).$$

You can multiply to check the factorization. We leave the check to you.

Factoring a Sum or Difference of Two Cubes

This product will lead us to another factoring pattern.

$$(a + b)(a^2 - ab + b^2)$$

To find the product, multiply each term in $(a + b)$
by each term in $(a^2 - ab + b^2)$.

$$= \mathbf{a} \cdot a^2 - \mathbf{a} \cdot ab + \mathbf{a} \cdot b^2 + \mathbf{b} \cdot a^2 - \mathbf{b} \cdot ab + \mathbf{b} \cdot b^2$$

$$= a^3 \quad - a^2b \quad + ab^2 \quad + a^2b \quad - ab^2 \quad + b^3$$

Combine like terms.

$$= a^3 + b^3$$

The four middle terms add to zero.

The result is $a^3 + b^3$, the **sum of two cubes**.

Note the structure of the two terms:

- The first term, a^3, is a perfect cube.

- The last term, b^3, is a perfect cube.

- The terms are added.

When we recognize this pattern, we can immediately factor the sum of
two cubes as follows:
$$a^3 + b^3 = (a + b)(a^2 - ab + b^2)$$

A similar factoring pattern holds for $a^3 - b^3$, the **difference of two cubes**.

*You may want to memorize a few
perfect cubes.*
$1^3 = 1$
$2^3 = 8$
$3^3 = 27$
$4^3 = 64$
$5^3 = 125$

*To check if a number is a perfect cube, use
the $\sqrt[3]{\ }$ key on your calculator to see if the
cube root is an integer.*

— Pattern —
To Factor the Sum or Difference of Two Cubes
$a^3 + b^3 = (a + b)(a^2 - ab + b^2)$ $a^3 - b^3 = (a - b)(a^2 + ab + b^2)$

Example 7.3.5

Factor: $y^3 + 64$

Solution

Step 1 Decide if the given polynomial fits a pattern.

The first term, y^3, is a perfect cube, $(y)^3$.

The last term, 64, is a perfect cube, $(4)^3$.

The terms are added.

Therefore, $y^3 + 64$ is a sum of two cubes.

Step 2 Identify a and b. Then substitute in the pattern and simplify.

In the factoring pattern for a sum of two cubes, substitute y for a and 4 for b.

$$a^3 + b^3 = (a + b)(a^2 - ab + b^2)$$

$$(y)^3 + (4)^3 = (y + 4)(y^2 - y \cdot 4 + 4^2)$$

Simplify.

$$= (y + 4)(y^2 - 4y + 16)$$

The result is:

$$y^3 + 64 = (y + 4)(y^2 - 4y + 16).$$

You can multiply to check the factorization. We leave the check to you.

Example 7.3.6

Factor: $8w^3 - 1$

Solution

Step 1 Decide if the given polynomial fits a pattern.

The first term, $8w^3$, is a perfect cube, $(2w)^3$.

The last term, 1, is a perfect cube, $(1)^3$.

The terms are subtracted.

Therefore, $8w^3 - 1$ is a difference of two cubes.

Step 2 Identify a and b. Then substitute in the pattern and simplify.

In the factoring pattern for a difference of two cubes, substitute $2w$ for a and 1 for b.

$$a^3 - b^3 = (a - b)(a^2 + ab + b^2)$$

$$(2w)^3 - (1)^3 = (2w - 1)[(2w)^2 + 2w \cdot 1 + (1)^2]$$

Simplify.

$$= (2w - 1)(4w^2 + 2w + 1)$$

The result is:

$$8w^3 - 1 = (2w - 1)(4w^2 + 2w + 1).$$

You can multiply to check the factorization. We leave the check to you.

Example 7.3.7

Factor: $27w^3 + 125y^{12}$

Solution

Step 1 Decide if the given polynomial fits a pattern.

The first term, $27w^3$, is a perfect cube, $(3w)^3$.

The last term, $125y^{12}$, is a perfect cube, $(5y^4)^3$.

The terms are added.

Therefore, $27w^3 + 125y^{12}$ is a sum of two cubes.

Step 2 Identify a and b. Then substitute in the pattern and simplify.

In the factoring pattern for a sum of two cubes, substitute $3w$ for a and $5y^4$ for b.

$$a^3 \ + \ b^3 \ = (a \ + \ b)(a^2 \ - \ ab \ + \ b^2)$$
$$(3w)^3 + (5y^4)^3 = (3w + 5y^4)[(3w)^2 - 3w \cdot 5y^4 + (5y^4)^2]$$

Simplify.
$$= (3w + 5y^4)(9w^2 - 15wy^4 + 25y^8)$$

The result is:
$$27w^3 + 125y^{12} = (3w + 5y^4)(9w^2 - 15wy^4 + 25y^8).$$

You can multiply to check the factorization. We leave the check to you.

Here is a summary of the factoring patterns presented in this lesson.

Patterns for Factoring

Perfect Square Trinomial

$$a^2 + 2ab + b^2 = (a + b)(a + b) \qquad a^2 - 2ab + b^2 = (a - b)(a - b)$$

Difference of Two Squares

$$a^2 - b^2 = (a + b)(a - b)$$

Sum of Two Cubes   ***Difference of Two Cubes***

$$a^3 + b^3 = (a + b)(a^2 - ab + b^2) \qquad a^3 - b^3 = (a - b)(a^2 + ab + b^2)$$

A General Strategy for Factoring

You have factored polynomials using a variety of methods. Some factoring problems require more than one method. Here is a systematic procedure for factoring a polynomial.

— Procedure —
General Strategy for Factoring a Polynomial

Step 1 Factor out the GCF of the terms of the polynomial.

Step 2 Count the number of terms and look for factoring patterns.

Two Terms: Look for the difference of two squares, the sum of two cubes, or the difference of two cubes.

Three Terms: • Look for a perfect square trinomial.
- If the trinomial has the form $x^2 + bx + c$, try to find two integers whose product is c and whose sum is b.
- If the trinomial has the form $ax^2 + bx + c$, try to find two integers whose product is ac and whose sum is b.

Four Terms: Try factoring by grouping.

Step 3 Factor completely.

To check the factorization, multiply the factors.

Example 7.3.8

Factor: $4wx^2 - 64wx + 256w$

Solution

Step 1 Factor out the GCF of the terms of the polynomial.

$$4wx^2 - 64wx + 256w$$

Factor out $4w$. $= 4w(x^2 - 16x + 64)$

Now we will try to factor the trinomial, $x^2 - 16x + 64$.

Step 2 Count the number of terms and look for factoring patterns.

There are three terms in $x^2 - 16x + 64$.

- The first term, x^2, is a perfect square, $(x)^2$.

- The third term, 64, is a perfect square, $(8)^2$.

- The middle term, $-16x$, is the opposite of twice the product of x and 8.

Therefore, $x^2 - 16x + 64$ has the form $a^2 - 2ab + b^2$ where a is x and b is 8.

$$a^2 - 2ab + b^2 = (a - b)(a - b)$$

In the pattern, substitute x for a and 8 for b. $\quad (x)^2 - 2(x)(8) + (8)^2 = (x - 8)(x - 8)$

Step 3 Factor completely.

$(x - 8)(x - 8)$ cannot be factored further.

But don't forget the original factor $4w$ that we factored out in Step 1. $\quad 4wx^2 - 64wx + 256w = \mathbf{4w(x - 8)(x - 8)}$

We multiply to check the factorization.

Is $\quad 4w(x - 8)(x - 8) = 4wx^2 - 64wx + 256w$?

Is $\quad 4w(x^2 - 16x + 64) = 4wx^2 - 64wx + 256w$?

Is $4wx^2 - 64wx + 256w = 4wx^2 - 64wx + 256w$? **Yes**

Example 7.3.9

Factor: $wx^2 + 5x^2 - 9w - 45$

Solution

Step 1 Factor out the GCF of the terms of the polynomial.

The GCF is 1.

Step 2 Count the number of terms and look for factoring patterns.

There are four terms, so try factoring by grouping.

$$wx^2 + 5x^2 - 9w - 45$$

Group the first pair of terms and factor out x^2.

$$= (wx^2 + 5x^2) + (-9w - 45)$$
$$= x^2(w + 5) + (-9w - 45)$$

Group the second pair of terms. Factor out -9 (rather than $+9$) to obtain $w + 5$, the same binomial as in the first grouping.

$$= x^2(w + 5) - 9(w + 5)$$

Factor out $(w + 5)$.

$$= (w + 5)(x^2 - 9)$$

Step 3 Factor completely.

$w + 5$ cannot be factored further.

$x^2 - 9$ is a difference of two squares, $(x)^2 - (3)^2$.

So we factor $x^2 - 9$ using the pattern for a difference of two squares.

$$= (w + 5)(x + 3)(x - 3)$$

The result is:
$$wx^2 + 5x^2 - 9w - 45 = (w + 5)(x + 3)(x - 3).$$

We multiply to check the factorization.

Is $(w + 5)(x + 3)(x - 3) = wx^2 + 5x^2 - 9w - 45$?

Is $(w + 5)(x^2 - 9) = wx^2 + 5x^2 - 9w - 45$?

Is $wx^2 - 9w + 5x^2 - 45 = wx^2 + 5x^2 - 9w - 45$? **Yes**

Here is a summary of this concept from *Academic Systems Algebra.*

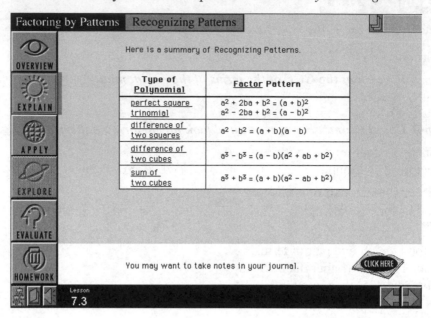

Factoring by Patterns   Recognizing Patterns

OVERVIEW
EXPLAIN
APPLY
EXPLORE
EVALUATE
HOMEWORK

Here is a summary of Recognizing Patterns.

Type of Polynomial	Factor Pattern
perfect square trinomial	$a^2 + 2ba + b^2 = (a + b)^2$ $a^2 - 2ba + b^2 = (a - b)^2$
difference of two squares	$a^2 - b^2 = (a + b)(a - b)$
difference of two cubes	$a^3 - b^3 = (a - b)(a^2 + ab + b^2)$
sum of two cubes	$a^3 + b^3 = (a + b)(a^2 - ab + b^2)$

You may want to take notes in your journal.   CLICK HERE

Lesson
7.3

Checklist Lesson 7.3

Here is what you should know after completing this lesson.

Words and Phrases

perfect square trinomial
difference of two squares

sum of two cubes
difference of two cubes

Ideas and Procedures

❶ **Factor a Perfect Square Trinomial**
Use a pattern to factor a perfect square trinomial.

Example 7.3.2
    Factor: $25y^2 - 40y + 18$

See also: Example 7.3.1
        Apply 1-11

❷ **Factor the Difference of Two Squares**
Use a pattern to factor the difference of two squares.

Example 7.3.4
    Factor: $16w^2 - 49y^2$

See also: Example 7.3.3.
        Apply 12-16

❸ **Factor the Sum or Difference of Two Cubes**
Use a pattern to factor the sum or difference of two cubes.

Example 7.3.7
    Factor: $27w^3 + 125y^{12}$

See also: Example 7.3.5, 7.3.6
        Apply 17-25

❹ **Factor a Polynomial**
Use a general strategy to factor a polynomial.

Example 7.3.8
    Factor: $4wx^2 - 64wx + 256w$

See also: Example 7.3.9
        Apply 26-28

Homework

Homework Problems

Circle the homework problems assigned to you by the computer, then complete them below.

 Explain

Recognizing Patterns

Factor the polynomials in questions 1 through 12.

1. $x^2 + 14x + 49$

2. $w^2 - 16$

3. $x^3 + 125$

4. $25y^2 - 30y + 9$

5. $9xy^2 - x$

6. $64y^3 - 27w^9$

7. $x^2 + 8w^2x + 16w^4$

8. $2x^6 - 72y^2$

9. $49y^2 - 28xy + 4x^2$

10. $x^3y^2 + 8y^2$

11. $2x^3 + 12x^2 + 18x$

12. $y^6 - 16y^2$

 **Apply**

Practice Problems

Here are some additional practice problems for you to try.

Recognizing Patterns

1. Factor: $a^2 + 18a + 81$

2. Factor: $y^2 + 14y + 49$

3. Factor: $9x^2 + 42x + 49$

4. Factor: $25m^2 + 30m + 9$

5. Factor: $4a^2 + 20a + 25$

6. Factor: $b^2 - 16b + 64$

7. Factor: $z^2 - 22z + 121$

8. Factor: $y^2 - 18y + 81$

9. Factor: $16a^2 - 40a + 25$

10. Factor: $4c^2 + 28c + 49$

11. Factor: $9x^2 - 12x + 4$

12. Factor: $m^2 - 144$

13. Factor: $x^2 - 36$

14. Factor: $9m^2 - 81n^2$

15. Factor: $25a^2 - 625b^2$

16. Factor: $16x^2 - 64y^2$

17. Factor: $a^3 - 216$

18. Factor: $m^3 - 1000$

19. Factor: $x^3 - 125$

20. Factor: $8b^3 - 125$

21. Factor: $27z^3 - 343$

22. Factor: $64a^3 - 216$

23. Factor: $c^3 + 64$

24. Factor: $p^3 + 512$

25. Factor: $y^3 + 27$

26. Factor: $3a^3 + 42a^2b + 147b^2$

27. Factor: $50m^3n - 128mn^3$

28. Factor: $5x^3 - 20xy^2$

Evaluate

Practice Test

Take this practice test to be sure that you are prepared for the final quiz in Evaluate.

1. Circle the expressions below that are perfect square trinomials.

   $9x^2 + 12x + 4$

   $0.25x^2 + 8x + 64$

   $25x^2 - 9$

   $9x^2 + 20x + 4$

   $x^2 - 2x + 1$

   $x^2 - 7x + 6$

2. Factor the polynomials below.

   a. $x^2 - 10x + 25$

   b. $49y^2 + 28y + 4$

   c. $16x^2 - 1$

   d. $9y^2 - 36$

3. Circle the polynomials below that **cannot** be factored any further using integers.

   $x^2 - 1000$

   $4y^2 - 4y + 1$

   $3x^2 - 27x + 9$

   $9m^2 - 24mn - 16n^2$

   $12x^3 - 8xy + 2y$

4. Factor: $12x^3 - 60x^2 + 75x$

5. Circle the expressions below that are perfect square trinomials.

   $36x^2 - 1$

   $4x^2 - 2x - 56$

   $x^2 + 8x + 16$

   $4x^2 - 12x + 9$

   $x^2 - 16x + 4$

6. Factor the polynomials below.

   a. $4x^2 - 24x + 36$

   b. $64z^2 + 16z + 1$

   c. $4w^2 - 49$

   d. $9m^2 - n^2$

7. Factor the polynomials below.

   a. $x^3 + 1000$

   b. $216y^3 - 1$

   c. $343x^3 + 8y^3$

8. Factor: $27w^3 + 90w^2 + 75w$

Cumulative Review Problems

These problems combine all of the material you have covered so far in this course. You may want to test your understanding of this material before you move on to the next topic, or you may wish to do these problems to review for a test.

1. Find: $(a^5 - 9a^3 + 5a^2 + 14a - 35) \div (a^2 - 7)$

2. Find the slope of the line perpendicular to the line through the points $(-3, 7)$ and $(9, -5)$.

3. Simplify this expression: $11x^2 + 6y + 2 - 4x^2 - y$

4. Graph the inequality $2x + 3y \le 6$.

5. Alfredo needs to make 250 ml of a 27% alcohol solution using a 15% solution and a 40% solution. How much of each should he use?

6. The point $(-2, -3)$ lies on a line with slope 2. Graph this line by finding another point that lies on the line.

7. Factor: $x^2 - 6x + 9$

8. Find the GCF of $6x^2y^2$ and $8xy^4$.

9. Circle the true statements below.

    $5(7 + 3) = 5(10)$

    $|9 - 20| = -11$

    The fraction $\frac{4}{6}$ is in lowest terms.

    The LCM of 45 and 75 is 225.

    $\frac{9}{11} \cdot \frac{22}{3} = 6$

10. Solve for x: $3(x + 1) = x + 2x + \frac{3}{2}2$

11. Graph the system of inequalities below to find its solution.

    $3x - 2y \le 7$
    $4x + y > 2$

12. Find the slope of the line parallel to the line through the points $(7, -1)$ and $(2, 8)$.

13. Factor: $a^4 + 4a^2 + 4$

14. Solve this system:

    $3x - y = 23$
    $2x + y = 22$

15. Solve $5 \le 3x - 13 < 17$ for x, then graph the solution on the number line below.

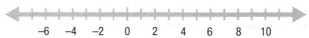

16. Factor: $6x + 3ax + 2b + ab$

17. Find the equation of the line through the point $(-7, 12)$ with slope $m = -2$:

    a. in point-slope form.

    b. in slope-intercept form.

    c. in standard form.

18. Find:

    a. $-2x^0 - \frac{4}{y^0}$ b. $\left(\frac{x^7yz^4}{x^2z}\right)^2$

    c. $a^0 \cdot a^0 \cdot a^0$

19. Solve for x by factoring: $x^2 - 5x - 14 = 0$

20. Find:

    a. $11^3 \cdot 11^5$

    b. $\frac{x}{x^8}$

    c. $(ab^6)^3$

21. Find the equation of the line through the point $(4, -3)$ with slope $-\frac{8}{5}$:

    a. in point-slope form.

    b. in slope-intercept form.

    c. in standard form.

22. Factor: $4y^2 - 28y + 49$

23. Find the slope of the line through the points $(31, 16)$ and $(-2, 8)$.

24. Find: $(5y - 3)^2$

25. Solve $5y + 5 = 5(2 + y)$ for y.

26. Find the slope and y-intercept of the line $\frac{9}{4}x - \frac{2}{3}y = 2$.

27. Factor: $5x^2 + 2x - 7$

28. Find:
$(xy^3 - 5x^2y + 11xy - 1) - (4xy^3 - 7 - x^2y + 3xy)$

29. Evaluate the expression $2a^3 - 8ab + 5b^2$ when $a = -2$ and $b = 4$.

30. Factor: $2x^2 + 9x - 18$

31. Use the FOIL method to find: $(a + 4)(a - 2)$

32. Graph the inequality $3x + 5y > 8$.

33. Jerome owed a total of $1820 on his two credit cards last year for which he paid $278.60 in interest. If one card charged 14% in interest and the other card charged 16% in interest, how much did he owe on each card?

34. Solve $-6 \leq 4y - 3 \leq 5$ for y.

35. Find the equation of the line through the point $(5, 3)$ with slope $m = \frac{5}{6}$:

    a. in point-slope form.

    b. in slope-intercept form.

    c. in standard form.

36. Factor: $x^2 - 7x + 12$

37. Graph the system of inequalities below to find its solution.
$$4x - 3y \leq 6$$
$$y \leq \frac{1}{2}x + 5$$

38. Circle the expressions below that are monomials.

    15 $\qquad\qquad$ $2x^4 + x$

    $9y$ $\qquad\qquad$ $a^3b^4c^2$

39. Graph the inequality $2x - 3y > 12$.

40. Hye was cleaning out her car and found a total of 44 nickels and quarters worth $4.80. How many of each did she find?

41. Factor: $36b^2 + 60b + 25$

42. Circle the true statements below.

$$\frac{17}{21} - \frac{7}{18} = \frac{10}{3}$$

$$\frac{15}{33} = \frac{5}{11}$$

$$|8| - |13| = |8 - 13|$$

The GCF of 120 and 252 is 12.

$$11^2(15 - 2) = 121(15 - 2)$$

43. Simplify this expression:
$8x^3 + 5xy^2 + 7 - 4x^3 + 2xy^2$

44. Graph the system of inequalities below to find its solution.
$$x + 2y < 6$$
$$x + 2y \geq -5$$

45. Solve this system:
$$5x + 7y = 25$$
$$5x - 3y = -25$$

46. Find the slope of the line through the points $(2, 11)$ and $(6, -8)$.

47. Find: $(x + 5)(5x + xy - 3y)$

48. Factor: $3x^2 - 5x - 2$

49. The length of a rectangle is 3 times its width. If the perimeter of the rectangle is 136 feet, what are its dimensions?

50. Solve this system:
$$6x + 5y = -7$$
$$2x + 5y = -9$$

TOPIC 8
RATIONAL EXPRESSIONS

We work with fractions every day: to cut a sandwich in half, to saw a board into four parts, or to divide a cake among eight people.

A fraction is a ratio of two real numbers. A ratio of two polynomials is called an algebraic fraction. Algebraic fractions are also called rational expressions.

In this topic, you will learn to work with rational expressions.

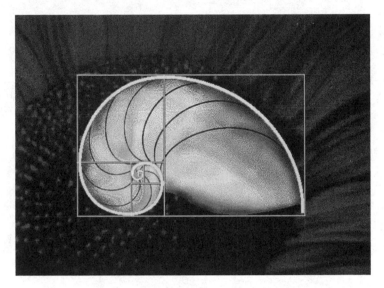

Lesson 8.1 Rational Expressions I

Concept 1: Multiplying and Dividing Rational Expressions
Determining When a Rational
    Expression is Undefined
Reducing a Rational Expression
    to Lowest Terms
Multiplying Rational Expressions
Dividing Rational Expressions
Simplifying a Complex Fraction

Concept 2: Adding and Subtracting Rational Expressions
Adding Rational Expressions
    with the Same Denominator
Subtracting Rational Expressions
    with the Same Denominator

Lesson 8.2 Rational Expressions II

Concept 1: Negative Exponents
Definition of a Negative Integer Exponent
Properties of Negative Exponents
Simplifying Expressions That Contain
    Negative Exponents
Scientific Notation

Concept 2: Multiplying and Dividing Rational Expressions Containing Binomials
Reducing Rational Expressions
    of the Form $\dfrac{a-b}{b-a}$
Multiplying Rational Expressions
Dividing Rational Expressions
Simplifying a Complex Fraction

Concept 3: Adding and Subtracting Rational Expressions Containing Binomials
Finding the Least Common Multiple (LCM)
    of a Set of Polynomials
Adding and Subtracting Rational Expressions
    with Different Denominators
Simplifying Complex Fractions Containing
    Addition or Subtraction

Lesson 8.3 Equations with Fractions

Concept 1: Solving Equations
Solving Equations That Contain
    Rational Expressions
Extraneous Solutions
Ratios and Proportions
Solving Proportions Using Cross
    Multiplication
Formulas

Lesson 8.4 Problem Solving

Concept 1: Rational Expressions
Work Problems
Distance Problems
Ratio and Proportion Problems
Direct Variation
Inverse Variation
Joint and Combined Variation

LESSON 8.1
RATIONAL EXPRESSIONS I

 Overview

 Over 2000 years ago, Eratosthenes, a mathematician from Alexandria, Egypt, was able to determine the circumference of the earth. He did this by setting up an equation that involved rational expressions, fractions in which the numerator and denominator are polynomials.

In this lesson, you will learn how to reduce, multiply, divide, add, and subtract some types of rational expressions.

 Explain

Concept 1 has sections on

- **Determining When a Rational Expression is Undefined**

- **Reducing a Rational Expression to Lowest Terms**

- **Multiplying Rational Expressions**

- **Dividing Rational Expressions**

- **Simplifying a Complex Fraction**

The integer -2 is a rational number, since it can be written as $\frac{-2}{1}$.
Likewise, 1.5 is a rational number, since it can be written as $\frac{3}{2}$.

Remember, constants such as 2 and 7 are monomials of degree 0.
So, $\frac{2}{7}$ is an example of a rational expression.

CONCEPT 1:
MULTIPLYING AND DIVIDING RATIONAL EXPRESSIONS

Determining When a Rational Expression is Undefined

A rational number is a number that can be written in the form $\frac{a}{b}$ where a and b are integers and $b \neq 0$.

For example,

$$\frac{7}{8}, -2, \text{ and } 1.5$$

are rational numbers.

We define a **rational expression** in a similar manner.

— Definition —
Rational Expression

A rational expression is an expression that can be written in the form

$$\frac{P}{Q},$$

where P and Q are polynomials and $Q \neq 0$.

Here are some examples of rational expressions:

$$\frac{4x + 15}{x + 8} \qquad \frac{1}{8x} \qquad \frac{3w - 14}{2} \qquad \frac{2}{7}$$

The denominator of a rational expression cannot equal 0. This is because division by 0 is undefined. Therefore, it is important to determine the values of the variable that make the denominator 0. We say that the rational expression is **undefined** for those values.

Example 8.1.1

Find the value(s) of x for which this rational expression is undefined: $\dfrac{4x + 15}{x + 8}$

Solution

The rational expression is undefined when its denominator is 0.

Set the denominator equal to 0.
Then solve for x. $\qquad\qquad x + 8 = 0$

Subtract 8 from both sides. $\qquad\qquad x = -8$

When $x = -8$, the denominator is 0. $\qquad \dfrac{4(-8) + 15}{-8 + 8}$

We have $\qquad\qquad = \dfrac{-17}{0}$

Therefore, $\dfrac{4x + 15}{x + 8}$ is undefined when $x = -8$.

*It's okay for the **numerator** of a rational expression to equal 0.*

For example, $\dfrac{2x}{x - 5}$ is defined when $x = 0$.

$\dfrac{2 \cdot 0}{0 - 5} = \dfrac{0}{-5} = 0$

*However, $\dfrac{2x}{x - 5}$ is **not** defined when $x = 5$.*

$\dfrac{2 \cdot 5}{5 - 5} = \dfrac{10}{0} =$ undefined

Example 8.1.2

Find the value(s) of x for which this rational expression is undefined: $\dfrac{x - 2}{x^2 - 9}$

Solution

Set the denominator equal to zero.
Then solve for x. $\qquad\qquad x^2 - 9 = 0$

Factor the left side of the equation. $\qquad (x - 3)(x + 3) = 0$

Use the Zero Product Property. $\qquad x - 3 = 0 \quad$ or $\quad x + 3 = 0$

Solve these equations. $\qquad\qquad x = 3 \quad$ or $\quad x = -3$

Therefore, $\dfrac{x - 2}{x^2 - 9}$ is undefined when $x = 3$ or $x = -3$.

In each rational expression that follows, we will assume that no value of a variable will make a denominator 0.

Reducing a Rational Expression to Lowest Terms

Like a fraction in arithmetic, a rational expression is usually easier to work with when written in **lowest terms**.

The procedure for reducing a rational expression to lowest terms is like the procedure for reducing a fraction to lowest terms.

— Procedure —
To Reduce a Rational Expression to Lowest Terms

Step 1 Factor the numerator and denominator.

Step 2 Cancel all pairs of factors common to the numerator and denominator.

*When we have **reduced** a rational expression to lowest terms, we also say we have **simplified** the rational expression.*

Here's an example from arithmetic.

Reduce to lowest terms: $\dfrac{30}{42}$

Step 1 Factor the numerator and denominator.

$$\frac{30}{42} = \frac{2 \cdot 3 \cdot 5}{2 \cdot 3 \cdot 7}$$

Step 2 Cancel all pairs of factors common to the numerator and denominator.

$$\frac{\cancel{2} \cdot \cancel{3} \cdot 5}{\underset{1}{\cancel{2}} \cdot \underset{1}{\cancel{3}} \cdot 7} = \frac{5}{7}$$

Thus,

$$\frac{30}{42} = \frac{5}{7}$$

Remember, that $w \neq 0$, $x \neq 0$, and $y \neq 0$.

Example 8.1.3

Reduce to lowest terms: $\dfrac{24w^3xy^2}{9wx^2y}$

Solution

Step 1 Factor the numerator and denominator.

$$\frac{24w^3xy^2}{9wx^2y} = \frac{2 \cdot 2 \cdot 2 \cdot 3 \cdot w \cdot w \cdot w \cdot x \cdot y \cdot y}{3 \cdot 3 \cdot w \cdot x \cdot x \cdot y}$$

Step 2 Cancel all pairs of factors common to the numerator and denominator.

$$= \frac{2 \cdot 2 \cdot 2 \cdot \cancel{3} \cdot \cancel{w} \cdot w \cdot w \cdot \cancel{x} \cdot \cancel{y} \cdot y}{\underset{1}{\cancel{3}} \cdot 3 \cdot \underset{1}{\cancel{w}} \cdot \underset{1}{\cancel{x}} \cdot x \cdot \underset{1}{\cancel{y}}}$$

$$= \frac{8w^2y}{3x}$$

Thus, $\dfrac{24w^3xy^2}{9wx^2y} = \dfrac{8w^2y}{3x}$.

We can also use the properties of exponents to simplify this fraction:

$$\frac{24w^3xy^2}{9wx^2y} = \frac{8w^{3-1}y^{2-1}}{3x^{2-1}}$$
$$= \frac{8w^2y}{3x}$$

Example 8.1.4

Remember, it is understood that x ≠ 3 and x ≠ −3.

Reduce to lowest terms: $\dfrac{x^2 - 2x - 15}{x^2 - 9}$

Solution

Step 1 Factor the numerator and denominator.

$$\dfrac{x^2 - 2x - 15}{x^2 - 9} = \dfrac{(x-5)(x+3)}{(x-3)(x+3)}$$

Step 2 Cancel all pairs of factors common to the numerator and denominator.

$$= \dfrac{(x-5)\cancel{(x+3)}}{(x-3)\cancel{(x+3)}}$$

$$= \dfrac{x-5}{x-3}$$

Thus, $\dfrac{x^2 - 2x - 15}{x^2 - 9} = \dfrac{x-5}{x-3}$.

Like a fraction in arithmetic, a rational expression should normally be written in lowest terms.

Multiplying Rational Expressions

Multiplying rational expressions is like multiplying fractions.

— Procedure —
To Multiply Rational Expressions

Step 1 Factor the numerators and denominators.

Step 2 Cancel all pairs of factors common to the numerators and denominators.

Step 3 Multiply the numerators. Multiply the denominators.

Here's an example from arithmetic:

Multiply $\dfrac{21}{18} \cdot \dfrac{3}{14}$ and write the answer in lowest terms:

Step 1 Factor the numerators and denominators.

$$\dfrac{21}{18} \cdot \dfrac{3}{14} = \dfrac{3 \cdot 7}{2 \cdot 3 \cdot 3} \cdot \dfrac{3}{2 \cdot 7}$$

Step 2 Cancel all pairs of factors common to the numerators and denominators.

$$= \dfrac{\cancel{3} \cdot \cancel{7}}{2 \cdot \cancel{3} \cdot 3} \cdot \dfrac{\cancel{3}}{2 \cdot \cancel{7}}$$

Step 3 Multiply the numerators. Multiply the denominators.

$$= \dfrac{1}{4}$$

Thus, $\dfrac{21}{18} \cdot \dfrac{3}{14} = \dfrac{1}{4}$.

Notice that $\dfrac{5x}{y}$ is in lowest terms.

Example 8.1.5

Find: $\dfrac{6x^2y}{15x} \cdot \dfrac{25x}{2xy^2}$

Solution

Step 1 Factor the numerators and denominators.

$$\dfrac{6x^2y}{15x} \cdot \dfrac{25x}{2xy^2}$$

$$= \dfrac{2 \cdot 3 \cdot x \cdot x \cdot y}{3 \cdot 5 \cdot x} \cdot \dfrac{5 \cdot 5 \cdot x}{2 \cdot x \cdot y \cdot y}$$

Step 2 Cancel all pairs of factors common to the numerators and denominators.

$$= \dfrac{\cancel{2} \cdot \cancel{3} \cdot \cancel{x} \cdot x \cdot \cancel{y}}{\cancel{3} \cdot \cancel{5} \cdot \cancel{x}} \cdot \dfrac{\cancel{5} \cdot 5 \cdot \cancel{x}}{\cancel{2} \cdot \cancel{x} \cdot \cancel{y} \cdot y}$$

Step 3 Multiply the numerators. Multiply the denominators.

$$= \dfrac{5x}{y}$$

Thus, $\dfrac{6x^2y}{15x} \cdot \dfrac{25x}{2xy^2} = \dfrac{5x}{y}$.

Example 8.1.6

Find: $\dfrac{9x^2y^2}{2wyz^2} \cdot \dfrac{10wz}{3x^2}$

Remember, it is understood that $w \neq 0$, $x \neq 0$, $y \neq 0$, and $z \neq 0$.

Solution

$$\frac{9x^2y^2}{2wyz^2} \cdot \frac{10wz}{3x^2}$$

Step 1 *Factor the numerators and denominators.*

$$= \frac{3 \cdot 3 \cdot x \cdot x \cdot y \cdot y}{2 \cdot w \cdot y \cdot z \cdot z} \cdot \frac{2 \cdot 5 \cdot w \cdot z}{3 \cdot x \cdot x}$$

Step 2 *Cancel all pairs of factors common to the numerators and denominators.*

$$= \frac{\cancel{3} \cdot 3 \cdot \cancel{x} \cdot \cancel{x} \cdot \cancel{y} \cdot y}{\cancel{2} \cdot \cancel{w} \cdot \cancel{y} \cdot \cancel{z} \cdot z} \cdot \frac{\cancel{2} \cdot 5 \cdot \cancel{w} \cdot \cancel{z}}{\cancel{3} \cdot \cancel{x} \cdot \cancel{x}}$$

Step 3 *Multiply the numerators. Multiply the denominators.*

$$= \frac{15y}{z}$$

Thus, $\dfrac{9x^2y^2}{2wyz^2} \cdot \dfrac{10wz}{3x^2} = \dfrac{15y}{z}$.

Dividing Rational Expressions

Dividing rational expressions is like dividing fractions.

> **— Procedure —**
> **To Divide Rational Expressions**
>
> **Step 1** Invert the second fraction and change the division symbol, $\div$, to the multiplication symbol, $\cdot$.
>
> **Step 2** Factor the numerators and denominators.
>
> **Step 3** Cancel all pairs of factors common to the numerators and denominators.
>
> **Step 4** Multiply the numerators. Multiply the denominators.

Here's an example of dividing fractions:

Divide and write the answer in lowest terms: $\dfrac{9}{18} \div \dfrac{3}{8}$

Step 1 *Invert the second fraction and change the division symbol, $\div$, to the multiplication symbol, $\cdot$.*

$$= \frac{9}{18} \cdot \frac{8}{3}$$

Step 2 *Factor the numerators and denominators.*

$$= \frac{3 \cdot 3}{2 \cdot 3 \cdot 3} \cdot \frac{2 \cdot 2 \cdot 2}{3}$$

Step 3 *Cancel all pairs of factors common to the numerators and denominators.*

$$= \frac{\cancel{3} \cdot \cancel{3}}{\cancel{2} \cdot \cancel{3} \cdot \cancel{3}} \cdot \frac{\cancel{2} \cdot 2 \cdot 2}{3}$$

Step 4 *Multiply the numerators. Multiply the denominators.*

$$= \frac{4}{3}$$

Thus, $\dfrac{9}{18} \div \dfrac{3}{8} = \dfrac{4}{3}$.

Example 8.1.7

Find: $\dfrac{45xy^2}{2w^2} \div \dfrac{30x^2y^3}{w^3}$

Solution

$$\frac{45xy^2}{2w^2} \div \frac{30x^2y^3}{w^3}$$

Step 1 *Invert the second fraction and change the division symbol, $\div$, to the multiplication symbol, $\cdot$.*

$$= \frac{45xy^2}{2w^2} \cdot \frac{w^3}{30x^2y^3}$$

Step 2 *Factor the numerators and denominators.*

$$= \frac{3 \cdot 3 \cdot 5 \cdot x \cdot y \cdot y}{2 \cdot w \cdot w} \cdot \frac{w \cdot w \cdot w}{2 \cdot 3 \cdot 5 \cdot x \cdot x \cdot y \cdot y \cdot y}$$

Step 3 *Cancel all pairs of factors common to the numerators and denominators.*

$$= \frac{\cancel{3} \cdot 3 \cdot \cancel{5} \cdot \cancel{x} \cdot \cancel{y} \cdot \cancel{y}}{2 \cdot \cancel{w} \cdot \cancel{w}} \cdot \frac{\cancel{w} \cdot \cancel{w} \cdot w}{2 \cdot \cancel{3} \cdot \cancel{5} \cdot \cancel{x} \cdot x \cdot \cancel{y} \cdot \cancel{y} \cdot y}$$

Step 4 ***Multiply the numerators. Multiply the denominators.***

$$= \frac{3w}{4xy}$$

Thus, $\frac{45xy^2}{2w^2} \div \frac{30x^2y^3}{w^3} = \frac{3w}{4xy}$.

Example 8.1.8

Find: $\frac{6a^2b^2}{5c^3} \div 3ab^3$

Solution

$$\frac{6a^2b^2}{5c^3} \div 3ab^3$$

$3ab^3$ may be written as $\frac{3ab^3}{1}$.

Inverting this results in $\frac{1}{3ab^3}$.

Step 1 ***Invert the second fraction and change the division symbol, ÷, to the multiplication symbol, ·.***

$$= \frac{6a^2b^2}{5c^3} \cdot \frac{1}{3ab^3}$$

Step 2 ***Factor the numerators and denominators.***

$$= \frac{2 \cdot 3 \cdot a \cdot a \cdot b \cdot b}{5 \cdot c \cdot c \cdot c} \cdot \frac{1}{3 \cdot a \cdot b \cdot b \cdot b}$$

Step 3 ***Cancel all pairs of factors common to the numerators and denominators.***

$$= \frac{2 \cdot \cancel{3} \cdot \cancel{a} \cdot a \cdot \cancel{b} \cdot \cancel{b}}{5 \cdot c \cdot c \cdot c} \cdot \frac{1}{\underset{1}{\cancel{3}} \cdot \underset{1}{\cancel{a}} \cdot \underset{1}{\cancel{b}} \cdot \underset{1}{\cancel{b}} \cdot b}$$

Notice that $\frac{2a}{5bc^3}$ is in lowest terms.

Step 4 ***Multiply the numerators. Multiply the denominators.***

$$= \frac{2a}{5bc^3}$$

Thus, $\frac{6a^2b^2}{5c^3} \div 3ab^3 = \frac{2a}{5bc^3}$.

Simplifying a Complex Fraction

Recall that a fraction can be written using the division symbol, ÷.

For example:

- $\frac{2}{3}$ can be written $2 \div 3$.

- $\frac{4x + 15}{x + 8}$ can be written $(4x + 15) \div (x + 8)$.

- $\frac{\frac{8w}{y}}{2w^3}$ can be written $\frac{8x}{y} \div 2w^3$

The expression, $\frac{\frac{8w}{y}}{2w^3}$, is called a complex fraction.

A **complex fraction** is a fraction that contains other fractions.

Here are some examples of complex fractions:

$$\frac{\frac{x + 6}{12x}}{x - 2} \qquad \frac{\frac{6x^4}{x - 3}}{\frac{12x}{x + 2}} \qquad \frac{1 - \frac{2}{x}}{\frac{5}{2x} + 2}$$

To simplify a complex fraction we first write it as a division problem. Then we follow the procedure for dividing rational expressions.

— Procedure —
To Simplify a Complex Fraction
Step 1 Write the complex fraction using a division symbol, $\div$.
Step 2 Invert the second fraction and change the division symbol, $\div$, to the multiplication symbol, $\cdot$.
Step 3 Factor the numerators and denominators.
Step 4 Cancel all pairs of factors common to the numerators and denominators.
Step 5 Multiply the numerators. Multiply the denominators.

Example 8.1.9

Simplify: $\dfrac{\dfrac{2x^3}{5y^4}}{\dfrac{6x}{25y^3}}$

Solution

$$\frac{\dfrac{2x^3}{5y^4}}{\dfrac{6x}{25y^3}}$$

Step 1 Write the complex fraction using a division symbol, $\div$.

$$= \frac{2x^3}{5y^4} \div \frac{6x}{25y^3}$$

Step 2 Invert the second fraction and change the division symbol, $\div$, to the multiplication symbol, $\cdot$.

$$= \frac{2x^3}{5y^4} \cdot \frac{25y^3}{6x}$$

Step 3 Factor the numerators and denominators.

$$= \frac{2 \cdot x \cdot x \cdot x}{5 \cdot y \cdot y \cdot y \cdot y} \cdot \frac{5 \cdot 5 \cdot y \cdot y \cdot y}{2 \cdot 3 \cdot x}$$

Step 4 Cancel all pairs of factors common to the numerators and denominators.

$$= \frac{\cancel{2} \cdot \cancel{x} \cdot x \cdot x}{\cancel{5} \cdot \cancel{y} \cdot \cancel{y} \cdot \cancel{y} \cdot y} \cdot \frac{\cancel{5} \cdot 5 \cdot \cancel{y} \cdot \cancel{y} \cdot \cancel{y}}{\cancel{2} \cdot 3 \cdot \cancel{x}}$$

Step 5 Multiply the numerators. Multiply the denominators.

$$= \frac{5x^2}{3y}$$

Thus, $\dfrac{\dfrac{2x^3}{5y^4}}{\dfrac{6x}{25y^3}} = \dfrac{5x^2}{3y}$.

Example 8.1.10

Simplify: $\dfrac{\dfrac{6x^3}{x+2}}{\dfrac{2x}{x+3}}$

Solution $\dfrac{\dfrac{6x^3}{x+2}}{\dfrac{2x}{x+3}}$

Step 1 *Write the complex fraction using a division symbol, ÷.*

$= \dfrac{6x^3}{x+2} \div \dfrac{2x}{x+3}$

Step 2 *Invert the second fraction and change the division symbol, ÷, to the multiplication symbol, ·.*

$= \dfrac{6x^3}{x+2} \cdot \dfrac{x+3}{2x}$

Step 3 *Factor the numerators and denominators.*

$= \dfrac{2 \cdot 3 \cdot x \cdot x \cdot x}{x+2} \cdot \dfrac{x+3}{2 \cdot x}$

Step 4 *Cancel all pairs of factors common to the numerators and denominators.*

$= \dfrac{\cancel{2} \cdot 3 \cdot \cancel{x} \cdot x \cdot x}{x+2} \cdot \dfrac{x+3}{\underset{1}{\cancel{2}} \cdot \underset{1}{\cancel{x}}}$

Step 5 *Multiply the numerators. Multiply the denominators.*

$= \dfrac{3x^2(x+3)}{x+2}$

In $\dfrac{3x^2(x+3)}{x+2}$, we cannot cancel x. Although x is a factor of the numerator, x is **not** a factor of the denominator. (In the denominator, x is in a term, not a factor.)

Thus, $\dfrac{\dfrac{6x^3}{x+2}}{\dfrac{2x}{x+3}} = \dfrac{3x^2(x+3)}{x+2}$.

Here is a summary of this concept from *Academic Systems Algebra*.

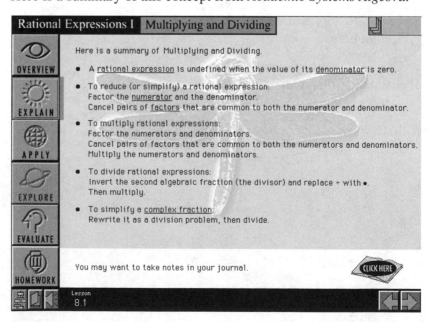

492   TOPIC 8   RATIONAL EXPRESSIONS

CONCEPT 2:
ADDING AND SUBTRACTING RATIONAL EXPRESSIONS

Concept 2 has sections on

- **Adding Rational Expressions with the Same Denominator**

- **Subtracting Rational Expressions with the Same Denominator**

Adding Rational Expressions with the Same Denominator

Adding rational expressions with the same denominator is like adding fractions with the same denominator.

— Procedure —
To Add Rational Expressions with the Same Denominator

Step 1 Add the numerators.

Write this sum as the numerator over the common denominator.

Step 2 Reduce to lowest terms.

Example 8.1.11

Find: $\dfrac{6x}{35y} + \dfrac{9x}{35y}$

Solution

The denominators are the same. $\dfrac{6x}{35y} + \dfrac{9x}{35y}$

Step 1 Add the numerators. Write this sum as the numerator over the common denominator. $= \dfrac{6x + 9x}{35y}$

Combine the like terms in the numerator. $= \dfrac{15x}{35y}$

Step 2 Reduce to lowest terms.

First, factor the numerator and denominator. $= \dfrac{3 \cdot 5 \cdot x}{5 \cdot 7 \cdot y}$

Next, cancel the common factor, 5. $= \dfrac{3x}{7y}$

Thus, $\dfrac{6x}{35y} + \dfrac{9x}{35y} = \dfrac{3x}{7y}$.

Here's an example of adding fractions:

Add and write the answer in lowest terms:
$$\frac{3}{4} + \frac{7}{4}$$

The denominators are the same. Add the numerators and write the sum over the common denominator, 4.

$$\frac{3}{4} + \frac{7}{4} = \frac{3+7}{4} = \frac{10}{4}$$

To reduce, cancel the common factor, 2, in the numerator and denominator.

$$\frac{10}{4} = \frac{\cancel{2} \cdot 5}{\cancel{2} \cdot 2} = \frac{5}{2}$$

Thus, $\dfrac{3}{4} + \dfrac{7}{4} = \dfrac{5}{2}$.

Example 8.1.12

Find: $\dfrac{2x - 4}{x^2 - 3x - 4} + \dfrac{x + 7}{x^2 - 3x - 4}$

Solution

The denominators are the same.

$$\dfrac{2x - 4}{x^2 - 3x - 4} + \dfrac{x + 7}{x^2 - 3x - 4}$$

Step 1 Add the numerators. Write this sum as the numerator over the common denominator.

$$= \dfrac{2x - 4 + x + 7}{x^2 - 3x - 4}$$

Combine the like terms in the numerator.

$$= \dfrac{3x + 3}{x^2 - 3x - 4}$$

Step 2 Reduce to lowest terms.

First, factor the numerator and denominator.

$$= \dfrac{3(x + 1)}{(x - 4)(x + 1)}$$

Next, cancel the common factor, $x + 1$.

$$= \dfrac{3}{x - 4}$$

Thus, $\dfrac{2x - 4}{x^2 - 3x - 4} + \dfrac{x + 7}{x^2 - 3x - 4} = \dfrac{3}{x - 4}$.

Subtracting Rational Expressions with the Same Denominator

Subtracting rational expressions with the same denominator is like subtracting fractions with the same denominator.

— Procedure —
To Subtract Rational Expressions with the Same Denominator
Step 1 Subtract the numerators. Write the difference as the numerator over the common denominator. **Step 2** Reduce to lowest terms.

Here's an example of subtracting fractions:

Subtract and write the answer in lowest terms: $\dfrac{5}{6} - \dfrac{1}{6}$

The denominators are the same.

Subtract the numerators and write the difference over the common denominator, 6.

$$\dfrac{5}{6} - \dfrac{1}{6} = \dfrac{5 - 1}{6} = \dfrac{4}{6}$$

To reduce, cancel the common factor, 2, in the numerator and denominator.

$$\dfrac{4}{6} = \dfrac{\cancel{2} \cdot 2}{\underset{1}{\cancel{2}} \cdot 3} = \dfrac{2}{3}$$

Thus, $\dfrac{5}{6} - \dfrac{1}{6} = \dfrac{2}{3}$.

Example 8.1.13

Find: $\dfrac{32w}{13x} - \dfrac{7w}{13x}$

Solution

The denominators are the same.

$$\dfrac{32w}{13x} - \dfrac{7w}{13x}$$

Step 1 Subtract the numerators. Write the difference as the numerator over the common denominator.

$$= \dfrac{32w - 7w}{13x}$$

Combine the like terms in the numerator.

$$= \dfrac{25w}{13x}$$

Step 2 Reduce to lowest terms.

First, factor the numerator and denominator.

$$= \dfrac{5 \cdot 5 \cdot w}{13 \cdot x}$$

There are no common factors to cancel.

$$= \dfrac{25w}{13x}$$

Thus, $\dfrac{32w}{13x} - \dfrac{7w}{13x} = \dfrac{25w}{13x}$.

Example 8.1.14

Find: $\dfrac{5x - 6}{x^2 + 6x + 5} - \dfrac{4x - 7}{x^2 + 6x + 5}$

Solution

The denominators are the same.

$$\dfrac{5x - 6}{x^2 + 6x + 5} - \dfrac{4x - 7}{x^2 + 6x + 5}$$

Step 1 Subtract the numerators. Write the difference as the numerator over the common denominator.

$$= \dfrac{5x - 6 - (4x - 7)}{x^2 + 6x + 5}$$

$$= \dfrac{5x - 6 - 4x + 7}{x^2 + 6x + 5}$$

Combine the like terms in the numerator.

$$= \dfrac{x + 1}{x^2 + 6x + 5}$$

Step 2 Reduce to lowest terms.

First, factor the numerator and denominator.

$$= \dfrac{x + 1}{(x + 1)(x + 5)}$$

Next, cancel the common factor, $x + 1$.

$$= \dfrac{1}{x + 5}$$

Thus, $\dfrac{5x - 6}{x^2 + 6x + 5} - \dfrac{4x - 7}{x^2 + 6x + 5} = \dfrac{1}{x + 5}$.

Here is a summary of this concept from *Academic Systems Algebra*.

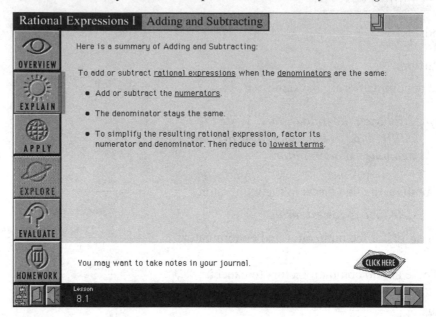

Rational Expressions I | Adding and Subtracting

OVERVIEW
EXPLAIN
APPLY
EXPLORE
EVALUATE
HOMEWORK

Here is a summary of Adding and Subtracting:

To add or subtract rational expressions when the denominators are the same:

- Add or subtract the numerators.

- The denominator stays the same.

- To simplify the resulting rational expression, factor its numerator and denominator. Then reduce to lowest terms.

You may want to take notes in your journal.

CLICK HERE

Lesson
8.1

Checklist Lesson 8.1

Here is what you should know after completing this lesson.

Words and Phrases

rational expression
undefined

lowest terms
complex fraction

Ideas and Procedures

❶ Determine Where a Rational Expression is Undefined
Determine the values of the variable that make a rational expression undefined.

Example 8.1.2
Find the value(s) of x for which this rational expression is undefined: $\dfrac{x-2}{x^2-9}$

See also: Example 8.1.1
Apply 1-4

---

❷ Reduce (Simplify) a Rational Expression
Reduce a rational expression to lowest terms.

Example 8.1.4
Reduce to lowest terms: $\dfrac{x^2-2x-15}{x^2-9}$

See also: Example 8.1.3
Apply 5-10

---

❸ Multiply Rational Expressions
Multiply rational expressions that contain monomials.

Example 8.1.6
Find: $\dfrac{9x^2y^2}{2wyz^2} \cdot \dfrac{10wz}{3x^2}$

See also: Example 8.1.5
Apply 11-16

---

❹ Divide Rational Expressions
Divide rational expressions that contain monomials.

Example 8.1.8
Find: $\dfrac{6a^2b^2}{5c^3} \div 3ab^3$

See also: Example 8.1.7
Apply 17-22

---

❺ Complex Fractions
Simplify a complex fraction.

Example 8.1.10
Simplify: $\dfrac{\dfrac{6x^3}{x+2}}{\dfrac{2x}{x+3}}$

See also: Example 8.1.9
Apply 23-28

❻ Add Rational Expressions

Add rational expressions that have the same denominator.

Example 8.1.12

Find: $\dfrac{2x-4}{x^2-3x-4} + \dfrac{x+7}{x^2-3x-4}$

See also: Example 8.1.11
   Apply 29-33, 39-47

❼ Subtract Rational Expressions

Subtract rational expressions that have the same denominator.

Example 8.1.14

Find: $\dfrac{5x-6}{x^2+6x+5} - \dfrac{4x-7}{x^2+6x+5}$

See also: Example 8.1.13
   Apply 34-38, 48-56

Homework

Homework Problems

Circle the homework problems assigned to you by the computer, then complete them below.

☀ Explain

Multiplying and Dividing Rational Expressions

1. For what values of x is the rational expression below undefined?
$$\frac{(x + 7)(x - 8)}{(x - 14)(x + 2)}$$

2. For what values of x is the rational expression below undefined?
$$\frac{x^2 - 9}{x^2 - 4}$$

3. Reduce to lowest terms: $\dfrac{3a^2b^5}{27ab^7}$

4. Reduce to lowest terms: $\dfrac{x^2 - 3x - 28}{x^2 + 5x + 4}$

5. Find: $\dfrac{3y^3}{z} \cdot \dfrac{yz}{7y^2}$

6. Find: $\dfrac{15a^2b^2}{2c^3d} \cdot \dfrac{2cd^3}{5ab^2}$

7. Find: $\dfrac{12xy}{w^2} \div \dfrac{4xy^3}{w^3}$

8. Find: $\dfrac{3ab^2}{13d^4} \div \dfrac{6a^2b}{11d^2}$

9. Simplify this complex fraction: $\dfrac{\frac{5}{a^3}}{\frac{9}{a^2}}$. Write your answer in lowest terms.

10. The ratio of the area of a circle to its circumference is given by $\dfrac{\pi r^2}{2\pi r}$.

   a. What value of r makes this ratio undefined?

   b. Simplify this expression and then determine what value of r will make the ratio equal to 2. That is, find the radius that will yield an area that is twice the circumference.

11. Simplify this complex fraction: $\dfrac{\frac{x}{x - 1}}{\frac{1}{x - 1}}$. Write your answer in lowest terms.

12. Simplify this complex fraction: $\dfrac{\frac{3y^4}{y + 2}}{\frac{9y^2}{y - 2}}$. Write your answer in lowest terms.

Adding and Subtracting Rational Expressions

13. Find: $\dfrac{3x}{5y} + \dfrac{18x}{5y}$

14. Find: $\dfrac{3 + 5a}{8 - a} + \dfrac{2a + 1}{8 - a}$

15. Find: $\dfrac{x}{x^2 - 4} + \dfrac{4}{x^2 - 4}$

16. Find: $\dfrac{3z + 4}{z - 11} + \dfrac{2z}{z - 11}$

17. Find: $\dfrac{2x - 5}{x^2 - 5x - 14} + \dfrac{3x + 15}{x^2 - 5x - 14}$

18. Find: $\dfrac{2z + 11}{z^2 - 3z - 18} + \dfrac{3z + 4}{z^2 - 3z - 18}$

19. Find: $\dfrac{9}{15x} - \dfrac{2}{15x}$

20. Find: $\dfrac{17}{13y} - \dfrac{5 + y}{13y}$

21. The volume, V, of a sphere of radius r is defined by the formula $V = \dfrac{4\pi r^3}{3}$. Find the volume of two identical spheres.
That is, find $\dfrac{4\pi r^3}{3} + \dfrac{4\pi r^3}{3}$.

22. Find: $\dfrac{y}{y^2 - 81} - \dfrac{9}{y^2 - 81}$

23. Find: $\dfrac{4y + 6}{3y + 6} - \dfrac{3y + 4}{3y + 6}$

24. Find: $\dfrac{4x - 4}{x^2 - 2x - 15} - \dfrac{3x - 7}{x^2 - 2x - 15}$

Practice Problems

Here are some additional practice problems for you to try.

Multiplying and Dividing Rational Expressions

1. For what value(s) of x is the rational expression below undefined?

$$\frac{1}{x+5}$$

2. For what value(s) of x is the rational expression below undefined?

$$\frac{2}{(x-3)(x+5)}$$

3. For what value(s) of x is the rational expression below undefined?

$$\frac{25}{3x^2-12}$$

4. For what value(s) of x is the rational expression below undefined?

$$\frac{17}{2x^2-18}$$

5. Reduce to lowest terms: $\frac{36m^5n^3}{27mn^6}$

6. Reduce to lowest terms: $\frac{75xy^2z^7}{45x^4y^3z^6}$

7. Reduce to lowest terms: $\frac{44a^2b^4c}{77a^7bc}$

8. Reduce to lowest terms: $\frac{x^2+10x+21}{x^2+5x+6}$

9. Reduce to lowest terms: $\frac{x^2+4x-5}{x^2-3x+2}$

10. Reduce to lowest terms: $\frac{x^2-x-12}{x^2+5x+6}$

11. Find: $\frac{6a}{b^3c^2} \cdot \frac{7b}{3a^3}$

12. Find: $\frac{8x}{y^2z} \cdot \frac{5y}{4x^2}$

13. Find: $\frac{10m^3n^5}{9mn^3} \cdot \frac{21m^5}{15n^6}$

14. Find: $\frac{5ab^4}{3c^2} \cdot \frac{6c}{10b^3}$

15. Find: $\frac{8m^5n}{7p^2} \cdot \frac{14mp}{24m^2n^4}$

16. Find: $\frac{3xy^3}{4z} \cdot \frac{2z^2}{9xy^2}$

17. Find: $\frac{4a^2b}{5c^3} \div \frac{8ab^2}{15c}$

18. Find: $\frac{12m^3n^4}{7p} \div \frac{18mn^5}{21p^4}$

19. Find: $\frac{3xy^2}{7z} \div \frac{6x^2y}{14z^2}$

20. Find: $\frac{5x^2y}{12z^3w} \div \frac{xy}{4z}$

21. Find: $\frac{9m^3n^4}{11pq^2} \div \frac{12mn^3}{22p^2q}$

22. Find: $\frac{7a^2b}{9c^2d^2} \div \frac{ab}{3cd}$

23. Simplify the complex fraction below.

$$\frac{\frac{4m^2}{n^3}}{\frac{2m}{n}}$$

24. Simplify the complex fraction below.

$$\frac{\frac{6x^5}{5y^3}}{\frac{3x^3}{10y}}$$

25. Simplify the complex fraction below.

$$\frac{\frac{6a^2}{b^3}}{\frac{3a}{2b}}$$

26. Simplify the complex fraction below.

$$\frac{\frac{6a^3}{a+5}}{\frac{12a}{a-4}}$$

27. Simplify the complex fraction below.

$$\frac{\frac{5x^2}{x+7}}{\frac{10x}{x-3}}$$

28. Simplify the complex fraction below.

$$\dfrac{\dfrac{15y^5}{y-3}}{\dfrac{18y^3}{y+3}}$$

Adding and Subtracting Rational Expressions

29. Find: $\dfrac{3a}{7b} + \dfrac{2a}{7b}$

30. Find: $\dfrac{2x}{5y} + \dfrac{7x}{5y}$

31. Find: $\dfrac{3b}{2b+1} + \dfrac{5}{2b+1}$

32. Find: $\dfrac{9n}{4n-7} + \dfrac{2}{4n-7}$

33. Find: $\dfrac{7x}{5x-1} + \dfrac{2}{5x-1}$

34. Find: $\dfrac{5y+2}{3y-2} - \dfrac{4y-5}{3y-2}$

35. Find: $\dfrac{7b+1}{2b+9} - \dfrac{5b+5}{2b+9}$

36. Find: $\dfrac{6x+1}{2x+3} - \dfrac{5x-3}{2x+3}$

37. Find: $\dfrac{15}{7n} - \dfrac{4-5n}{7n}$

38. Find: $\dfrac{11}{9x} - \dfrac{7-5x}{9x}$

39. Add and reduce your answer to lowest terms:
$$\dfrac{3x+4}{x^2+5x+6} + \dfrac{5}{x^2+5x+6}$$

40. Add and reduce your answer to lowest terms:
$$\dfrac{4x+7}{x^2+7x+10} + \dfrac{1}{x^2+7x+10}$$

41. Add and reduce your answer to lowest terms:
$$\dfrac{2x+5}{x^2+x-12} + \dfrac{3}{x^2+x-12}$$

42. Add and reduce your answer to lowest terms:
$$\dfrac{3x+12}{x^2+2x-3} + \dfrac{2x+3}{x^2+2x-3}$$

43. Add and reduce your answer to lowest terms:
$$\dfrac{3x+19}{x^2+3x-10} + \dfrac{x-1}{x^2+3x-10}$$

44. Add and reduce your answer to lowest terms:
$$\dfrac{2x+15}{x^2+5x-14} + \dfrac{x+6}{x^2+5x-14}$$

45. Add and reduce your answer to lowest terms:
$$\dfrac{x^2-5x+2}{x^2+7x+12} + \dfrac{2(5x+1)}{x^2+7x+12}$$

46. Add and reduce your answer to lowest terms:
$$\dfrac{x^2-3x+2}{x^2+3x+2} + \dfrac{4(2x+1)}{x^2+3x+2}$$

47. Add and reduce your answer to lowest terms:
$$\dfrac{x^2-7x+12}{x^2+9x+18} + \dfrac{5(3x+1)-2}{x^2+9x+18}$$

48. Subtract and reduce your answer to lowest terms:
$$\dfrac{4x+7}{3x-9} - \dfrac{3x+10}{3x-9}$$

49. Subtract and reduce your answer to lowest terms:
$$\dfrac{5x+6}{2x+10} - \dfrac{2x-9}{2x+10}$$

50. Subtract and reduce your answer to lowest terms:
$$\dfrac{3x+2}{2x+14} - \dfrac{2x-5}{2x+14}$$

51. Subtract and reduce your answer to lowest terms:
$$\dfrac{2x+5}{x^2+3x-10} - \dfrac{x+7}{x^2+3x-10}$$

52. Subtract and reduce your answer to lowest terms:
$$\dfrac{4x+2}{x^2-x-20} - \dfrac{3x-2}{x^2-x-20}$$

53. Subtract and reduce your answer to lowest terms:
$$\dfrac{3x+5}{x^2-4x+3} - \dfrac{2x+8}{x^2-4+3}$$

54. Subtract and reduce your answer to lowest terms:
$$\dfrac{8x+5}{4x-4} - \dfrac{5x+8}{4x-4}$$

55. Subtract and reduce your answer to lowest terms:
$$\dfrac{5x+9}{5x+20} - \dfrac{2x-3}{5x+20}$$

56. Subtract and reduce your answer to lowest terms:
$$\dfrac{7x-2}{3x+3} - \dfrac{5x-4}{3x+3}$$

Evaluate

Practice Test

Take this practice test to be sure that you are prepared for the final quiz in Evaluate.

1. For what values of x is the following expression undefined?
$$\frac{x^2 - 16}{(x + 3)(x - 2)}$$

2. Reduce to lowest terms: $\dfrac{x^2 - 3x - 28}{x^2 + 10x + 24}$

3. Find:
   a. $\dfrac{5y^2}{9z^2} \cdot \dfrac{z}{y^2}$
   b. $\dfrac{12x^2y^2}{z^3w} \cdot \dfrac{2zw}{3xy^2}$

4. a. Find: $\dfrac{3x^2}{yz} \div \dfrac{7x}{2yz}$

   b. Simplify this complex fraction: $\dfrac{\frac{2x^2y}{9w}}{\frac{10xy^2}{3w^2}}$. Write your answer in lowest terms.

5. Find:
   a. $\dfrac{5x}{13y} + \dfrac{2x}{13y}$
   b. $\dfrac{3w}{z - 8} + \dfrac{14}{z - 8}$

6. Find: $\dfrac{15y}{7x} - \dfrac{3 + 6y}{7x}$

7. Find the following. Reduce your answer to lowest terms.
$$\frac{x + 7}{x^2 - 3x - 18} + \frac{3x + 5}{x^2 - 3x - 18}$$

8. Find the following. Reduce your answer to lowest terms.
$$\frac{9y}{y - 7} - \frac{3y - 4}{y - 7}$$

LESSON 8.2
RATIONAL EXPRESSIONS II

Overview

In this lesson, you will learn about negative exponents. You will also study scientific notation. Finally, you will learn more about how to multiply, divide, add, and subtract rational expressions.

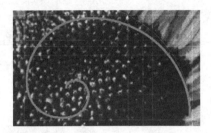

Explain

Concept 1 has sections on

- **Definition of a Negative Integer Exponent**

- **Properties of Negative Exponents**

- **Simplifying Expressions that Contain Negative Exponents**

- **Scientific Notation**

Recall:
$2^3 = 2 \cdot 2 \cdot 2$
$2^0 = 1$

CONCEPT 1:
NEGATIVE EXPONENTS

Definition of a Negative Integer Exponent

You have seen how to work with exponents that are positive integers or 0.

Now, we will investigate exponents that are negative integers.

We'll begin with this expression: $\dfrac{2^4}{2^7}$

We can simplify the expression by canceling common factors.

$$\frac{2^4}{2^7} = \frac{\overset{1}{\cancel{2}} \cdot \overset{1}{\cancel{2}} \cdot \overset{1}{\cancel{2}} \cdot \overset{1}{\cancel{2}}}{\underset{1}{\cancel{2}} \cdot \underset{1}{\cancel{2}} \cdot \underset{1}{\cancel{2}} \cdot \underset{1}{\cancel{2}} \cdot 2 \cdot 2 \cdot 2} = \frac{1}{2^3}$$

We can also simplify the expression by subtracting exponents.

$$\frac{2^4}{2^7} = 2^{4-7} = \mathbf{2^{-3}}$$

Since $\dfrac{2^4}{2^7}$ simplifies to both $\dfrac{1}{2^3}$ and 2^{-3}, we conclude $2^{-3} = \dfrac{1}{2^3}$.

This relationship holds in general.

— Definition —
Negative Integer Exponent
$x^{-n} = \dfrac{1}{x^n}$
Here, $x \neq 0$ and n is a nonnegative integer.

Example 8.2.1

Find: 5^{-2}

Solution

Use the definition of a negative exponent: $\qquad x^{-n} = \dfrac{1}{x^n}$

$$5^{-2} = \frac{1}{5^2} = \frac{1}{5 \cdot 5} = \frac{1}{25}$$

So, $5^{-2} = \dfrac{1}{25}$.

Be careful!

*Here, 5 is raised to a **negative** power.*
*But the result is a **positive** number.*

$5^{-2} = \dfrac{1}{5^2}$

$5^{-2} \neq 5 \cdot (-2)$

$5^{-2} \neq (-5)^2$

We can also define $\dfrac{1}{x^{-n}}$, as follows:

$$\frac{1}{x^{-n}} = \frac{1}{\frac{1}{x^n}} = 1 \div \frac{1}{x^n} = 1 \cdot \frac{x^n}{1} = x^n$$

> **— Definition —**
> $\dfrac{1}{x^{-n}}$
>
> $\dfrac{1}{x^{-n}} = x^n$
> Here, $x \neq 0$ and n is a nonnegative integer.

Example 8.2.2

a. Find: $\dfrac{1}{2^{-3}}$ b. Find: $\dfrac{1}{(-2)^{-3}}$

Solution

a. Use the definition $\dfrac{1}{x^{-n}} = x^n$. $\dfrac{1}{2^{-3}} = 2^3 = 2 \cdot 2 \cdot 2 = 8$

b. Use the definition $\dfrac{1}{x^{-n}} = x^n$.

$$\frac{1}{(-2)^{-3}} = (-2)^3$$
$$= (-2) \cdot (-2) \cdot (-2)$$
$$= -8$$

A negative exponent does not determine
if an expression is positive or negative.
For example:

$5^{-2} = \dfrac{1}{5^2} = \dfrac{1}{25}$ *positive*

$-5^{-2} = -\dfrac{1}{5^2} = -\dfrac{1}{25}$ *negative*

Here is a summary of our work with **negative exponents**:

Definition	*Example 1*	*Example 2*
$x^{-n} = \dfrac{1}{x^n}$	$2^{-3} = \dfrac{1}{2^3}$	$m^{-6} = \dfrac{1}{m^6}$
$\dfrac{1}{x^{-n}} = x^n$	$\dfrac{1}{4^{-2}} = 4^2$	$\dfrac{1}{y^{-5}} = y^5$

Here, the variables represent nonzero real numbers and n is a nonnegative integer.

Example 8.2.3

Find: $\dfrac{5}{2^{-1} - 3^{-2}}$

Solution

$$\dfrac{5}{2^{-1} - 3^{-2}}$$

Use the definition of a negative exponent, $x^{-n} = \dfrac{1}{x^n}$.

$$= \dfrac{5}{\dfrac{1}{2^1} - \dfrac{1}{3^2}}$$

Evaluate the exponential expressions.

$$= \dfrac{5}{\dfrac{1}{2} - \dfrac{1}{9}}$$

In the denominator of the expression, write each fraction using the LCD, 18.

$$= \dfrac{5}{\dfrac{9}{18} - \dfrac{2}{18}}$$

In the denominator of the expression, subtract the fractions.

$$= \dfrac{5}{\dfrac{7}{18}}$$

Rewrite the division using $\div$.

$$= 5 \div \dfrac{7}{18}$$

To divide 5 by a fraction, multiply $\dfrac{5}{1}$ by the reciprocal of the fraction.

$$= \dfrac{5}{1} \cdot \dfrac{18}{7}$$

Multiply the numerators and multiply the denominators.

$$= \dfrac{90}{7}$$

Thus,

$$\dfrac{5}{2^{-1} - 3^{-2}} = \dfrac{90}{7}.$$

Example 8.2.4

Rewrite using only positive exponents: $\dfrac{5y^{-7}}{x^2}$

Solution

Since -7 is the exponent of y, not $5y$, $5y^{-7} = 5 \cdot y^{-7}$.

$$\dfrac{5y^{-7}}{x^2}$$

Use the definition $x^{-n} = \dfrac{1}{x^n}$.

$$= \dfrac{5}{x^2 y^7}$$

Thus, $\dfrac{5y^{-7}}{x^2} = \dfrac{5}{x^2 y^7}$.

Properties of Negative Exponents

The properties of whole number exponents also hold for negative exponents. This table contains an example of each property.

Property	Positive Integer Exponents	Negative Integer Exponents
Multiplication	$3^2 \cdot 3^4 = 3^{2+4} = 3^6$	$3^{-2} \cdot 3^{-4} = 3^{(-2)+(-4)}$ $= 3^{-6} = \dfrac{1}{3^6}$
Division	$\dfrac{4^7}{4^5} = 4^{7-5} = 4^2$	$\dfrac{4^{-7}}{4^{-5}} = 4^{(-7)-(-5)}$ $= 4^{-7+5} = 4^{-2} = \dfrac{1}{4^2}$
Power of a Power	$(5^2)^3 = 5^{2\cdot 3} = 5^6$	$(5^{-2})^{-3} = 5^{(-2)(-3)} = 5^6$
Power of a Product	$(5 \cdot 7)^3 = 5^3 \cdot 7^3$	$(5 \cdot 7)^{-3} = 5^{-3} \cdot 7^{-3} = \dfrac{1}{5^3} \cdot \dfrac{1}{7^3}$
Power of a Quotient	$\left(\dfrac{3}{5}\right)^4 = \dfrac{3^4}{5^4}$	$\left(\dfrac{3}{5}\right)^{-4} = \dfrac{3^{-4}}{5^{-4}}$

Now we will find two additional **properties of negative exponents**.

We'll begin by simplifying $\dfrac{2^{-4}}{5^{-3}}$.

$$\dfrac{2^{-4}}{5^{-3}}$$

We apply the definition of a negative exponent.

$$= \dfrac{\frac{1}{2^4}}{\frac{1}{5^3}}$$

Rewrite the division using $\div$.

$$= \dfrac{1}{2^4} \div \dfrac{1}{5^3}$$

To divide by a fraction, multiply by its reciprocal.

$$= \dfrac{1}{2^4} \cdot \dfrac{5^3}{1}$$

Multiply the numerators. Multiply the denominators.

$$= \dfrac{5^3}{2^4}$$

Thus, $\dfrac{2^{-4}}{5^{-3}} = \dfrac{5^3}{2^4}$.

Notice that the bases, 2 and 5, have moved to the opposite side of the division bar, and the signs of the their exponents changed.

This turns out to be true in general.

Next, we'll use this relationship to rewrite a quotient raised to a negative power.

For example, we'll simplify $\left(\dfrac{3}{7}\right)^{-2}$.

$$\left(\dfrac{3}{7}\right)^{-2}$$

We use the Power of a Quotient Property.

$$= \dfrac{3^{-2}}{7^{-2}}$$

As in the previous example, we move each base to the opposite side of the division bar and change the sign of each exponent.

$$= \frac{7^2}{3^2}$$

Again, we use the Power of a Quotient Property.

$$= \left(\frac{7}{3}\right)^2$$

We see that $\left(\frac{3}{7}\right)^{-2} = \left(\frac{7}{3}\right)^2$.

Notice that the new base, $\frac{7}{3}$, is the reciprocal of the original base. Also notice the new exponent, 2, is the opposite of the original exponent.

To rewrite a fraction raised to a negative power, just "flip" the fraction and change the negative power to positive.

— Properties —
To Rewrite a Quotient Using Positive Exponents

A factor that contains a negative exponent may be rewritten on the other side of the division bar by changing the sign of the exponent.

Property	*Example 1*	*Example 2*
$\dfrac{x^{-m}}{y^{-n}} = \dfrac{y^n}{x^m}$	$\dfrac{7^{-1}}{5^{-3}} = \dfrac{5^3}{7^1}$	$\dfrac{3a^{-4}}{5b^{-2}} = \dfrac{3b^2}{5a^4}$

Here, $x \neq 0$ and $y \neq 0$.

A fraction raised to a negative exponent may be rewritten as the reciprocal of the fraction raised to the corresponding positive exponent.

Property	*Example 1*	*Example 2*
$\left(\dfrac{x}{y}\right)^{-n} = \left(\dfrac{y}{x}\right)^n$	$\left(\dfrac{2x}{y}\right)^{-3} = \left(\dfrac{y}{2x}\right)^3$	$\left(\dfrac{1}{2x^4}\right)^{-2} = (2x^4)^2$

Here, $x \neq 0$ and $y \neq 0$.

Example 8.2.5

Simplify and write using only positive exponents: $\dfrac{3x^{-2}}{4^{-3}}$

Solution

Use this property: $\dfrac{x^{-m}}{y^{-n}} = \dfrac{y^n}{x^m}$.

$$\frac{3x^{-2}}{4^{-3}} = \frac{3 \cdot 4^3}{x^2} = \frac{3 \cdot 64}{x^2} = \frac{192}{x^2}$$

Example 8.2.6

Simplify and write using only positive exponents: $\left(\dfrac{m}{5}\right)^{-2}$

Solution

Use this property: $\left(\dfrac{x}{y}\right)^{-n} = \left(\dfrac{y}{x}\right)^n$

$$\left(\frac{m}{5}\right)^{-2} = \left(\frac{5}{m}\right)^2$$

Use the Power of a Quotient Property.

$$= \frac{5^2}{m^2}$$

Simplify.

$$= \frac{25}{m^2}$$

Simplifying Expressions that Contain Negative Exponents

When we write an exponential expression in simplified form, we typically use only positive exponents.

Example 8.2.7

Simplify and write using only positive exponents: $(3^{-1}r^4s^{-5}t)^{-2}$

Solution

Use the Power of a Product Property. $= (3^{-1})^{-2}(r^4)^{-2}(s^{-5})^{-2}(t)^{-2}$

Use the Power of a Power Property. $= 3^2 \cdot r^{-8} \cdot s^{10} \cdot t^{-2}$

Rewrite using only positive exponents. $= \dfrac{3^2}{1} \cdot \dfrac{1}{r^8} \cdot \dfrac{s^{10}}{1} \cdot \dfrac{1}{t^2}$

Simplify. $= \dfrac{9s^{10}}{r^8t^2}$

So, $(3^{-1}r^4s^{-5}t)^{-2} = \dfrac{9s^{10}}{r^8t^2}$.

There's more than one way to simplify the original expression. For example, you could begin like this:

$$(3^{-1}r^4s^{-5}t)^{-2} = \dfrac{1}{(3^{-1}r^4s^{-5}t)^2}$$

Then use the Power of a Product Property.

Example 8.2.8

Simplify and write using only positive exponents: $\dfrac{2^{-5}c^3d^{-6}}{c^{-2}d^4}$

Solution

For each factor with a negative exponent, move the factor to the other side of the division bar and make its exponent positive. $\dfrac{c^3c^2}{2^5d^4d^6}$

Use the Multiplication Property of Exponents. $= \dfrac{c^5}{2^5d^{10}}$

Evaluate 2^5. $= \dfrac{c^5}{32d^{10}}$

So, $\dfrac{2^{-5}c^3d^{-6}}{c^{-2}d^4} = \dfrac{c^5}{32d^{10}}$.

Scientific Notation

It is often difficult to read and work with very large or very small numbers.

For example,

The national debt is continually changing, minute by minute, day by day.

- In mid-2002, the U. S. national debt was approximately $5,600,000,000,000. To calculate the amount of money owed by each American, we would divide this number by the U. S. population. Unfortunately, 5600000000000 will not fit in the display of most calculators.

- The rest mass of an electron is about 0.00000000000000000000000000000911 kilograms. It is very difficult to work with a number that has so many zeros.

Numbers such as 0.00000000000000000000000000000911 and 5,600,000,000,000 are said to be written in **expanded form**.

To make it easier to read and work with very large or very small numbers, we often use **scientific notation**.

For example, 2.1×10^5 is written in scientific notation.

In expanded form we write,

$$2.1 \times 10^5 = 2.1 \cdot 10 \cdot 10 \cdot 10 \cdot 10 \cdot 10 = 210,000.$$

The term "rest mass" means the mass when the electron is not moving. As an electron moves faster, its mass increases (according to Einstein's Theory of Special Relativity).

— Definition —
Scientific Notation

A number is written in scientific notation when it has the form

$$N \times 10^n$$

where $1 \leq N < 10$, N is written in decimal notation, and n is an integer.

Here's how to convert a number from expanded form to scientific notation.

— Procedure —
To Convert From Expanded Form to Scientific Notation

Step 1 Move the decimal point until there is only one nonzero digit to its left.

Step 2 Write the number from Step 1 multiplied by a power of 10.

To find the power, count the number of places you moved the decimal point.

- If you moved the decimal point to the **left**, the power is **positive**.

- If you moved the decimal point to the **right**, the power is **negative**.

Step 3 Check the sign of the power.

- If the original number was **greater** than or equal to 10, the power should be **positive**.

- If the original number was greater than 0 and **less** than 1, the power should be **negative**.

Remember, you can write a whole number using a decimal point.
For example: $239 = 239.0$

Example 8.2.9

The distance from the sun to the earth is approximately 93,000,000 miles.

Write 93,000,000 in scientific notation.

Solution

Step 1 Move the decimal point until there is only one nonzero digit to its left.

The original number is not written with a decimal point.   93,000,000

Since the number is a whole number, we can rewrite it with a decimal point to the right of the last digit. $= 93,000,000.$

Then we move that decimal point seven places to the left.

$$9.\underset{7\ 6\ 5\ 4\ 3\ 2\ 1}{3000000.}$$

Step 2 Write the number from Step 1 multiplied by a power of 10.

We moved the decimal point **7** places to the **left**.

So the power of 10 is 7. $= 9.3 \times 10^7$

Step 3 Check the sign of the power.

The original number is **greater** than 10, so the power should be **positive**, and it is.

We can also check our result by expanding 9.3×10^7.

$$9.3 \times 10^7 = 9.3 \cdot 10 \cdot 10 \cdot 10 \cdot 10 \cdot 10 \cdot 10 \cdot 10$$
$$= 93,000,000$$

Thus, 93,000,000 miles $= 9.3 \times 10^7$ miles.

Example 8.2.10

The rest mass of an electron is approximately
0.00000000000000000000000000000911 kg.

Write this number in scientific notation.

Solution

Step 1 Move the decimal point until there is only one nonzero digit to its left.

Move the decimal point until it is between the 9 and the 1.

$$0.\underset{1\ 2\ 3\ 4\ 5\ 6\ 7\ 8\ 9\ 10\ 11\ 12\ 13\ 14\ 15\ 16\ 17\ 18\ 19\ 20\ 21\ 22\ 23\ 24\ 25\ 26\ 27\ 28\ 29\ 30\ 31}{00000000000000000000000000000009.}11$$

Step 2 Write the number from Step 1 multiplied by a power of 10.

We moved the decimal point 31 places to the **right**.

So the power of 10 is -31. 9.11×10^{-31}

Step 3 Check the sign of the power.

The original number is **less** than 1, so the power should be **negative**, and it is.

Thus,

$$0.000000000000000000000000000000911 \text{ kg} = 9.11 \times 10^{-31} \text{ kg}.$$

We can also convert a number from scientific notation to expanded form.

— Procedure —
To Convert From Scientific Notation to Expanded Form

Move the decimal point the same number of places as the exponent of 10.

- If the exponent is **positive**, move the decimal point **right**.
- If the exponent is **negative**, move the decimal point **left**.

As a check, note the following:

- If the power of 10 is positive, the number written in expanded form will be greater than or equal to 10.
- If the power of 10 is negative, the number written in expanded form will be greater than 0 and less than 1.

Example 8.2.11

A light year is a measure of distance.
Its value is approximately 5.87×10^{12} miles.

Write in expanded form: 5.87×10^{12}

Solution

The exponent, 12, is **positive**, so move the decimal point 12 places to the **right**.

As you move the decimal point, you will have to append zeros to the right of 587 to serve as place holders.

The result is: 5,870,000,000,000

A light year is almost 6 trillion miles.

Be careful! The power of 10 does NOT tell us how many zeros to append to the right of the number.
To write 5.87×10^{12} in expanded form, we append 10 zeros (not 12).

Example 8.2.12

The gravitational force of attraction between two masses, m_1 and m_2, that are a distance r apart is given by $\dfrac{Gm_1m_2}{r^2}$.

The G in the formula represents the universal gravitational constant, $6.673 \times 10^{-11}\ \dfrac{\mathrm{N} \cdot \mathrm{m}^2}{\mathrm{kg}^2}$.

Write 6.673×10^{-11} in expanded form.

Solution

The exponent, -11, is **negative**, so move the decimal point 11 places to the **left**.

As you move the decimal point, you will have to append zeros to the left of 6673 to serve as place holders.

$$6.673 \times 10^{-11} \rightarrow 0.\underbrace{00000000006}_{1\ 2\ 3\ 4\ 5\ 6\ 7\ 8\ 9\ 10\ 11}673$$

Thus,

$$6.673 \times 10^{-11}\ \frac{\mathrm{N} \cdot \mathrm{m}^2}{\mathrm{kg}^2} = 0.0000000000673\ \frac{\mathrm{N} \cdot \mathrm{m}^2}{\mathrm{kg}^2}$$

Here is a summary of this concept from *Academic Systems Algebra*.

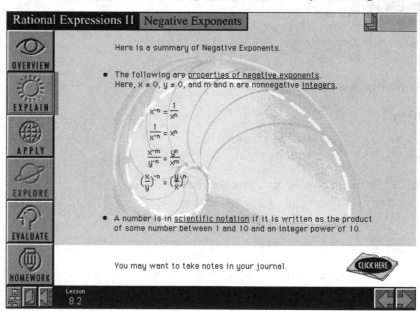

In $\dfrac{\mathrm{N} \cdot \mathrm{m}^2}{\mathrm{kg}^2}$, the abbreviations are:

N *for Newton, a unit of force*
m *for meter, a unit of length*
kg *for kilogram, a unit of mass.*

CONCEPT 2: MULTIPLYING AND DIVIDING RATIONAL EXPRESSIONS CONTAINING BINOMIALS

Concept 2 has sections on

- **Reducing Rational Expressions of the Form** $\dfrac{a-b}{b-a}$

- **Multiplying Rational Expressions**

- **Dividing Rational Expressions**

- **Simplifying a Complex Fraction**

Reducing Rational Expressions of the Form $\dfrac{a-b}{b-a}$

Sometimes we need to simplify an expression such as the following:

$$= \frac{7-x}{x-7}$$

In the expression, notice that the numerator and denominator are the same except for the signs of the terms.

To reduce the expression, we first factor -1 out of the numerator.

$$\frac{7-x}{x-7} = \frac{-1(-7+x)}{x-7}$$

Notice that $\dfrac{-1(-7+x)}{x-7} = \dfrac{-1(x-7)}{x-7}$.

Then we cancel common factors.

$$= \frac{-1(\cancel{x-7})}{\cancel{x-7}}$$

The result is -1.

$$= -1$$

— Formula —
To Simplify a Rational Expression of the Form $\dfrac{a-b}{b-a}$

$$\frac{a-b}{b-a} = -1$$

Here, a and b are real numbers and $a \neq b$.

Example 8.2.13

Reduce to lowest terms: $\dfrac{x^2 + 6x - 27}{9 - x^2}$

Solution

Step 1 Factor the numerator and denominator.

For the numerator, find two numbers whose product is -27 and whose sum is 6. These numbers are -3 and 9.

$$= \frac{x^2 + 6x - 27}{9 - x^2}$$

The denominator is the difference of two squares: $3^2 - x^2$.

$$= \frac{(x-3)(x+9)}{(3-x)(3+x)}$$

Step 2 Cancel all pairs of factors common to the numerator and denominator.

Since $\dfrac{(x-3)}{(3-x)}$ has the form $\dfrac{a-b}{b-a}$, it reduces to -1.

$$= -1 \cdot \frac{(x+9)}{(3+x)}$$

$$= -\frac{x+9}{3+x}$$

Thus, $\dfrac{x^2 + 6x - 27}{9 - x^2} = -\dfrac{x+9}{3+x}$.

The answer may be written in several ways.

Here is an example of multiplying rational expressions that contain monomials:

$$\frac{9x^2}{5z^2} \cdot \frac{10z}{6x} = \frac{3 \cdot 3 \cdot x \cdot x}{5 \cdot z \cdot z} \cdot \frac{2 \cdot 5 \cdot z}{2 \cdot 3 \cdot x}$$

$$= \frac{\overset{1}{\cancel{3}} \cdot 3 \cdot \overset{1}{\cancel{x}} \cdot x}{5 \cdot \underset{1}{\cancel{z}} \cdot z} \cdot \frac{\overset{1}{\cancel{2}} \cdot 5 \cdot \overset{1}{\cancel{z}}}{\underset{1}{\cancel{2}} \cdot 3 \cdot \underset{1}{\cancel{x}}}$$

$$= \frac{3 \cdot x}{z} \cdot \frac{1}{1} = \frac{3x}{z}$$

Multiplying Rational Expressions

In Lesson 8.1 you multiplied rational expressions that contain monomials.

Now, we will use the same procedure to multiply rational expressions that contain binomials or trinomials.

> **— Procedure —**
> **To Multiply Rational Expressions**
>
> **Step 1** Factor the numerators and denominators.
>
> **Step 2** Cancel all pairs of factors common to the numerators and denominators.
>
> **Step 3** Multiply the numerators. Multiply the denominators.
>
> We usually leave the answer in factored form.

Example 8.2.14

Find: $\dfrac{5x^2 - 15x}{x^2 - x - 12} \cdot \dfrac{x^2 - 6x + 8}{x - 3}$

Solution

$$\frac{5x^2 - 15x}{x^2 - x - 12} \cdot \frac{x^2 - 6x + 8}{x - 3}$$

Step 1 Factor the numerators and denominators.

$$= \frac{5x(x - 3)}{(x + 3)(x - 4)} \cdot \frac{(x - 4)(x - 2)}{x - 3}$$

Step 2 Cancel all pairs of factors common to the numerators and denominators.

$$= \frac{5x\overset{1}{\cancel{(x - 3)}}}{(x + 3)\underset{1}{\cancel{(x - 4)}}} \cdot \frac{\overset{1}{\cancel{(x - 4)}}(x - 2)}{\underset{1}{\cancel{(x - 3)}}}$$

Step 3 Multiply the numerators, and then multiply the denominators.

$$= \frac{5x(x - 2)}{x + 3}$$

Thus, $\dfrac{5x^2 - 15x}{x^2 - x - 12} \cdot \dfrac{x^2 - 6x + 8}{x - 3} = \dfrac{5x(x - 2)}{x + 3}.$

Example 8.2.15

Find: $\dfrac{4x^2 - 24x}{x^2 - 10x + 25} \cdot \dfrac{x^2 - 25}{6 - x}$

Solution

$$\frac{4x^2 - 24x}{x^2 - 10x + 25} \cdot \frac{x^2 - 25}{6 - x}$$

Step 1 Factor the numerators and denominators.

$$= \frac{4x(x - 6)}{(x - 5)(x - 5)} \cdot \frac{(x - 5)(x + 5)}{6 - x}$$

Step 2 Cancel all pairs of factors common to the numerators and denominators.

$$= \frac{4x(x - 6)}{(x - 5)\underset{1}{\cancel{(x - 5)}}} \cdot \frac{\overset{1}{\cancel{(x - 5)}}(x + 5)}{6 - x}$$

Replace $\dfrac{x - 6}{6 - x}$ with -1.

$$= \frac{4x}{(x - 5)} \cdot (x + 5) \cdot (-1)$$

Step 3 *Multiply the numerators, and then multiply the denominators.*

$$= \frac{-4x(x+5)}{x-5}$$

So, $\dfrac{4x^2-24x}{x^2-10x+25} \cdot \dfrac{x^2-25}{6-x} = \dfrac{-4x(x+5)}{x-5}$.

Dividing Rational Expressions

In Lesson 8.1 you divided rational expressions containing monomials.

Now, we will use the same procedure to divide rational expressions that contain binomials or trinomials.

— Procedure —
To Divide Rational Expressions

Step 1 Invert the second fraction and change the division symbol, $\div$, to the multiplication symbol, $\cdot$.

Step 2 Factor the numerators and denominators.

Step 3 Cancel all pairs of factors common to the numerators and denominators.

Step 4 Multiply the numerators. Multiply the denominators.

We usually leave the answer in factored form.

Here is an example of dividing rational expressions that contain monomials:

$$\frac{15w}{4y} \div \frac{10w^2}{12y} = \frac{15w}{4y} \cdot \frac{12y}{10w^2}$$

$$= \frac{3 \cdot 5 \cdot w}{2 \cdot 2 \cdot y} \cdot \frac{2 \cdot 2 \cdot 3 \cdot y}{2 \cdot 5 \cdot w \cdot w}$$

$$= \frac{3 \cdot 5 \cdot w}{2 \cdot 2 \cdot y} \cdot \frac{2 \cdot 2 \cdot 3 \cdot y}{2 \cdot 5 \cdot w \cdot w}$$

$$= \frac{3}{1} \cdot \frac{3}{2 \cdot w}$$

$$= \frac{9}{2w}$$

Example 8.2.16

Find: $\dfrac{2x^2+5x-3}{x^2-6x+5} \div \dfrac{2x^2+x-1}{x^2-4x-5}$

Solution

$$\frac{2x^2+5x-3}{x^2-6x+5} \div \frac{2x^2+x-1}{x^2-4x-5}$$

Step 1 *Invert the second fraction and change the division symbol, ÷, to the multiplication symbol, ·.*

$$= \frac{2x^2+5x-3}{x^2-6x+5} \cdot \frac{x^2-4x-5}{2x^2+x-1}$$

Step 2 *Factor the numerators and denominators.*

$$= \frac{(2x-1)(x+3)}{(x-1)(x-5)} \cdot \frac{(x+1)(x-5)}{(2x-1)(x+1)}$$

Step 3 *Cancel all pairs of factors common to the numerators and denominators.*

$$= \frac{(2x-1)(x+3)}{(x-1)(x-5)} \cdot \frac{(x+1)(x-5)}{(2x-1)(x+1)}$$

$$= \frac{(x+3)}{(x-1)} \cdot \frac{1}{1}$$

Step 4 *Multiply the numerators. Multiply the denominators.*

$$= \frac{x+3}{x-1}$$

Thus, $\dfrac{2x^2+5x-3}{x^2-6x+5} \div \dfrac{2x^2+x-1}{x^2-4x-5} = \dfrac{x+3}{x-1}$.

Example 8.2.17

Find: $\dfrac{y^2 + 7y + 10}{16 - 2y} \div \dfrac{y^2 + 10y + 16}{y^2 - 64}$

Solution

$$\dfrac{y^2 + 7y + 10}{16 - 2y} \div \dfrac{y^2 + 10y + 16}{y^2 - 64}$$

Step 1 *Invert the second fraction and change the division symbol, ÷, to the multiplication symbol, ·.*

$$= \dfrac{y^2 + 7y + 10}{16 - 2y} \cdot \dfrac{y^2 - 64}{y^2 + 10y + 16}$$

Step 2 *Factor the numerators and denominators.*

$$= \dfrac{(y + 5)(y + 2)}{2(8 - y)} \cdot \dfrac{(y - 8)(y + 8)}{(y + 2)(y + 8)}$$

Step 3 *Cancel all pairs of factors common to the numerators and denominators.*

$$= \dfrac{(y + 5)\cancel{(y + 2)}^{\,1}}{2(8 - y)} \cdot \dfrac{(y - 8)\cancel{(y + 8)}}{\cancel{(y + 2)}\cancel{(y + 8)}}$$

$$= \dfrac{(y + 5)}{2(8 - y)} \cdot \dfrac{(y - 8)}{1}$$

Replace $\dfrac{y - 8}{8 - y}$ with -1.

$$= \dfrac{(y + 5)}{2} \cdot \dfrac{-1}{1}$$

Step 4 *Multiply the numerators. Multiply the denominators.*

$$= \dfrac{-y - 5}{2}$$

Thus, $\dfrac{y^2 + 7y + 10}{16 - 2y} \div \dfrac{y^2 + 10y + 16}{y^2 - 64} = \dfrac{-y - 5}{2}$.

You can also write the answer as follows:

$$-\dfrac{y + 5}{2}$$

Simplifying a Complex Fraction

A **complex fraction** is a fraction that contains other fractions.

You have already used this procedure to simplify a complex fraction.

— Procedure —
To Simplify a Complex Fraction

Step 1 Write the complex fraction using a division symbol, ÷.

Step 2 Invert the second fraction and change the division symbol, ÷, to the multiplication symbol, ·.

Step 3 Factor the numerators and denominators.

Step 4 Cancel all pairs of factors common to the numerators and denominators.

Step 5 Multiply the numerators. Multiply the denominators.

Example `8.2.18`

Simplify: $\dfrac{\dfrac{x^3 + 2x^2}{3x}}{\dfrac{2x + 4}{9}}$

Solution

Step 1 Write the complex fraction using a division symbol, ÷.

$$\frac{x^3 + 2x^2}{3x} \div \frac{2x + 4}{9}$$

Step 2 Invert the second fraction and change the division symbol, ÷, to the multiplication symbol, ·.

$$= \frac{x^3 + 2x^2}{3x} \cdot \frac{9}{2x + 4}$$

Step 3 Factor the numerators and denominators.

$$= \frac{x \cdot x(x + 2)}{3 \cdot x} \cdot \frac{3 \cdot 3}{2(x + 2)}$$

Step 4 Cancel all pairs of factors common to the numerators and denominators.

$$= \frac{\overset{1}{x} \cdot x \overset{1}{\cancel{(x + 2)}}}{\underset{11}{\cancel{3x}}} \cdot \frac{\overset{1}{\cancel{3}} \cdot 3}{2(x + 2)}$$

Step 5 Multiply the numerators. Multiply the denominators.

$$= \frac{3x}{2}$$

Thus, $\dfrac{\dfrac{x^3 + 2x^2}{3x}}{\dfrac{2x + 4}{9}} = \dfrac{3x}{2}$.

Example `8.2.19`

Simplify: $\dfrac{\dfrac{x^2 - 4}{x^2 - 8x + 15}}{\dfrac{12x + 24}{3x - 15}}$

Solution

Step 1 Write the complex fraction using a division symbol, ÷.

$$\frac{x^2 - 4}{x^2 - 8x + 15} \div \frac{12x + 24}{3x - 15}$$

Step 2 Invert the second fraction and change the division symbol, ÷, to the multiplication symbol, ·.

$$= \frac{x^2 - 4}{x^2 - 8x + 15} \cdot \frac{3x - 15}{12x + 24}$$

Step 3 Factor the numerators and denominators.

$$= \frac{(x - 2)(x + 2)}{(x - 3)(x - 5)} \cdot \frac{3(x - 5)}{2 \cdot 2 \cdot 3(x + 2)}$$

Step 4 *Cancel all pairs of factors*
common to the numerators
and denominators.

$$= \frac{(x-2)\cancel{(x+2)}}{(x-3)\overset{1}{\cancel{(x-5)}}} \cdot \frac{\overset{1}{\cancel{3}}\overset{1}{\cancel{(x-5)}}}{2 \cdot 2 \cdot \overset{1}{\cancel{3}}(x+2)}$$

Step 5 *Multiply the numerators.*
Multiply the denominators.

$$= \frac{x-2}{4(x-3)}$$

Thus, $\dfrac{\dfrac{x^2-4}{x^2-8x+15}}{\dfrac{12x+24}{3x-15}} = \dfrac{x-2}{4(x-3)}$.

Here is a summary of this concept from *Academic Systems Algebra*.

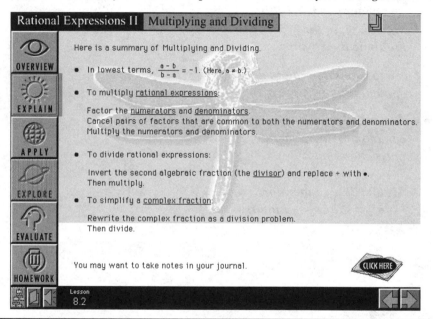

Concept 3 has sections on

- **Finding the Least Common Multiple (LCM) of a Set of Polynomials**

- **Adding and Subtracting Rational Expressions with Different Denominators**

- **Simplifying a Complex Fraction that Contains Addition or Subtraction**

CONCEPT 3: ADDING AND SUBTRACTING RATIONAL EXPRESSIONS CONTAINING BINOMIALS

Finding the Least Common Multiple (LCM) of a Set of Polynomials

Adding and subtracting rational expressions with different denominators is like adding and subtracting fractions with different denominators.

We begin by finding the **least common denominator** (**LCD**) of a set of rational expressions.

The LCD of two or more rational expressions is the **least common multiple** (**LCM**) of their denominators.

We can find the LCM of a set of polynomials in much the same manner that we found the LCM of a set of whole numbers.

```
—— Procedure ——
To Find the Least Common Multiple (LCM) of a Set of Polynomials
```

Step 1 Factor each polynomial.

Step 2 For each factor, list it the greatest number of times it appears in any factorization.

Step 3 Find the product of the factors in the list.

We usually leave the LCM in factored form.

To find the LCM of a set of numbers, say 10, 15, and 18, follow these steps:

Step 1 Write the prime factorization of each number.

$10 = 2 \cdot 5$
$15 = 3 \cdot 5$
$18 = 2 \cdot 3 \cdot 3$

Step 2 List each prime factor the greatest number of times it appears in any factorization:

2, 3, 3, 5

Step 3 Multiply the prime factors in the list:

$2 \cdot 3 \cdot 3 \cdot 5 = 90$

The LCM of 10, 15, and 18 is 90.

Example 8.2.20

Find the LCM of $15xy$, $10x^2y$, and $6xy^2$.

Solution

Step 1 Factor each polynomial.
$$15xy = 3 \cdot 5 \cdot x \cdot y$$
$$10x^2y = 2 \cdot 5 \cdot x \cdot x \cdot y$$
$$6xy^2 = 2 \cdot 3 \cdot x \cdot y \cdot y$$

Step 2 For each factor, list it the greatest number of times it appears in any factorization.
$$2, 3, 5, x, x, y, y$$

Step 3 Find the product of the factors in the list.
$$\text{LCM} = 2 \cdot 3 \cdot 5 \cdot x \cdot x \cdot y \cdot y$$
$$= 30x^2y^2$$

The LCM of $15xy$, $10x^2y$, and $6xy^2$ is $30x^2y^2$.

Example 8.2.21

Find the LCM of $x^2 - 2x$, $x^2 + x - 6$, and $x^2 + 6x + 9$

Solution

Step 1 Factor each polynomial.
$$x^2 - 2x = x(x - 2)$$
$$x^2 + x - 6 = (x + 3)(x - 2)$$
$$x^2 + 6x + 9 = (x + 3)(x + 3)$$

Step 2 For each factor, list it the greatest number of times it appears in any factorization.
$$x, (x - 2), (x + 3), (x + 3)$$

Step 3 Find the product of the factors in the list.
$$\text{LCM} = x(x - 2)(x + 3)(x + 3)$$

The LCM of $x^2 - 2x$, $x^2 + x - 6$, and $x^2 + 6x + 9$ is $x(x - 2)(x + 3)(x + 3)$.

To add (or subtract) fractions with different denominators, say

$$\frac{5}{24} + \frac{7}{15},$$

follow these steps:

Step 1 Find the LCD.

$24 = 2 \cdot 2 \cdot 2 \cdot 3$

$15 = 3 \cdot 5$

$LCD = 2 \cdot 2 \cdot 2 \cdot 3 \cdot 5 = 120$

Step 2 Rewrite each fraction with the LCD as the denominator.

$$\frac{5}{24} = \frac{5}{24} \cdot \frac{5}{5} = \frac{25}{120}$$

$$\frac{7}{15} = \frac{7}{15} \cdot \frac{8}{8} = \frac{56}{120}$$

Step 3 Add (or subtract) the numerators. The denominator stays the same.

$$\frac{25}{120} + \frac{56}{120} = \frac{81}{120}$$

Step 4 Reduce to lowest terms.

$$\frac{81}{120} = \frac{\overset{1}{\cancel{3}} \cdot 3 \cdot 3 \cdot 3}{2 \cdot 2 \cdot 2 \cdot \underset{1}{\cancel{3}} \cdot 5} = \frac{3 \cdot 3 \cdot 3}{2 \cdot 2 \cdot 2 \cdot 5} = \frac{27}{40}$$

Adding and Subtracting Rational Expressions with Different Denominators

We add or subtract rational expressions in the same way that we add or subtract fractions.

You have already learned how to add and subtract rational expressions with the same denominator. Now we will add and subtract rational expressions with different denominators.

> — Procedure —
> **To Add (or Subtract) Rational Expressions That Have Different Denominators**
>
> **Step 1** Find the LCD.
> **Step 2** Rewrite each rational expression with the LCD as the denominator.
> **Step 3** Add (or subtract) the numerators. The denominator stays the same.
> **Step 4** Reduce to lowest terms.
> We usually leave the answer in factored form.

Example 8.2.22

Find: $\dfrac{x}{3w} + \dfrac{5}{9x}$

Solution

Step 1 Find the LCD.

$$\frac{x}{3w} + \frac{5}{9x}$$

Factor each denominator.

$$= \frac{x}{3 \cdot w} + \frac{5}{3 \cdot 3 \cdot x}$$

List each factor the greatest number of times it appears in any factorization.

$3, 3, w, x$

The LCD is $3 \cdot 3 \cdot w \cdot x = 9wx$.

Step 2 Rewrite each rational expression with the LCD as the denominator.

$$= \frac{x}{3 \cdot w} \cdot \frac{\mathbf{3 \cdot x}}{\mathbf{3 \cdot x}} + \frac{5}{3 \cdot 3 \cdot x} \cdot \frac{\mathbf{w}}{\mathbf{w}}$$

$$= \frac{3x^2}{9wx} + \frac{5w}{9wx}$$

Step 3 Add (or subtract) the numerators. The denominator stays the same.

$$= \frac{3x^2 + 5w}{9wx}$$

Step 4 Reduce to lowest terms.

The numerator and denominator have no common factors other than 1 and -1.

Therefore, $\dfrac{3x^2 + 5w}{9wx}$ is in lowest terms.

Thus, $\dfrac{x}{3w} + \dfrac{5}{9x} = \dfrac{3x^2 + 5w}{9wx}$.

In $\dfrac{3x^2 + 5w}{9wx}$, we CANNOT cancel w or x because the operation in the numerator is addition, not multiplication.

Example 8.2.23

Find: $\dfrac{16}{x^2 + 2x - 3} + \dfrac{4}{x + 3}$

Solution

Step 1 Find the LCD.

Factor each denominator.

$$\dfrac{16}{(x - 1)(x + 3)} + \dfrac{4}{x + 3}$$

The LCD is $(x - 1)(x + 3)$.

Step 2 Rewrite each rational expression with the LCD as the denominator.

The denominator of the first fraction is already the LCD.

The denominator of the second fraction needs another factor, $(x - 1)$.

$$= \dfrac{16}{(x - 1)(x + 3)} + \dfrac{4}{(x + 3)} \cdot \dfrac{(x - 1)}{(x - 1)}$$

$$= \dfrac{16}{(x - 1)(x + 3)} + \dfrac{4(x - 1)}{(x + 3)(x - 1)}$$

At the end of Step 2, you may be tempted to cancel common factors.

But that would get you back to where you started.

Remember to add first, then factor and cancel factors.

Step 3 Add (or subtract) the numerators. The denominator stays the same.

Add the numerators.

$$= \dfrac{16 + 4(x - 1)}{(x + 3)(x - 1)}$$

Distribute the 4.

$$= \dfrac{16 + 4x - 4}{(x + 3)(x - 1)}$$

Combine like terms.

$$= \dfrac{4x + 12}{(x + 3)(x - 1)}$$

Step 4 Reduce to lowest terms.

Factor the numerator.

$$= \dfrac{4(x + 3)}{(x + 3)(x - 1)}$$

Cancel the common factor, $(x + 3)$.

$$= \dfrac{4}{x - 1}$$

So, $\dfrac{16}{x^2 + 2x - 3} + \dfrac{4}{x + 3} = \dfrac{4}{x - 1}$.

Find: $\dfrac{5y}{w^2 - 6w} - \dfrac{7}{4wy}$

Solution

Step 1 Find the LCD.

Factor each denominator.

The LCD is $w(w - 6) \cdot 2 \cdot 2 \cdot y$.

$$\dfrac{5y}{w(w - 6)} - \dfrac{7}{2 \cdot 2 \cdot w \cdot y}$$

At the end of Step 2, you may be tempted to cancel common factors.

But that would get you back to where you started.

Remember to subtract first, then factor and cancel factors.

Step 2 Rewrite each rational expression with the LCD as the denominator.

$$= \dfrac{5y}{w(w - 6)} \dfrac{\mathbf{2 \cdot 2 \cdot y}}{\mathbf{2 \cdot 2 \cdot y}} - \dfrac{7}{2 \cdot 2 \cdot w \cdot y} \cdot \dfrac{\mathbf{(w - 6)}}{\mathbf{(w - 6)}}$$

$$= \dfrac{20y^2}{4wy(w - 6)} - \dfrac{7(w - 6)}{4wy(w - 6)}$$

Step 3 Add (or subtract) the numerators. The denominator stays the same.

Subtract the numerators.

$$= \dfrac{20y^2 - 7(w - 6)}{4wy(w - 6)}$$

Distribute the -7.

$$= \dfrac{20y^2 - 7w + 42}{4wy(w - 6)}$$

Step 4 Reduce to lowest terms.

The numerator cannot be factored using integers. Since there are no factors, other than 1 or -1, common to the numerator and denominator, the expression is in lowest terms.

So, $\dfrac{5y}{w^2 - 6w} - \dfrac{7}{4wy} = \dfrac{20y^2 - 7w + 42}{4wy(w - 6)}$.

Find: $\dfrac{x}{x^2 - 6x + 9} - \dfrac{3}{x^2 - 9}$

Solution

Step 1 Find the LCD.

Factor each denominator.

$$\dfrac{x}{(x - 3)(x - 3)} - \dfrac{3}{(x - 3)(x + 3)}$$

The LCD is $(x - 3)(x - 3)(x + 3)$.

Step 2 Rewrite each rational expression with the LCD as the denominator.

$$= \dfrac{x}{(x - 3)(x - 3)} \cdot \dfrac{\mathbf{(x + 3)}}{\mathbf{(x + 3)}} - \dfrac{3}{(x + 3)(x - 3)} \cdot \dfrac{\mathbf{(x - 3)}}{\mathbf{(x - 3)}}$$

$$= \dfrac{x(x + 3)}{(x - 3)(x - 3)(x + 3)} - \dfrac{3(x - 3)}{(x + 3)(x - 3)(x - 3)}$$

Step 3 ***Add (or subtract) the numerators. The denominator stays the same.***

Subtract the numerators.

$$= \frac{x(x + 3) - 3(x - 3)}{(x - 3)(x - 3)(x + 3)}$$

In the numerator, distribute the x and the -3.

$$= \frac{x^2 + 3x - 3x + 9}{(x - 3)(x - 3)(x + 3)}$$

Combine like terms.

$$= \frac{x^2 + 9}{(x - 3)(x - 3)(x + 3)}$$

Step 4 ***Reduce to lowest terms.***

The numerator cannot be factored over the integers.

Since there are no factors, other than 1 or -1, common to the numerator and the denominator, the expression is in lowest terms.

So, $\dfrac{x}{x^2 - 6x + 9} - \dfrac{3}{x^2 - 9} = \dfrac{x^2 + 9}{(x - 3)(x - 3)(x + 3)}$.

Simplifying a Complex Fraction That Contains Addition or Subtraction

You have already simplified some complex fractions. Now we will learn how to simplify a complex fraction that contains addition or subtraction.

One way to begin is to carry out the addition or subtraction.

— Procedure —
To Simplify a Complex Fraction
That Contains Addition or Subtraction.

Step 1 Perform any addition or subtraction.

Step 2 Rewrite the complex fraction using a division symbol, $\div$.

Step 3 Invert the second fraction and change the division symbol, $\div$, to the multiplication symbol, $\cdot$.

Step 4 Factor the numerators and denominators.

Step 5 Cancel all pairs of factors common to the numerators and denominators.

Step 6 Multiply the numerators. Multiply the denominators.

Example 8.2.26

Simplify: $\dfrac{\dfrac{8}{w} + \dfrac{4}{y}}{\dfrac{6}{w} - \dfrac{10}{y}}$

Solution

Step 1 Perform any addition or subtraction.

In both the numerator and denominator the LCD of the fractions is wy.

We write each fraction with LCD.

$\dfrac{\dfrac{8}{w} \cdot \dfrac{y}{y} + \dfrac{4}{y} \cdot \dfrac{w}{w}}{\dfrac{6}{w} \cdot \dfrac{y}{y} - \dfrac{10}{y} \cdot \dfrac{w}{w}}$

Then we add the fractions in the numerator and subtract the fractions in the denominator.

$= \dfrac{\dfrac{8y + 4w}{wy}}{\dfrac{6y - 10w}{wy}}$

Step 2 Rewrite the complex fraction using a division symbol, $\div$.

$= \dfrac{8y + 4w}{wy} \div \dfrac{6y - 10w}{wy}$

Step 3 Invert the second fraction and change the division symbol, $\div$, to the multiplication symbol, $\cdot$.

$= \dfrac{8y + 4w}{wy} \cdot \dfrac{wy}{6y - 10w}$

Step 4 Factor the numerators and denominators.

$= \dfrac{4(2y + w)}{wy} \cdot \dfrac{wy}{2(3y - 5w)}$

Step 5 Cancel all pairs of factors common to the numerators and denominators.

The common factors are 2, w, and y.

$= \dfrac{2(2y + w)}{1} \cdot \dfrac{1}{(3y - 5w)}$

Step 6 Multiply the numerators. Multiply the denominators.

$= \dfrac{2(2y + w)}{3y - 5w}$

Thus, $\dfrac{\dfrac{8}{w} + \dfrac{4}{y}}{\dfrac{6}{w} - \dfrac{10}{y}} = \dfrac{2(2y + w)}{3y - 5w}$.

Example 8.2.27

Simplify: $\dfrac{\dfrac{3}{x-1}+\dfrac{5}{x}}{4-\dfrac{2}{x-1}}$

Solution

Step 1 Perform any addition or subtraction.

In the numerator, the LCD of the fractions is $x(x-1)$.

In the denominator, the LCD of the fractions is $x-1$.

$$\dfrac{\dfrac{3}{x-1}\cdot\dfrac{x}{x}+\dfrac{5}{x}\cdot\dfrac{x-1}{x-1}}{4\cdot\dfrac{x-1}{x-1}-\dfrac{2}{x-1}}$$

Add the fractions in the numerator. Subtract the fractions in the denominator.

$$=\dfrac{\dfrac{3x+5(x-1)}{x(x-1)}}{\dfrac{4(x-1)-2}{x-1}}$$

Distribute the 5 in the numerator of the complex fraction.

Distribute the 4 in the denominator of the complex fraction.

$$=\dfrac{\dfrac{3x+5x-5}{x(x-1)}}{\dfrac{4x-4-2}{x-1}}$$

Combine like terms.

$$=\dfrac{\dfrac{8x-5}{x(x-1)}}{\dfrac{4x-6}{x-1}}$$

Step 2 Rewrite the complex fraction using a division symbol, $\div$.

$$=\dfrac{8x-5}{x(x-1)}\div\dfrac{4x-6}{x-1}$$

Step 3 Invert the second fraction and change the division symbol, $\div$, to the multiplication symbol, $\cdot$.

$$=\dfrac{8x-5}{x(x-1)}\cdot\dfrac{x-1}{4x-6}$$

Step 4 Factor the numerators and denominators.

$$=\dfrac{8x-5}{x(x-1)}\cdot\dfrac{x-1}{2(2x-3)}$$

Step 5 Cancel all pairs of factors common to the numerators and denominators.

Cancel the common factor, $x-1$.

$$=\dfrac{8x-5}{x}\cdot\dfrac{1}{2(2x-3)}$$

Step 6 Multiply the numerators. Multiply the denominators.

$$=\dfrac{8x-5}{2x(2x-3)}$$

Thus, $\dfrac{\dfrac{3}{x-1}+\dfrac{5}{x}}{4-\dfrac{2}{x-1}}=\dfrac{8x-5}{2x(2x-3)}$.

Here is a summary of this concept from *Academic Systems Algebra*.

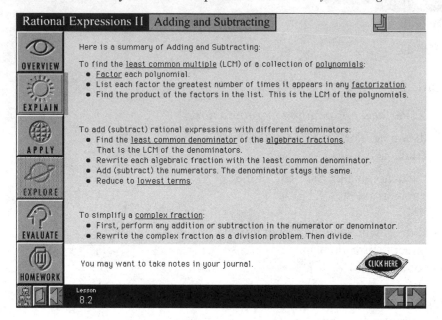

Rational Expressions II | Adding and Subtracting

OVERVIEW
EXPLAIN
APPLY
EXPLORE
EVALUATE
HOMEWORK

Here is a summary of Adding and Subtracting:

To find the least common multiple (LCM) of a collection of polynomials:
- Factor each polynomial.
- List each factor the greatest number of times it appears in any factorization.
- Find the product of the factors in the list. This is the LCM of the polynomials.

To add (subtract) rational expressions with different denominators:
- Find the least common denominator of the algebraic fractions.
  That is the LCM of the denominators.
- Rewrite each algebraic fraction with the least common denominator.
- Add (subtract) the numerators. The denominator stays the same.
- Reduce to lowest terms.

To simplify a complex fraction:
- First, perform any addition or subtraction in the numerator or denominator.
- Rewrite the complex fraction as a division problem. Then divide.

You may want to take notes in your journal.

CLICK HERE

Lesson
8.2

Checklist Lesson 8.2

Here is what you should know after completing this lesson.

Words and Phrases

negative exponents
properties of negative exponents
expanded form
scientific notation

complex fraction
least common denominator (LCD)
least common multiple (LCM)

Ideas and Procedures

❶ Negative Exponent
Use the definition of a negative exponent to simplify an expression.

Example 8.2.3
  Find: $\dfrac{5}{2^{-1} - 3^{-2}}$
See also: Example 8.2.1, 8.2.2, 8.2.4
    Apply 1-12

❷ Properties of Negative Exponents
Use the properties of negative exponents to write an exponential expression using only positive exponents.

Example 8.2.8
  Simplify and write using only positive exponents:
  $\dfrac{2^{-5}c^3 d^{-6}}{c^{-2}d^4}$
See also: Example 8.2.5, 8.2.6, 8.2.7
    Apply 13-24

❸ Scientific Notation
Write a number in scientific notation.

Example 8.2.9
  Write 93,000,000 in scientific notation.

See also: Example 8.2.10
    Apply 25, 26

Convert a number from scientific notation to expanded form.

Example 8.2.12
  Write 6.673×10^{-11} in expanded form.

See also: Example 8.2.11
    Apply 27, 28

❹ Reduce a Rational Expression of the Form $\dfrac{a - b}{b - a}$
Reduce a rational expression using the relationship $\dfrac{a - b}{b - a} = -1$

Example 8.2.13
  Reduce to lowest terms: $\dfrac{x^2 + 6x - 27}{9 - x^2}$
See also: Apply 29, 30, 32, 33, 35

❺ Multiply Rational Expressions
Multiply rational expressions.

Example 8.2.14
  Find: $\dfrac{5x^2 - 15x}{x^2 - x - 12} \cdot \dfrac{x^2 - 6x + 8}{x - 3}$
See also: Example 8.2.15
    Apply 36-44

⑥ Divide Rational Expressions

Divide rational expressions.

Example 8.2.16

Find: $\dfrac{2x^2 + 5x - 3}{x^2 - 6x + 5} \div \dfrac{2x^2 + x - 1}{x^2 - 4x - 5}$

See also: Example 8.2.17

Apply 45-50

---

⑦ Complex Fractions

Simplify a complex fraction.

Example 8.2.19

Simplify: $\dfrac{\dfrac{x^2 - 4}{x^2 - 8x + 15}}{\dfrac{12x + 24}{3x - 15}}$

See also: Example 8.2.18

Apply 51-56

---

⑧ Least Common Multiple (LCM)

Find the LCM of a set of rational expressions.

Example 8.2.21

Find the LCM of $x^2 - 2x$, $x^2 + x - 6$, and $x^2 + 6x + 9$

See also: Example 8.2.20

Apply 57-60

---

⑨ Add Rational Expressions

Add rational expressions that have different denominators.

Example 8.2.23

Find: $\dfrac{16}{x^2 + 2x - 3} + \dfrac{4}{x + 3}$

See also: Example 8.2.22

Apply 61-72

---

⑩ Subtract Rational Expressions

Subtract rational expressions that have different denominators.

Example 8.2.24

Find: $\dfrac{5y}{w^2 - 6w} - \dfrac{7}{4wy}$

See also: Example 8.2.25

Apply 73-81

---

⑪ Complex Fractions

Simplify a complex fraction that contains addition or subtraction.

Example 8.2.26

Simplify: $\dfrac{\dfrac{8}{w} + \dfrac{4}{y}}{\dfrac{6}{w} - \dfrac{10}{y}}$

See also: Example 8.2.27

Apply 82-84

Homework

Homework Problems

Circle the homework problems assigned to you by the computer, then complete them below.

☀ Explain

Negative Exponents

1. Find: 5^{-3}

2. Find: $7^{-2} \cdot 7^3$

3. Find: $\dfrac{50}{10^{-2} + 5^{-2}}$

In questions 4 through 9, simplify each expression. Use only positive exponents in your answers.

4. $\left(\dfrac{2m}{n}\right)^{-3}$

5. $\dfrac{2m^{-3}}{n^3}$

6. $(n^4 p^{-3})^5$

7. $(2s^3 t)^{-5} \cdot (2st^3)^6$

8. $\dfrac{(3uv^4)(9u^3v)^{-2}}{(3u^5v^{-4})^{-3}}$

9. All matter is made up of tiny particles called atoms. Through experimentation, it has been found that the diameters of atoms range from 1×10^{-8} cm to 5×10^{-8} cm. Rewrite each of these numbers in expanded form.

10. The monthly payment E on a loan of amount P can be computed by using the formula below, where r is the monthly interest rate, and n is the number of months for which the loan is made. Find the monthly payment on a $15,000 loan for 4 years (48 months) if the monthly interest rate is 1%.

$$E = \dfrac{Pr}{1 - (1 + r)^{-n}}$$

11. Write $\left(\dfrac{3x^4y}{z^5}\right)^{-2}$ using only positive exponents.

12. Suppose $x = 3$ and $y = 5$.

   a. Is $x^{-1}y^{-1} = \dfrac{1}{x} \cdot \dfrac{1}{y}$?

   b. Is $x^{-1}y^{-1} = \dfrac{1}{xy}$?

   c. Is $x^{-1} + y^{-1} = \dfrac{1}{x} + \dfrac{1}{y}$?

   d. Is $x^{-1} + y^{-1} = \dfrac{1}{x + y}$?

Multiplying and Dividing Rational Expressions Containing Binomials

13. Reduce to lowest terms: $\dfrac{y - 13}{13 - y}$

14. Reduce to lowest terms: $\dfrac{y^2 + y - 20}{16 - y^2}$

15. Find: $\dfrac{6 - x}{x + 7} \cdot \dfrac{x^2 + 7x}{x - 6}$

16. $\dfrac{a^2 - 5a - 14}{a^2 - 2a - 35} \cdot \dfrac{a^2 + 6a + 5}{a^2 - a - 6}$

17. Find: $\dfrac{3x^2 - 7x + 2}{x^2 + 4x - 12} \cdot \dfrac{2x^2 + 12x}{3x^2 + 2x - 1}$

18. Find: $\dfrac{(x + 3)(x - 2)}{x^2 - 4} \div \dfrac{(x + 3)(x - 4)}{x^2 - 16}$

19. Find: $\dfrac{y^2 + 15y + 56}{8y^2 - 10y + 3} \div \dfrac{y + 7}{4y - 3}$

20. Find: $\dfrac{x(x - 9)}{x^2 + 3x + 2} \div \dfrac{x^2 - 81}{x(x + 2)}$

21. Find: $\dfrac{z^2 + 8z + 15}{z^2 - 16} \div \dfrac{z^2 + 10z + 25}{z + 4}$

In questions 22, 23 and 24, simplify the complex fractions. Reduce your answer to lowest terms.

22. $\dfrac{\dfrac{x^2 - 13x + 42}{x^2 - 4}}{\dfrac{3x - 18}{3x - 6}}$

23. $\dfrac{\dfrac{2z^2 - 4z}{3z^3 + 6z^2}}{\dfrac{z - 2}{z + 2}}$

24. $\dfrac{\dfrac{2w^2 - 4w}{2w^2 - 2}}{\dfrac{w^2 - 5w + 6}{w^2 - 2w - 3}}$

Adding and Subtracting Rational Expressions Containing Binomials

25. Find the LCM of $x^2 + 10x + 25$ and $x^2 - 3x - 40$.

26. Find the LCM of x, $x^2 - 16$, and $x^2 + 7x + 12$.

27. Find: $\dfrac{5}{xy^3} + \dfrac{14}{x^2y^2}$

28. Find: $\dfrac{-1}{x^2 + 3x + 2} + \dfrac{2}{x^2 + 2x}$

29. Find: $\dfrac{4}{xy^2z} - \dfrac{3}{xyz^2}$

30. Find: $\dfrac{8}{x^2 + 14x + 49} - \dfrac{4}{x^2 - 49}$

31. Find: $\dfrac{-1}{y + 2} + \dfrac{2}{y - 2} - \dfrac{4}{y^2 - 4}$

32. Find: $\dfrac{1}{x^2 + 8x} - \dfrac{3}{x^2 - 64} + \dfrac{2}{x^2 + 6x - 16}$

33. Simplify the left side of the equation below to show it equals $\dfrac{1}{n}$. Then use the equation to find two fractions with 1 in the numerator whose difference is $\dfrac{1}{5}$. (Hint: let $n = 5$).
$$\dfrac{1}{n - 1} - \dfrac{1}{n(n - 1)} = \dfrac{1}{n}$$

34. Optometrists use the formula below to find the strength to be used for the lenses of glasses. Simplify the right side of this formula, then find the value of P that corresponds to $a = 12$ and $b = 0.3$.
$$P = \dfrac{1}{a} + \dfrac{1}{b}$$

35. The total resistance, R, of a circuit that consists of two resistors connected in parallel with resistance R_1 and R_2 is given by the formula below. Simplify this formula, then find the resistance, R, if $R_1 = 3$ ohms and $R_2 = 4$ ohms.
$$R = \dfrac{1}{\dfrac{1}{R_1} + \dfrac{1}{R_2}}$$

36. Simplify this complex fraction: $\dfrac{1}{\dfrac{1}{a} + \dfrac{1}{ab^2}}$

Apply

Practice Problems

Here are some additional practice problems for you to try.

Negative Exponents

1. Find: 2^{-3}

2. Find: 4^{-2}

3. Find: 3^{-4}

4. Find: 5^{-2}

5. Find: $\dfrac{1}{3^{-4}}$

6. Find: $\dfrac{1}{5^{-3}}$

7. Find: $4^{-7} \cdot 4^5$

8. Find: $2^8 \cdot 2^{-5}$

9. Find: $5^{-9} \cdot 5^6$

10. Find: $\dfrac{1}{3^{-2} + 2^{-3}}$

11. Find: $\dfrac{3}{4^{-3} + 5^{-2}}$

12. Find: $\dfrac{2}{4^{-2} + 7^{-1}}$

13. Rewrite using only positive exponents: $(a^4 b^6)^{-1}$

14. Rewrite using only positive exponents: $(x^3 y^5)^{-2}$

15. Rewrite using only positive exponents: $(m^6 n^3 p)^{-4}$

16. Rewrite using only positive exponents: $(x^{-5} b^2)^5$

17. Rewrite using only positive exponents: $(a^{-3} b^7)^4$

18. Rewrite using only positive exponents: $(x^{-6} y z^{-3})^5$

19. Rewrite using only positive exponents: $\left(\dfrac{c^4 d^{-5}}{a^2}\right)^{-2}$

20. Rewrite using only positive exponents: $\left(\dfrac{x^3 w^{-2}}{y^4}\right)^{-3}$

21. Rewrite using only positive exponents: $\left(\dfrac{m^{-4} n^5}{p^{-3}}\right)^{-4}$

22. Rewrite using only positive exponents: $(3x^3 y)^{-2} \cdot (3x^2 y^{-1} z^3)^4$

23. Rewrite using only positive exponents: $(4a^4 b^2)^4 \cdot (4a^{-3} bc^2)^{-3}$

24. Rewrite using only positive exponents: $(5x^{-3} y^{-1} z)^{-3} \cdot (5xz^{-5})^4$

25. Write in scientific notation: 0.000057

26. Write in scientific notation: 148,000,000

27. The following number is written in scientific notation. Write it in expanded form: 4.3×10^6

28. The following number is written in scientific notation. Write it in expanded form: 1.785×10^{-4}

Multiplying and Dividing Rational Expressions Containing Binomials

29. Reduce to lowest terms: $\dfrac{x - 5}{5 - x}$

30. Reduce to lowest terms: $\dfrac{x - 3}{3 - x}$

31. Reduce to lowest terms: $\dfrac{x^2 - 2x - 35}{x^2 - 25}$

32. Reduce to lowest terms: $\dfrac{x^2 + 2x - 24}{16 - x^2}$

33. Reduce to lowest terms: $\dfrac{x^2 - 8x + 7}{49 - x^2}$

34. Reduce to lowest terms: $\dfrac{x^2 - 11x + 30}{x^2 - 36}$

35. Reduce to lowest terms: $\dfrac{x^2 - 8x - 9}{81 - x^2}$

36. Find: $\dfrac{x^2 + 9x + 14}{x^2 + 2x - 15} \cdot \dfrac{x^2 - 4x + 3}{x^2 + 6x - 7}$

37. Find: $\dfrac{x^2 - 7x + 12}{x^2 + 2x - 15} \cdot \dfrac{x^2 - x - 30}{x^2 - 3x - 18}$

38. Find: $\dfrac{x^2 + 5x + 6}{x^2 - 5x - 6} \cdot \dfrac{x^2 - 10x + 24}{x^2 - x - 12}$

39. Find: $\dfrac{3x^2 - 6x}{x + 1} \cdot \dfrac{x - 1}{2 - x}$

40. Find: $\dfrac{5x^2 - 25x}{x - 3} \cdot \dfrac{x + 3}{5 - x}$

41. Find: $\dfrac{2x^2 - 6x}{x - 5} \cdot \dfrac{x + 5}{3 - x}$

42. Find: $\dfrac{x^2 + 2x - 15}{x^2 - 25} \cdot \dfrac{x^2 + 3x + 2}{x^2 - 2x - 3}$

43. Find: $\dfrac{x^2 + 4x - 45}{x^2 - 81} \cdot \dfrac{x^2 - 4x - 45}{x^2 - 7x + 10}$

44. Find: $\dfrac{x^2 + 10x + 21}{x^2 - 2x - 15} \cdot \dfrac{x^2 - x - 20}{x^2 - 16}$

45. Find: $\dfrac{x^2 + 2x - 35}{x^2 + x - 90} \div \dfrac{x^2 + 10x + 21}{x^2 + x - 90}$

46. Find: $\dfrac{x^2 + 2x - 35}{x^2 + x - 90} \div \dfrac{x^2 + 10x + 21}{x^2 + x - 90}$

47. Find: $\dfrac{x^2 - 2x - 3}{x^2 + 4x - 5} \div \dfrac{x^2 - 10x + 21}{x^2 + 4x - 5}$

48. Find: $\dfrac{5x - 25}{x^2 - 49} \div \dfrac{x^2 - 9x + 20}{x^2 - 11x + 28}$

49. Find: $\dfrac{x^2 + 7x + 6}{x^2 - 5x - 6} \div \dfrac{3x + 18}{x^2 + 5x - 66}$

50. Find: $\dfrac{4x - 16}{x^2 - 36} \div \dfrac{x^2 - x - 12}{x^2 + 9x + 18}$

51. Simplify the complex fraction below. Write your answer in lowest terms.
$$\dfrac{\frac{x^2 + 3x - 70}{x^2 - 49}}{\frac{x^2 + 9x - 10}{3x^2 - 3x}}$$

52. Simplify the complex fraction below. Write your answer in lowest terms.
$$\dfrac{\frac{x^2 - 4x - 45}{4x^2 + 20x}}{\frac{x^2 + 2x - 99}{x^2 - 121}}$$

53. Simplify the complex fraction below. Write your answer in lowest terms.
$$\dfrac{\frac{x^2 - 8x - 33}{x^2 - 9}}{\frac{x^2 - 9x - 22}{5x^2 + 10x}}$$

54. Simplify the complex fraction below. Write your answer in lowest terms.
$$\dfrac{\frac{x^2 - 7x + 6}{x^2 + 8x + 12}}{\frac{3x^2 - 3x}{x^2 - 36}}$$

55. Simplify the complex fraction below. Write your answer in lowest terms.
$$\dfrac{\frac{x^2 + 2x - 15}{5x^2 + 15x}}{\frac{x^2 - 2x - 35}{x^2 - 9}}$$

56. Simplify the complex fraction below. Write your answer in lowest terms.
$$\dfrac{\frac{x^2 + x - 20}{x^2 + 5x + 4}}{\frac{2x^2 + 10x}{x^2 - 16}}$$

Adding and Subtracting Rational Expressions Containing Binomials

57. Find the LCM of $x^2 + 7x + 12$ and $x^2 - 3x - 28$.

58. Find the LCM of $x^2 + 11x + 28$ and $x^2 + 2x - 8$.

59. Find the LCM of $x^2 + 4x$, $x^2 + 3x - 4$, and $x^2 - 2x + 1$.

60. Find the LCM of $x^2 - 6x$, $x^2 - 5x - 6$, and $x^2 + 2x + 1$.

61. Find: $\dfrac{4}{9a} + \dfrac{2}{3b}$

62. Find: $\dfrac{3}{8m} + \dfrac{7}{10n}$

63. Find: $\dfrac{2}{3x} + \dfrac{2}{6y}$

64. Find: $\dfrac{4}{x^2 - 4x - 12} + \dfrac{3}{x - 6}$

65. Find: $\dfrac{2}{x + 10} + \dfrac{5}{x^2 + 5x - 50}$

66. Find: $\dfrac{5}{x^2 + 4x - 21} + \dfrac{1}{x + 7}$

67. Find: $\dfrac{x}{x + 1} + \dfrac{x + 4}{x - 4}$

68. Find: $\dfrac{3x}{x + 3} + \dfrac{x + 2}{x - 7}$

69. Find: $\dfrac{5x}{x - 3} + \dfrac{x + 1}{x + 2}$

70. Find: $\dfrac{x + 2}{x^2 + 7x + 12} + \dfrac{x - 1}{x^2 + x - 12}$

71. Find: $\dfrac{x + 4}{x^2 + 5x + 6} + \dfrac{x - 3}{x^2 - 3x - 10}$

72. Find: $\dfrac{x - 5}{x^2 - 6x + 8} + \dfrac{x + 3}{x^2 + 2x - 8}$

73. Find: $\dfrac{4}{m^2 n} - \dfrac{1}{mn^2}$

74. Find: $\dfrac{5}{abc} - \dfrac{7}{b^2}$

75. Find: $\dfrac{3}{xyz} - \dfrac{2}{x^2}$

76. Find: $\dfrac{7x}{x + 6} - \dfrac{5}{x - 1}$

77. Find: $\dfrac{3x}{x-8} - \dfrac{11}{x+3}$

78. Find: $\dfrac{8x}{x-7} - \dfrac{3}{x+1}$

79. Find: $\dfrac{x+2}{x^2+6x+5} - \dfrac{x+3}{x^2+4x-5}$

80. Find: $\dfrac{x+5}{x^2-8x+12} - \dfrac{x-1}{x^2-3x-18}$

81. Find: $\dfrac{x+4}{x^2+x-2} - \dfrac{x+1}{x^2+2x-3}$

82. Simplify this complex fraction: $\dfrac{\dfrac{4}{x}+\dfrac{1}{y}}{\dfrac{3}{x}-\dfrac{5}{y}}$

83. Simplify this complex fraction: $\dfrac{\dfrac{1}{x+1}+\dfrac{2}{x}}{\dfrac{4}{x}-\dfrac{3}{x+1}}$

84. Simplify this complex fraction: $\dfrac{\dfrac{7}{x}-\dfrac{3}{y}}{\dfrac{1}{x}+\dfrac{2}{y}}$

Evaluate

Practice Test

Take this practice test to be sure that you are prepared for the final quiz in Evaluate.

1. Find: $\left(\dfrac{1}{2}\right)^{-3}$

2. Fill in the blanks below by writing the numbers in either scientific notation or expanded form.

$$73901 = \underline{\hspace{1.5cm}} \times 10^4$$

$$0.00004003 = 4.003 \times \underline{\hspace{1cm}}$$

$$2.081 \times 10^2 = \underline{\hspace{2cm}}$$

$$9.019 \times 10^{-5} = \underline{\hspace{2cm}}$$

3. Rewrite $\dfrac{a^{-8}b^{13}}{a^{-2}b^{-2}}$ using only positive exponents.

4. Rewrite $\dfrac{(2xy^5)(8x^2y)^{-3}}{(2x^4y^{-5})^{-2}}$ using only positive exponents.

5. Reduce to lowest terms: $\dfrac{2x^3 - 8x}{4x - 2x^2}$

6. Multiply and reduce to lowest terms:

   a. $\dfrac{x + 3}{x^2 - 4} \cdot \dfrac{x^2 - 10x + 16}{x - 8}$

   b. $\dfrac{x^2 + x - 2}{x^3 - 6x^2} \cdot \dfrac{2x^2 - 14x + 12}{x + 2}$

7. Divide and reduce your result to lowest terms:

   a. $\dfrac{3x^2 - 75}{x^2 - 10x + 25} \div \dfrac{-x - 5}{x - 5}$

   b. $\dfrac{y^2 + 5y + 4}{y^2 + y - 30} \div \dfrac{y^2 + 2y + 1}{y - 5}$

8. Simplify this complex fraction: $\dfrac{\dfrac{4x + 12}{5x - 5}}{\dfrac{2x^2 - 18}{x^2 - 2x + 1}}$

9. Find the LCM of x, $x^2 + 12x + 35$, and $x^2 - 25$.

10. Add and reduce your answer to lowest terms.

    $$\dfrac{4}{b^2 + 4b + 3} + \dfrac{3}{b^2 + 3b + 2}$$

11. Subtract and reduce your answer to lowest terms.

    $$\dfrac{3y}{y^2 + 7y + 10} - \dfrac{2y}{y^2 + 6y + 8}$$

12. Simplify this complex fraction: $\dfrac{\dfrac{3}{5}}{\dfrac{1}{x} + 3}$

LESSON 8.3
EQUATIONS WITH FRACTIONS

 Overview

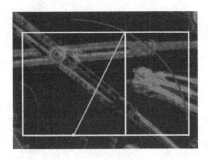

Suppose you want to estimate the population of fish in a lake or use a scale model to determine the height of a building. In each of these examples, you can find the answer by setting up and solving an equation that contains rational expressions.

In this lesson, you will learn how to solve equations that contain rational expressions. You will also learn how to identify extraneous, or false, solutions of such equations.

 Explain

Concept 1 has sections on

- **Solving Equations That Contain Rational Expressions**

- **Extraneous Solutions**

- **Ratios and Proportions**

- **Solving Proportions Using Cross Multiplication**

- **Formulas**

CONCEPT 1: SOLVING EQUATIONS

Solving Equations That Contain Rational Expressions

Solving an equation that contains rational expressions is like solving an equation that contains fractions. Let's begin by solving an equation that has only integers in the denominators of the rational expressions.

Example 8.3.1

Solve: $\dfrac{x}{3} - \dfrac{1}{4} = \dfrac{2x + 1}{12}$

Solution

To clear the fractions, multiply each side of the equation by the LCD of all the rational expressions.

$$\dfrac{x}{3} - \dfrac{1}{4} = \dfrac{2x + 1}{12}$$

In this example, the LCD is 12.

$$12 \cdot \left[\dfrac{x}{3} - \dfrac{1}{4}\right] = 12 \cdot \left[\dfrac{2x + 1}{12}\right]$$

Distribute 12 to each term on the left side.

$$12 \cdot \dfrac{x}{3} - 12 \cdot \dfrac{1}{4} = 12 \cdot \left[\dfrac{2x + 1}{12}\right]$$

If there are two or more terms on one side of an equation, be sure to use brackets when you multiply by the LCD. Then, distribute the LCD to the terms inside the brackets.

To reduce, cancel common factors.

$$\overset{4}{\cancel{12}} \cdot \dfrac{x}{\underset{1}{\cancel{3}}} - \overset{3}{\cancel{12}} \cdot \dfrac{1}{\underset{1}{\cancel{4}}} = \overset{1}{\cancel{12}} \cdot \left[\dfrac{2x + 1}{\underset{1}{\cancel{12}}}\right]$$

Simplify.

$$4x - 3 = 2x + 1$$

Subtract $2x$ from both sides and add 3 to both sides.

$$2x = 4$$

Divide both sides by 2.

$$x = 2$$

The result is $x = 2$.

To check the solution, substitute 2 for x in the original equation and simplify.

Check x = 2

$$\dfrac{x}{3} - \dfrac{1}{4} = \dfrac{2x + 1}{12}$$

Is $\quad \dfrac{\mathbf{2}}{3} - \dfrac{1}{4} = \dfrac{2(2) + 1}{12}$?

Is $\quad \dfrac{8}{12} - \dfrac{3}{12} = \dfrac{5}{12}$?

Is $\quad \dfrac{5}{12} = \dfrac{5}{12}$? **Yes**

Now, let's consider the case where some of the rational expressions have a variable in the denominator.

Example 8.3.2

Solve: $\dfrac{2}{x} + \dfrac{x-2}{4} = \dfrac{23}{4x}$

Solution

$$\frac{2}{x} + \frac{x-2}{4} = \frac{23}{4x}$$

Multiply each side of the equation by $4x$, the LCD of the rational expressions.

$$\mathbf{4x} \cdot \left[\frac{2}{x} + \frac{x-2}{4} \right] = \mathbf{4x} \cdot \left[\frac{23}{4x} \right]$$

Distribute $4x$ to each term on the left side.

$$4x \cdot \frac{2}{x} + 4x \cdot \frac{x-2}{4} = 4x \cdot \left[\frac{23}{4x} \right]$$

Reduce by canceling common factors.

$$4\overset{1}{\cancel{x}} \cdot \frac{2}{\underset{1}{\cancel{x}}} + \overset{1}{\cancel{4}}x \cdot \frac{x-2}{\underset{1}{\cancel{4}}} = \overset{1}{\cancel{4x}} \cdot \left[\frac{23}{\underset{1}{\cancel{4x}}} \right]$$

$$8 + x(x-2) = 23$$

Once you cancel common factors, you should no longer have any fractions.

Distribute x.

$$8 + x^2 - 2x = 23$$

The fractions have been eliminated and we are left with the quadratic equation $8 + x^2 - 2x = 23$.

To solve this equation, first write it in standard form, $ax^2 + bx + c = 0$.

$$x^2 - 2x - 15 = 0$$

To factor $x^2 - 2x - 15$, find two integers whose product is -15 and whose sum is -2. They are -5 and 3.

$$(x-5)(x+3) = 0$$

Use the Zero Product Property.

$$x - 5 = 0 \quad \text{or} \quad x + 3 = 0$$

Solve each equation.

$$x = 5 \quad \text{or} \quad x = -3$$

So, the equation has two solutions: 5 and -3.

To check the solutions, we substitute each value of x in the original equation and simplify.

Check $x = 5$	*Check $x = -3$*
$\dfrac{2}{x} + \dfrac{x-2}{4} = \dfrac{23}{4x}$	$\dfrac{2}{x} + \dfrac{x-2}{4} = \dfrac{23}{4x}$
Is $\dfrac{2}{\mathbf{5}} + \dfrac{\mathbf{5}-2}{4} = \dfrac{23}{4(\mathbf{5})}$?	Is $\dfrac{2}{\mathbf{-3}} + \dfrac{\mathbf{-3}-2}{4} = \dfrac{23}{4(\mathbf{-3})}$?
Is $\dfrac{2}{5} + \dfrac{3}{4} = \dfrac{23}{20}$?	Is $-\dfrac{2}{3} + \left(-\dfrac{5}{4}\right) = -\dfrac{23}{12}$?
Is $\dfrac{8}{20} + \dfrac{15}{20} = \dfrac{23}{20}$?	Is $-\dfrac{8}{12} + \left(-\dfrac{15}{12}\right) = -\dfrac{23}{12}$?
Is $\dfrac{23}{20} = \dfrac{23}{20}$? **Yes**	Is $-\dfrac{23}{12} = -\dfrac{23}{12}$? **Yes**

Extraneous Solutions

If an equation contains a variable in the denominator of a rational expression, then it is possible that the equation may not have a solution.

For example, let's try to solve this equation:

$$\frac{x - 12}{x - 4} = 2 - \frac{2x}{x - 4}$$

Multiply both sides by $(x - 4)$.

$$(x - 4) \cdot \left[\frac{x - 12}{x - 4}\right] = (x - 4) \cdot \left[2 - \frac{2x}{x - 4}\right]$$

$$(x - 4) \cdot \frac{x - 12}{x - 4} = (x - 4) \cdot 2 - (x - 4) \cdot \frac{2x}{x - 4}$$

Cancel.

$$\overset{1}{(\cancel{x - 4})} \cdot \frac{x - 12}{\underset{1}{(\cancel{x - 4})}} = (x - 4) \cdot 2 - \overset{1}{(\cancel{x - 4})} \cdot \frac{2x}{(x - 4)}$$

$$x - 12 = (x - 4) \cdot 2 - 2x$$

Distribute the 2.

$$x - 12 = 2x - 8 - 2x$$

Simplify the right side.

$$x - 12 = -8$$

Add 12 to both sides.

$$x = 4$$

The result is $x = 4$.

However, notice what happens when we check the solution.

Substitute 4 for x:

Is $\dfrac{4 - 12}{4 - 4} = 2 - \dfrac{2(4)}{4 - 4}$?

Simplify.

$$\frac{-8}{0} = 2 - \frac{8}{0}$$

The result is division by zero, which is undefined.

This means that $x = 4$ is not a solution.

Therefore, the equation has no solution.

We call 4 an **extraneous solution**. It is a number that results from solving an equation, but it is not a solution of the equation.

Since it does not satisfy the original equation, an extraneous solution is not really a solution. An extraneous solution is sometimes called a **false solution**.

Example 8.3.3

Solve: $\dfrac{4}{x+3} = \dfrac{1}{x} - \dfrac{12}{x(x+3)}$

Solution

Multiply each side by $x(x+3)$, the LCD of the rational expression.

$$x(x+3) \cdot \left[\dfrac{4}{x+3}\right] = x(x+3) \cdot \left[\dfrac{1}{x} - \dfrac{12}{x(x+3)}\right]$$

Distribute $x(x+3)$ to each term on the right side.

$$x(x+3) \cdot \left[\dfrac{4}{x+3}\right] = x(x+3) \cdot \left[\dfrac{1}{x}\right] - x(x+3) \cdot \left[\dfrac{12}{x(x+3)}\right]$$

Cancel common factors. $4x = x + 3 - 12$

Subtract x from both sides
and simplify the right side. $3x = -9$

Divide both sides by 3. $x = -3$

It appears that $x = -3$ is a solution.

However, if we substitute -3
for x in the original equation
the result is division by 0.

Is $\dfrac{4}{-3+3} = \dfrac{1}{-3} - \dfrac{12}{(-3)(-3+3)}$?

$$\dfrac{4}{0} = -\dfrac{1}{3} - \dfrac{12}{(-3)(0)}$$

Division by 0 is undefined, so $x = -3$ is not a solution.

Therefore, the equation has no solution.

Even before we solve $\dfrac{4}{x+3} = \dfrac{1}{x} - \dfrac{12}{x(x+3)}$, we can see that $x = 0$ and $x = -3$ cannot be solutions.
This is because replacing x with 0 or -3 would make a denominator zero.

Ratios and Proportions

A **ratio** is a way to compare two quantities using division.

Ratios are often written as fractions.

For example:

- If a class of 24 students contains 11 women and 13 men, then the ratio of women to men is 11 to 13, which we can write as $\dfrac{11}{13}$.

- If 10 pounds of watermelon costs \$3, then the ratio of cost to weight is $\dfrac{3}{10}$.

A **proportion** is an equation that sets one ratio equal to another ratio.

— Definition —
Proportion

A proportion is an equation that can be written in the form

$$\frac{a}{b} = \frac{c}{d}.$$

Here $b \neq 0$ and $d \neq 0$.

Here's a problem we can solve with a proportion.

If an 18-pound melon costs \$3.60, what is the cost of a 26-pound melon?

If we assume that the ratio of cost to weight is the same for all melons, then we can write this proportion.

$$\frac{\text{cost of small melon}}{\text{weight of small melon}} = \frac{\text{cost of big melon}}{\text{weight of big melon}}$$

We let x represent the cost (in dollars) of the big melon and we substitute the given values.

$$\frac{\$3.60}{18 \text{ pounds}} = \frac{x}{26 \text{ pounds}}$$

$$\frac{3.6}{18} = \frac{x}{26}$$

To solve this equation for x, we can multiply both sides by 26.

$$26\left[\frac{3.6}{18}\right] = 26\left[\frac{x}{26}\right]$$

We simplify.

$$5.2 = x$$

The cost of the big melon is \$5.20.

Solving Proportions Using Cross Multiplication

Let's consider this proportion:

$$\frac{a}{b} = \frac{c}{d}$$

To clear the fractions, we multiply both sides by bd, the LCD of the fractions.

$$bd \cdot \frac{a}{b} = bd \cdot \frac{c}{d}$$

To simplify each side, we cancel common factors.

$$\overset{1}{\cancel{b}}d \cdot \frac{a}{\cancel{b}} = b\overset{1}{\cancel{d}} \cdot \frac{c}{\cancel{d}}$$

The result is:

$$ad = bc$$

Now look again at the original proportion.

$$\frac{a}{b} = \frac{c}{d}$$

We draw a line from a to d, and draw a line from b to c.

$$\frac{a}{b} \diagdown \frac{c}{d}$$

The lines form a "cross" and we obtain the previous result:

$$ad = bc$$

This process is often called **cross multiplication**.

— Definition —
Cross Multiplication

To clear the fractions from a proportion, multiply the numerator of each fraction by the denominator of the other fraction.

That is,

 is equivalent to $ad = bc$.

Example 8.3.4

Solve the proportion for x: $\dfrac{26}{5} = \dfrac{182}{x}$

Solution

$$\frac{26}{5} = \frac{182}{x}$$

Cross multiply.

$$26x = 5 \cdot 182$$

Divide both sides by 26. Simplify.

$$x = 35$$

We leave the check to you.

Example 8.3.5

Solve the proportion for w: $\dfrac{10}{w + 4} = \dfrac{6}{w}$

Solution

$$\frac{10}{w + 4} = \frac{6}{w}$$

Cross multiply.

$$10w = (w + 4)6$$

Distribute the 6.

$$10w = 6w + 24$$

Subtract $6w$ from both sides.

$$4w = 24$$

Divide both sides by 4.

$$w = 6$$

We leave the check to you.

Example **8.3.6**

Solve the proportion for x: $\dfrac{-1}{x+3} = \dfrac{x-5}{12}$

Solution $\qquad\qquad\qquad\qquad\qquad\qquad\qquad \dfrac{-1}{x+3} = \dfrac{x-5}{12}$

Cross multiply. $\qquad\qquad\qquad\qquad\qquad\qquad -1 \cdot 12 = (x+3)(x-5)$

Simplify. $\qquad\qquad\qquad\qquad\qquad\qquad\qquad\quad -12 = x^2 - 2x - 15$

This is a quadratic equation.
We write it in standard form. $\qquad\qquad\qquad\qquad 0 = x^2 - 2x - 3$

Factor the right side. $\qquad\qquad\qquad\qquad\qquad\quad 0 = (x-3)(x+1)$

Use the Zero Product Property. $\qquad\quad x - 3 = 0 \quad \text{or} \quad x + 1 = 0$

Solve each equation. $\qquad\qquad\qquad\qquad\qquad x = 3 \quad \text{or} \quad x = -1$

We leave the check to you.

Formulas

A **formula** is an equation that contains at least two variables. Sometimes it is useful to solve a formula for one of the variables. That is, we write that variable in terms of the other variables.

Example **8.3.7**

The density, d, of an object can be found by dividing its mass, m, by its volume, v.

That is: $d = \dfrac{m}{v}$.

Solve this formula for v.

Solution $\qquad\qquad\qquad\qquad\qquad\qquad\qquad\qquad\qquad d = \dfrac{m}{v}$

Multiply both sides of the equation $\qquad\qquad\qquad v \cdot d = v \cdot \dfrac{m}{v}$
by v, the denominator of the fraction.

Simplify. $\qquad\qquad\qquad\qquad\qquad\qquad\qquad\qquad dv = m$

Divide both sides by d. $\qquad\qquad\qquad\qquad\qquad\qquad v = \dfrac{m}{d}$

Thus, $v = \dfrac{m}{d}$.

We could also solve for v by cross multiplying.

$$d = \frac{m}{v}$$

$$\frac{d}{1} = \frac{m}{v}$$

$$dv = 1m$$

$$dv = m$$

To check the solution, substitute $\frac{m}{d}$ for v in the original equation.

$$d = \frac{m}{v}$$

Is $\quad d = \dfrac{m}{\frac{m}{d}}$?

Is $\quad d = m \div \dfrac{m}{d}$?

Is $\quad d = m \cdot \dfrac{d}{m}$?

Is $\quad d = d$? **Yes**

Example **8.3.8**

The focal length, f, of a thin lens is related to p, the distance between the lens and the object, and q, the distance between the lens and the image, by the formula: $\dfrac{1}{f} = \dfrac{1}{p} + \dfrac{1}{q}$

p = object distance   q = image distance

image

f = focal length

Solve this formula for f.

Solution

Multiply each side by fpq, the LCD of the fractions.

$$fpq\left[\frac{1}{f}\right] = fpq\left[\frac{1}{p}\right] + fpq\left[\frac{1}{q}\right]$$

Cancel common factors.

$$pq = fq + fp$$

On the right side of the equation, factor out f.

$$pq = f(q + p)$$

Divide both sides by $(q + p)$, the coefficient of f.

$$\frac{pq}{q + p} = f$$

We leave the check to you.

Here is a summary of this concept from *Academic Systems Algebra*.

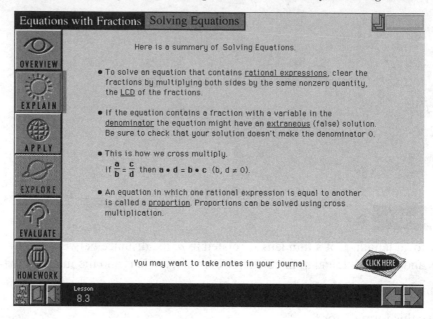

Equations with Fractions | Solving Equations

OVERVIEW
EXPLAIN
APPLY
EXPLORE
EVALUATE
HOMEWORK

Here is a summary of Solving Equations.

• To solve an equation that contains <u>rational expressions</u>, clear the fractions by multiplying both sides by the same nonzero quantity, the <u>LCD</u> of the fractions.

• If the equation contains a fraction with a variable in the <u>denominator</u> the equation might have an <u>extraneous</u> (false) solution. Be sure to check that your solution doesn't make the denominator 0.

• This is how we cross multiply.

If $\dfrac{a}{b} = \dfrac{c}{d}$ then $a \bullet d = b \bullet c$ $(b, d \neq 0)$.

• An equation in which one rational expression is equal to another is called a <u>proportion</u>. Proportions can be solved using cross multiplication.

You may want to take notes in your journal. CLICK HERE

Lesson 8.3

Checklist Lesson 8.3

Here is what you should know after completing this lesson.

Words and Phrases

extraneous solution
false solution
ratio

proportion
cross multiplication
formula

Ideas and Procedures

❶ Solve an Equation
Solve an equation that contains a rational
expression.

Example 8.3.2
  Solve: $\dfrac{2}{x} + \dfrac{x-2}{4} = \dfrac{23}{4x}$
See also: Example 8.3.1
              Apply 1-26

❷ Extraneous Solution
Determine if the result of solving an equation
is an extraneous solution.

Example 8.3.3
  Solve: $\dfrac{4}{x+3} = \dfrac{1}{x} - \dfrac{12}{x(x+3)}$
See also: Apply 27, 28

❸ Proportion
Solve a proportion.

Example 8.3.5
  Solve the proportion for w: $\dfrac{10}{w+4} = \dfrac{6}{w}$
See also: Example 8.3.4, 8.3.6

❹ Solve a Formula
Solve a formula for a specified variable.

Example 8.3.8
  Solve for f: $\dfrac{1}{f} = \dfrac{1}{p} + \dfrac{1}{q}$
See also: Example 8.3.7

Homework

Homework Problems

Circle the homework problems assigned to you by the computer, then complete them below.

 Explain

Solving Equations That Contain Rational Expressions

In problems 1 through 12 solve for the variable. Be sure to check whether your answer is an extraneous solution.

1. Solve for x: $\dfrac{5}{x} - \dfrac{2}{x} = 1$

2. Solve for y: $\dfrac{4}{7}y = -\dfrac{2}{7}$

3. Solve for x: $\dfrac{3}{x} + \dfrac{2}{x-2} = 1$

4. Solve for y: $\dfrac{y}{y-5} - \dfrac{2}{5} = \dfrac{5}{y-5}$

5. Solve for x: $\dfrac{3x+1}{11x-9} = \dfrac{1}{3}$

6. Solve for x: $\dfrac{2}{1-x} - \dfrac{1}{x} = \dfrac{7}{6}$

7. Solve for y: $\dfrac{4y-9}{8} = \dfrac{6-8y}{16}$

8. Solve for x: $\dfrac{3}{2x-3} - x = \dfrac{2}{4x-6}$

9. A person who weighs 100 pounds on Earth would weigh 38 pounds on Mars. Use the proportion below to figure out how much someone who weighs 160 pounds on Earth would weigh on Mars.

$$\dfrac{\text{weight on Mars}}{\text{weight on Earth}} = \dfrac{38}{100} = \dfrac{x}{160}$$

10. A person who weighs 100 pounds on Earth would weigh 234 pounds on Jupiter. Use the proportion below to figure out how much someone who weighs 160 pounds on Earth would weigh on Jupiter.

$$\dfrac{\text{weight on Jupiter}}{\text{weight on Earth}} = \dfrac{234}{100} = \dfrac{x}{160}$$

11. Solve for x: $\dfrac{6}{x-2} - \dfrac{3}{x} = \dfrac{-5}{x-4}$

12. Solve for x: $\dfrac{6}{x-2} - \dfrac{1}{3} = \dfrac{3x}{x-2}$

 **Apply**

Practice Problems

Here are some additional practice problems for you to try.

Solving Equations That Contain Rational Expressions

1. Solve for x: $\dfrac{4}{x} + \dfrac{3}{x} = 1$

2. Solve for x: $\dfrac{8}{x} - \dfrac{4}{x} = 1$

3. Solve for x: $\dfrac{1}{x+1} + \dfrac{5}{x+1} = 2$

4. Solve for x: $\dfrac{10}{x-3} - \dfrac{4}{x-3} = -3$

5. Solve for x: $\dfrac{3}{x+2} + \dfrac{4}{x+2} = -1$

6. Solve for x: $\dfrac{x}{1-x} + \dfrac{3}{1-x} = -5$

7. Solve for x: $\dfrac{7}{x+3} - \dfrac{x}{x+3} = -3$

8. Solve for x: $\dfrac{4}{x-2} - \dfrac{x}{x-2} = -3$

9. Solve for x: $\dfrac{x-1}{4} + \dfrac{x}{3} = -2$

10. Solve for x: $\dfrac{x+2}{6} - \dfrac{x}{2} = 5$

11. Solve for x: $\dfrac{x+2}{3} + \dfrac{3x}{4} = 5$

12. Solve for x: $\dfrac{x-1}{5} + \dfrac{x}{3} = \dfrac{3x+2}{15}$

13. Solve for x: $\dfrac{x+3}{6} - \dfrac{x}{5} = \dfrac{9x-5}{30}$

14. Solve for x: $\dfrac{x+3}{5} + \dfrac{x}{4} = \dfrac{8x+4}{20}$

15. Solve for x: $\dfrac{4}{x} + \dfrac{2}{x+1} = 5$

16. Solve for x: $\dfrac{3}{x-2} - \dfrac{1}{x} = -4$

17. Solve for x: $\dfrac{2}{x} - \dfrac{1}{x-3} = 2$

18. Solve for x: $\dfrac{x}{5} + \dfrac{15}{3x} = \dfrac{x+3}{4}$

19. Solve for x: $\dfrac{24}{8x} - \dfrac{x}{3} = \dfrac{3-x}{6}$

20. Solve for x: $\dfrac{x}{6} + \dfrac{12}{2x} = \dfrac{x-2}{4}$

21. Solve for x: $\dfrac{x+1}{5} - \dfrac{3}{x} = \dfrac{x-2}{x}$

22. Solve for x: $\dfrac{3}{x} - \dfrac{x-2}{3} = \dfrac{x+1}{2x}$

23. Solve for x: $\dfrac{x-2}{7} - \dfrac{5}{x} = \dfrac{x+5}{x}$

24. Solve for x: $\dfrac{2}{3(x+4)} - \dfrac{4}{3} = \dfrac{2}{x}$

25. Solve for x: $\dfrac{6}{4(x-2)} + \dfrac{1}{4} = \dfrac{4}{x}$

26. Solve for x: $\dfrac{8}{5(x-3)} + \dfrac{1}{5} = \dfrac{5}{x}$

27. Solve for x: $2 - \dfrac{2x}{x-4} = \dfrac{x-12}{x-4}$

28. Solve for x: $\dfrac{1}{x-2} + 3 = \dfrac{x-1}{x-2}$

Practice Test

Take this practice test to be sure that you are prepared for the final quiz in Evaluate.

1. Solve $\dfrac{2}{3x} - \dfrac{1}{x} = \dfrac{1}{15}$ for x. Is the solution extraneous?

2. Solve $\dfrac{4y}{y+3} - \dfrac{1}{2} = \dfrac{9}{y+3}$ for y. Is the solution extraneous?

3. The volume V of a right circular cone is $V = \dfrac{1}{3}\pi r^2 h$, where r is the radius, and h is the height. Solve this formula for h.

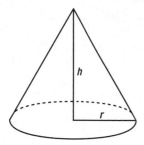

4. Solve this proportion for x: $\dfrac{5x-8}{2x+1} = \dfrac{4}{3}$

5. Solve $\dfrac{5}{4y} - \dfrac{2}{2y} = \dfrac{1}{16}$ for y. Is the solution extraneous?

6. Solve $\dfrac{x}{x+5} - \dfrac{1}{5} = \dfrac{3}{x+5}$ for x. Is the solution extraneous?

7. The surface area, S, of a right circular cylinder is $S = 2\pi rh + 2\pi r^2$, where r is the radius, and h is the height. Solve this formula for h.

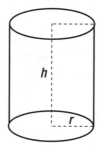

8. Solve this proportion for y: $\dfrac{6y-4}{6y+6} = \dfrac{4}{9}$

LESSON 8.4
PROBLEM SOLVING

 Overview

Have you ever wondered how fast you could complete a job if someone else helped you, or what speed you should drive to complete a trip in a certain amount of time?

In this lesson, you will apply what you have learned about rational equations to solve a variety of problems like these.

 Explain

Concept 1 has sections on

- **Work Problems**
- **Distance Problems**
- **Ratio and Proportion Problems**
- **Direct Variation**
- **Inverse Variation**
- **Joint and Combined Variation**

CONCEPT 1: RATIONAL EXPRESSIONS

Work Problems

If two people work on the same job, then the work needed to complete the job is the sum of the work done by each person. That is,

$$\begin{bmatrix} \text{Fraction of job} \\ \text{done by first person} \end{bmatrix} + \begin{bmatrix} \text{Fraction of job done} \\ \text{by second person} \end{bmatrix} = \begin{bmatrix} \text{1 whole job} \\ \text{completed} \end{bmatrix}$$

Example 8.4.1

Simone and Pierre want to paint their living room. If Pierre worked alone, it would take him 6 hours. If Simone worked alone, it would take her 5 hours. How long will it take them to paint the room if they work together?

Solution

Step 1 List the quantities to be found. Use English phrases.

The time it will take to paint the room if they work together.

Step 2 Represent these quantities algebraically.

Let t represent the time it takes them working together.

t = time working together (hours)

They work until the job is done; that is, they each work for t hours. therefore:

$$\begin{bmatrix} \text{Fraction of job} \\ \text{done by Simone} \\ \text{in } t \text{ hours} \end{bmatrix} + \begin{bmatrix} \text{Fraction of job} \\ \text{done by Pierre} \\ \text{in } t \text{ hours.} \end{bmatrix} = \begin{bmatrix} \text{1 whole job} \\ \text{completed} \\ \text{in } t \text{ hours} \end{bmatrix}$$

We can also find the fraction of the job done by each person by multiplying their rate by the time they work. For example, Simone can paint 1 room in 5 hours so her rate can be written in either of following ways:

$$rate = \frac{1 \; room}{5 \; hours} \; or \; \frac{\frac{1}{5} room}{1 \; hour}$$

Multiplying one of these rates by the t hours she works results in the fraction of the room she paints in t hours:

$$\left(\frac{\frac{1}{5} room}{1 \; hour} \right) \cdot (t \; hours) = \frac{1}{5} \cdot t \; room$$

$$= \frac{t}{5} room$$

To find the fraction of the job done by each person in t hours, we can think about what happens after each hour they work:

Simone can paint the whole room alone in 5 hours. So,

- in 1 hour she can paint $\frac{1}{5}$ of the room;

- in 2 hours she can paint $\frac{1}{5} \cdot 2 = \frac{2}{5}$ of the room;

- in t hours she can paint $\frac{1}{5} \cdot t = \frac{t}{5}$ of the room.

Likewise Pierre can paint the whole room alone in 6 hours. So,

- in 1 hour he can paint $\frac{1}{6}$ of the room;

- in 2 hours he can paint $\frac{1}{6} \cdot 2 = \frac{2}{6}$ of the room;

- in t hours he can paint $\frac{1}{6} \cdot t = \frac{t}{6}$ of the room.

Thus, in t hours, the fraction of the room painted by Simone is $\frac{t}{5}$ and the fraction of the room painted by Pierre is $\frac{t}{6}$.

In the t hours they work, Simone and Pierre together will paint 1 whole room.

$$\begin{bmatrix} \text{Fraction of job} \\ \text{done by Simone} \end{bmatrix} + \begin{bmatrix} \text{Fraction of job} \\ \text{done by Pierre} \end{bmatrix} = \begin{bmatrix} \text{1 whole job} \\ \text{completed} \end{bmatrix}$$

We write this equation: $\quad \frac{t}{5} \quad + \quad \frac{t}{6} \quad = 1$

Step 4 Solve the equation.

Multiply both sides by 30, the LCD of the fractions. $\qquad 30 \cdot \left[\frac{t}{5} + \frac{t}{6} \right] = 30 \cdot 1$

Distribute 30 and simplify. $\qquad 6t + 5t = 30$

Combine like terms. $\qquad 11t = 30$

Divide both sides by 11. $\qquad t = \frac{30}{11}$

To convert $\frac{8}{11}$ hours to minutes, set up and solve this proportion:

$$\frac{8}{11} = \frac{x}{60}.$$

Thus, working together, it takes them $\frac{30}{11}$ hours, or $2\frac{8}{11}$ hours.

This corresponds to about 2 hours and 44 minutes.

Step 5 Check that the numbers work in the original problem.

Condition	Check

- Simone can paint the room by herself in 5 hours.

- Simone can paint $\frac{1}{5}$ of the room in 1 hour.

  In $\frac{30}{11}$ hours she can paint

  $\frac{1}{5} \cdot \frac{30}{11} = \frac{6}{11}$ of the room.

- Pierre can paint the room by himself in 6 hours.

- Pierre can paint $\frac{1}{6}$ of the room in 1 hour

  In $\frac{30}{11}$ hours he can paint

  $\frac{1}{6} \cdot \frac{30}{11} = \frac{5}{11}$ of the room.

- Together they paint 1 room.

- $\frac{6}{11}$ room $+ \frac{5}{11}$ room $= \frac{11}{11}$ room

  $= 1$ room. ✓

Even though they work the same amount of time, 2 hours and 44 minutes, Simone paints $\frac{6}{11}$ of the room while Pierre only paints $\frac{5}{11}$ of the room. Simone does more work because she works faster.

Distance Problems

To find the distance traveled by a car moving at a constant speed, we multiply the speed (rate) by the time of travel.

$$\text{distance traveled} = (\text{rate of travel}) \cdot (\text{time of travel})$$

We can write this as a formula, $d = rt$.

Two other forms of this formula are sometimes useful.

- If we divide both sides by r, we get $t = \dfrac{d}{r}$.

- If we divide both sides by t, we get $r = \dfrac{d}{t}$.

Example 8.4.2

Gretchen runs as fast as Petra. Last Saturday, Gretchen ran 4 miles farther than Petra. If Gretchen ran for 3 hours and Petra ran for 2 hours, how far did Gretchen run?

Solution

Step 1 List the quantities to be found. Use English phrases.

The distance Gretchen ran.

Step 2 Represent these quantities algebraically.

Since Gretchen's distance is given in terms of Petra's, let d represent the distance Petra ran.

$d = $ Petra's distance

Gretchen ran 4 miles farther than Petra.

$d + 4 = $ Gretchen's distance

Step 3 Write an equation that describes the problem.

Gretchen and Petra run at the same speed.

Gretchen's **rate** = Petra's **rate**

To calculate their rates, use $r = \dfrac{d}{t}$.

$$\frac{\text{Gretchen's distance}}{\text{Gretchen's time}} = \frac{\text{Petra's distance}}{\text{Petra's time}}$$

$$\frac{d + 4}{3} = \frac{d}{2}$$

Step 4 Solve the equation.

This is a proportion, so we cross multiply.

$(d + 4)2 = 3d$

Distribute the 2.

$2d + 8 = 3d$

Subtract $2d$ from both sides.

$8 = d$

Thus, Petra ran 8 miles.

Gretchen's distance is $d + 4$, which is $8 + 4$ or 12 miles.

Step 5 Check that the numbers satisfy the original problem.

Condition	Check
• Petra ran for 2 hours.	• Since Petra ran 8 miles in 2 hours, her rate was $\dfrac{8 \text{ miles}}{2 \text{ hours}} = 4$ miles per hour.
• Gretchen ran for 3 hours.	• Since Gretchen ran 12 miles in 3 hours, her rate was $\dfrac{12 \text{ miles}}{3 \text{ hours}} = 4$ miles per hour.
• Gretchen can run as fast as Petra.	• Gretchen and Petra each ran at a rate of 4 miles per hour. ✓

Ratio and Proportion Problems

Recall that a proportion is an equation that sets one **ratio** equal to another ratio. A **proportion** has the form $\dfrac{a}{b} = \dfrac{c}{d}$.

Example 8.4.3

To estimate the number of fish in a lake, a biologist catches, tags, and releases 54 fish. A week later, the biologist catches 85 fish at random, 6 of which have tags. Estimate the total number of fish in the lake.

Solution

Step 1 List the quantities to be found. Use English phrases.

The total number of fish in the lake.

Step 2 Represent these quantities algebraically.

Let n represent the total number of fish in the lake.

n = total number of fish

Step 3 Write an equation that describes the problem.

We assume that the ratio of tagged fish to all fish in the entire lake is the same as the ratio for the sample.

$$\frac{\text{tagged fish in sample}}{\text{all fish in sample}} = \frac{\text{tagged fish in lake}}{\text{all fish in lake}}$$

Substitute the values.

$$\frac{6 \text{ tagged fish in sample}}{85 \text{ fish in sample}} = \frac{54 \text{ tagged fish in lake}}{n \text{ fish in lake}}$$

To make it easier to solve the equation, we remove the units.

$$\frac{6}{85} = \frac{54}{n}$$

Step 4 Solve the equation.

Cross multiply. $6n = 85 \cdot 54$

Divide both sides by 6 and simplify. $n = 765$

Therefore, the estimated number of fish in the lake is 765.

Step 5 Check that the numbers work in the original problem.

Condition

The ratio of tagged fish to all fish, both in the sample and in the entire lake, is expected to be the same.

Check

Is $\dfrac{\text{tagged fish in sample}}{\text{all fish in sample}} = \dfrac{\text{tagged fish in lake}}{\text{all fish in lake}}$?

Is $\qquad\qquad \dfrac{6}{85} = \dfrac{54}{765}$?

Cross multiply. $4590 = 4590$ ✓

Another way to show that $\frac{6}{85} = \frac{54}{765}$ is to change each fraction to a decimal.

Example 8.4.4

Kim's Catering is hired to cater a dinner party where she will need to provide 21 cups of cooked rice. The Basmati rice she will use requires a ratio of 3 parts dry rice to 5 parts water. Using this ratio, 1 cup of dry rice will produce 3 cups of cooked rice.

- How much rice should she use?

- How much water should she use?

Solution

Step 1 List the quantities to be found. Use English phrases.

The amount of rice needed.

The amount of water needed.

Step 2 Represent these quantities algebraically.

Let r represent the amount of rice needed. r = rice needed (cups)

Let w represent the amount of water needed. w = water needed (cups)

Step 3 *Write an equation that describes the problem.*

First, let's find the amount of rice she should use.

Since 1 cup of dry rice is needed for every 3 cups of cooked rice we can set up a proportion.

$$\frac{1 \text{ cup dry rice}}{3 \text{ cups cooked rice}} = \frac{r \text{ cups dry rice}}{21 \text{ cups cooked rice}}$$

$$\frac{1}{3} = \frac{r}{21}$$

Step 4 *Solve the equation.*

Cross multiply. $1 \cdot 21 = 3r$

Divide both sides by 3 and simplify. $7 = r$

So, 7 cups of dry rice are needed.

Now, let's find the amount of water, w, needed to cook this rice.

Since 3 cups of dry rice require 5 cups of water, we can set up another proportion.

$$\frac{3 \text{ cups dry rice}}{5 \text{ cups water}} = \frac{7 \text{ cups dry rice}}{w \text{ cups water}}$$

$$\frac{3}{5} = \frac{7}{w}$$

This is a proportion so we may cross multiply. $3w = 5 \cdot 7$

Divide both sides by 3 and simplify. $w = \frac{35}{3}$

Thus, she needs $\frac{35}{3}$ or $11\frac{2}{3}$ of cups of water.

Step 5 *Check that the numbers work in the original problem.*

Condition	Check
• The ratio of dry rice to water should be 3 to 5.	• She needs 7 cups of rice and $\frac{35}{3}$ cups of water. Write this as a ratio: $\frac{7}{\frac{35}{3}} = 7 \div \frac{35}{3} = \frac{7}{1} \cdot \frac{3}{35} = \frac{3}{5}$ ✓
• Kim needs to provide 21 cups of cooked rice.	• One cup of dry rice produces 3 cups of cooked rice. Therefore, 7 cups of dry rice produce $7 \cdot 3 = 21$ cups of cooked rice. ✓

Direct Variation

Suppose you travel at a constant rate of 50 miles per hour for t hours. The distance you travel, d, may be calculated using $d = 50t$.

As you can see from the data table and graph, as the value of t **increases**, the value of d also **increases** proportionately.

time (hours)	distance (miles)
0.0	0
0.2	10
0.4	20
1.0	50
2.0	100
5.0	250

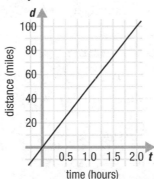

This is an example of **direct variation**. We say that the distance varies directly with time.

— Definition —
Direct Variation

Two quantities, represented by x and y, vary directly when the relation between them can be written in the form $y = kx$, where k is a nonzero constant.

Example 8.4.5

Sally plans to buy a car that costs $15,400. She knows that the amount of sales tax varies directly with the price of the car. She's not sure of the sales tax rate, but she has a receipt that shows she paid $1.47 in sales tax on an item that cost $24.50.

a. Find the direct variation equation for this situation.

b. Use the equation from part (a) to calculate the sales tax on the car.

Solution

a. Let y represent the sales tax on the car. y = sales tax (dollars)

Let x represent the price of the car. x = cost (dollars)

The sales tax varies directly with the price of the car.

Therefore, the relation between tax
and price has the form $y = kx$. $y = kx$

To find the value of k, use the fact that Sally
paid $1.47 in sales tax on a $24.50 purchase.

In the formula, substitute 1.47 for y
and 24.50 for x. $1.47 = k(24.50)$

Divide both sides by 24.50. $0.06 = k$

Now, we can write the direct variation equation, $y = 0.06x$.

The formula for direct variation, $y = kx$, is a linear equation, in slope-intercept form, $y = mx + b$.

Here the y-intercept, b, is 0, and the slope, m, is the constant k.

$$y = mx + b$$
$$y = kx + 0$$
$$y = kx$$

So the graph of $y = kx$ is a straight line that passes through the origin.

For this problem, the constant k is the sales tax rate, $0.06 = 6\%$.

b. To find the tax on a car that costs
    $15,400, substitute 15,400 for x
    and then solve for y.

$$y = 0.06x$$
$$y = 0.06 \cdot 15,400$$

Multiply.

$$y = 924$$

So, Sally can expect to pay $924 in sales tax.

Inverse Variation

The frequency of pitch, f, of a guitar string is related to the length of the string, L, by the formula $f = \dfrac{k}{L}$.

length (cm)	frequency (Hz)
32	880
40	704
44	640
55	512
64	440

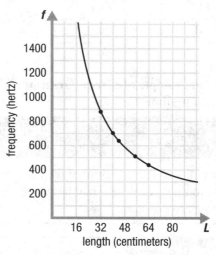

The formula shows that as the length of the string **increases**, the string frequency **decreases** proportionally. (The sound gets lower in pitch.)

This is an example of **inverse variation**.

We say that the frequency, f, varies inversely with the length, L.

— Definition —
Inverse Variation

Two quantities, represented by x and y, vary inversely when the relation between them can be written in the form $y = \dfrac{k}{x}$, where k is a nonzero constant.

Example 8.4.6

Gage often drives between his house and a friend's house in another state. When he drives 50 miles per hour the trip takes him 6 hours.

a. Assuming that his travel time varies inversely with his rate, find the inverse variation equation for this situation.

b. Use the equation from part (a) to calculate the speed he must drive to make the trip in 4 hours.

Solution

a. Let r represent his rate r = rate (mph)

    Let t represent his time. t = time (hours)

    His time varies inversely with his rate.

    So, use the inverse variation formula,
$y = \dfrac{k}{x}$, with t in place of y and r in
place of x. $t = \dfrac{k}{r}$

    To find the value of k, use the fact that it
takes Gage 6 hours when he travels at
50 mph. In the formula, substitute 6 for
t and 50 for r. $\mathbf{6} = \dfrac{k}{\mathbf{50}}$

    Multiply both sides by 50. $300 = k$

    Now, we can write the indirect variation equation, $t = \dfrac{300}{r}$.

Here, the constant k represents the number of miles driven.

b. To find the rate when the time is 4 hours, $\mathbf{4} = \dfrac{300}{r}$
substitute 4 for t.

    To solve for r, multiply both sides by r. $4r = 300$

    Divide both sides by 4. $r = 75$

    So, Gage must drive 75 mph to make the trip in 4 hours.

Joint and Combined Variation

In some situations, one quantity may vary with several quantities, directly
or inversely.

For example, the pressure, P, of an enclosed gas varies directly as its
absolute temperature, T, and inversely as its volume, V.

We can write this relation as follows: $P = \dfrac{kT}{V}$.

> **— Definition —**
> **Joint Variation**
> **Combined Variation**
>
> *Joint variation* can be expressed in the form $y = kxz$, where k is a
> nonzero constant.
>
> In joint variation, one quantity varies directly with two or more
> quantities.
>
> *Combined variation* can be expressed the form $y = \dfrac{kx}{z}$, where k is a
> nonzero constant.
>
> In combined variation, one quantity varies directly with one or more
> quantities and inversely with one or more quantities.

Example 8.4.7

The pressure of an enclosed gas varies directly as the absolute temperature and inversely as the volume. At a temperature of 200° K, 300 cubic inches of a particular gas results in a pressure of 20 pounds per square inch.

a. Write a combined variation equation for this situation.

b. Use the equation from part (a) to calculate the pressure of the same gas if the volume is decreased to 100 cubic inches while the temperature is increased to 250° K.

Solution

a. Let P represent the gas pressure. P = pressure (pounds per sq in)

Let T represent the gas temperature. T = temperature (° K)

Let V represent the gas volume. V = volume (cubic inch)

The relation involves both direct and inverse variation. Therefore, we may use the combined variation formula.

$$y = \frac{kx}{z}$$

Since pressure varies directly with temperature, write T in the numerator. Since pressure varies inversely with volume, write V in the denominator.

$$P = \frac{kT}{V}$$

To find the value of k, substitute the given values for P, T, and V.

$$20 = \frac{k \cdot 200}{300}$$

Multiply both sides by 300.
Divide both sides by 200.

$$30 = k$$

Now, we can write the combined variation equation.

$$P = \frac{30T}{V}$$

b. To find the pressure when the volume is decreased to 100 cubic inches and the temperature is increased to 250° K, substitute 100 for V and 250 for T.

$$P = \frac{30 \cdot 250}{100}$$

Simplify. $P = 75$

Thus, the new pressure is 75 pounds per square inch.

Here is a summary of this concept from *Academic Systems Algebra*.

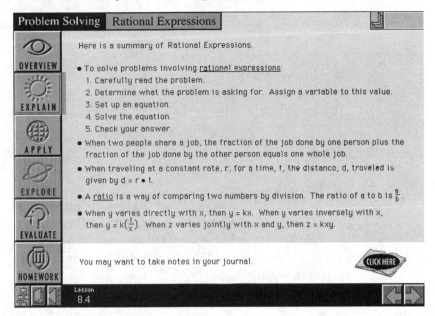

Problem Solving | Rational Expressions

OVERVIEW

EXPLAIN

APPLY

EXPLORE

EVALUATE

HOMEWORK

Here is a summary of Rational Expressions.

- To solve problems involving <u>rational expressions</u>:
  1. Carefully read the problem.
  2. Determine what the problem is asking for. Assign a variable to this value.
  3. Set up an equation.
  4. Solve the equation.
  5. Check your answer.
- When two people share a job, the fraction of the job done by one person plus the fraction of the job done by the other person equals one whole job.
- When traveling at a constant rate, r, for a time, t, the distance, d, traveled is given by $d = r \bullet t$.
- A <u>ratio</u> is a way of comparing two numbers by division. The ratio of a to b is $\frac{a}{b}$.
- When y varies directly with x, then $y = kx$. When y varies inversely with x, then $y = k\left(\frac{1}{x}\right)$. When z varies jointly with x and y, then $z = kxy$.

You may want to take notes in your journal.

CLICK HERE

Lesson
8.4

Checklist Lesson 8.4

Here is what you should know after completing this lesson.

Words and Phrases

ratio
proportion
direct variation

inverse variation
joint variation
combined variation

Ideas and Procedures

❶ **Work Problem**
Solve word problems that involve shared work.

Example 8.4.1
Simone and Pierre want to paint their living room. If Pierre worked alone, it would take him 6 hours. If Simone worked alone, it would take her 5 hours. How long will it take them to paint the room if they work together?

See also: Apply 1-8

❷ **Distance Word Problem**
Solve word problems that involve distances, rates, and times.

Example 8.4.2
Gretchen runs as fast as Petra. Last Saturday, Gretchen ran 4 miles farther than Petra. If Gretchen ran for 3 hours and Petra ran for 2 hours, how far did Gretchen run?

See also: Apply 15-20

❸ **Ratio and Proportion Word Problem**
Solve word problems that involve ratio and proportion.

Example 8.4.3
To estimate the number of fish in a lake, a biologist catches, tags, and releases 54 fish. A week later, the biologist catches 85 fish at random, 6 of which have tags. Estimate the total number of fish in the lake.

See also: Example 8.4.4
Apply 9-14

❹ **Direct Variation**
Define direct variation.

Write an equation that states:
    y varies directly with x.
    Answer: $y = kx$, where k is a nonzero constant.

Solve word problems that involve direct variation.

Example 8.4.5
Sally plans to buy a car that costs $15,400. She knows that the amount of sales tax varies directly with the price of the car. She's not sure of the sales tax rate, but she has a receipt that shows she paid $1.47 in sales tax on an item that cost $24.50.

See also: Apply 21-23

⑤ Inverse Variation

Define inverse variation.

Write an equation that states:

    y varies inversely with x.

    Answer: $y = \dfrac{k}{x}$, where k is a nonzero constant.

Solve word problems that involve direct variation.

Example 8.4.6

Gage often drives between his house and a friend's house in another state. When he drives 50 miles per hour the trip takes him 6 hours. Assuming that his travel time varies inversely with his rate, find the inverse variation equation for this situation.

See also: Apply 24-26

---

⑥ Joint or Combined Variation

Define joint variation.

Write an equation that states:

    y varies jointly with both x and z.

    Answer: $y = kxz$, where k is a nonzero constant.

Define combined variation.

Write an equation that states:

    y varies directly with x and inversely with z.

    Answer: $y = \dfrac{kx}{z}$, where k is a nonzero constant.

Solve word problems that involve joint or combined variation.

Example 8.4.7

The pressure of an enclosed gas varies directly as the absolute temperature and inversely as the volume. At a temperature of 200° K, 300 cubic feet of a particular gas results in a pressure of 20 pounds per square foot.

See also: Apply 27, 28

Homework

Homework Problems

Circle the homework problems assigned to you by the computer, then complete them below.

 Explain

Rational Expressions

1. To fill up their swimming pool, the Johnsons decided to use both their high volume hose and their neighbor's regular garden hose. If they had used only their hose, it would have taken them 12 hours to fill the pool, but using both hoses it took them only 7 hours. How long would it have taken them to fill the pool using only their neighbor's hose?

2. On her camping trip, Li spent as much time hiking as she did rafting. She traveled 2.5 miles per hour when she was rafting and 3 miles per hour when she was hiking. If she went 3 miles more hiking than she did rafting, how far did she hike?

3. The ratio of jellybeans to gummy bears in a bag of candy is 7 to 2. If there are 459 pieces of candy in the bag, how many jellybeans are there?

4. The mass of an object varies jointly with its density and its volume. If 156 grams of iron has a volume of 20 cm^3 and a density of $7.8\frac{grams}{cm^3}$, what is the volume of 312 grams of iron with the same density?

5. To empty their swimming pool, the Johnsons decided to use both the regular drain and a pump. If it takes 15 hours for the pool to empty using the drain alone and 7 hours for the pool to empty using the pump alone, how long will it take for the pool to empty using both the drain and the pump?

6. One cyclist can ride 2 miles per hour faster than another cyclist. If it takes the first cyclist 2 hours and 20 minutes to ride as far as the second cyclist rides in 2 hours, how fast can each go?

7. The ratio of the length of a rectangle to its width is 3 to 1. If the perimeter of the rectangle is 32 inches, what are its dimensions?

8. The amount of energy that can be derived from particles varies directly with their mass. If $8.184 \cdot 10^{-14}$ Nm of energy is obtained from a particle whose mass is $9.1066 \cdot 10^{-31}$ kg, how much energy can be derived from particles whose mass is 0.001 kg?

9. Melanie and Alex have to prune all of the trees in their yard. Working alone, it would take Melanie 7 hours to do all of the pruning. It would take Alex 11 hours to do all of the pruning by himself. How long will it take them working together?

10. A bicyclist and a horseback rider are going the same speed. The rider stops after 11.1 miles. The bicyclist goes for another hour and travels a total of 18.5 miles. How fast is each one going?

11. Fish and game wardens can estimate the population of fish in a lake if they take a sample of fish, tag them, return them to the lake, take another sample of fish, and look at the ratio of tagged fish to untagged fish. If a warden tags 117 fish in the first sample, and then finds 13 out of 642 fish have tags in the second sample, how many fish were in the lake?

12. The height of a pyramid of constant volume is inversely proportional to the area of its base. If a pyramid of volume 300 $meters^3$ has a base area of 90 $meters^2$ and a height of 10 meters, what is the height of a pyramid whose base area is 100 $meters^2$?

 **Apply**

Practice Problems

Here are some additional practice problems for you to try.

Rational Expressions

1. Working alone it would take Josie 4 hours to paint a room. It would take Curtis 5 hours to paint the same room by himself. How long would it take them to paint the room if they work together?

2. Before the library is remodeled, all of the books must be packed in boxes. Working alone, it would take Gail 15 workdays to do the packing. It would take Rob 18 workdays. How long will it take them working together?

3. Two computers are available to process a batch of data. The faster computer can process the batch in 36 minutes. If both computers run at the same time, they can process the batch in 20 minutes. How long would it take the slower computer to process the batch alone?

4. Two copy machines are available to print final exams. The faster copy machine can do the whole job in 75 minutes. If both machines print at the same time, they can do the whole job in 50 minutes. How long would it take the slower machine to do the whole job alone?

5. Two tomato harvesters are available to harvest a field of tomatoes. The slower harvester can harvest the whole field in 7 hours. If both machines harvest at the same time, they can harvest the whole field in 3 hours. How long would it take the faster machine to harvest the whole field by itself?

6. There are two overflow pipes at a dam. The larger overflow pipe can lower the level of the water in the reservoir by 1 foot in 45 minutes. The smaller one lowers the level of water by 1 foot in 2 hours 15 minutes. If both overflow pipes are open at the same time, how long will it take them to lower the level of water by 1 foot?

7. Two fire hoses are being used to flood the skating rink at the park. The larger hose alone can flood the park in 50 minutes. The smaller hose alone can flood the park in 1 hour and 15 minutes. If both hoses run at the same time, how long will it take them to flood the park?

8. Used by itself, the cold water faucet can fill a bathtub in 12 minutes. It takes 15 minutes for the hot water faucet to fill the bathtub. If both faucets are on, how long will it take to fill the bathtub?

9. A box of chocolates contains caramel chocolates and nougat chocolates. The ratio of the number of caramels in the box to the number of nougats in the box is 4 to 3. There are a total of 42 chocolates in the box. How many caramel chocolates are in the box? How many nougat chocolates are in the box?

10. A fast food stand sells muffins and cookies. Last Monday, the ratio of the number of muffins sold to the number of cookies sold was 16 to 13. A total of 145 muffins and cookies were sold. How many muffins were sold? How many cookies were sold?

11. At a certain animal shelter, the ratio of puppies to adult dogs is 7 to 4. This week, there are a total of 55 dogs in the shelter. How many puppies are in the shelter this week? How many adult dogs are in the shelter this week?

12. In a certain cookie recipe, the ratio of cups of flour to cups of sugar is 3 to 1. If the recipe uses $2\frac{1}{4}$ cups of flour, how much sugar does it use?

13. In one multivitamin pill, the ratio of the number of units of Vitamin C to the number of units of Vitamin E is 40 to 13. If the pill contains 200 units of Vitamin C, how many units of Vitamin E does it contain?

14. The ratio of the amount of caffeine, in milligrams, in a 12-ounce serving of coffee to the amount of caffeine, in milligrams, in a 12-ounce serving of cola is 25 to 9. If a 12-ounce serving of cola contains 72 milligrams of caffeine, how much caffeine does a 12-ounce serving of coffee contain?

15. Jayme can ride his bike as fast as Terry. Each day, Jayme rides his bike for one hour and 20 minutes. Each day, Terry rides his bike for two hours and rides 15 miles further than Jayme. How far does each ride?

16. Saskia runs as fast as Tanya. Each day, Tanya runs for 40 minutes. Each day, Saskia runs for one hour and runs 2 miles farther than Tanya. How far does each run?

17. Leroy rows a boat as fast as Sasha rows a boat. If Leroy rows for 30 minutes, he travels 1 mile farther than Sasha when she rows for 20 minutes. How far does each row?

18. Pietro and Maria spend the same amount of time driving to school. Pietro averages 50 miles per hour and Maria averages 30 miles per hour. Pietro drives 10 miles farther than Maria. How far does each drive to school?

19. Ranji and Paula spend the same amount of time driving to work. Ranji averages 60 miles per hour and Paula averages 40 miles per hour. Ranji drives 15 miles farther than Paula. How far does each drive to work?

20. A car averages 55 miles per hour and an airplane averages 75 miles per hour. If the airplane and the car travel for the same amount of time, the airplane travels 100 miles farther than the car. How far does each travel?

21. The accuracy of a car's speedometer varies directly with the actual speed of the car. A car's speedometer reads 24 miles per hour when the car is actually traveling at 32 miles per hour. When the speedometer reads 51 miles per hour, how fast is the car actually going?

22. The force needed to stretch a spring a certain distance varies directly with the distance. An 8 pound force stretches a spring 3.5 inches. How much force is needed to stretch the spring 12 inches?

23. A person's weight on the moon varies directly as the person's weight on Earth. A person weighing 144 pounds on Earth weighs only 24 pounds on the moon. How much does a person weigh on Earth who weighs 30 pounds on the moon?

24. The current, i, in an electrical circuit with constant voltage varies inversely as the resistance, r, of the circuit. The current in a circuit with constant voltage is 5 amperes when the resistance is 8 ohms. What is the current in the circuit if the resistance is increased to 10 ohms?

25. For storage boxes with the same volume, the area of the bottom of the box varies inversely with the height of the box. The area of the bottom of the box is 108 square inches when the height is 20 inches. What is the area when the height is 16 inches?

26. The time it takes a car to travel a fixed distance varies inversely with the rate at which it travels. It takes the car 4 hours to travel a fixed distance when it travels at a rate of 50 miles per hour. How fast does the car have to travel to cover the same distance in $2\frac{1}{2}$ hours?

27. The volume of a gas is directly proportional to the temperature of the gas and inversely proportional to the pressure exerted on the gas. Write a formula expressing this property. Use V for volume, T for temperature, and P for pressure.

28. The resistance of an electric wire is directly proportional to the length of the wire and inversely proportional to the square of its diameter. Write a formula expressing this property using R for resistance, L for length, and D for diameter.

Evaluate

Practice Test

Take this practice test to be sure that you are prepared for the final quiz in Evaluate.

1. Caleb and Daria are going to wash windows. Working alone, it would take Daria 4 hours to wash the windows. It would take Caleb 3 hours to wash the windows by himself. How long will it take them to wash the windows working together?

2. Trisha ran to the park and then walked home. It took her $\frac{1}{2}$ hour to get to the park and 1 hour and 20 minutes to get home. If she runs 5 miles an hour faster than she walks, how far does she live from the park?

3. The ratio of raisins to peanuts in a bag of party mix is 5 to 6. If the bag contains 462 items, how many peanuts are there?

4. The area of a kite varies jointly with the lengths of its two diagonals. If a kite with area 30 inches^2 has one diagonal of length 10 inches and the other diagonal of length 6 inches, what is the area of a kite with diagonals of length 8 inches and 13 inches?

5. Marta is helping Ned wash dishes after a big party. If Ned could do all of the dishes by himself in 60 minutes and Marta could do all of the dishes by herself in 90 minutes, how long will it take them to do the dishes working together?

6. A harpy eagle can fly 35 kilometers per hour faster than a ruby topaz hummingbird. In the same amount of time, an eagle can fly 8.5 kilometers and a hummingbird can fly 5 kilometers. How fast can each bird fly?

7. The ratio of roses to carnations that a florist ordered was 3 to 4. If the florist received a total of 441 flowers, how many of those were roses?

8. The speed of a wave varies jointly with the wavelength and the frequency of the wave. If the speed of a wave is 20 feet per second, its wavelength is 50 feet and its frequency is 0.4 waves per second. What is the speed of a wave whose wavelength is 1 foot and whose frequency is 8 waves per second?

Cumulative Review Problems

These problems combine all of the material you have covered so far in this course. You may want to test your understanding of this material before you move on to the next topic, or you may wish to do these problems to review for a test.

1. Solve $-13 \le 5x - 3 < 4$ for x.

2. Find: $a^2b^3c \cdot ab^2c^3$

3. Factor: $a^2 - b^2$

4. Circle the true statements.

$\dfrac{1}{2} + \dfrac{1}{3} = \dfrac{2}{5}$

$|19 + 4| = |19| + |4|$

If $R = \{1, 2, 3\}$ and $S = \{1, 2, 3, 4, 5\}$, then $R \subset S$.

$7 + 3 \cdot 6 = 60$

$\dfrac{56}{63} = \dfrac{8}{9}$

The GCF and LCM of two numbers is usually the same.

5. Use the Pythagorean Theorem to find the distance between the points $(2, -5)$ and $(-3, 7)$. See Figure 8.1.

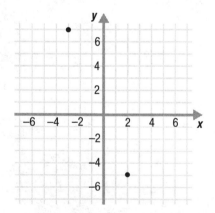

Figure 8.1

6. Factor: $18ab^4c^3 + 9a^4b^3c^2 + 12ab^2c^5$

7. Find the equation of the line parallel to the line $y = 3x + 2$ that passes through the point $(-2, 5)$.

8. Find: $(4a^2b + 3a - 9b) - (7a + 2b - 8a^2b)$

9. Solve $\dfrac{5}{x + 3} - \dfrac{3}{x + 3} = 1$ for x.

10. Write in scientific notation:

a. 42,789,400

b. 0.0025815

11. Find the slope and y-intercept of this line:
$9x + 5y = 11$

12. Find:

a. $3^4 \cdot 3$

b. $\dfrac{a}{a^9}$

c. $(x^7y^0)^5$

13. It would take Kendra 4 hours to type a report. It would take Gerri $2\dfrac{1}{2}$ hours to type the same report. How long would it take them to type the report working together?

14. Write the equation of the circle with radius 3 whose center is at $(1, 5)$.

15. Find: $\dfrac{3}{x - 2} + \dfrac{1}{x - 3}$

16. Factor: $6ab - 10a + 9b - 15$

17. Factor: $x^4 - y^4$

18. Evaluate the expression $5x^2 - 6xy^4 - 4 + 7y$ when $x = 3$ and $y = 0$.

19. Solve $2(3 + y) = 5\left(\dfrac{2}{5}y + 1\right)$ for y.

20. Solve for x: $\dfrac{2}{x} - \dfrac{1}{x - 1} = \dfrac{5}{2x}$

21. Use the distance formula to find the square of the distance between the points $(1, 1)$ and $(7, -4)$.

22. For what values of x is the expression $\dfrac{7}{x^2 - 9}$ undefined?

23. Find: $(9a^8b^3c - 12a^4b^3c^6) \div 3a^7b^3c^4$

Use Figure 8.2 to answer questions 24 through 26.

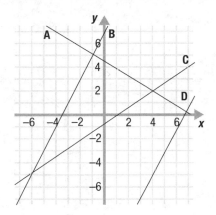

Figure 8.2

24. Which two lines form a system that has a solution of (4, 2)?

25. Which two lines form a system that has a solution of (−1, 5)?

26. Which two lines form a system that has no solution?

27. Graph the inequality $\frac{6}{5}x + 2y \geq 1$.

28. The ratio of dark brown candies to light brown candies in a bag is 3 to 1. If there are 53 light brown candies in the bag, how many are dark brown?

29. Find the slope of the line through the points (6, −2) and (4, −11).

30. Find: $-2s^3t(7r^2st^5 - r^3t)$

31. Factor: $6a^3b^2 - 24a^2b^3 + 24ab^2$

32. Graph the system of inequalities below to find its solution.

$$y \leq -\frac{2}{3}x + 3$$
$$y > -3x - 4$$

33. Find: $\frac{x^2 - x - 6}{x^2 - 25} \cdot \frac{x^2 - 5x}{x^2 - x - 6}$

34. Factor: $8x^2y - 6xy^2 + 12x - 9y$

35. Solve $2 - \frac{x}{x + 3} = \frac{-3}{x + 3}$ for x.

36. Find the slope of the line that is perpendicular to the line that passes through the points (8, −9) and (−3, 11).

37. Find the equation of the line through the point (−2, 6) that has slope $\frac{4}{3}$:

   a. in point-slope form.

   b. in slope-intercept form.

   c. in standard form.

38. Emily withdrew $985 in 5-dollar and 20-dollar bills from her savings account. If she had 65 bills altogether, how many of each did she have?

39. Find:

   a. $2x^0 - 3x^0 + 4x^0$

   b. $(x^0 \cdot x^0 \cdot x^0)^2$

   c. $\frac{a^2 \cdot c}{a^5 \cdot b^6 \cdot c^4}$

40. Factor: $2x^2 + xy - 3y^2$

41. Find the radius and the center of the circle whose equation is: $(x - 2)^2 + (y + 6)^2 = 25$

42. Find: $\frac{23}{\frac{9}{4^3} + \frac{5}{6^2}}$

43. Factor: $49x^2 - 14x + 1$

44. Find:
$(a^2b^2 - 4a^2b - 4ab^2 + 16ab + 2b - 8) \div (b - 4)$

45. Solve $3(x + 2) = 3x + 6$ for x.

46. Graph the line $x = -2.5$.

47. Find the equation of the line perpendicular to the line $y = 2x - 5$ that passes through the point (6, −1).

48. Find the slope of the line through the points (6, −14) and (22, 17).

49. Factor: $x^2 - 4x + 3$

50. Write in expanded form:

   a. $7.1047 \cdot 10^{12}$

   b. $4.294036 \cdot 10^{-8}$

TOPIC 9
RATIONAL EXPONENTS AND RADICALS

You are already familiar with numbers such as the square root of 2. In this topic, you will learn more about square roots as well as other roots and their properties. You will also learn how to represent roots using exponents.

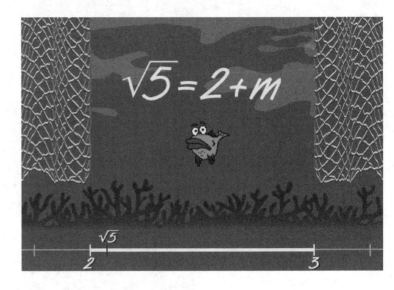

LESSON 9.1
ROOTS AND RADICALS

Overview

In this lesson, you will learn how to add, subtract, multiply, and divide square roots and cube roots. You will also learn how to simplify an expression that contains a square root or a cube root in its denominator. Finally, you will learn how to solve certain equations that contain square roots.

Explain

Concept 1 has sections on

- **Definition of Square Root**

- **Definition of Cube Root**

- **Multiplication Property of Square Roots; of Cube Roots**

- **Division Property of Square Roots; of Cube Roots**

- **Simplifying Square Roots That Contain Whole Numbers**

- **Simplifying Cube Roots That Contain Integers**

- **Simplifying Square Roots That Contain Variables**

- **Simplifying Cube Roots That Contain Variables**

CONCEPT 1:
SQUARE ROOTS AND CUBE ROOTS

Definition of Square Root

Before we define the square root of a number, let's review what we mean by the square of a number.

- The square of 5 is 5^2, which is 25.

- The square of -5 is $(-5)^2$, which is also 25.

Now we will reverse the squaring process and obtain the square roots of a number.

The **square root** of a number is a number that when multiplied by itself, gives the original number.

The number 25 has two square roots, $+5$ and -5. Squaring 5 gives 25, squaring -5 also gives 25.

Each positive real number has two square roots, one positive and the other negative.

The **positive square root** of a number is called the **principal square root**. The principal square root of 25 is $+5$.

The number 0 has a single square root, 0.

*A negative real number, for example −25, does not have square roots that are **real** numbers. That's because a real number times itself always gives a **nonnegative** number.*

$$5^2 = +25 \qquad (-5)^2 = +25$$

The **radical symbol**, $\sqrt{}$, is used to denote the principle square root of a number.

For example,

$$\sqrt{25} = 5.$$

The negative of the radical symbol, $-\sqrt{}$, denotes the negative square root.

For example,

$$-\sqrt{25} = -5.$$

The expression under the radical symbol is called the **radicand**.

For example, in the expression $\sqrt{49}$, the radicand is 49.

A **radical** is the part of an expression that consists of a radical symbol and a radicand. In this example, the radical is $\sqrt{7}$.

A **radical expression** is an expression that contains a radical.

radical symbol

$$8 - 2\sqrt{7}$$

radicand

radical

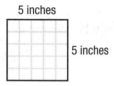

5 inches

5 inches

> — Definition —
> ## Square Root
>
> For a nonnegative real number, a, the principal square root of a is written
>
> $$\sqrt{a}.$$
>
> If b is a nonnegative real number and $b^2 = a$, then $\sqrt{a} = b$.
>
> Example:
>
> $$\sqrt{49} = 7 \text{ because 7 is nonnegative and } 7^2 = 49.$$

We can use geometry to provide a visual interpretation of a positive square root.

For example, suppose a square has an area of 25 square inches. The length of each side is the principal square root of the area. That is,

the length of a side of the square = $\sqrt{25 \text{ inches}^2}$ = 5 inches.

A **perfect square** is a number that has a *rational* square root.

As we work with square roots, we will find it helpful to recognize perfect squares and their square roots. The table lists some whole number perfect squares and their principle square roots.

To approximate the square root of a number that is not a perfect square, we can estimate or use the $\boxed{\sqrt{}}$ key on a calculator.

Perfect Squares	Principal Square Roots
$0^2 = 0$	$\sqrt{0} = 0$
$1^2 = 1$	$\sqrt{1} = 1$
$2^2 = 4$	$\sqrt{4} = 2$
$3^2 = 9$	$\sqrt{9} = 3$
$4^2 = 16$	$\sqrt{16} = 4$
$5^2 = 25$	$\sqrt{25} = 5$
$6^2 = 36$	$\sqrt{36} = 6$
$7^2 = 49$	$\sqrt{49} = 7$
$8^2 = 64$	$\sqrt{64} = 8$
$9^2 = 81$	$\sqrt{81} = 9$
$10^2 = 100$	$\sqrt{100} = 10$
$\vdots$	$\vdots$

Example 9.1.1

The area of a square room is 90 ft^2 (square feet).

Which of the following values best approximates the length of each side of the room:

    8.7 ft   9 ft   9.5 ft   10 ft?

Solution

The area of the room is 90 ft^2, so the length of each side of the room is $\sqrt{90}$ ft.

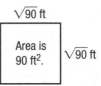

Since 90 is not a perfect square, its principal square root is not a rational number.

However, 90 lies between two perfect squares, 81 and 100. $81 < 90 < 100$

Therefore, we estimate that $\sqrt{90}$ lies between $\sqrt{81}$ and $\sqrt{100}$. $\sqrt{81} < \sqrt{90} < \sqrt{100}$

That is, $\sqrt{90}$ lies between 9 and 10. $9 < \sqrt{90} < 10$

Of the values given, 9.5 ft best approximates the length of each side of the room.

If you use a calculator to approximate $\sqrt{90}$, the display will read 9.486832981. Rounding to one decimal place, we write

$$\sqrt{90} \approx 9.5.$$

The symbol $\approx$ means "approximately equal to."

Now we will summarize the relationship between squares and square roots.

— Property —
Squares and Square Roots

English Squaring and taking a square root "undo" each other.

Algebra If a is a nonnegative real number, then
$$\sqrt{a^2} = a \text{ and } \left(\sqrt{a}\right)^2 = a$$
Example $\sqrt{17^2} = 17 \text{ and } \left(\sqrt{17}\right)^2 = 17.$

Example 9.1.2

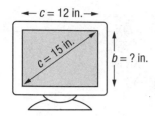

Joe has a 15-inch computer monitor. This means that the diagonal of the screen is 15 inches. If the screen is 12 inches wide, how high is it?

Solution

Picture the screen width and height as the legs of a right triangle. The diagonal is the hypotenuse.

The Pythagorean Theorem gives the relation between the legs, a and b, and the hypotenuse, c.

$$c^2 = a^2 + b^2$$

Replace c with 15 in. and a with 12 in.

$$(\mathbf{15\ in})^2 = (\mathbf{12\ in})^2 + b^2$$

Simplify.

$$225\ \text{in}^2 = 144\ \text{in}^2 + b^2$$

Subtract 144 from both sides.

$$81\ \text{in}^2 = b^2$$

Since $b^2 = 81\ \text{in}^2$, b is 9 inches or b is -9 inches.
But b is length, so b must be positive.
Therefore, b is 9 inches.

So, the height of the screen is 9 inches.

Definition of Cube Root

To indicate a **cube root**, we use the same radical symbol we used for square roots, but we write a small 3 just above the $\sqrt{}$ on the radical symbol to indicate a cube root. The small 3 is called the **index** of the radical.

For example, the cube root of 64 is written $\sqrt[3]{64}$.

For a square root, the index is 2.

However, we usually do not write the index. For example, $\sqrt{16}$ and $\sqrt[2]{16}$ each represent the principal square root of 16.

index   radical symbol

radical   radicand

— Definition —
Cube Root

The cube root of a real number, a, is written
$$\sqrt[3]{a}.$$
If b is a real number and $b^3 = a$, then $\sqrt[3]{a} = b$.
Example:
$$\sqrt[3]{64} = 4 \text{ because } 4^3 = 64.$$

To find the cube root of a number, we reverse the operation of cubing.

For example, to find $\sqrt[3]{8}$ we ask "What number cubed is 8?".

The answer is 2.

Therefore, $\sqrt[3]{8} = 2$.

Here are some examples:

$$\sqrt[3]{125} = 5 \text{ because } 5^3 = 5 \cdot 5 \cdot 5 = 125$$

$$\sqrt[3]{1} = 1 \text{ because } 1^3 = 1 \cdot 1 \cdot 1 = 1.$$

$$\sqrt[3]{-1} = -1 \text{ because } (-1)^3 = (-1)(-1)(-1) = -1.$$

$$\sqrt[3]{-8} = -2 \text{ because } (-2)^3 = (-2)(-2)(-2) = -8.$$

The last two examples show that a cube root, unlike a square root, can have a negative radicand.

We can use geometry to provide a visual interpretation of a cube root.

For example, suppose a cube has a volume of 125 cubic inches. The length of each side is the cube root of the volume.

That is,

$$\text{the length of a side of the cube} = \sqrt[3]{125 \text{ in}^3} = 5 \text{ in.}$$

A **perfect cube** is a number that has a rational cube root.

For example, 125 is a perfect cube because $5^3 = 125$.

As we work with cube roots, we will find it useful to recognize perfect cubes and their cube roots.

Now we will summarize the relationship between cubes and cube roots.

Unlike square roots, there are no "principal" cube roots.

The sign of a cube root depends on the sign of its radicand.

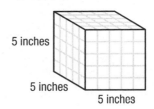

5 inches
5 inches
5 inches

Perfect Cubes	Cube Roots
$0^3 = 0$	$\sqrt[3]{0} = 0$
$1^3 = 1$	$\sqrt[3]{1} = 1$
$2^3 = 8$	$\sqrt[3]{8} = 2$
$3^3 = 27$	$\sqrt[3]{27} = 3$
$4^3 = 64$	$\sqrt[3]{64} = 4$
$5^3 = 125$	$\sqrt[3]{125} = 5$
$6^3 = 216$	$\sqrt[3]{216} = 6$
$7^3 = 343$	$\sqrt[3]{343} = 7$
$8^3 = 512$	$\sqrt[3]{512} = 8$
$9^3 = 729$	$\sqrt[3]{729} = 9$
$10^3 = 1000$	$\sqrt[3]{1000} = 10$

— Property —
Cubes and Cube Roots

English Cubing and taking a cube root "undo" each other.

Algebra If a is a real number, then
$$\sqrt[3]{a^3} = a \text{ and } \left(\sqrt[3]{a}\right)^3 = a$$

Example $\sqrt[3]{12^3} = 12$ and $\left(\sqrt[3]{12}\right)^3 = 12.$

Multiplication Property of Square Roots; of Cube Roots

To indicate multiplication of square roots or of cube roots, we often write the radicals next to each other, without a multiplication dot between them.

For example,

$$\sqrt{4}\sqrt{9} \text{ means } \sqrt{4} \cdot \sqrt{9}.$$

When a radical is multiplied by a factor that does not contain a radical, we usually write the radical factor on the right.

For example,

$$\sqrt{15} \cdot 2 \text{ is usually written } 2\sqrt{15}.$$

To simplify a square-root radical or a cube-root radical, we often use these multiplication properties.

English The root of a product is the product of the roots.

	Square Roots	*Cube Roots*
Algebra	$\sqrt{ab} = \sqrt{a}\sqrt{b}$	$\sqrt[3]{ab} = \sqrt[3]{a}\sqrt[3]{b}$
	Here, a and b are nonnegative real numbers.	Here, a and b are real numbers.
Example	$\sqrt{2 \cdot 6} = \sqrt{2}\sqrt{6}$	$\sqrt[3]{7 \cdot 15} = \sqrt[3]{7}\sqrt[3]{15}$

These properties allow us to write a single radical as the product of two radicals. Sometimes we can simplify one (or both) of the radicals.

For example,

$$\sqrt{36 \cdot 7} = \sqrt{36} \cdot \sqrt{7} = 6\sqrt{7}.$$

The property can also be used to write the product of two radicals as a single radical, provided the radicals have the same index.

For example,

$$\sqrt{2} \cdot \sqrt{8} = \sqrt{2 \cdot 8} = \sqrt{16} = 4.$$

The Multiplication Property applies only when the indices of the radicals are the same. So we cannot use it to multiply a square root by a cube root:

$$\sqrt{2} \cdot \sqrt[3]{4}$$

Example 9.1.3

Simplify: a. $\sqrt{16 \cdot 5}$ b. $\sqrt[3]{8 \cdot 6}$

Solution

To simplify, use the Multiplication Property to rewrite each radical.

a. $\sqrt{16 \cdot 5}$

Write the radical as the product of two radicals. $\quad = \sqrt{16} \cdot \sqrt{5}$

Simplify $\sqrt{16}$. $\quad = 4\sqrt{5}$

b. $\sqrt[3]{8 \cdot 6}$

Write the radical as the product of two radicals. $\quad = \sqrt[3]{8} \cdot \sqrt[3]{6}$

Simplify $\sqrt[3]{8}$. $\quad = 2\sqrt[3]{6}$

Example 9.1.4

Simplify: a. $\sqrt{3}\sqrt{27}$ b. $\sqrt[3]{5}\sqrt[3]{25}$

Solution

Use the Multiplication Property of Square Roots or Cube Roots to rewrite each expression. Then simplify the result.

a. $$\sqrt{3}\sqrt{27}$$

Write the product as a single radical.	$= \sqrt{3 \cdot 27}$
Multiply the numbers under the radical symbol.	$= \sqrt{81}$
Simplify the radical.	$= 9$

b. $$\sqrt[3]{5}\sqrt[3]{25}$$

Write the product as a single radical.	$= \sqrt[3]{5 \cdot 25}$
Multiply the numbers under the radical symbol.	$= \sqrt[3]{125}$
Simplify the radical.	$= 5$

Division Property of Square Roots; of Cube Roots

It is often useful to write a single radical that contains a fraction as the quotient of two radicals, and vice versa.

— Property —
The Division Property of Square Roots and
The Division Property of Cube Roots

English The root of a quotient is the quotient of the roots.

	Square Roots	*Cube Roots*
Algebra	$\sqrt{\dfrac{a}{b}} = \dfrac{\sqrt{a}}{\sqrt{b}}$	$\sqrt[3]{\dfrac{a}{b}} = \dfrac{\sqrt[3]{a}}{\sqrt[3]{b}}$
	Here, a and b are nonnegative real numbers and $b \neq 0$.	Here, a and b are real numbers and $b \neq 0$.
Example	$\sqrt{\dfrac{7}{38}} = \dfrac{\sqrt{7}}{\sqrt{38}}$	$\sqrt[3]{\dfrac{5}{6}} = \dfrac{\sqrt[3]{5}}{\sqrt[3]{6}}$

This property allows us to write a single radical as the quotient of two radicals.

For example,

$$\sqrt{\frac{10}{9}} = \frac{\sqrt{10}}{\sqrt{9}} = \frac{\sqrt{10}}{3}.$$

The property can also be used to write the quotient of two radicals as a single radical, provided the radicals have the same index.

For example,

$$\frac{\sqrt{50}}{\sqrt{2}} = \sqrt{\frac{50}{2}} = \sqrt{25} = 5.$$

*The Division Property applies only when the indices of the radicals are the same. So we **cannot** use it to divide a square root by a cube root.*

*That is, we **cannot** use the Division Property to find*

$$\frac{\sqrt{45}}{\sqrt[3]{5}}$$

Example 9.1.5

Simplify: a. $\sqrt{\dfrac{5}{16}}$ b. $\sqrt[3]{\dfrac{10}{27}}$

Solution

a. $\sqrt{\dfrac{5}{16}}$

Write the radical as the quotient of two radicals.	$= \dfrac{\sqrt{5}}{\sqrt{16}}$
Simplify the radical in the denominator.	$= \dfrac{\sqrt{5}}{4}$

b. $\sqrt[3]{\dfrac{10}{27}}$

Write the radical as the quotient of two radicals.	$= \dfrac{\sqrt[3]{10}}{\sqrt[3]{27}}$
Simplify the radical in the denominator.	$= \dfrac{\sqrt[3]{10}}{3}$

Example 9.1.6

Simplify: a. $\dfrac{\sqrt{27}}{\sqrt{3}}$ b. $\dfrac{\sqrt[3]{72}}{\sqrt[3]{9}}$

Solution

a. $\dfrac{\sqrt{27}}{\sqrt{3}}$

Write the quotient as a single radical.	$= \sqrt{\dfrac{27}{3}}$
Divide the numbers under the radical symbol.	$= \sqrt{9}$
Simplify the radical.	$= 3$

b. $\dfrac{\sqrt[3]{72}}{\sqrt[3]{9}}$

Write the quotient as a single radical.	$= \sqrt[3]{\dfrac{72}{9}}$
Divide the numbers under the radical symbol.	$= \sqrt[3]{8}$
Simplify the radical.	$= 2$

Simplifying Square Roots That Contain Whole Numbers

To make it easier to work with an algebraic expression, we often simplify it.

For example, you have simplified expressions as follows:

- $5(x - 4) + 2x = 7x - 20$

- $\dfrac{24x^{10}}{6x^7} = 4x^3$

To simplify a square root radical, we examine the factors of the radicand.

If any of those factors are perfect squares, we rewrite the radical so there are no perfect square factors under the radical sign.

To do this, we use the Multiplication Property of Square Roots.

We will learn two methods for simplifying square-root radicals.

To see how each method works, let's simplify $\sqrt{600}$.

- *Method 1 Use Perfect Square Factors*

   Identify perfect square factors of 600.

   The numbers 4, 25, and 100 are each perfect square factors of 600.

   Using those factors, we can write $\sqrt{600}$ in several ways:

   $$\sqrt{600} = \sqrt{4 \cdot 150}$$
   $$\sqrt{600} = \sqrt{25 \cdot 24}$$
   $$\sqrt{600} = \sqrt{4 \cdot 25 \cdot 6}$$
   $$\sqrt{600} = \sqrt{100 \cdot 6}$$

The factorization $100 \cdot 6$ contains 100, the largest perfect square that is a factor of 600. So we use that form.	$\sqrt{600}$ $= \sqrt{100 \cdot 6}$
Use the Multiplication Property of Square Roots to write $\sqrt{100 \cdot 6}$ as the product of two radicals.	$= \sqrt{100} \cdot \sqrt{6}$
Simplify $\sqrt{100}$.	$= 10\sqrt{6}$

   Thus, in simplified form,

   $$\sqrt{600} = 10\sqrt{6}.$$

Here is another way to use perfect squares to simplify $\sqrt{600}$:

$$\sqrt{600}$$
$$= \sqrt{4 \cdot 25 \cdot 6}$$
$$= \sqrt{4}\sqrt{25}\sqrt{6}$$
$$= 2 \cdot 5 \cdot \sqrt{6}$$
$$= 10\sqrt{6}$$

• **Method 2 Use Prime Factors**

If you have trouble finding a perfect square factor of the radicand, write its prime factorization. Then, group the factors to form perfect squares.

$$\sqrt{600}$$

Write the prime factorization of 600.

$$= \sqrt{2 \cdot 2 \cdot 2 \cdot 3 \cdot 5 \cdot 5}$$

Group pairs of factors to form perfect squares.

$$= \sqrt{(2 \cdot 2) \cdot 2 \cdot 3 \cdot (5 \cdot 5)}$$
$$= \sqrt{4 \cdot 6 \cdot 25}$$

Write as a product of three radicals.

$$= \sqrt{4} \cdot \sqrt{6} \cdot \sqrt{25}$$

Simplify $\sqrt{4}$ and simplify $\sqrt{25}$.

$$= 2 \cdot \sqrt{6} \cdot 5$$
$$= 10\sqrt{6}$$

Thus, in simplified form,

$$\sqrt{600} = 10\sqrt{6}.$$

Example **9.1.7**

Simplify: $\sqrt{8}$

Solution

$$\sqrt{8}$$

The largest perfect square factor of 8 is 4.

$$= \sqrt{4 \cdot 2}$$

Write as a product of two radicals.

$$= \sqrt{4}\sqrt{2}$$

Simplify $\sqrt{4}$.

$$= 2\sqrt{2}$$

In general, 4 is a factor of a number if the last two digits of the number are divisible by 4.

For example:

4 is a factor of 236 since 36 is divisible by 4.

Thus, in simplified form,

$$\sqrt{8} = 2\sqrt{2}.$$

Example **9.1.8**

Simplify: $\sqrt{108}$

Solution

$$\sqrt{108}$$

Write the prime factorization of 108.

$$= \sqrt{2 \cdot 2 \cdot 3 \cdot 3 \cdot 3}$$

Group pairs of factors to form perfect squares.

$$= \sqrt{(2 \cdot 2) \cdot (3 \cdot 3) \cdot 3}$$
$$= \sqrt{4 \cdot 9 \cdot 3}$$

Write as a product of three radicals.

$$= \sqrt{4} \cdot \sqrt{9} \cdot \sqrt{3}$$

Simplify $\sqrt{4}$ and simplify $\sqrt{9}$.

$$= 2 \cdot 3 \cdot \sqrt{3}$$
$$= 6\sqrt{3}$$

In general, 9 is a factor of a number if the sum of the digits of the number is divisible by 9.

For example:

9 is a factor of 198 since $1 + 9 + 8 = 18$ and 18 is divisible by 9.

If you realize that 36 is the largest perfect square factor of 108, the you can write:

$$\sqrt{108}$$
$$= \sqrt{36 \cdot 3}$$
$$= \sqrt{36}\sqrt{3}$$
$$= 6\sqrt{3}$$

Thus, in simplified form,

$$\sqrt{108} = 6\sqrt{3}.$$

Simplifying Cube Roots That Contain Integers

To simplify a cube-root radical, we look for perfect cube factors of the radicand.

Example 9.1.9

Simplify: $\sqrt[3]{250}$

Solution

$\sqrt[3]{250}$

Write the prime factorization of 250.

$= \sqrt[3]{2 \cdot 5 \cdot 5 \cdot 5}$

Group **triples** of like factors to form perfect **cubes**.

$= \sqrt[3]{2 \cdot (5 \cdot 5 \cdot 5)}$

$= \sqrt[3]{2 \cdot 125}$

Write as a product of two radicals.

$= \sqrt[3]{2} \cdot \sqrt[3]{125}$

Simplify $\sqrt[3]{125}$.

$= 5\sqrt[3]{2}$

Thus, in simplified form,

$$\sqrt[3]{250} = 5\sqrt[3]{2}.$$

If you realize that 125 is the largest perfect cube factor of 250, then you can write:

$$\sqrt[3]{250}$$
$$= \sqrt[3]{125 \cdot 2}$$
$$= \sqrt[3]{125} \cdot \sqrt[3]{2}$$
$$= 5\sqrt[3]{2}$$

Example 9.1.10

Simplify: $\sqrt[3]{\dfrac{-40}{27}}$

Solution

To simplify this expression, we'll use the Division Property of Cube Roots to rewrite the radical as a quotient of radicals. Then we'll simplify each of those radicals.

$\sqrt[3]{\dfrac{-40}{27}}$

Write the numerator and denominator under separate radical symbols.

$= \dfrac{\sqrt[3]{-40}}{\sqrt[3]{27}}$

Write -40 using a perfect cube factor, -8.

$= \dfrac{\sqrt[3]{-8 \cdot 5}}{\sqrt[3]{27}}$

Write the numerator as the product of two radicals.

$= \dfrac{\sqrt[3]{-8} \cdot \sqrt[3]{5}}{\sqrt[3]{27}}$

Simplify the cube roots of any perfect cubes.

$= \dfrac{-2\sqrt[3]{5}}{3}$

Thus, in simplified form,

$$\sqrt[3]{\dfrac{-40}{27}} = \dfrac{-2\sqrt[3]{5}}{3}.$$

If you have difficulty seeing the largest perfect cube that is a factor of -40 or 27, write their prime factorizations.

$$\dfrac{\sqrt[3]{-40}}{\sqrt[3]{27}} = \dfrac{\sqrt[3]{(-2) \cdot (-2) \cdot (-2) \cdot 5}}{\sqrt[3]{3 \cdot 3 \cdot 3}}$$

$$= \dfrac{\sqrt[3]{(-2)^3 \cdot 5}}{\sqrt[3]{(3)^3}}$$

Simplifying Square Roots That Contain Variables

Next we will simplify a square-root radical whose radicand contains a variable.

Let's look at these examples.

If x is a *nonnegative* real number, then:

$$\sqrt{x^2} = x \text{ since } x \cdot x = x^2$$

$$\sqrt{x^6} = x^3 \text{ since } (x^3)^2 = x^6 \qquad \text{Notice that } \sqrt{x^6} = x^{6 \div 2} = x^3.$$

$$\sqrt{x^{10}} = x^5 \text{ since } (x^5)^2 = x^{10} \qquad \text{Notice that } \sqrt{x^{10}} = x^{10 \div 2} = x^5.$$

$$\sqrt{x^{16}} = x^8 \text{ since } (x^8)^2 = x^{16} \qquad \text{Notice that } \sqrt{x^{16}} = x^{16 \div 2} = x^8.$$

In each example, the exponent of the variable in the simplified expression is one-half the exponent of the variable in the radicand.

If the power of x in the radicand is not a multiple of 2, we rewrite the radicand as a product of x^1 and an even power of x.

For example, let's simplify $\sqrt{x^{37}}$, where x is a nonnegative real number.

$$\sqrt{x^{37}}$$

Write x^{37} as $x^{36} \cdot x^1$.

$$= \sqrt{x^{36} \cdot x^1}$$

Write $\sqrt{x^{36} \cdot x^1}$ as the product of two radicals.

$$= \sqrt{x^{36}} \cdot \sqrt{x^1}$$

Simplify.

$$= x^{18}\sqrt{x}$$

In the remainder of this Topic, we will assume that each variable under a radical represents a *nonnegative* real number.

Be careful:

$\sqrt{x^{16}} \neq x^4$

$\sqrt{x^{16}} = x^{16 \div 2} = x^8$

Be careful:

$\sqrt{x^{36}} \neq x^6$

$\sqrt{x^{36}} = x^{36 \div 2} = x^{18}$

If x is negative, then $\sqrt{x^2} = |x|$.

For example, if $x = -3$:
$\sqrt{x^2} = \sqrt{(-3)^2} = \sqrt{9} = +3 = |x|$

Example 9.1.11

Simplify: $\sqrt{49x^{13}}$

Solution

$$\sqrt{49x^{13}}$$

Factor the radicand, using perfect square factors when possible.

$$= \sqrt{49 \cdot x^{12} \cdot x^1}$$

Write as a product of three radicals.

$$= \sqrt{49} \cdot \sqrt{x^{12}} \cdot \sqrt{x^1}$$

Simplify the square root of each perfect square radicand.

$$= 7 \cdot x^6 \cdot \sqrt{x}$$

$$= 7x^6\sqrt{x}$$

So,

$$\sqrt{49x^{13}} = 7x^6\sqrt{x}.$$

Example 9.1.12

Simplify: $\sqrt{50y^7}$

Solution

$$\sqrt{50y^7}$$

Factor the radicand, using perfect square factors when possible.

$$= \sqrt{25 \cdot 2 \cdot y^6 \cdot y^1}$$

Use the Multiplication Property of Square Roots to write as the product of four radicals.

$$= \sqrt{25} \cdot \sqrt{2} \cdot \sqrt{y^6} \cdot \sqrt{y^1}$$

Simplify the square root of each perfect square radicand.

$$= 5 \cdot \sqrt{2} \cdot y^3 \cdot \sqrt{y^1}$$

Use the Multiplication Property of Square Roots to combine the remaining radicals into a single radical.

$$= 5y^3\sqrt{2y}$$

So,

$$\sqrt{50y^7} = 5y^3\sqrt{2y}.$$

Simplifying Cube Roots That Contain Variables

Next we will simplify a cube-root radical whose radicand contains a variable.

We will use a procedure similar to the one we used to simplify square-root radicals. However, when we simplify a cube-root radical, we divide the exponent of the variable by 3 (instead of 2).

Here are some examples.

If x is any real number, then:

$\sqrt[3]{x^3} = x$ since $x \cdot x \cdot x = x^3$

$\sqrt[3]{x^{12}} = x^4$ since $x^4 \cdot x^4 \cdot x^4 = x^{12}$ Notice that $\sqrt[3]{x^{12}} = x^{12 \div 3} = x^4$.

$\sqrt[3]{x^{27}} = x^9$ since $x^9 \cdot x^9 \cdot x^9 = x^{27}$ Notice that $\sqrt[3]{x^{27}} = x^{27 \div 3} = x^9$.

Be careful:

$$\sqrt[3]{x^{27}} \neq x^3$$

$$\sqrt[3]{x^{27}} = x^{27 \div 3} = x^9$$

In each example, the exponent of the variable in the simplified expression is one-third the exponent of the variable in the radicand.

If the power of x in the radicand is not a multiple of 3, we rewrite the radicand as a product where one of the factors has a power that is a multiple of 3 and the other factor is x^1 or x^2.

For example, let's simplify $\sqrt[3]{x^{14}}$.

$\sqrt[3]{x^{14}}$

Write x^{14} as $x^{12} \cdot x^2$.

$= \sqrt[3]{x^{12} \cdot x^2}$

Notice that **12** is a multiple of 3.

Write as the product of two radicals.

$= \sqrt[3]{x^{12}} \cdot \sqrt[3]{x^2}$

Simplify.

$= x^4 \cdot \sqrt[3]{x^2}$

So, $x^{14} = x^4\sqrt[3]{x^2}$

Example 9.1.13

Simplify: $\sqrt[3]{8x^2y^7}$

Solution

$\sqrt[3]{8x^2y^7}$

We rewrote y^7 as $y^6 \cdot y^1$.

Factor the radicand, using perfect cube factors when possible.

$= \sqrt[3]{8 \cdot x^2 \cdot y^6 \cdot y^1}$

*Notice that **6** is a multiple of 3.*

Write as a product of four radicals.

$= \sqrt[3]{8} \cdot \sqrt[3]{x^2} \cdot \sqrt[3]{y^6} \cdot \sqrt[3]{y^1}$

Simplify the cube root of each perfect cube.

$= 2 \cdot \sqrt[3]{x^2} \cdot y^2 \cdot \sqrt[3]{y^1}$

Combine the remaining radicals.

$= 2y^2 \cdot \sqrt[3]{x^2y}$

So, $\sqrt[3]{8x^2y^7} = 2y^2\sqrt[3]{x^2y}$.

Here is a summary of this concept from *Academic Systems Algebra.*

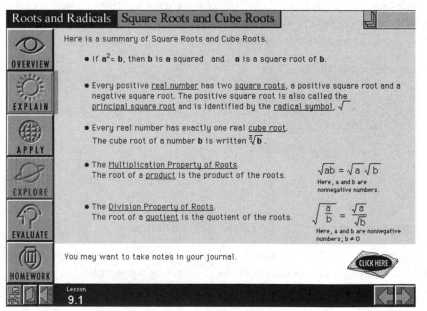

CONCEPT 2:
RADICAL EXPRESSIONS

Simplified Form of a Square Root; of a Cube Root

Here is what we mean by simplified form for a square root or cube root.

> **— Definition —**
> **Simplified Form of a Square Root; of a Cube Root**
>
> When we work with a square root or a cube root, we say a radical expression is in simplified form when there are:
> - No perfect square factors under a square root symbol.
> - No perfect cube factors under a cube root symbol.
> - No fractions under a radical symbol.
> - No radicals in the denominator of a fraction.

Here are some examples: ***Not simplified***

- No perfect square factors under a square root. $\sqrt{48} = \sqrt{\mathbf{16 \cdot 3}}$

    $\sqrt{3x^8} = \sqrt{3 \cdot (x^4)^2}$

- No perfect cube factors under a cube root. $\sqrt[3]{40} = \sqrt[3]{\mathbf{8 \cdot 5}}$

    $\sqrt[3]{25y^{12}} = \sqrt[3]{25 \cdot (y^4)^3}$

- No fractions under a radical symbol. $\sqrt{\dfrac{\mathbf{5}}{\mathbf{4}}}$

- No radicals in the denominator of a fraction. $\dfrac{\sqrt[3]{10}}{\sqrt[3]{8}} = \dfrac{\sqrt[3]{10}}{\sqrt[3]{(2)^3}}$

Like Radical Terms

You have already learned how to recognize like terms. These are terms that have the same variables raised to the same power. For example, $2x$ and $3x$ are like terms.

Like radical terms are terms whose radical parts have the same index and and the same radicand.

Concept 2 has sections on

- **Simplified Form of a Square Root; of a Cube Root**
- **Like Radical Terms**
- **Combining Like Radical Terms**
- **Multiplying Square Roots; Multiplying Cube Roots**
- **Conjugates**
- **Rationalizing the Denominator**
- **Solving an Equation That Contains a Square Root**

Example 9.1.14

Identify the like radical terms:

$$4\sqrt{6} \qquad \frac{13\sqrt{6}}{5} \qquad 8\sqrt[3]{6} \qquad -3\sqrt{2} \qquad -3\sqrt{6} \qquad \frac{\sqrt[3]{6}}{5}$$

Solution

$4\sqrt{6}, \dfrac{13\sqrt{6}}{5}, -3\sqrt{6}$ are like radical terms.

Each radical has index 2 and radicand 6.

$8\sqrt[3]{6}, \dfrac{\sqrt[3]{6}}{5}$, are like radical terms.

Each radical has index 3 and radicand 6.

$-3\sqrt{2}$ is not "like" any of the other radicals.

Example 9.1.15

Identify the like radical terms:

$$\sqrt[3]{15} \qquad 7\sqrt{15} \qquad -4\sqrt[3]{15} \qquad 27\sqrt[3]{15} \qquad 2\sqrt[3]{5}$$

Solution

$\sqrt[3]{15}, -4\sqrt[3]{15}$, and $27\sqrt[3]{15}$ are like radical terms.
Each radical has index 3 and radicand of 15.

$7\sqrt{15}$ has index 2, while $2\sqrt[3]{5}$ has radicand 5.
Neither of these terms is "like" any of the other radical expressions.

Combining Like Radical Terms

Adding and subtracting radical expressions is like adding and subtracting polynomials.

- With polynomials, to add like terms, we add their coefficients.

$$5x \;+\; 7x \;= (5 + 7)x \;\;= 12x$$

- With radical expressions, to add like radical terms, we add the numbers in front of the radicals.

$$5\sqrt{x} + 7\sqrt{x} = (5 + 7)\sqrt{x} = 12\sqrt{x}$$

Example 9.1.16

a. Find $5\sqrt{3} + \sqrt{3}$ b. Find $4\sqrt[3]{7} - \dfrac{\sqrt[3]{7}}{2}$

Solution

a. $5\sqrt{3}$ and $\sqrt{3}$ are like radical terms.
    So we add the numbers in front of the radicals.
    Remember: $\sqrt{3}$ is $1 \cdot \sqrt{3}$.

$5\sqrt{3} + \sqrt{3}$

$= 5\sqrt{3} + 1\sqrt{3}$

$= (5 + 1)\sqrt{3}$

$= 6\sqrt{3}$

Thus, $5\sqrt{3} + \sqrt{3}$ simplifies to $6\sqrt{3}$.

b. $4\sqrt[3]{7}$ and $\dfrac{\sqrt[3]{7}}{2}$ are like radical terms.

$4\sqrt[3]{7} - \dfrac{\sqrt[3]{7}}{2}$

To subtract them, first write $\dfrac{\sqrt[3]{7}}{2}$ as $\dfrac{1}{2} \cdot \sqrt[3]{7}$.

$= 4\sqrt[3]{7} - \dfrac{1}{2} \cdot \sqrt[3]{7}$

To subtract the terms, we must subtract $\dfrac{1}{2}$ from 4.

The LCD of 4 and $\dfrac{1}{2}$ is 2.

Therefore, write: $4 = \dfrac{4}{1} = \dfrac{4}{1} \cdot \dfrac{2}{2} = \dfrac{8}{2}$.

$= \dfrac{8}{2} \cdot \sqrt[3]{7} - \dfrac{1}{2} \cdot \sqrt[3]{7}$

$= \left(\dfrac{8}{2} - \dfrac{1}{2}\right) \cdot \sqrt[3]{7}$

$= \dfrac{7}{2} \cdot \sqrt[3]{7}$ *We can also write the result as:* $\dfrac{7\sqrt[3]{7}}{2}$

Therefore, $4\sqrt[3]{7} - \dfrac{\sqrt[3]{7}}{2} = \dfrac{7}{2} \cdot \sqrt[3]{7}$.

Before we can combine like radical terms, we sometimes need to simplify the individual radicals to obtain like terms.

Example 9.1.17

Find: $\sqrt{24} + 8\sqrt[3]{6} + 9\sqrt{6} - 4$

Solution

First simplify $\sqrt{24}$. The radicand, 24, has a perfect square factor, 4.

$$\sqrt{24} = \sqrt{4 \cdot 6}$$
$$= \sqrt{4} \cdot \sqrt{6}$$
$$= 2\sqrt{6}$$

$$\sqrt{24} + 8\sqrt[3]{6} + 9\sqrt{6} - 4$$

Replace $\sqrt{24}$ with $2\sqrt{6}$.

$$= 2\sqrt{6} + 8\sqrt[3]{6} + 9\sqrt{6} - 4$$

Combine the like radical terms, $2\sqrt{6}$ and $9\sqrt{6}$.

$$= (2 + 9)\sqrt{6} + 8\sqrt[3]{6} - 4$$

Simplify.

$$= 11\sqrt{6} + 8\sqrt[3]{6} - 4$$

So,

$$\sqrt{24} + 8\sqrt[3]{6} + 9\sqrt{6} - 4 = 11\sqrt{6} + 8\sqrt[3]{6} - 4$$

Example 9.1.18

Find: $5\sqrt[3]{4} - 5 - 8\sqrt[3]{4} + 3\sqrt[3]{32} - 2$

Solution

First simplify $\sqrt[3]{32}$. The radicand, 32, has a perfect cube factor, 8.

$$\sqrt[3]{32} = \sqrt[3]{8 \cdot 4}$$
$$= \sqrt[3]{8} \cdot \sqrt[3]{4}$$
$$= 2\sqrt[3]{4}$$

$$5\sqrt[3]{4} - 5 - 8\sqrt[3]{4} + 3\sqrt[3]{32} - 2$$

Replace $\sqrt[3]{32}$ with $2\sqrt[3]{4}$.

$$= 5\sqrt[3]{4} - 5 - 8\sqrt[3]{4} + 3 \cdot 2\sqrt[3]{4} - 2$$

Multiply $3 \cdot 2\sqrt[3]{4}$.

$$= 5\sqrt[3]{4} - 5 - 8\sqrt[3]{4} + 6\sqrt[3]{4} - 2$$

Combine the like radical terms, $5\sqrt[3]{4}$, $-8\sqrt[3]{4}$, and $6\sqrt[3]{4}$.

Also, combine the like terms -5 and -2.

$$= (5 - 8 + 6)\sqrt[3]{4} + (-5 - 2)$$

Simplify.

$$= 3\sqrt[3]{4} - 7$$

So,

$$5\sqrt[3]{4} - 5 - 8\sqrt[3]{4} + 3\sqrt[3]{32} - 2 = 3\sqrt[3]{4} - 7$$

Multiplying Square Roots; Multiplying Cube Roots

Now we will look at several examples of multiplying radical expressions.

We have already used the Multiplication Property of Square Roots to multiply two square roots by multiplying their radicands.

$$\sqrt{2} \cdot \sqrt{5} = \sqrt{2 \cdot 5}$$
$$= \sqrt{10}$$

Here, the factors 3 and 4 lie outside the radical symbols.

$$3\sqrt{2} \cdot 4\sqrt{5} = (3 \cdot 4)\sqrt{2 \cdot 5}$$

We multiply 3 by 4, and we multiply the radicands.

$$= 12\sqrt{10}$$

We use the Distributive Property to remove the parentheses.

$$\sqrt{5}(\sqrt{3} - 4) = \sqrt{5} \cdot \sqrt{3} - \sqrt{5} \cdot 4$$
$$= \sqrt{15} - 4\sqrt{5}$$

We use the FOIL method to multiply two radical expressions, each with two terms.

$$(2\sqrt{5} + 3)(\sqrt{7} - \sqrt{2})$$

$$\overset{\mathbf{F}}{=} \overset{\mathbf{O}}{2\sqrt{5} \cdot \sqrt{7}} - \overset{\mathbf{I}}{2\sqrt{5} \cdot \sqrt{2}} + \overset{\mathbf{I}}{3 \cdot \sqrt{7}} - \overset{\mathbf{L}}{3 \cdot \sqrt{2}}$$
$$= 2\sqrt{35} - 2\sqrt{10} + 3\sqrt{7} - 3\sqrt{2}$$

Example 9.1.19

Find: $2\sqrt{6}(5\sqrt{3} + \sqrt{6})$

Solution

Distribute $2\sqrt{6}$.

$$2\sqrt{6}(5\sqrt{3} + \sqrt{6})$$
$$= 2\sqrt{6} \cdot 5\sqrt{3} + 2\sqrt{6} \cdot \sqrt{6}$$

For each term, multiply the integers in front of the radicals and multiply the radicands.

$$= 10\sqrt{18} + 2\sqrt{36}$$

Write $\sqrt{18}$ as $\sqrt{9 \cdot 2}$.

$$= 10\sqrt{\mathbf{9 \cdot 2}} + 2\sqrt{36}$$

Rewrite $\sqrt{9 \cdot 2}$ as the product $\sqrt{9}\sqrt{2}$.

$$= 10\sqrt{\mathbf{9}}\sqrt{2} + 2\sqrt{36}$$

Simplify $\sqrt{9}$ and simplify $\sqrt{36}$.

$$= 10 \cdot \mathbf{3}\sqrt{2} + 2 \cdot \mathbf{6}$$

Multiply.

$$= 30\sqrt{2} + 12$$

Thus,

$$2\sqrt{6}(5\sqrt{3} + \sqrt{6}) = 30\sqrt{2} + 12.$$

Example 9.1.20

Find: $(5 + \sqrt{10})(7 - \sqrt{10})$

Solution
$$(5 + \sqrt{10})(7 - \sqrt{10})$$

Use the FOIL method.
$$= 5 \cdot 7 - 5 \cdot \sqrt{10} + \sqrt{10} \cdot 7 - \sqrt{10} \cdot \sqrt{10}$$

Simplify each term.
$$= 35 - 5\sqrt{10} + 7\sqrt{10} - \sqrt{100}$$

Simplify $\sqrt{100}$.
$$= 35 - 5\sqrt{10} + 7\sqrt{10} - \mathbf{10}$$

Combine the like radical terms, $-5\sqrt{10}$ and $7\sqrt{10}$.
$$= 35 + \mathbf{2\sqrt{10}} - 10$$

Combine the like terms 35 and -10.
$$= 25 + 2\sqrt{10}$$

So,
$$(5 + \sqrt{10})(7 - \sqrt{10}) = 25 + 2\sqrt{10}$$

Example 9.1.21

Find: $\sqrt[3]{6}(\sqrt[3]{4} - 7)$

Solution
$$\sqrt[3]{6}(\sqrt[3]{4} - 7)$$

Distribute $\sqrt[3]{6}$.
$$= \sqrt[3]{6} \cdot \sqrt[3]{4} - \sqrt[3]{6} \cdot 7$$

In the first term, multiply the radicands.
$$= \sqrt[3]{\mathbf{24}} - \sqrt[3]{6} \cdot 7$$

Simplify $\sqrt[3]{\mathbf{24}}$.
The radicand, 24, has a perfect cube factor, 8.
So, write 24 as the product $8 \cdot 3$.
$$= \sqrt[3]{\mathbf{8 \cdot 3}} - \sqrt[3]{6} \cdot 7$$

Rewrite $\sqrt[3]{8 \cdot 3}$ as the product $\sqrt[3]{8}\sqrt[3]{3}$.
$$= \sqrt[3]{\mathbf{8}}\sqrt[3]{\mathbf{3}} - \sqrt[3]{6} \cdot 7$$

Simplify $\sqrt[3]{8}$.
$$= 2\sqrt[3]{3} - \sqrt[3]{6} \cdot 7$$

Write 7 to the left of $\sqrt[3]{6}$.
$$= 2\sqrt[3]{3} - 7\sqrt[3]{6}$$

So,
$$\sqrt[3]{6}(\sqrt[3]{4} - 7) = 2\sqrt[3]{3} - 7\sqrt[3]{6}$$

If you have difficulty "seeing" that 24 has a perfect cube factor, find the prime factorization of 24.

$24 = 2 \cdot 2 \cdot 2 \cdot 3$

$\quad = 2^3 \cdot 3$

Example 9.1.22

Find: $\left(\sqrt{3} - 5\right)\left(\sqrt{3} + 5\right)$

Solution	$\left(\sqrt{3} - 5\right)\left(\sqrt{3} + 5\right)$
Use the FOIL method.	$= \sqrt{3} \cdot \sqrt{3} + 5 \cdot \sqrt{3} - 5 \cdot \sqrt{3} - 5 \cdot 5$
Multiply.	$= \sqrt{9} + 5\sqrt{3} - 5\sqrt{3} - 25$
The middle terms are opposites and cancel.	$= \sqrt{9} - 25$
Simplify $\sqrt{9}$.	$= 3 - 25$
Subtract.	$= -22$

Conjugates

In the previous example, we multiplied two radical expressions, $\left(\sqrt{3} - 5\right)$ and $\left(\sqrt{3} + 5\right)$.

You may have been surprised that the result -22, does not contain a radical.

Let's recall why that is so.

We used the FOIL method to multiply:

$$\left(\sqrt{3} - 5\right)\left(\sqrt{3} + 5\right) = \overset{\mathbf{F}}{\sqrt{9}} + \overset{\mathbf{O}}{5\sqrt{3}} - \overset{\mathbf{I}}{5\sqrt{3}} - \overset{\mathbf{L}}{25}$$

9 is a
perfect square

These two terms are
opposites and add
to zero.

$$= \quad 3 \qquad\qquad\qquad -25$$

$$= \quad -22$$

Let's look again at the original two radical expressions.

The first terms are the same.

$$\left(\sqrt{3} - 5\right) \text{ and } \left(\sqrt{3} + 5\right)$$

The last terms are the same *except* for their signs.

Such binomial radical expressions are called **conjugates**.

Here are some other examples of conjugates:

$$\sqrt{5} + 7 \text{ and } \sqrt{5} - 7$$

$$6 + \sqrt{15} \text{ and } 6 - \sqrt{15}$$

$$\sqrt{3} + \sqrt{2} \text{ and } \sqrt{3} - \sqrt{2}$$

When we multiply two conjugate radical expressions, the result is a rational number. For this reason, conjugates are used to simplify certain types of radical expressions.

Example 9.1.23

Multiply $5 - \sqrt{2}$ by its conjugate.

Solution

The conjugate of $5 - \sqrt{2}$ is $5 + \sqrt{2}$. $(5 - \sqrt{2})(5 + \sqrt{2})$

Use the FOIL method. $= 5 \cdot 5 + 5\sqrt{2} - 5\sqrt{2} - \sqrt{2}\sqrt{2}$

Multiply. $= 25 + 5\sqrt{2} - 5\sqrt{2} - \sqrt{4}$

The two middle terms are opposites and add to zero. $= 25 - \sqrt{4}$

Simplify $\sqrt{4}$. $= 25 - 2$

Subtract. $= 23$

Rationalizing the Denominator

The radical expression $\dfrac{13}{\sqrt{5}}$ is not in simplified form because it has a radical in the denominator. To write it in simplified form we **rationalize** the denominator. That is, we make the denominator a rational number and eliminate the radical.

Example 9.1.24

Rationalize the denominator: $\dfrac{6}{5\sqrt{7}}$

Solution

To eliminate $\sqrt{7}$ from the denominator, we multiply $\dfrac{6}{5\sqrt{7}}$ by 1 in the written form $\dfrac{\sqrt{7}}{\sqrt{7}}$.

$$\dfrac{6}{5\sqrt{7}}$$

$$= \dfrac{6}{5\sqrt{7}} \cdot \dfrac{\sqrt{7}}{\sqrt{7}}$$

Multiply the numerators and multiply the denominators.

$$= \dfrac{6\sqrt{7}}{5\sqrt{49}}$$

Simplify $\sqrt{49}$.

$$= \dfrac{6\sqrt{7}}{5 \cdot 7}$$

Simplify the denominator.

$$= \dfrac{6\sqrt{7}}{35}$$

So,

$$\dfrac{6}{5\sqrt{7}} = \dfrac{6\sqrt{7}}{35}$$

When we multiply $\dfrac{6}{5\sqrt{7}}$ by 1, we do not change its value.

Here, we write 1 in the form $\dfrac{\sqrt{7}}{\sqrt{7}}$.

We can use a calculator to verify that $\dfrac{6}{5\sqrt{7}} = \dfrac{6\sqrt{7}}{35}$.

Use the $\boxed{\sqrt{\ }}$ key to approximate $\sqrt{7} \approx 2.645751$.

Example 9.1.25

Rationalize the denominator: $\dfrac{10}{7\sqrt[3]{2}}$

Solution

There is a cube root in the denominator, so we must multiply it by factors that will make the radicand a perfect cube.

Since $\sqrt[3]{2}$ occurs once as a factor, we need two more such factors to obtain a perfect cube.

$$\dfrac{10}{7\sqrt[3]{2}} \cdot \dfrac{\sqrt[3]{2} \cdot \sqrt[3]{2}}{\sqrt[3]{2} \cdot \sqrt[3]{2}}$$

Here we multiply the original expression by 1 written as:

$$\dfrac{\sqrt[3]{2} \cdot \sqrt[3]{2}}{\sqrt[3]{2} \cdot \sqrt[3]{2}}$$

Multiply.

$$= \dfrac{10\sqrt[3]{2 \cdot 2}}{7\sqrt[3]{2 \cdot 2 \cdot 2}}$$

Simplify the radicals.
$\sqrt[3]{2 \cdot 2 \cdot 2} = \sqrt[3]{8} = 2$.

$$= \dfrac{10\sqrt[3]{4}}{7 \cdot 2}$$

Cancel the common factor, 2, in the numerator and denominator.

$$= \dfrac{5\sqrt[3]{4}}{7}$$

Example 9.1.26

Rationalize the denominator: $\dfrac{9}{2 + \sqrt{6}}$

Solution

To eliminate the square root, we can multiply by the conjugate of $2 + \sqrt{6}$.

We multiply $\dfrac{9}{2 + \sqrt{6}}$ by 1 written in the form $\dfrac{2 - \sqrt{6}}{2 - \sqrt{6}}$.

$$\dfrac{9}{2 + \sqrt{6}} \cdot \dfrac{2 - \sqrt{6}}{2 - \sqrt{6}}$$

Multiply the numerators and multiply the denominators.

$$= \dfrac{9(2 - \sqrt{6})}{(2 + \sqrt{6})(2 - \sqrt{6})}$$

In the numerator, use the Distributive Property.

$$= \dfrac{18 - 9\sqrt{6}}{(2 + \sqrt{6})(2 - \sqrt{6})}$$

In the denominator, use the FOIL method.

$$= \dfrac{18 - 9\sqrt{6}}{4 - 2\sqrt{6} + 2\sqrt{6} - 6}$$

In the denominator, combine like terms.

$$= \dfrac{18 - 9\sqrt{6}}{-2}$$

We normally do not leave a negative number in the denominator. Therefore, multiply by 1 in the form $\dfrac{-1}{-1}$.

$$= \dfrac{18 - 9\sqrt{6}}{-2} \cdot \dfrac{-1}{-1}$$

Multiply the numerators and multiply the denominators.

$$= \dfrac{-18 + 9\sqrt{6}}{2}$$

Solving an Equation That Contains a Square Root

An equation with a variable in a radicand is called a **radical equation**. Here are three examples:

$$\sqrt{x} = 7 \qquad\qquad \sqrt{x} + 3 = 12 \qquad\qquad \sqrt{x+4} - 5 = 2$$

The following procedure may be used to solve an equation that contains a variable under a square root symbol.

— Procedure —
To Solve an Equation That Contains a Variable Under a Square Root Symbol

Step 1 Isolate the square-root radical on one side of the equation.

Step 2 Square both sides of the equation.

Step 3 Solve for the variable.

Step 4 Check the answer.

Example 9.1.27

Solve: $\sqrt{2x} - 3 = 7$

Solution $\hfill \sqrt{2x} - 3 = 7$

Step 1 Isolate the square-root radical on one side of the equation.

Add 3 to both sides of the equation. $\hfill \sqrt{2x} = 10$

Remember, squaring "undoes" the square root.

Step 2 Square both sides of the equation. $\hfill \left(\sqrt{2x}\right)^2 = 10^2$

  Simplify. $\hfill 2x = 100$

Step 3 Solve for the variable.

Divide both sides by 2. $\hfill x = 50$

Step 4 Check the answer.

To check, substitute 50 for x in the original equation and simplify. $\hfill \sqrt{2x} - 3 = 7$

$$\text{Is} \quad \sqrt{2(\mathbf{50})} - 3 = 7\,?$$

$$\text{Is} \quad \sqrt{100} - 3 = 7\,?$$

$$\text{Is} \quad 10 - 3 = 7\,?$$

$$\text{Is} \quad 7 = 7\,? \ \textbf{Yes}$$

So, $x = 50$ is the solution of the radical equation.

Example 9.1.28

Solve: $\sqrt{2x-5} + 4 = 11$

Solution
$$\sqrt{2x-5} + 4 = 11$$

Step 1 Isolate the square-root radical on one side of the equation.

Subtract 4 from both sides of the equation.
$$\sqrt{2x-5} = 7$$

Step 2 Square both sides of the equation.
$$\left(\sqrt{2x-5}\right)^2 = 7^2$$

Simplify.
$$2x - 5 = 49$$

Step 3 Solve for the variable.

Add 5 to both sides of the equation.
$$2x = 54$$

Divide both sides by 2.
$$x = 27$$

Step 4 Check the answer.

To check, substitute 27 for x in the original equation and simplify.
$$\sqrt{2x-5} + 4 = 11$$

$$\text{Is } \sqrt{2\cdot\mathbf{27}-5} + 4 = 11 \text{ ?}$$
$$\text{Is } \sqrt{49} + 4 = 11 \text{ ?}$$
$$\text{Is } 7 + 4 = 11 \text{ ?}$$
$$\text{Is } 11 = 11 \text{ ? } \textbf{Yes}$$

So, $x = 27$ is the solution of the radical equation.

Example 9.1.29

The distance, d, from the center of the Earth to the surface can be calculated using the formula

$$d = \sqrt{\frac{GM}{a}},$$

where

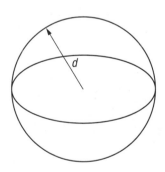

G = the universal gravitation constant,
   = 6.7×10^{-11} Newton · meter^2/kilogram^2;

M = the mass of the Earth;

a = acceleration due to gravity at the surface of the Earth.

Solve the equation for M to find an equation that can be used to calculate the mass of the Earth.

A Newton is a measure of force used in the Metric System. One Newton corresponds to about 0.22 pounds.

To calculate the mass of the earth, substitute these values for the variables:

$a = 9.8$ meters/second^2

$d = 6.4 \times 10^6$ meters

$G = 6.7 \times 10^{-11}$ Newton $\cdot$ meters^2/kilogram^2

$$M = \frac{9.8(6.4 \times 10^6)^2}{6.7 \times 10^{-11}}$$

$$\cong \frac{9.8 \cdot 4.1 \times 10^{13}}{6.7 \times 10^{-11}}$$

$$\cong \frac{4.0 \times 10^{14}}{6.7 \times 10^{-11}}$$

$$\cong 6.0 \times 10^{24} \text{ kg}$$

So, the mass of the earth is approximately 6,000,000,000,000,000,000,000,000 kilograms.

Solution

Since the square root is already isolated, begin by squaring both sides of the equation.

$$d = \sqrt{\frac{GM}{a}}$$

$$(d)^2 = \left(\sqrt{\frac{GM}{a}}\right)^2$$

Simplify.

$$d^2 = \frac{GM}{a}$$

Multiply both sides by a.

$$ad^2 = GM$$

Divide both sides by G.

$$\frac{ad^2}{G} = M$$

So,

$$M = \frac{ad^2}{G}.$$

Here is a summary of this concept from *Academic Systems Algebra*.

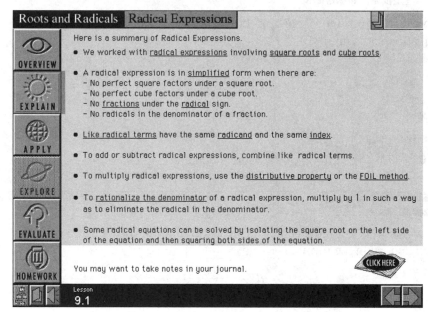

Roots and Radicals   Radical Expressions

OVERVIEW
EXPLAIN
APPLY
EXPLORE
EVALUATE
HOMEWORK

Here is a summary of Radical Expressions.

- We worked with radical expressions involving square roots and cube roots.

- A radical expression is in simplified form when there are:
  - No perfect square factors under a square root.
  - No perfect cube factors under a cube root.
  - No fractions under the radical sign.
  - No radicals in the denominator of a fraction.

- Like radical terms have the same radicand and the same index.

- To add or subtract radical expressions, combine like radical terms.

- To multiply radical expressions, use the distributive property or the FOIL method.

- To rationalize the denominator of a radical expression, multiply by 1 in such a way as to eliminate the radical in the denominator.

- Some radical equations can be solved by isolating the square root on the left side of the equation and then squaring both sides of the equation.

You may want to take notes in your journal.   CLICK HERE

Lesson 9.1

Checklist Lesson 9.1

Here is what you should know after completing this lesson.

Words and Phrases

square root
positive square root
principal square root
radical symbol
radicand
radical
radical expression
perfect square

cube root
index
perfect cube
like radical terms
conjugates
rationalize
radical equation

Ideas and Procedures

❶ **Square Root**
Define the principal square root of a number.

The principal square root of a nonnegative real number, a, is written $\sqrt{a}$.

If b is a nonnegative real number and $b^2 = a$, then $\sqrt{a} = b$.

Estimate the square root of a number.

Example 9.1.1
The area of a square room is 90 ft² (square feet). Which of the following values best approximates the length of each side of the room: 8.7 feet, 9 feet, 9.5 feet, or 10 feet?

See also: Example 9.1.2
Apply 1-6

❷ **Perfect Square**
Define perfect square and list some whole numbers that are perfect squares.

A perfect square is a number that has a rational square root. The following whole numbers are examples of perfect squares:
1, 4, 9, 16, 25, 36, 49, 64, 81, and 100.

❸ **Squares and Square Roots**
State the relationship between squaring and taking a square root.

If a is a nonnegative real number, then $\sqrt{a^2} = a$ and $\left(\sqrt{a}\right)^2 = a$.

❹ **Cube Root**
Define the cube root of a number.

The cube root of a real number, a, is written $\sqrt[3]{a}$.
If b is a real number and $b^3 = a$, then $\sqrt[3]{a} = b$.

❺ **Perfect Cube**
Define perfect cube and list some whole numbers that are perfect cubes.

A perfect cube is a number that has a rational cube root.
The following whole numbers are examples of perfect cubes: 1, 8, 27, 64, 125, and 216.

⑥ Cubes and Cube Roots

State the relationship between cubing and taking a cube root.

If a is a real number, then $\sqrt[3]{a^3} = a$ and $\left(\sqrt[3]{a}\right)^3 = a$.

⑦ Multiplication Property of Square Roots; of Cube Roots

State the Multiplication Property of Square Roots; of Cube Roots.

Square roots: $\sqrt{ab} = \sqrt{a}\sqrt{b}, a \geq 0, b \geq 0$
Cube roots: $\sqrt[3]{ab} = \sqrt[3]{a}\sqrt[3]{b}$

Use the Multiplication Property to simplify an expression.

Example 9.1.3
Simplify: $\sqrt[3]{8 \cdot 6}$

See also: Example 9.1.4

⑧ Division Property of Square Roots; of Cube Roots

State the Division Property of Square Roots; of Cube Roots.

Square roots: $\sqrt{\dfrac{a}{b}} = \dfrac{\sqrt{a}}{\sqrt{b}}, a \geq 0, b > 0$

Cube roots: $\sqrt[3]{\dfrac{a}{b}} = \dfrac{\sqrt[3]{a}}{\sqrt[3]{b}}, b \neq 0$

Use the Division Property to simplify an expression.

Example 9.1.6

Simplify: $\dfrac{\sqrt{27}}{\sqrt{3}}$

See also: Example 9.1.5
Apply 7, 8

⑨ Simplify a Square-Root Radical Expression With a Whole Number Radicand

Simplify the square root of a whole number.

Example 9.1.8
Simplify: $\sqrt{108}$

See also: Example 9.1.7

⑩ Simplify a Cube-Root Radical Expression With an Integer Radicand

Simplify the cube root of an expression that contains only integers.

Example 9.1.10

Simplify: $\sqrt[3]{\dfrac{-40}{27}}$

See also: Example 9.1.9

⑪ Simplify a Square-Root Radical Expression With Variables in the Radicand

Simplify the square root of an expression that contains variables.

Example 9.1.12
Simplify: $\sqrt{50y^7}$

See also: Example 9.1.11
Apply 9

⑫ Simplify a Cube-Root Radical Expression With Variables in the Radicand

Simplify the cube root of an expression that contains variables.

Example 9.1.13
Simplify: $\sqrt[3]{8x^2y^7}$

See also: Apply 10

⑬ Like Radical Terms
Identify like radical terms.

Example 9.1.15
Identify the like radical terms:
$$\sqrt[3]{15}, \quad 7\sqrt{15}, \quad -4\sqrt[3]{15}, \quad 27\sqrt[3]{15}, \quad 2\sqrt[3]{5}$$

See also: Example 9.1.14

⑭ Combine Like Radical Terms
Add and subtract like radical terms.

Example 9.1.17
Find: $\sqrt{24} + 8 \cdot \sqrt[3]{6} + 9\sqrt{6} - 4$

See also: Example 9.1.16, 9.1.18
Apply 11, 12

⑮ Multiply Square Roots; Multiply Cube Roots
Multiply radical expressions that contain square roots or cube roots.

Example 9.1.20
Find: $\left(5 + \sqrt{10}\right)\left(7 - \sqrt{10}\right)$

See also: Example 9.1.19, 9.1.21
Apply 13, 14

⑯ Conjugates
Multiply conjugate radical expressions.

Example 9.1.23
Multiply $5 - \sqrt{2}$ by its conjugate.

See also: Example 9.1.22
Apply 15, 16

⑰ Rationalize a Denominator
Rationalize the denominator of a radical expression.

Example 9.1.26
Rationalize the denominator: $\dfrac{9}{2 + \sqrt{6}}$

See also: Example 9.1.24, 9.1.25
Apply 17, 18

⑱ Equations That Contain a Square Root
Solve an equation that contains a square root.

Example 9.1.28
Solve: $\sqrt{2x - 5} + 4 = 11$

See also: Example 9.1.27, 9.1.29
Apply 19, 20

Homework

Homework Problems

Circle the homework problems assigned to you by the computer, then complete them below.

☀ Explain

Square Roots and Cube Roots

1. For the expression $\sqrt[3]{27}$:

   a. Identify the radical.

   b. Identify the radicand.

   c. Identify the index.

   d. Evaluate the radical.

2. Evaluate: $\sqrt{49}$

3. Evaluate: $\sqrt[3]{-1000}$

4. Simplify: $\sqrt{162}$

5. Simplify: $\sqrt{\dfrac{108}{25}}$

6. Find two consecutive integers between which $\sqrt{50}$ lies.

7. Simplify: $\sqrt[3]{750}$

8. Simplify: $\sqrt[3]{\dfrac{80}{125}}$

9. The area of a circle is given by the formula $A = \pi r^2$, where A is the area of the circle and r is the radius of the circle. If the radius of a circle is $\sqrt{38}$ cm, what is the area of the circle?

10. If the volume of a cube is 216 cubic inches, what is the length of each edge of the cube? (Hint: The volume, V, of a cube with edges, each of length e is $V = e^3$.)

11. Simplify: $\sqrt{147a^{20}b^3}$

12. Simplify: $\sqrt[3]{216x^{21}y^4}$

13. Find: $2\sqrt{3} + \sqrt{13} - \sqrt{3} + 5\sqrt{13} + 3$

14. Find: $4\sqrt[3]{6} - 2\sqrt[3]{6} - 5\sqrt[3]{12} + 4\sqrt[3]{12}$

15. Find: $\sqrt{5}\left(3\sqrt{11} + 8\right)$

16. Find: $6\sqrt{98} - 2\sqrt{2} + 4 - \sqrt{128}$

17. Find: $4\sqrt[3]{24} - 2\sqrt[3]{81} + 5\sqrt[3]{3}$

18. Find: $\left(4\sqrt{5} + 3\right)\left(2\sqrt{7} - 5\right)$

19. Rationalize the denominator: $\dfrac{9}{11\sqrt{10}}$

20. Rationalize the denominator: $\dfrac{3}{6 + \sqrt{5}}$

21. The radius, r, of a sphere with surface area A is given by the formula $r = \dfrac{1}{2}\sqrt{\dfrac{A}{\pi}}$. If a sphere has radius 5 feet, what is its surface area?

22. The radius, r, of a sphere with volume V is given by the formula $r = \sqrt[3]{\dfrac{3V}{4\pi}}$. If a sphere has radius 3 inches, what is its volume?

23. Solve for x: $13 - \sqrt{x} = 4$

24. Solve for y: $\sqrt{3y - 2} - 5 = 5$

 **Apply**

Practice Problems

Here are some additional practice problems for you to try.

1. Find the negative square root of 25.

2. 25 and -25 are square roots of what number?

3. A square rug has area 110 square feet. Of the following values, which best approximates the length of an edge of the rug?

   a. 8.8 feet

   b. 10.5 feet

   c. 11.0 feet

   d. 27.5 feet

4. The area of a square table top is 6 square feet. Of the following values, which best approximates the length of an edge of the table top?

   a. 1.5 feet

   b. 2.0 feet

   c. 2.4 feet

   d. 3.0 feet

5. In a right triangle, the sum of the squares of the lengths of the legs is equal to the square of the length of the hypotenuse. Suppose the length of one leg of a right triangle is 5 cm and the length of the hypotenuse is 13 cm. What is the length of the other leg?

6. In a right triangle, the sum of the squares of the lengths of the legs is equal to the square of the length of the hypotenuse. Suppose the length of one leg of a right triangle is 24 inches and the length of the hypotenuse is 25 inches. What is the length of the other leg?

7. Simplify: $\dfrac{\sqrt{125}}{\sqrt{5}}$

8. Simplify: $\dfrac{\sqrt[3]{81}}{\sqrt[3]{-3}}$

9. Simplify: $\sqrt{x^5 y^2}$

10. Simplify: $\sqrt[3]{-x^5 y^2}$

11. Find: $\sqrt{3} - \sqrt{12} + \sqrt{27}$

12. Find: $-\sqrt[3]{5} + \sqrt[3]{135} - \sqrt[3]{40}$

13. Use the FOIL method to do this multiplication:
$(3 + \sqrt{5})(\sqrt{5} - 2)$

14. Use the FOIL method to do this multiplication:
$(\sqrt{6} + 1)(3 - \sqrt{6})$

15. Multiply $4 + \sqrt{6}$ by its conjugate. What is the result?

16. Multiply $-4 + 3\sqrt{5}$ by its conjugate. What is the result?

17. Which of the following expressions, when multiplied by $\dfrac{3}{2 + \sqrt{14}}$, rationalizes the

    denominator of $\dfrac{3}{2 + \sqrt{14}}$?

    a. $\dfrac{2 - \sqrt{14}}{2 - \sqrt{14}}$

    b. $\dfrac{-2 + \sqrt{14}}{-2 + \sqrt{14}}$

    c. $\dfrac{-2 - \sqrt{14}}{-2 - \sqrt{14}}$

18. Which of the following expressions, when multiplied by $\dfrac{8}{\sqrt[3]{10}}$, rationalizes

    the denominator of $\dfrac{8}{\sqrt[3]{10}}$?

    a. $\dfrac{\sqrt{10} \cdot \sqrt{10}}{\sqrt{10} \cdot \sqrt{10}}$

    b. $\dfrac{\sqrt[3]{10} \cdot \sqrt[3]{10}}{\sqrt[3]{10} \cdot \sqrt[3]{10}}$

    c. $\dfrac{\sqrt[3]{10}}{\sqrt[3]{10}}$

19. Solve this radical equation for x:
$\sqrt{2x - 3} + 16 = 19$

20. Solve this radical equation for x: $\dfrac{3x + 1}{5} = 20$

Evaluate

Practice Test

Take this practice test to be sure that you are prepared for the final quiz in Evaluate.

1. A positive number, a, has principal square root 1.1.

   a. What is another square root of a?

   b. What is the value of a?

2. The number $\sqrt[3]{-30}$ lies between what two consecutive integers?

3. Simplify the quotient of these square roots: $\dfrac{\sqrt{147}}{\sqrt{3}}$

4. Use prime factorization to simplify this radical: $\sqrt{28u^3}$ Here, u is a nonnegative number.

5. Find: $\sqrt{99} + \sqrt{44} - \sqrt{50} - \sqrt{2}$

6. Multiply $3 - 5\sqrt{2}$ by its conjugate. Enter the result.

7. For each given radical expression, rationalize the denominator.

   a. $\dfrac{5}{\sqrt[3]{-6}}$

   b. $\dfrac{3}{1 + \sqrt{7}}$

8. Solve this equation for x: $3\sqrt{5 - x} = 12$

LESSON 9.2
RATIONAL EXPONENTS

 Overview

You have already learned about square roots and cube roots. In this lesson, you will extend your study of radicals to simplify, add, subtract, multiply, and divide radical expressions.

First, you will learn about rational exponents and their relationship to radicals. You will use the properties of exponents to simplify expressions that contain rational exponents.

 Explain

Concept 1 has sections on

- **Square Roots**

- **n^{th} Roots**

- **Rational Exponents**

- **Properties of Rational Exponents**

CONCEPT 1:
ROOTS AND EXPONENTS

Square Roots

To square a number, we raise the number to the second power.

For example, $6^2 = 36$.

To find the **square root** of a number, we reverse the squaring process.

For example,

- one square root of 36 is 6, because $6^2 = 36$;

- another square root of 36 is -6, because $(-6)^2 = 36$.

Each positive real number has a positive square root and a negative square root.

The positive square root is called the **principal square root**.

The **radical symbol**, $\sqrt{\ }$, is used to denote the principal square root of a number.

For example, the principal square root of 36 is written like this: $\sqrt{36}$.

Since the principle square root is the positive square root, we have:
$$\sqrt{36} = 6.$$

The expression under the radical symbol is called the **radicand**.

Here, the radicand is 36: $\sqrt{36}$.

A **radical** is the part of an expression that consists of a radical symbol and a radicand.

A **radical expression** is an expression that contains a radical.

In this example, the radical is $\sqrt{3}$.

$$13 - 5\sqrt{3}$$

radical symbol
radicand
radical

A negative number, for example -36, does not have square roots that are *real* numbers. That's because a real number times itself always gives a *nonnegative* number.

$$6^2 = +36 \qquad\qquad (-6)^2 = +36$$

— Definition —
Square Root

For a nonnegative real number, a, the principal square root of a is written $\sqrt{a}$.

If b is a nonnegative real number and $b^2 = a$, then $\sqrt{a} = b$.

Example:

$\sqrt{36} = 6$ because b is nonnegative and $6^2 = 36$.

When you square the square root of a nonnegative number, the result is the original number.

For example,

$$\left(\sqrt{14}\right)^2 = 14.$$

Likewise, when you take the square root of a nonnegative number squared, the result is the original number.

For example,

$$\sqrt{(14)^2} = 14.$$

nth Roots

Now we will study higher order roots, such as cube roots. Like square roots, these roots can be written using a radical symbol. To indicate the specific root, a number called the **index** is written just above the $\sqrt{}$ on the radical symbol.

For example, the cube root of 8 is written like this: $\sqrt[3]{8}$.

The index, 3, indicates the radical is a cube root.

The cube root of 8 is 2 because $2^3 = 8$.

We write: $\sqrt[3]{8} = 2$.

The square root of a number is also called the 2nd root of the number.

The index of a square root is 2, but we rarely write it. Thus,

$$\sqrt{5} = \sqrt[2]{5}.$$

The cube root of a number is also called the 3rd root of the number.

In a similar way, we define 4th roots, 5th roots, 6th roots, and so on.

For example,

- The 4th root of 81 is written like this: $\sqrt[4]{81}$
  The index is 4.
  $\sqrt[4]{81} = 3$ because $3^4 = 81$.

- The 10th root of 1 is written like this: $\sqrt[10]{1}$
  The index is 10.
  $\sqrt[10]{1} = 1$ because $1^{10} = 1$.

To indicate an nth root, we use the letter n for the index.

- If n is odd, then $\sqrt[n]{a}$ is always a real number.

  For example, $\sqrt[3]{8}$ and $\sqrt[3]{-8}$ are both real numbers:

  $$\sqrt[3]{8} = 2 \text{ and } \sqrt[3]{-8} = -2.$$

- If n is even, then $\sqrt[n]{a}$ is a real number only when $a \geq 0$.

  For example, $\sqrt{25} = 5$, but $\sqrt{-25}$ is not a real number because $5 \cdot 5 \neq -25$ and $(-5) \cdot (-5) \neq -25$. In fact, no real number multiplied by itself will equal -25.

n	n^{th} root	symbol
2	square root	$\sqrt{}$
3	cube root	$\sqrt[3]{}$
4	fourth root	$\sqrt[4]{}$
5	fifth root	$\sqrt[5]{}$
⋮	⋮	⋮

Example 9.2.1

a. Find: $\sqrt[4]{625}$ b. Find the 5th root of 243.

Solution

a. Find the prime factorization of 625.

  $$625 = 5 \cdot 5 \cdot 5 \cdot 5 = 5^4$$

  Since $5^4 = 625$, and 5 is positive, $\sqrt[4]{625} = 5$.

b. The 5th root of 243 may be written $\sqrt[5]{243}$.

  Find the prime factorization of 243.

  $$243 = 3 \cdot 3 \cdot 3 \cdot 3 \cdot 3 = 3^5.$$

  Since $3^5 = 243$, $\sqrt[5]{243} = 3$.

Rational Exponents

We can also use exponential notation to represent a radical. To do so, we use a **rational exponent**.

Recall that a rational number is a number that may be written as the ratio of two integers.

So, a rational exponent may be a fraction, such as $\frac{1}{2}$ or $\frac{5}{3}$, or an integer such as $2 = \frac{2}{1}$.

— Definition —
Rational Exponent With Numerator 1

If a is a real number, then

$$a^{1/n} = \sqrt[n]{a}.$$

Here, n is a positive integer.

If n is odd, then $a^{1/n}$ is a real number.

If n is even, then $a^{1/n}$ is a real number only when $a \geq 0$.

The way we interpret 2^n depends upon the value of n:

* *n is a whole number*
$$2^3 = \underbrace{2 \cdot 2 \cdot 2}_{3\ factors}$$

* *n is zero*
$$2^0 = 1$$

* *n is a negative integer*
$$2^{-3} = \frac{1}{2^3}$$

* *n is a fraction*
$$2^{1/3} = \sqrt[3]{2}$$

Using this definition, we write:

$$\sqrt{6} = 6^{1/2}$$
$$3^{1/5} = \sqrt[5]{3}$$

Example 9.2.2

Rewrite using a radical and evaluate: $125^{1/3}$

Solution

Write the radical symbol. $\qquad\qquad\qquad\qquad\qquad\qquad \sqrt{}$

The index is 3, the denominator of the exponent $\frac{1}{3}$. $\qquad\quad \sqrt[3]{}$

The radicand is 125, the base of the exponential expression. $\quad \sqrt[3]{125}$

Find the prime factorization of 125.

$$125 = 5 \cdot 5 \cdot 5 = 5^3.$$

Since $5^3 = 125$, the cube root of 125 is 5.

So,

$$125^{1/3} = \sqrt[3]{125} = 5.$$

Properties of Rational Exponents

The properties of integer exponents also hold for rational exponents. This table contains an example of each property.

Property	Integer Exponents	Rational Exponents
Multiplication	$3^2 \cdot 3^4 = 3^{2+4} = 3^6$	$3^{7/5} \cdot 3^{3/5} = 3^{7/5 + 3/5} = 3^{10/5}$ $= 3^2 = 9$
Division	$\dfrac{4^7}{4^5} = 4^{7-5} = 4^2$	$\dfrac{4^{1/2}}{4^{1/3}} = 4^{1/2 - 1/3} = 4^{3/6 - 2/6}$ $= 4^{1/6} = \sqrt[6]{4}$
Power of a Power	$(5^2)^3 = 5^{2 \cdot 3} = 5^6$	$(5^{1/2})^{2/3} = 5^{\frac{1}{2} \cdot \frac{2}{3}} = 5^{1/3} = \sqrt[3]{5}$
Power of a Product	$(5 \cdot 7)^3 = 5^3 \cdot 7^3$	$(5 \cdot 7)^{1/6} = 5^{1/6} \cdot 7^{1/6}$ $= \sqrt[6]{5} \cdot \sqrt[6]{7}$
Power of a Quotient	$\left(\dfrac{3}{5}\right)^4 = \dfrac{3^4}{5^4}$	$\left(\dfrac{3}{4}\right)^{1/2} = \dfrac{3^{1/2}}{4^{1/2}} = \dfrac{\sqrt{3}}{\sqrt{4}} = \dfrac{\sqrt{3}}{2}$

The Power of a Power Property is particularly useful when we work with rational exponents.

	Notation 1	Notation 2
For example, let's use this property to rewrite $5^{3/4}$ in two different, but equivalent, ways.	$5^{3/4}$	$5^{3/4}$
Rewrite the fraction 3/4 as $3 \cdot (1/4)$ and as $(1/4) \cdot 3$.	$= 5^{3 \cdot (1/4)}$	$= 5^{(1/4) \cdot 3}$
Use the Power of a Power Property.	$= (5^3)^{1/4}$	$= (5^{1/4})^3$
Use radical notation.	$= \sqrt[4]{5^3}$	$= (\sqrt[4]{5})^3$

Thus, $5^{3/4} = \sqrt[4]{5^3} = (\sqrt[4]{5})^3$.

Let's compare the original exponential expression, $5^{3/4}$, with the final radical expressions, $\sqrt[4]{5^3}$ and $(\sqrt[4]{5})^3$.

- In the original expression $5^{3/4}$, the exponent is $\dfrac{3}{4}$.

- The denominator, **4**, is the index of the radical $\sqrt[4]{}$.

- The numerator, **3**, is a power in the radical expression.

$$\sqrt[4]{5^3} \leftarrow \text{power of the radicand}$$

$$(\sqrt[4]{5})^3 \leftarrow \text{power of the radical}$$

This relationship is true in general.

— Definition —
Rational Exponent With Numerator m

If a is a real number, m is a nonnegative integer, n is a positive integer, and $\dfrac{m}{n}$ is in lowest terms, then
$$a^{m/n} = \left(\sqrt[n]{a}\right)^m = \sqrt[n]{a^m}$$
If n is even, then $a^{m/n}$ is a real number only when $a \geq 0$.

Examples:
$$5^{2/3} = \sqrt[3]{5^2} = \left(\sqrt[3]{5}\right)^2$$
$$6^{3/8} = \sqrt[8]{6^3} = \left(\sqrt[8]{6}\right)^3$$

When $m = 1$, we have
$$a^{m/n} = a^{1/n} = \left(\sqrt[n]{a}\right)^1 = \sqrt[n]{a}.$$

That is $a^{1/n} = \sqrt[n]{a}$.

Example 9.2.3

Rewrite using a radical and evaluate: $32^{3/5}$

Solution

We will use three different methods to solve this problem.

Method 1 Use $a^{m/n} = \left(\sqrt[n]{a}\right)^m$ $32^{3/5}$

Here, $a = 32$, $m = 3$, and $n = 5$. $= \left(\sqrt[5]{32}\right)^3$

Find the prime factorization of 32.

    $32 = 2 \cdot 2 \cdot 2 \cdot 2 \cdot 2 = 2^5.$ $= \left(\sqrt[5]{2^5}\right)^3$

Simplify the radical. $= (2)^3$

Evaluate 2^3. $= 8$

Method 2 typically means dealing with larger numbers since we first evaluate the power.

Method 2 Use $a^{m/n} = \sqrt[n]{a^m}$ $32^{3/5}$

Comparing $a^{m/n}$ to $32^{3/5}$ we see that $a = 32$, $= \sqrt[5]{32^3}$
$m = 3$, and $n = 5$.

Use your calculator to find 32^3. $= \sqrt[5]{32{,}768}$

Use your calculator to find $\sqrt[5]{32{,}768}$. $= 8$

Method 3 Use the Power of a Power Property
of Exponents, $(a^m)^n = a^{mn}$. $32^{3/5}$

Find the prime factorization of 32.

    $32 = 2 \cdot 2 \cdot 2 \cdot 2 \cdot 2 = 2^5.$ $= \left(2^5\right)^{3/5}$

Use the Power of a Power Property of Exponents. $= 2^{5 \cdot \frac{3}{5}}$

Multiply the exponents and write the result
in lowest terms. $= 2^3$

Evaluate 2^3. $= 8$

In summary, all three methods lead to the same result:
$$32^{3/5} = 8$$

Before we rewrite an exponential expression as a radical, we must make sure that the rational exponent is reduced to lowest terms.

Example 9.2.4

Simplify and write using only positive exponents: $w^{1/3} \cdot w^{(-3/2)} \cdot w^{1/6}$

Solution

Each factor has the same base, w.

$$w^{1/3} \cdot w^{(-3/2)} \cdot w^{1/6}$$

Therefore, add the exponents and keep w as the base.

$$= w^{1/3 + (-3/2) + 1/6}$$

Write each fraction with the LCD, 6.

$$= w^{2/6 - 9/6 + 1/6}$$

Add the exponents.

$$= w^{-6/6}$$

Simplify.

$$= w^{-1}$$

Use $a^{-n} = \dfrac{1}{a^n}$ to write the expression using a positive exponent.

$$= \dfrac{1}{w}$$

Therefore,

$$w^{1/3} \cdot w^{(-3/2)} \cdot w^{1/6} = \dfrac{1}{w}.$$

Example 9.2.5

Simplify and write using only positive exponents: $\left(\dfrac{2wx^{-1/5}}{5w^{2/3}}\right)^{-3}$

Solution

There is more than one way to start simplifying.

We begin with the Power of a Quotient Property.

$$= \dfrac{\left(2wx^{-1/5}\right)^{-3}}{\left(5w^{2/3}\right)^{-3}}$$

Use the Power of a Product Property to raise each factor to the power -3.

$$= \dfrac{(2)^{-3} \cdot (w)^{-3} \cdot \left(x^{-1/5}\right)^{-3}}{(5)^{-3} \cdot \left(w^{2/3}\right)^{-3}}$$

Use the Power of a Power Property.

$$= \dfrac{2^{-3} \cdot w^{-3} \cdot x^{3/5}}{5^{-3} \cdot w^{-2}}$$

Use the following to write the coefficients with positive exponents: $a^{-n} = \dfrac{1}{a^n}$ and $a^n = \dfrac{1}{a^{-n}}$

$$= \dfrac{5^3 \cdot w^2 \cdot x^{3/5}}{2^3 \cdot w^3}$$

Evaluate the coefficients and simplify $\dfrac{w^2}{w^3}$.

$$= \dfrac{125x^{3/5}}{8w}$$

So,

$$\left(\dfrac{2wx^{-1/5}}{5w^{2/3}}\right)^{-3} = \dfrac{125x^{3/5}}{8w}$$

We could use radical notation to write $\dfrac{125x^{3/5}}{8w}$ as $\dfrac{125\sqrt[5]{x^3}}{8w}$

Here is a summary of this concept from *Academic Systems Algebra*.

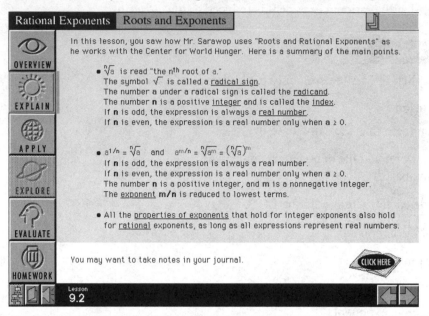

Rational Exponents	Roots and Exponents

OVERVIEW

EXPLAIN

APPLY

EXPLORE

EVALUATE

HOMEWORK

In this lesson, you saw how Mr. Sarawop uses "Roots and Rational Exponents" as he works with the Center for World Hunger. Here is a summary of the main points.

- $\sqrt[n]{a}$ is read "the nth root of a."
  The symbol $\sqrt{}$ is called a <u>radical sign</u>.
  The number a under a radical sign is called the <u>radicand</u>.
  The number **n** is a positive <u>integer</u> and is called the <u>index</u>.
  If **n** is odd, the expression is always a <u>real number</u>.
  If **n** is even, the expression is a real number only when a ≥ 0.

- $a^{1/n} = \sqrt[n]{a}$ and $a^{m/n} = \sqrt[n]{a^m} = \left(\sqrt[n]{a}\right)^m$
  If **n** is odd, the expression is always a real number.
  If **n** is even, the expression is a real number only when a ≥ 0.
  The number **n** is a positive integer, and m is a nonnegative integer.
  The <u>exponent</u> **m/n** is reduced to lowest terms.

- All the <u>properties of exponents</u> that hold for integer exponents also hold for <u>rational</u> exponents, as long as all expressions represent real numbers.

You may want to take notes in your journal.

CLICK HERE

Lesson 9.2

Concept 2 has sections on

- **Multiplication Property of Radicals**

- **Division Property of Radicals**

- **The Relationship Between Roots and Powers**

- **Simplifying Radical Expressions Containing One Term**

CONCEPT 2: SIMPLIFYING RADICALS

Multiplication Property of Radicals

The Multiplication Property of Radicals allows us to write a single radical as the product of two radicals.

Here are two examples: ***Square Root***   ***Cube Root***

$$\sqrt{2w} = \sqrt{2} \cdot \sqrt{w} \qquad \sqrt[3]{18y^2} = \sqrt[3]{18} \cdot \sqrt[3]{y^2}$$

The property can also be used to write the product of two radicals as a single radical, provided the two radicals have the same index.

Here are two examples: ***Square Root***   ***Cube Root***

$$\sqrt{11} \cdot \sqrt{5x} = \sqrt{11 \cdot 5x} \quad \sqrt[3]{2} \cdot \sqrt[3]{6} = \sqrt[3]{2 \cdot 6}$$

— Property —
Multiplication Property of Radicals

English The nth root of a product is the product of the nth roots.

Algebra $\sqrt[n]{a \cdot b} = \sqrt[n]{a} \cdot \sqrt[n]{b}$
where $\sqrt[n]{a}$ and $\sqrt[n]{b}$ are real numbers and n is a positive integer.

Example $\sqrt[7]{5x^6} = \sqrt[7]{5} \cdot \sqrt[7]{x^6}$

*If x is **negative**, then $\sqrt{x^2} = |x|$.*

For example, if x = −3:
$\sqrt{x^2} = \sqrt{(-3)^2} = \sqrt{9} = +3 = |x|$

In the remainder of this Topic, we will assume that each variable under a radical represents a nonnegative real number.

Example 9.2.6

Simplify: a. $\sqrt{25x^2}$ b. $\sqrt[4]{16y^5}$

Solution

To simplify, use the Multiplication Property of Radicals to rewrite each radical.

a. $\sqrt{25x^2}$

Write the radical as a product of radicals. $= \sqrt{25} \cdot \sqrt{x^2}$

Simplify each radical. $= 5 \cdot x$

                                                $= 5x$

If possible, write the radicand as a product where one exponent is a multiple of the index. Use the largest multiple possible.

Here are three examples:

$\sqrt{3^5} = \sqrt{3^4 \cdot 3^1} = \sqrt{3^4} \cdot \sqrt{3^1}$
$\qquad = 3^2 \cdot \sqrt{3^1}$

$\sqrt[3]{w^5} = \sqrt[3]{w^3 \cdot w^2} = \sqrt[3]{w^3} \cdot \sqrt[3]{w^2}$
$\qquad = w \cdot \sqrt[3]{w^2}$

$\sqrt[4]{y^{15}} = \sqrt[4]{y^{12} \cdot y^3} = \sqrt[4]{y^{12}} \cdot \sqrt[4]{y^3}$
$\qquad = y^3 \cdot \sqrt[4]{y^2}$

b. $\sqrt[4]{16y^5}$

Write the radical as a product of radicals. $= \sqrt[4]{16} \cdot \sqrt[4]{y^4} \cdot \sqrt[4]{y^1}$

Simplify $\sqrt[4]{16}$ and $\sqrt[4]{y^4}$. $= 2 \cdot y \cdot \sqrt[4]{y^1}$

                                                $= 2y\sqrt[4]{y}$

Example 9.2.7

Use the Multiplication Property of Radicals to rewrite each expression. Then simplify the result.

a. $\sqrt{2} \cdot \sqrt{32}$ b. $\sqrt[4]{w^3} \cdot \sqrt[4]{w}$

Solution

a. $\sqrt{2} \cdot \sqrt{32}$

Write the product as a single radical. $= \sqrt{2 \cdot 32}$

Multiply the factors under the radical symbol. $= \sqrt{64}$

Simplify the radical. $= 8$

b. $\sqrt[4]{w^3} \cdot \sqrt[4]{w}$

Write the product as a single radical. $= \sqrt[4]{w^3 \cdot w}$

Multiply the factors under the radical symbol. $= \sqrt[4]{w^4}$

Simplify the radical. $= w$

Division Property of Radicals

The Division Property of Radicals allows us to write a single radical as the quotient of two radicals.

Here are two examples:

Square Root

$$\sqrt{\frac{x}{14}} = \frac{\sqrt{x}}{\sqrt{14}}$$

Cube Root

$$\sqrt[3]{\frac{2}{25}} = \frac{\sqrt[3]{2}}{\sqrt[3]{25}}$$

It can also be used to write the quotient of two radicals as a single radical, provided they have the same index.

Here are two examples:

Square Root

$$\frac{\sqrt{3}}{\sqrt{2}} = \sqrt{\frac{3}{2}}$$

Cube Root

$$\frac{\sqrt[3]{6x^2}}{\sqrt[3]{5}} = \sqrt[3]{\frac{6x^2}{5}}$$

— Property —
Division Property of Radicals

English The nth root of a quotient is the quotient of the nth roots.

Algebra $\sqrt{\dfrac{a}{b}} = \dfrac{\sqrt[n]{a}}{\sqrt[n]{b}}$

where $\sqrt[n]{a}$ and $\sqrt[n]{b}$ are real numbers, $b \neq 0$, and n is a positive integer.

Example $\sqrt[5]{\dfrac{12x^4}{y^3}} = \dfrac{\sqrt[5]{12x^4}}{\sqrt[5]{y^3}}$

Example 9.2.8

Simplify: a. $\sqrt{\dfrac{23}{49}}$ b. $\sqrt[3]{\dfrac{15}{64}}$

Solution

To simplify, use the Division Property of Radicals to rewrite each radical.

a.
$$\sqrt{\frac{23}{49}}$$

Write each radical as a quotient of radicals. $= \dfrac{\sqrt{23}}{\sqrt{49}}$

Simplify $\sqrt{49}$. $= \dfrac{\sqrt{23}}{7}$

b.
$$\sqrt[3]{\frac{15}{64}}$$

Write each radical as a quotient of radicals. $= \dfrac{\sqrt[3]{15}}{\sqrt[3]{64}}$

Simplify $\sqrt[3]{64}$. $= \dfrac{\sqrt[3]{15}}{4}$

Example 9.2.9

Use the Division Property of Radicals to rewrite each radical. Then simplify the result.

a. $\dfrac{\sqrt{72w^3}}{\sqrt{2w}}$　　b. $\dfrac{\sqrt[4]{32x^6}}{\sqrt[4]{2x^2}}$

Solution

a.

$$\dfrac{\sqrt{72w^3}}{\sqrt{2w}}$$

Write the quotient as a single radical.　　$= \sqrt{\dfrac{72w^3}{2w}}$

Simplify the radicand.　　$= \sqrt{36w^2}$

Simplify the radical.　　$= 6w$

b.

$$\dfrac{\sqrt[4]{32x^6}}{\sqrt[4]{2x^2}}$$

Write the quotient as a single radical.　　$= \sqrt[4]{\dfrac{32x^6}{2x^2}}$

Simplify the radicand.　　$= \sqrt[4]{16x^4}$

Simplify the radical.　　$= 2x$

The Relationship Between Roots and Powers

Let's look again at the relationship between taking a square root and squaring.

For example, let's start with the number 6.　　6

Take its square root.　　$\sqrt{6}$

Square the square root.　　$\left(\sqrt{6}\right)^2 = \sqrt{6} \cdot \sqrt{6}$

Write the product as a single radical.　　$= \sqrt{6 \cdot 6}$

Multiply.　　$= \sqrt{36}$

Simplify.　　$= 6$

The result, 6, is the number that we started with.

Thus, squaring "undoes" taking a square root.
Here, we saw that $\left(\sqrt{6}\right)^2 = 6$.

This is true in general.

English Raising the nth root of a number to the nth power results in the original number.

Algebra If $\sqrt[n]{x}$ is defined, then
$$\left(\sqrt[n]{x}\right)^n = x.$$
Here, n is a positive integer.

Example $\left(\sqrt[8]{13}\right)^8 = 13.$

Example 9.2.10

Simplify: a. $\left(\sqrt[3]{10}\right)^3$ b. $\left(\sqrt[5]{w}\right)^5$ c. $\left(\sqrt[4]{x}\right)^4$ Here, $x \geq 0$

Solution

Use this relationship to simplify each radical: $\left(\sqrt[n]{x}\right)^n = x$

a. $\left(\sqrt[3]{10}\right)^3 = 10$ b. $\left(\sqrt[5]{w}\right)^5 = w$ c. $\left(\sqrt[4]{x}\right)^4 = x$

$\left(\sqrt[4]{x}\right)^4 = x$ only when $x \geq 0$. An even root of a negative number is **not** a real number.

Now, let's see what happens when we first square a negative number, and then take its square root.

For example, let's start with the number -4. -4

Square the number. The result is positive. $(-4)^2 = 16$

Take the square root. $\sqrt{16}$

Simplify. $= 4$

The result, 4, is the opposite of the number we started with.

Thus, when we square a negative number, and then take the square root, we obtain the opposite of the original number.

This relationship holds true, in general for *even* roots.

		Examples
$\sqrt[n]{x^n} = x$	if n is an *odd* positive integer and x is *any real number*.	$\sqrt[5]{17^5} = 17$
$\sqrt[n]{x^n} = x$	if n is an *even* positive integer and $x \geq 0$.	$\sqrt[4]{17^4} = 17$
$\sqrt[n]{x^n} = -1 \cdot x$	if n is an *even* positive integer and $x < 0$.	$\sqrt[4]{(-17)^4} = -1(-17)$ $= 17$

Example 9.2.11

Simplify: a. $\sqrt[3]{10^3}$ b. $\sqrt[5]{(-7)^5}$ c. $\sqrt[6]{y^6}$ Here, $y \geq 0$

Solution

Use this relationship to simplify each radical: $\sqrt[n]{x^n} = x$

a. $\sqrt[3]{10^3} = 10$ b. $\sqrt[5]{(-7)^5} = -7$ c. $\sqrt[6]{y^6} = y$

Example 9.2.12

Simplify: $\sqrt[4]{(-12)^4}$

Solution

This has the form $\sqrt[n]{x^n}$ where $x < 0$.

Therefore, use this relationship:
$\sqrt[n]{x^n} = -1 \cdot x$. $\sqrt[4]{(-12)^4} = -1 \cdot (-12) = 12$

Simplifying Radical Expressions Containing One Term

Here is what we mean by the simplified form of a radical expression that contains one term.

— Definition —
Simplified Form of a Radical Expression That Contains One Term

A radical expression that contains one term is in simplified form when:

• For $\sqrt[n]{x}$ there are no factors of x, other than 1, that are perfect n^{th} powers.

• There are no fractions under the radical symbol.

• There are no radicals in the denominator of an expression.

Here are some examples: ***Not simplified***

•   For $\sqrt[n]{x}$ there are no factors of x, other $\sqrt[3]{8w^3y^4}$
    than 1, that are perfect n^{th} powers.

•   There are no fractions under the radical symbol. $\sqrt{\dfrac{5x}{7}}$

•   There are no radicals in the denominator of a fraction. $\dfrac{\sqrt{10x}}{\sqrt{3w}}$

Example 9.2.13

Simplify: $\sqrt[3]{-24w^6x^2y^4}$

Solution

This radical is a cube root. It is not in simplified form because the radicand has some factors that are perfect cubes. To begin, we identify those factors.

$$\sqrt[3]{-24w^6x^2y^4}$$

Factor the radicand. Use perfect cube factors when possible.

$$= \sqrt[3]{-1 \cdot 2 \cdot 2 \cdot 2 \cdot 3 \cdot w^3 \cdot w^3 \cdot x^2 \cdot y^3 \cdot y^1}$$

Write as a product of radicals. Place each perfect cube under its own radical symbol. You can leave the "noncube" factors under the same radical symbol.

$$= \sqrt[3]{-1} \cdot \sqrt[3]{2^3} \cdot \sqrt[3]{w^3} \cdot \sqrt[3]{w^3} \cdot \sqrt[3]{y^3} \cdot \sqrt[3]{3x^2y^1}$$

Simplifying the cube root of each perfect cube.

$$= -1 \cdot 2 \cdot w \cdot w \cdot y \cdot \sqrt[3]{3x^2y^1}$$

Multiply the factors outside the radical symbol.

$$= -2w^2y\sqrt[3]{3x^2y^1}$$

So,

$$\sqrt[3]{-24w^6x^2y^4} = -2w^2y\sqrt[3]{3x^2y}$$

Example 9.2.14

Simplify: $\dfrac{\sqrt{108w^5y^{11}}}{\sqrt{6w}}$

Solution

This radical expression is not in simplified form because it has a radical in its denominator.

To begin, we will write the expression as a quotient under a single radical symbol.

Then we will try to simplify that quotient so that it can be written without a denominator.

$$\frac{\sqrt{108w^5y^{11}}}{\sqrt{6w}}$$

Use the Division Property of Radicals to write the quotient under one radical symbol.

$$= \sqrt{\frac{108w^5y^{11}}{6w}}$$

Simplify the radicand.

$$= \sqrt{\frac{\overset{1}{\cancel{6}} \cdot 18 \cdot w^4 \cdot \overset{1}{\cancel{w}} \cdot y^{11}}{\underset{1}{\cancel{6}}\underset{1}{\cancel{w}}}}$$

| We have rewritten the radicand without a denominator. However, the radicand has some factors that are perfect squares. | $= \sqrt{18w^4y^{11}}$ |

Factor the radicand. Use perfect square factors when possible.

$$= \sqrt{2 \cdot 3 \cdot 3 \cdot w^2 \cdot w^2 \cdot y^{10} \cdot y^1}$$

Write as a product of radicals. Place each perfect square under its own radical symbol.

$$= \sqrt{3^2} \cdot \sqrt{w^2} \cdot \sqrt{w^2} \cdot \sqrt{y^{10}} \cdot \sqrt{2y^1}$$

Simplify the square root of each perfect square.

$$= 3 \cdot w \cdot w \cdot y^5 \cdot \sqrt{2y}$$

Multiply the factors outside the radical symbol.

$$= 3w^2y^5\sqrt{2y}$$

So,

$$\frac{\sqrt{108w^5y^{11}}}{\sqrt{6w}} = 3w^2y^5\sqrt{2y}$$

Example 9.2.15

Simplify: $\sqrt[4]{\dfrac{81w^{11}x^6}{16y^{12}}}$

Solution

This radical is not in simplified form because it has a fraction under the radical symbol.

We cannot simplify the fraction because the numerator and denominator have no common factors except 1 and -1. Instead we will write the radical as a quotient of two radicals. Then we will try to simplify each radical so that we can write the expression without a radical in the denominator.

$$\sqrt[4]{\frac{81w^{11}x^6}{16y^{12}}}$$

Use the Division Property of Radicals to write the radical as a quotient of two radicals.

$$= \frac{\sqrt[4]{81w^{11}x^6}}{\sqrt[4]{16y^{12}}}$$

For each radical, factor the radicand. Use perfect fourth power factors when possible.

$$= \frac{\sqrt[4]{3 \cdot 3 \cdot 3 \cdot 3 \cdot w^4 \cdot w^4 \cdot w^3 \cdot x^4 \cdot x^2}}{\sqrt[4]{2 \cdot 2 \cdot 2 \cdot 2 \cdot y^4 \cdot y^4 \cdot y^4}}$$

Write as a product of radicals. Place each perfect fourth power under its own radical symbol.

$$= \frac{\sqrt[4]{3^4} \cdot \sqrt[4]{w^4} \cdot \sqrt[4]{w^4} \cdot \sqrt[4]{x^4} \cdot \sqrt[4]{w^3x^2}}{\sqrt[4]{2^4} \cdot \sqrt[4]{y^4} \cdot \sqrt[4]{y^4} \cdot \sqrt[4]{y^4}}$$

Simplify the fourth root of each perfect fourth power.

$$= \frac{3 \cdot w \cdot w \cdot x \cdot \sqrt[4]{w^3 x^2}}{2 \cdot y \cdot y \cdot y}$$

Multiply the factors outside the radical.

$$= \frac{3w^2 x \sqrt[4]{w^3 x^2}}{2y^3}$$

So,

$$\sqrt[4]{\frac{81w^{11} x^6}{16y^{12}}} = \frac{3w^2 x \sqrt[4]{w^3 x^2}}{2y^3}$$

There is often more than one way to simplify a radical expression. With practice, you may be able to decrease the amount of writing required.

Here is a summary of this concept from *Academic Systems Algebra*.

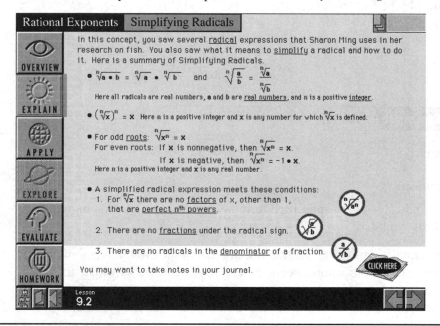

| Rational Exponents | Simplifying Radicals |

OVERVIEW

In this concept, you saw several <u>radical</u> expressions that Sharon Ming uses in her research on fish. You also saw what it means to <u>simplify</u> a radical and how to do it. Here is a summary of Simplifying Radicals.

EXPLAIN

- $\sqrt[n]{a \cdot b} = \sqrt[n]{a} \cdot \sqrt[n]{b}$ and $\sqrt[n]{\frac{a}{b}} = \frac{\sqrt[n]{a}}{\sqrt[n]{b}}$

  Here all radicals are real numbers, a and b are <u>real numbers</u>, and n is a positive <u>integer</u>.

- $\left(\sqrt[n]{x}\right)^n = x$ Here n is a positive integer and x is any number for which $\sqrt[n]{x}$ is defined.

APPLY

- For odd <u>roots</u>: $\sqrt[n]{x^n} = x$
  For even roots: If x is nonnegative, then $\sqrt[n]{x^n} = x$.
  If x is negative, then $\sqrt[n]{x^n} = -1 \bullet x$.
  Here n is a positive integer and x is any real number.

EXPLORE

- A simplified radical expression meets these conditions:
  1. For $\sqrt[n]{x}$ there are no <u>factors</u> of x, other than 1, that are <u>perfect nth powers</u>.

  2. There are no <u>fractions</u> under the radical sign.

EVALUATE

  3. There are no radicals in the <u>denominator</u> of a fraction.

You may want to take notes in your journal.

HOMEWORK

Lesson 9.2

Concept 3 has sections on

- **Like Radical Terms**

- **Combining Like Radical Terms**

- **Multiplying Radical Expressions**

- **Conjugates**

- **Dividing Radical Expressions**

- **Rationalizing the Denominator**

- **Combining Operations**

CONCEPT 3: OPERATIONS WITH RADICALS

Like Radical Terms

Like terms are terms that have the same variables raised to the same power. For example, $3y^2$ and $8y^2$ are like terms. **Like radical terms** are terms whose radical parts have the same index and the same radicand.

For example, $5\sqrt[3]{4x}$ and $-4\sqrt[3]{4x}$ are like radical terms. Each radical has index 3 and radicand $4x$.

However, $2\sqrt{10w}$ and $2\sqrt[3]{10w}$ are *not* like radical terms because each radical has a different index. In particular, one radical is a square root and the other is a cube root.

Example 9.2.16

Identify the like radical terms.

$$6\sqrt{7xy}, \quad \frac{2\sqrt[3]{7xy}}{9}, \quad 6\sqrt[3]{7xy}, \quad -3\sqrt{7xy}$$

Solution

- $6\sqrt{7xy}$ and $-3\sqrt{7xy}$ are like radical terms.
  Each has index 2 and radicand $7xy$.

- $\dfrac{2\sqrt[3]{7xy}}{9}$ and $6\sqrt[3]{7xy}$ are like radical terms.
  Each has index 3 and radicand $7xy$.

Remember, the index of a square root is 2.

Combining Like Radical Terms

Adding and subtracting radical expressions is like adding and subtracting polynomials.

- With polynomials, to add like terms, we add their coefficients.

$$2x + 3x = (2 + 3)x \quad = 5x$$

- With radical expressions, to add like radical terms, we add the numbers in front of the radicals.

$$2\sqrt{x} + 3\sqrt{x} = (2 + 3)\sqrt{x} = 5\sqrt{x}$$

Before we can combine radical terms, we sometimes need to simplify the individual radicals to obtain like terms.

Consider this example:

$$\sqrt{8} + 3\sqrt{2}$$

At first glance, we may think we cannot add the radical terms because the radicands are different.

However, if we simplify $\sqrt{8}$, we can combine like radical terms:

$$\sqrt{8} + 3\sqrt{2}$$
$$= \sqrt{\mathbf{4 \cdot 2}} + 3\sqrt{2}$$
$$= 2\sqrt{\mathbf{2}} + 3\sqrt{\mathbf{2}}$$
$$= (2 + 3)\sqrt{2}$$
$$= 5\sqrt{2}$$

Example 9.2.17

Simplify: $\sqrt{75y} - 8\sqrt[3]{3y} - 2\sqrt{3y} + 7y$

Solution

First simplify $\sqrt{75y}$.

The radicand, $75y$, has a perfect square factor, 25.

$$\sqrt{75y} = \sqrt{\mathbf{25} \cdot 3y}$$
$$= \sqrt{\mathbf{25}} \cdot \sqrt{3y}$$
$$= 5\sqrt{3y}$$

$$\sqrt{75y} - 8\sqrt[3]{3y} - 2\sqrt{3y} + 7y$$

Replace $\sqrt{75y}$ with $5\sqrt{3y}$.

$$= \mathbf{5}\sqrt{\mathbf{3y}} - 8\sqrt[3]{3y} - 2\sqrt{3y} + 7y$$

Combine the like radical terms, $5\sqrt{3y}$ and $-2\sqrt{3y}$.

$$= (\mathbf{5 - 2})\sqrt{3y} - 8\sqrt[3]{3y} + 7y$$

Simplify.

$$= \mathbf{3}\sqrt{\mathbf{3y}} - 8\sqrt[3]{3y} + 7y$$

So,

$$\sqrt{75y} - 8\sqrt[3]{3y} - 2\sqrt{3y} + 7y = 3\sqrt{3y} - 8\sqrt[3]{3y} + 7y$$

Example 9.2.18

Simplify: $3\sqrt[3]{2x} - 5\sqrt{2x} - 8\sqrt[3]{54x} + 2$

Solution

First, simplify $\sqrt[3]{54x}$.

The radicand, $54x$, has a perfect cube factor, 27.

$$\sqrt[3]{54x} = \sqrt[3]{\mathbf{27} \cdot 2x}$$
$$= \sqrt[3]{\mathbf{27}} \cdot \sqrt[3]{2x}$$
$$= \mathbf{3}\sqrt[3]{2x}$$

$$3\sqrt[3]{2x} - 5\sqrt{2x} - 8\sqrt[3]{54x} + 2$$

Replace $\sqrt[3]{54x}$ with $3\sqrt[3]{2x}$.

$$= 3\sqrt[3]{\mathbf{2x}} - 5\sqrt{2x} - 8 \cdot \mathbf{3}\sqrt[3]{\mathbf{2x}} + 2$$

Multiply $8 \cdot 3\sqrt[3]{2x}$.

$$= \mathbf{3}\sqrt[3]{\mathbf{2x}} - 5\sqrt{2x} - \mathbf{24}\sqrt[3]{\mathbf{2x}} + 2$$

Combine the like radical terms $3\sqrt[3]{2x}$ and $-24\sqrt[3]{2x}$.

$$= (\mathbf{3 - 24})\sqrt[3]{2x} - 5\sqrt{2x} + 2$$

Simplify.

$$= \mathbf{-21}\sqrt[3]{\mathbf{2x}} - 5\sqrt{2x} + 2$$

So,

$$3\sqrt[3]{2x} - 5\sqrt{2x} - 8\sqrt[3]{54x} + 2 = -21\sqrt[3]{2x} - 5\sqrt{2x} + 2$$

Multiplying Radical Expressions

We can multiply radicals provided they have the same index. To multiply the radicals, we multiply their radicands. The resulting radical has the common index.

For example, let's find this product: $\sqrt[4]{8}\sqrt[4]{2}$

    We multiply the radicands. $\quad = \sqrt[4]{16}$

    Finally, we simplify. $\quad = 2$

If the expressions being multiplied contain factors that are not under a radical symbol, multiply those factors. Then multiply the radicands of radicals that have the same index.

For example, let's find this product: $\quad 8w\sqrt[3]{7y} \cdot 5y\sqrt[3]{4x}$

    Multiply $8w$ by $5y$. Multiply $7y$ by $4x$. $\quad = (8w \cdot 5y) \cdot \sqrt[3]{7y \cdot 4x}$

    Simplify. $\quad = 40wy\sqrt[3]{28xy}$

In the following multiplication problem, we use the Distributive Property to remove the parentheses.

Find this product: $\quad \sqrt[3]{5w}\left(\sqrt[3]{6} - 9\right)$

    Distribute $\sqrt[3]{5w}$ to each term inside the parentheses. $\quad = \sqrt[3]{5w} \cdot \sqrt[3]{6} - \sqrt[3]{5w} \cdot 9$

    Simplify. $\quad = \sqrt[3]{30w} - 9\sqrt[3]{5w}$

Caution! When you multiply radicals, be sure to write the index in the result.

For example, $\sqrt[4]{8} \cdot \sqrt[4]{2} = \sqrt[4]{16}$

It is possible to use rational exponents to multiply radicals with different indices, such as $\sqrt{3}$ and $\sqrt[3]{9}$. However, such examples are beyond the scope of this lesson.

Example 9.2.19

Multiply and simplify: $8\sqrt{10y}\left(4\sqrt{5} - \sqrt{6y}\right)$

Solution

$\qquad\qquad 8\sqrt{10y}\left(4\sqrt{5} - \sqrt{6y}\right)$

Distribute $8\sqrt{10y}$. $\quad = 8\sqrt{10y} \cdot 4\sqrt{5} - 8\sqrt{10y} \cdot \sqrt{6y}$

Multiply. $\quad = 8 \cdot 4\sqrt{10y \cdot 5} - 8\sqrt{10y \cdot 6y}$

Factor each radicand. Use perfect square factors when possible. $\quad = 32\sqrt{2 \cdot 5^2 \cdot y} - 8\sqrt{2^2 \cdot 5 \cdot 3 \cdot y^2}$

Write each radical as a product of radicals. Place each perfect square under its own radical symbol. $\quad = 32 \cdot \sqrt{5^2} \cdot \sqrt{2y} - 8 \cdot \sqrt{2^2} \cdot \sqrt{y^2} \cdot \sqrt{5 \cdot 3}$

Simplify each radical. $\quad = 32 \cdot 5 \cdot \sqrt{2y} - 8 \cdot 2 \cdot y \cdot \sqrt{15}$

$\qquad\qquad\qquad = 160\sqrt{2y} - 16y\sqrt{15}$

Thus,

$$8\sqrt{10y}\left(4\sqrt{5} - \sqrt{6y}\right) = 160\sqrt{2y} - 16y\sqrt{15}.$$

Example 9.2.20

Multiply and simplify: $5\sqrt[3]{12y}\left(15\sqrt[3]{10y^2} - 4\sqrt[3]{9y}\right)$

Solution

Distribute $5\sqrt[3]{12y}$.

$$= 5\sqrt[3]{12y} \cdot 15\sqrt[3]{10y^2} - 5\sqrt[3]{12y} \cdot 4\sqrt[3]{9y}$$

Multiply. $= 5 \cdot 15\sqrt[3]{12y \cdot 10y^2} - 5 \cdot 4\sqrt[3]{12y \cdot 9y}$

Factor the radicands.

$$= 75\sqrt[3]{2 \cdot 2 \cdot 3 \cdot y \cdot 2 \cdot 5 \cdot y \cdot y} - 20\sqrt[3]{2 \cdot 2 \cdot 3 \cdot y \cdot 3 \cdot 3 \cdot y}$$

Rewrite the factors as perfect cubes, when possible.

$$= 75\sqrt[3]{2^3 \cdot 3 \cdot 5 \cdot y^3} - 20\sqrt[3]{2^2 \cdot 3^3 \cdot y^2}$$

Write each radical as a product of radicals.
Place each perfect cube under its own radical symbol.

$$= 75\sqrt[3]{2^3}\sqrt[3]{y^3}\sqrt[3]{3 \cdot 5} - 20\sqrt[3]{3^3}\sqrt[3]{2^2 \cdot y^2}$$

Simplify each radical.

$$= 75 \cdot 2 \cdot y\sqrt[3]{15} - 20 \cdot 3\sqrt[3]{4y^2}$$

$$= 150y\sqrt[3]{15} - 60\sqrt[3]{4y^2}$$

Thus,

$$5\sqrt[3]{12y}\left(15\sqrt[3]{10y^2} - 4\sqrt[3]{9y}\right) = 150y\sqrt[3]{15} - 60\sqrt[3]{4y^2}.$$

Example 9.2.21

Multiply and simplify: $\left(3\sqrt{5w} - \sqrt{6}\right)\left(4\sqrt{2w} + \sqrt{3}\right)$

Solution

Use the FOIL method.

$$= 3\sqrt{5w} \cdot 4\sqrt{2w} + 3\sqrt{5w} \cdot \sqrt{3} - \sqrt{6} \cdot 4\sqrt{2w} - \sqrt{6} \cdot \sqrt{3}$$

Multiply radicals.

$$= 3 \cdot 4\sqrt{5w \cdot 2w} + 3\sqrt{5w \cdot 3} - 4\sqrt{6 \cdot 2w} - \sqrt{6 \cdot 3}$$

Factor each radicand.

$$= 12\sqrt{5 \cdot w \cdot 2 \cdot w} + 3\sqrt{5 \cdot w \cdot 3} - 4\sqrt{2 \cdot 3 \cdot 2 \cdot w} - \sqrt{2 \cdot 3 \cdot 3}$$

Rewrite the factors as perfect squares, when possible.

$$= 12\sqrt{2 \cdot 5 \cdot w^2} + 3\sqrt{3 \cdot 5 \cdot w} - 4\sqrt{2^2 \cdot 3 \cdot w} - \sqrt{2 \cdot 3^2}$$

Write each radical as a product of radicals.
Place each perfect square under its own radical symbol.

$$= 12\sqrt{w^2} \cdot \sqrt{2 \cdot 5} + 3\sqrt{3 \cdot 5 \cdot w} - 4\sqrt{2^2} \cdot \sqrt{3 \cdot w} - \sqrt{3^2} \cdot \sqrt{2}$$

Simplify the radicals.

$$= 12w \cdot \sqrt{10} + 3\sqrt{15w} - 4 \cdot 2 \cdot \sqrt{3w} - 3 \cdot \sqrt{2}$$

$$= 12w\sqrt{10} + 3\sqrt{15w} - 8\sqrt{3w} - 3\sqrt{2}$$

Thus,

$$\left(3\sqrt{5w} - \sqrt{6}\right)\left(4\sqrt{2w} + \sqrt{3}\right) = 12w\sqrt{10} + 3\sqrt{15w} - 8\sqrt{3w} - 3\sqrt{2}.$$

Conjugates

Now we will work with special pairs of binomial radical expression such as the following:

$$\sqrt{3} + 5 \text{ and } \sqrt{3} - 5$$

$$5\sqrt{2} - \sqrt{7} \text{ and } 5\sqrt{2} + \sqrt{7}.$$

Notice that in each binomial pair, the first terms are the same and the second terms differ only in sign.

Such pairs of binomial radical expressions are called **conjugates**.

— Definition —
Conjugates

Two binomial radical expressions of the form

$$a\sqrt{b} + c\sqrt{d} \text{ and } a\sqrt{b} - c\sqrt{d}$$

are called conjugates.

Here, a, b, c, and d are rational numbers. Also, $\sqrt{b}$ and $\sqrt{d}$ are *not both* rational.

The product of conjugates is a rational number.

Example 9.2.22

Find: $\left(\sqrt{10} - 3\sqrt{2}\right)\left(\sqrt{10} + 3\sqrt{2}\right)$

Solution

$$\left(\sqrt{10} - 3\sqrt{2}\right)\left(\sqrt{10} + 3\sqrt{2}\right)$$

Use the FOIL method.

$$= \sqrt{10}\sqrt{10} + 3\sqrt{2}\sqrt{10} - 3\sqrt{2}\sqrt{10} - 3\sqrt{2} \cdot 3\sqrt{2}$$

Multiply.

$$= \sqrt{100} + 3\sqrt{20} - 3\sqrt{20} - 9\sqrt{4}$$

The two middle terms are opposites and add to zero.

$$= 10 - 9 \cdot 2$$

Simplify.

$$= 10 - 18$$

$$= -8$$

Thus,

$$\left(\sqrt{10} - 3\sqrt{2}\right)\left(\sqrt{10} + 3\sqrt{2}\right) = -8.$$

Dividing Radical Expressions

To find the quotient of two radicals, we can sometimes use the Division Property of Radicals in this form:

$$\frac{\sqrt[n]{a}}{\sqrt[n]{b}} = \sqrt[n]{\frac{a}{b}}.\ \text{Here, } b \neq 0.$$

Example 9.2.23

Divide and simplify: $\dfrac{\sqrt[3]{81w^7y^9}}{\sqrt[3]{3w^4y}}$

Solution

$$\frac{\sqrt[3]{81w^7y^9}}{\sqrt[3]{3w^4y}}$$

Write the numerator and denominator under the same radical symbol.

$$= \sqrt[3]{\frac{81w^7y^9}{3w^4y}}$$

Simplify the radicand by canceling common factors.

$$= \sqrt[3]{27w^3y^8}$$

Factor the radical. Use perfect cube factors where possible.

$$= \sqrt[3]{3^3 \cdot w^3 \cdot y^3 \cdot y^3 \cdot y^2}$$

Write the radical as a product of radicals. Place each perfect cube under its own radical symbol.

$$= \sqrt[3]{3^3} \cdot \sqrt[3]{w^3} \cdot \sqrt[3]{y^3} \cdot \sqrt[3]{y^3} \cdot \sqrt[3]{y^2}$$

Simplify the cube root of each perfect cube.

$$= 3wy^2\sqrt[3]{y^2}$$

Thus,

$$\frac{\sqrt[3]{81w^7y^9}}{\sqrt[3]{3w^4y}} = 3wy^2\sqrt[3]{y^2}.$$

Rationalizing the Denominator

The radical expression $\dfrac{24}{\sqrt{10x}}$ is not in simplified form because it has a radical in the denominator.

To write the radical expression in simplified form, we must **rationalize** its denominator. That is, we rewrite the expression to make the denominator a rational number and eliminate the radical.

$$\dfrac{24}{\sqrt{10x}}$$

To do this, we multiply $\dfrac{24}{\sqrt{10x}}$ by 1 written in the form $\dfrac{\sqrt{10x}}{\sqrt{10x}}$.

$$= \dfrac{24}{\sqrt{10x}} \cdot \dfrac{\sqrt{10x}}{\sqrt{10x}}$$

Multiply the numerators. Multiply the denominators.

$$= \dfrac{24\sqrt{10x}}{\sqrt{100x^2}}$$

Simplify the denominator.

$$= \dfrac{24\sqrt{10x}}{10x}$$

The denominator has been rationalized since it no longer contains a radical. The radical expression is now in simplified form.

Example 9.2.24

Simplify: $\dfrac{10}{2\sqrt{18x}}$

Solution

$$\dfrac{10}{2\sqrt{18x}}$$

In the numerator and denominator, cancel the common factor, 2.

$$= \dfrac{5}{\sqrt{18x}}$$

Simplify the radical by removing the perfect square factor, 9.

$$= \dfrac{5}{\sqrt{9}\sqrt{2x}}$$

Simplify $\sqrt{9}$.

$$= \dfrac{5}{3\sqrt{2x}}$$

To eliminate $\sqrt{2x}$ in the denominator, multiply the expression by 1 written in the form $\dfrac{\sqrt{2x}}{\sqrt{2x}}$.

$$= \dfrac{5}{3\sqrt{2x}} \cdot \dfrac{\sqrt{2x}}{\sqrt{2x}}$$

Multiply the numerators. Multiply the denominators.

$$= \dfrac{5\sqrt{2x}}{3\sqrt{4x^2}}$$

Simplify $\sqrt{4x^2}$ and multiply the result by 3.

$$= \dfrac{5\sqrt{2x}}{6x}$$

$\dfrac{5\sqrt{2x}}{6x}$ is in simplified form.

So,

$$\dfrac{10}{2\sqrt{18x}} = \dfrac{5\sqrt{2x}}{6x}$$

We cannot cancel the x's since the x in the numerator is under the radical symbol, while the x in the denominator is not. The same is true for a factor of 2.

Example 9.2.25

Simplify: $\dfrac{7}{5\sqrt[3]{4w}}$

Solution $\dfrac{7}{5\sqrt[3]{4w}}$

Factor the radicand. $= \dfrac{7}{5\sqrt[3]{2 \cdot 2 \cdot w}}$

The radical in the denominator is a cube root. To rationalize the denominator, we want to make the radicand a perfect cube.

We do not need additional factors of 5 because 5 is not under the radical symbol.

- 2 occurs twice as a factor. To make a perfect cube, we multiply by 2.

- w occurs once as a factor. To make a perfect cube, we multiply by w^2.

We multiply by 1 written in the form $\dfrac{\sqrt[3]{2w^2}}{\sqrt[3]{2w^2}}$. $= \dfrac{7}{5\sqrt[3]{2 \cdot 2 \cdot w}} \cdot \dfrac{\sqrt[3]{2w^2}}{\sqrt[3]{2w^2}}$

Multiply the numerators and multiply the denominators. $= \dfrac{7\sqrt[3]{2w^2}}{5\sqrt[3]{2^3 w^3}}$

Simplify the denominator. $= \dfrac{7\sqrt[3]{2w^2}}{5 \cdot 2w}$

$= \dfrac{7\sqrt[3]{2w^2}}{10w}$

So,

$$\dfrac{7}{5\sqrt[3]{4w}} = \dfrac{7\sqrt[3]{2w^2}}{10w}$$

Suppose we have a radical expression such as $\dfrac{3}{x - \sqrt{10}}$.

Recall that when we multiply conjugates, the result is always a rational number.

Therefore, to eliminate the radical in the denominator of the expression, we multiply the numerator and denominator by $x + \sqrt{10}$, the conjugate of the denominator.

Example 9.2.26

Simplify: $\dfrac{3}{x - \sqrt{10}}$

Solution

$$\dfrac{3}{x - \sqrt{10}}$$

To rationalize the denominator we multiply the numerator and denominator by $x + \sqrt{10}$, the conjugate of $x - \sqrt{10}$.

$$= \dfrac{3}{x - \sqrt{10}} \cdot \dfrac{x + \sqrt{10}}{x + \sqrt{10}}$$

Multiply the numerators and multiply the denominators.

$$= \dfrac{3(x + \sqrt{10})}{(x - \sqrt{10})(x + \sqrt{10})}$$

Remove the parentheses.

$$= \dfrac{3x + 3\sqrt{10}}{x \cdot x + x \cdot \sqrt{10} - x \cdot \sqrt{10} - \sqrt{10} \cdot \sqrt{10}}$$

Simplify the denominator. The two middle terms add to zero.

$$= \dfrac{3x + 3\sqrt{10}}{x^2 - 10}$$

So,

$$\dfrac{3}{x - \sqrt{10}} = \dfrac{3x + 3\sqrt{10}}{x^2 - 10}.$$

Combining Operations

Now we will simplify some radical expressions that involve more than one operation.

Example 9.2.27

Simplify: $\sqrt{50x^3} - x\sqrt{18x}$

Solution

$$\sqrt{50x^3} - x\sqrt{18x}$$

Factor each radicand.

$$= \sqrt{25 \cdot 2 \cdot x^2 \cdot x} - x\sqrt{9 \cdot 2 \cdot x}$$

Write each radical as the product of radicals.

$$= \sqrt{25} \cdot \sqrt{2} \cdot \sqrt{x^2} \cdot \sqrt{x} - x \cdot \sqrt{9} \cdot \sqrt{2} \cdot \sqrt{x}$$

Simplify square roots of perfect squares.

$$= 5 \cdot \sqrt{2} \cdot x \cdot \sqrt{x} - x \cdot 3 \cdot \sqrt{2} \cdot \sqrt{x}$$

For each term, multiply the radicals.

$$= 5x\sqrt{2x} - 3x\sqrt{2x}$$

Combine like radical terms.

$$= 2x\sqrt{2x}$$

Therefore,

$$\sqrt{50x^3} - x\sqrt{18x} = 2x\sqrt{2x}.$$

Example 9.2.28

Simplify: $\sqrt{5x} + \sqrt{6}(\sqrt{30x} - 2)$

Solution

$$\sqrt{5x} + \sqrt{6}(\sqrt{30x} - 2)$$

To remove the parentheses, distribute $\sqrt{6}$.

$$= \sqrt{5x} + \sqrt{6} \cdot \sqrt{30x} - 2 \cdot \sqrt{6}$$

Multiply $\sqrt{6}$ by $\sqrt{30x}$. Then factor the radicand.

$$= \sqrt{5x} + \sqrt{2 \cdot 2 \cdot 3 \cdot 3 \cdot 5 \cdot x} - 2\sqrt{6}$$

Simplify the second term: $\sqrt{2 \cdot 2 \cdot 3 \cdot 3 \cdot 5 \cdot x} = 2 \cdot 3\sqrt{5x}$.

$$= \sqrt{5x} + 6\sqrt{5x} - 2\sqrt{6}$$

Combine like radical terms.

$$= 7\sqrt{5x} - 2\sqrt{6}$$

Thus,

$$\sqrt{5x} + \sqrt{6}(\sqrt{30x} - 2) = 7\sqrt{5x} - 2\sqrt{6}.$$

Example 9.2.29

Simplify: $\dfrac{5}{4}\sqrt[3]{16x^3} - \dfrac{x}{\sqrt[3]{4}}$

Solution

$$\dfrac{5}{4}\sqrt[3]{16x^3} - \dfrac{x}{\sqrt[3]{4}}$$

To rationalize the denominator of the second term, multiply the term by $\dfrac{\sqrt[3]{2}}{\sqrt[3]{2}}$.

$$= \dfrac{5}{4}\sqrt[3]{16x^3} - \dfrac{x}{\sqrt[3]{4}} \cdot \dfrac{\sqrt[3]{2}}{\sqrt[3]{2}}$$

Simplify the second term.

$$= \dfrac{5}{4}\sqrt[3]{16x^3} - \dfrac{x\sqrt[3]{2}}{2}$$

Write the radicand of $\sqrt[3]{16x^3}$ using perfect cube factors.

$$= \dfrac{5}{4}\sqrt[3]{2 \cdot 2^3 \cdot x^3} - \dfrac{x\sqrt[3]{2}}{2}$$

Simplify the first term.

$$= \dfrac{5}{4} \cdot 2 \cdot x \cdot \sqrt[3]{2} - \dfrac{x\sqrt[3]{2}}{2}$$

In the first term, cancel the common factor, 2.

$$= \dfrac{5x}{2} \cdot \sqrt[3]{2} - \dfrac{x}{2} \cdot \sqrt[3]{2}$$

Combine like radical terms.

$$= \left(\dfrac{5x}{2} - \dfrac{x}{2}\right) \cdot \sqrt[3]{2}$$

$$= \dfrac{4x}{2} \cdot \sqrt[3]{2}$$

Cancel the common factor of 2.

$$= 2x\sqrt[3]{2}$$

Thus,

$$\dfrac{5}{4}\sqrt[3]{16x^3} - \dfrac{x}{\sqrt[3]{4}} = 2x\sqrt[3]{2}.$$

Here is a summary of this concept from *Academic Systems Algebra*.

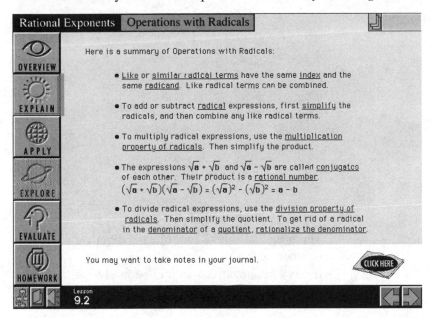

Rational Exponents	Operations with Radicals

OVERVIEW

EXPLAIN

APPLY

EXPLORE

EVALUATE

HOMEWORK

Here is a summary of Operations with Radicals:

- **Like** or **similar radical terms** have the same **index** and the same **radicand**. Like radical terms can be combined.

- To add or subtract **radical** expressions, first **simplify** the radicals, and then combine any like radical terms.

- To multiply radical expressions, use the **multiplication property of radicals**. Then simplify the product.

- The expressions $\sqrt{a} + \sqrt{b}$ and $\sqrt{a} - \sqrt{b}$ are called **conjugates** of each other. Their product is a **rational number**.
$(\sqrt{a} + \sqrt{b})(\sqrt{a} - \sqrt{b}) = (\sqrt{a})^2 - (\sqrt{b})^2 = a - b$

- To divide radical expressions, use the **division property of radicals**. Then simplify the quotient. To get rid of a radical in the **denominator** of a **quotient**, **rationalize the denominator**.

You may want to take notes in your journal.

CLICK HERE

Lesson
9.2

Checklist Lesson 9.2

Here is what you should know after completing this lesson.

Words and Phrases

square root
principal square root
radical symbol
radicand
radical
radical expression

index
rational exponent
like radical terms
conjugates
rationalize

Ideas and Procedures

❶ Square Root
Define the principal square root of a number.

The principal square root of a nonnegative real number, a, is written $\sqrt{a}$.
If b is a nonnegative real number and $b^2 = a$, then $\sqrt{a} = b$.

❷ n^{th} root
Calculate the nth root of a number.

Example 9.2.1
Find the 5th root of 243.

See also: Apply 6-11

❸ Rational Exponent
Describe the relationship between rational exponential notation and radical notation.

If a is a real number, m is a nonnegative integer, n is a positive integer, and $\dfrac{m}{n}$ is in lowest terms, then
$$a^{m/n} = \left(\sqrt[n]{a}\right)^m = \sqrt[n]{a^m}$$
If n is even, then $a^{m/n}$ is a real number only when $a \geq 0$.

Convert between rational exponential notation and radical notation.

Example 9.2.3
Rewrite using a radical and evaluate: $32^{3/5}$

See also: Example 9.2.2
        Apply 1-5, 12-16

Use the properties of exponents to simplify an expression written in rational exponential notation.

Example 9.2.4
Simplify: $w^{1/3} \cdot w^{(-3/2)} \cdot w^{1/6}$

See also: Example 9.2.5
        Apply 17-28

❹ Multiplication Property of Radicals
State the Multiplication Property of Radicals.

$\sqrt[n]{a \cdot b} = \sqrt[n]{a} \cdot \sqrt[n]{b}$ where $\sqrt[n]{a}$ and $\sqrt[n]{b}$ are real numbers and n is a positive integer.

Use the Multiplication Property of Radicals to simplify a radical expression.

Example 9.2.6
Simplify: $\sqrt[4]{16y^5}$

See also: Example 9.2.7

❺ Division Property of Radicals
State the Division Property of Radicals.

$$\sqrt[n]{\dfrac{a}{b}} = \dfrac{\sqrt[n]{a}}{\sqrt[n]{b}} \text{ where } \sqrt[n]{a} \text{ and } \sqrt[n]{b} \text{ are real numbers,}$$
$b \neq 0$, and n is a positive integer.

Use the Division Property of Radicals to simplify a radical expression.

Example 9.2.9
Simplify: $\dfrac{\sqrt[4]{32x^6}}{\sqrt[4]{2x^2}}$

See also: Example 9.2.8
Apply 29-37

❻ Raising an nth Root to the nth Power
State a general relationship between roots and powers.

If $\sqrt[n]{x}$ is defined, then $\left(\sqrt[n]{x}\right)^n = x$.

Use the relationship between roots and powers to simplify a radical expression.

Example 9.2.10
Simplify: $\left(\sqrt[5]{w}\right)^5$

❼ Taking the nth Root of an nth Power
State a general relationship between roots and powers.

$\sqrt[n]{x^n} = x$ if n is an odd positive integer and x is any real number.
$\sqrt[n]{x^n} = x$ if n is an even positive integer and $x \geq 0$.
$\sqrt[n]{x^n} = -1 \cdot x$ if n is an even positive integer and $x < 0$.

Use the relationship between roots and powers to simplify a radical.

Example 9.2.12
Simplify: $\sqrt[4]{(-12)^4}$

See also: Example 9.2.11
Apply 38-42

❽ Simplified Form of a Radical Expression Containing One Term
Define simplified form.

A radical expression that contains one term is in simplified form when:
- For $\sqrt[n]{x}$ there are no factors of x, other than 1, that are perfect n^{th} powers.
- There are no fractions under the radical symbol.
- There are no radicals in the denominator of an expression.

See also: Apply 43, 44

Simplify a radical expression that contains one term.

Example 9.2.13
Simplify: $\sqrt[3]{-24w^6x^2y^4}$

See also: Example 9.2.14, 9.2.15
Apply 45-56

❾ Like Radical Terms
Identify like radical terms.

Example 9.2.16
Which of the following are like radical terms?

$$6\sqrt{7xy}, \quad \dfrac{2\sqrt[3]{7xy}}{9}, \quad 6\sqrt[3]{7xy}, \quad -3\sqrt{7xy}$$

See also: Apply 57, 58

⑩ **Combine Like Radical Terms**
Add and subtract like radical terms.

Example 9.2.17
   Simplify: $\sqrt{75y} - 8\sqrt[3]{3y} - 2\sqrt{3y} + 7y$

See also: Example 9.2.18
   Apply 59-67

⑪ **Multiply Radical Expressions**
Multiply radical expressions.

Example 9.2.20
   Multiply and simplify: $5\sqrt[3]{12y}\left(15\sqrt[3]{10y^2} - 4\sqrt[3]{9y}\right)$

See also: Example 9.2.19, 9.2.21
   Apply 68-76

⑫ **Conjugates**
Multiply conjugates.

Example 9.2.22
   Find: $\left(\sqrt{10} - 3\sqrt{2}\right)\left(\sqrt{10} + 3\sqrt{2}\right)$

See also: Apply 77-79

⑬ **Divide Radical Expressions**
Divide radical expressions.

Example 9.2.23
   Divide and simplify: $\dfrac{\sqrt[3]{81w^7y^9}}{\sqrt[3]{3w^4y}}$

⑭ **Rationalize a Denominator**
Rationalize the denominator of
a radical expression.

Example 9.2.24
   Simplify: $\dfrac{10}{2\sqrt{18x}}$

See also: Example 9.2.25, 9.2.26
   Apply 80-84

⑮ **Combine Operations**
Write a radical expression in simplified form.

Example 9.2.28
   Simplify: $\sqrt{5x} + \sqrt{6}\left(\sqrt{30x} - 2\right)$

See also: Example 9.2.27, 9.2.29

 **Homework**

Homework Problems

Circle the homework problems assigned to you by the computer, then complete them below.

 Explain

Roots and Exponents

1. Rewrite using a radical, then evaluate: $8^{\frac{1}{3}}$

2. Evaluate: $\sqrt[3]{-216}$

3. Evaluate: $2^{\frac{1}{4}} \cdot 2^{\frac{2}{5}}$

4. Rewrite using a radical, then evaluate: $4^{\frac{3}{2}}$

5. Evaluate: $\sqrt[5]{1024}$

6. Simplify the expression below. Write your answer using only positive exponents.

$$\left(x^{\frac{1}{3}} \cdot y^{\frac{1}{2}}\right)^{-2}$$

7. Evaluate: $\sqrt[4]{-81}$

8. Simplify: $x^{\frac{4}{3}} \cdot x^{\frac{1}{3}}$

9. The number of cells of one type of bacteria doubles every 5 hours according to the formula $n_f = n_i \cdot 2^{\frac{t}{5}}$ where n_f is the final number of cells, n_i is the initial number of cells, and t is the initial number of hours since the growth began. If a biologist starts with a single cell of the bacteria, how many cells will she have after 50 hours?

10. Alan invests $100 in a savings account. How much money would he have after a year if the interest rate for this account is 3% compounded every 4 months?

    The amount A in a savings account can be expressed as

    $$A = P\left(1 + \frac{r}{n}\right)^{nt}$$

    where P is the amount of money initially invested, t is the number of years the money has been invested, r is the annual rate of interest, and n is the number of times the interest is compounded each year.

11. Evaluate the expression below. Express your answer using only positive exponents.

$$\left(x^{\frac{5}{7}} \cdot x^{-\frac{3}{4}} \cdot y^{\frac{5}{4}}\right)^{-4}$$

12. Evaluate the expression below. Express your answer using only positive exponents.

$$\left(\sqrt[3]{-1331}\right)\left(x^{\frac{2}{9}}\right)^{-3}\left(\frac{1}{x^{-\frac{1}{3}}}\right)$$

Simplifying Radicals

Simplify the expressions in questions 13–20. Assume x, y, and z are positive numbers.

13. $\sqrt[3]{\dfrac{54}{250}}$

14. $\sqrt{\dfrac{49x}{4}}$

15. $\dfrac{\sqrt{5x^3}}{\sqrt{5x^2}}$

16. $\sqrt{\dfrac{-1048}{775}}$

17. $\sqrt[3]{-27x^6y^3}$

18. $\dfrac{\sqrt{x}}{\sqrt{y^4z^{12}}}$

19. $\sqrt[3]{16x^9y^4z^2}$

20. $\sqrt{\dfrac{242xy^{12}}{288y^2z^4}}$

21. One of the three unsolved problems of antiquity was to "double a cube"—that is, to construct a cube with twice the volume of a given cube. What would be the length of a side of a cube with twice the volume of 1 m^3? (Hint: The volume, V, of a cube with sides of length L is $V = L \cdot L \cdot L = L^3$.)

22. In a cube with surface area, A, the length, s, of each side is given by this formula:

$$s = \sqrt{\frac{A}{6}}$$

The volume, V, of the cube is:

$$V = s^3$$

What is the volume of a cube with a surface area of 48 ft^2?

Simplify the expressions in questions 23 and 24. Assume x, y, and z are positive numbers.

23. $\sqrt{4x^5y^7z^2}$

24. $\dfrac{\sqrt[3]{-8x^6y^3z^3}}{\sqrt{36x^2y^6z^2}}$

Operations on Radicals

25. Circle the like terms:

$7\sqrt[4]{360}$

$72\sqrt{360}$

$\dfrac{\sqrt[4]{360}}{72}$

$360\sqrt[4]{72}$

$-22\sqrt[3]{360}$

$-\dfrac{11}{4}\sqrt[4]{360}$

$\sqrt[4]{36}$

26. Simplify: $7\sqrt{125} + 2\sqrt{500} - \dfrac{3}{2}\sqrt{20} - 2\sqrt{10}$

27. Simplify: $5\sqrt{12}\left(6\sqrt{3} - 7\sqrt{27}\right)$

28. Circle the like terms:

79      $\sqrt{79}$

$\sqrt[3]{79}$ $\sqrt[2]{79}$

$\dfrac{1}{44}\sqrt{799}$ $-\sqrt{79}$

$2\sqrt{3} \cdot \sqrt{79}$ $-\sqrt[2]{79^2}$

29. Simplify: $8\sqrt[3]{24} - \dfrac{\sqrt{16}}{2} + \dfrac{1}{4}\sqrt[3]{2} - \sqrt[3]{-3^3}$

30. Simplify: $\left(7\sqrt{2} - 8\sqrt{3}\right)\left(5\sqrt{2} + 6\sqrt{3}\right)$

31. Circle the like terms:

$\sqrt[3]{24}$

$2\sqrt[3]{3}$

$\sqrt[3]{8} \cdot \sqrt[3]{3}$

$\sqrt{(-3)^2}$

$\dfrac{\sqrt[3]{3}}{27}$

3^{-3}

$3^{\frac{1}{3}}$

32. Simplify: $\dfrac{1 - \sqrt{5}}{\sqrt{5} - 9}$

33. The period of a simple pendulum is given by the formula $t = 2\pi\sqrt{\dfrac{L}{32}}$ where t is the period of the pendulum in seconds, and L is the length of the pendulum in feet. What is the period of a 16 foot pendulum?

34. The Pythagorean Theorem, $a^2 + b^2 = c^2$, gives the relationship between the lengths of the two legs of a right triangle, a and b, and the length of the hypotenuse of the triangle, c. If the lengths of the legs of a right triangle are $\sqrt{2}$ cm and $\sqrt{6}$ cm, how long is the hypotenuse?

35. Simplify: $\dfrac{\sqrt[3]{22}}{\sqrt[3]{77}}$

36. Simplify: $\dfrac{6\sqrt[3]{2} - 2\sqrt[3]{4}(2\sqrt[3]{32} - 2\sqrt[3]{4})}{2\sqrt[3]{2} - \sqrt[3]{2} \cdot \sqrt[3]{2}}$

 **Apply**

Practice Problems

Here are some additional practice problems for you to try.

Roots and Exponents

1. Rewrite using a radical, then evaluate: $9^{\frac{5}{2}}$

2. Rewrite using a radical, then evaluate: $16^{\frac{3}{2}}$

3. Rewrite using a radical, then evaluate: $27^{\frac{2}{3}}$

4. Rewrite using a radical, then evaluate: $32^{\frac{4}{5}}$

5. Rewrite using a radical, then evaluate: $81^{\frac{3}{4}}$

6. Evaluate: $\sqrt[4]{625}$

7. Evaluate: $\sqrt[5]{7776}$

8. Evaluate: $\sqrt[5]{1024}$

9. Evaluate: $-\sqrt[4]{81}$

10. Evaluate: $\sqrt[5]{-32}$

11. Evaluate: $\sqrt[3]{-216}$

12. Rewrite using rational exponents: $\sqrt[4]{245^3}$

13. Rewrite using rational exponents: $\sqrt[5]{312^4}$

14. Rewrite using rational exponents: $\sqrt[3]{315^2}$

15. Rewrite using rational exponents: $\sqrt[7]{200^5}$

16. Rewrite using rational exponents: $\sqrt[8]{400^3}$

17. Find: $y^{\frac{2}{3}} \cdot y^{\frac{1}{4}}$

18. Find: $x^{\frac{1}{3}} \cdot x^{\frac{2}{5}}$

19. Find: $x^{\frac{1}{6}} \cdot x^{\frac{1}{5}}$

20. Find: $x^{\frac{1}{7}} \cdot x^{\frac{3}{7}} \cdot x^{\frac{2}{7}}$

21. Find: $x^{\frac{2}{9}} \cdot x^{\frac{5}{9}} \cdot x^{\frac{2}{9}}$

22. Find: $x^{\frac{3}{4}} \cdot x^{\frac{1}{2}} \cdot x^{\frac{3}{4}}$

23. Evaluate the expression below. Express your answer using only positive exponents.
$$\left(\frac{3a^{\frac{3}{4}}}{2b^2}\right)^{-4}$$

24. Evaluate the expression below. Express your answer using only positive exponents.
$$\left(\frac{x^{-\frac{4}{5}}}{2y}\right)^5$$

25. Evaluate the expression below. Express your answer using only positive exponents.
$$\left(\frac{4x^{-\frac{2}{3}}}{3y}\right)^3$$

26. Evaluate the expression below. Express your answer using only positive exponents.
$$\left(a^{\frac{3}{7}} \cdot b^{-\frac{2}{5}}\right)^3$$

27. Evaluate the expression below. Express your answer using only positive exponents.
$$\left(x^{-\frac{4}{9}} \cdot y^{\frac{6}{11}}\right)^2$$

28. Evaluate the expression below. Express your answer using only positive exponents.
$$\left(x^{-\frac{2}{3}} \cdot y^{\frac{3}{5}} \cdot z^{-\frac{4}{7}}\right)^3$$

Simplifying Radicals

29. Simplify: $\sqrt{\dfrac{121}{64}}$

30. Simplify: $\sqrt{\dfrac{289}{361}}$

31. Simplify: $\sqrt{\dfrac{169}{576}}$

32. Simplify: $\sqrt[3]{\dfrac{27}{8}}$

33. Simplify: $\sqrt[3]{\dfrac{-64}{125}}$

34. Simplify: $\sqrt[3]{\dfrac{-343}{27}}$

35. Simplify: $\sqrt[5]{\dfrac{-32}{243}}$

36. Simplify: $\sqrt[4]{\dfrac{625}{1296}}$

37. Simplify: $\sqrt[6]{\dfrac{729}{64}}$

38. Calculate: $\sqrt{(-35^2)}$

39. Calculate: $\sqrt{(-56)^2}$

40. Calculate: $\sqrt[3]{(13^3)}$

41. Calculate: $\sqrt[5]{(-47^5)}$

42. Calculate: $\sqrt[3]{(-29)^3}$

43. Which of the radical expressions below is in simplified form?

$$\frac{\sqrt{81}}{x} \qquad \sqrt{\frac{25}{49}} \qquad \frac{6}{\sqrt{30}} \qquad \frac{\sqrt[4]{7}}{x}$$

44. Which of the radical expressions below is in simplified form?

$$\frac{\sqrt[3]{5}}{x} \qquad \frac{4}{\sqrt{20}} \qquad \sqrt{\frac{16}{9}} \qquad \frac{\sqrt{49}}{x}$$

45. Simplify: $\sqrt{36a^2b^6}$

46. Simplify: $\sqrt{100m^6n^4}$

47. Simplify: $\sqrt{64x^4y^6z^{10}}$

48. Simplify: $\sqrt{54a^3b^8}$

49. Simplify: $\sqrt{108m^5n^9}$

50. Simplify: $\sqrt{72x^4y^7}$

51. Simplify: $\sqrt[3]{192a^3b^5c^9}$

52. Simplify: $\sqrt[3]{-250x^4y^6z^8}$

53. Simplify: $\sqrt[5]{160m^2n^7p^{12}}$

54. Simplify: $\dfrac{\sqrt{49a^3b^8}}{\sqrt{7ab^7}}$

55. Simplify: $\dfrac{\sqrt[3]{64m^7n^5}}{\sqrt[3]{2mn^3}}$

56. Simplify: $\dfrac{\sqrt[4]{81x^9y^6}}{\sqrt[4]{3xy^4}}$

Operations with Radicals

57. Circle the like terms:

$$\frac{\sqrt{-5}}{4}$$

$$\sqrt{5}$$

$$\frac{1}{3}\sqrt{5}$$

$$-9\sqrt{50}$$

$$\frac{7\sqrt{5}}{8}$$

$$\frac{6\sqrt[5]{50}}{13}$$

$$\sqrt[5]{-2}$$

58. Circle the like terms:

$$\frac{5}{2}\sqrt{3}$$

$$-\sqrt[3]{2}$$

$$\frac{\sqrt{-3}}{3}$$

$$-6\sqrt{30}$$

$$\frac{4\sqrt[3]{30}}{15}$$

$$\sqrt{3}$$

$$\frac{6\sqrt{3}}{5}$$

59. Simplify: $7\sqrt{5} + \sqrt{20} - 3\sqrt{80}$

60. Simplify: $10\sqrt{2} - \sqrt{128} + 3\sqrt{32}$

61. Simplify: $8\sqrt{3} + \sqrt{12} - 4\sqrt{27}$

62. Simplify: $\sqrt{40} + 3\sqrt{10} - \sqrt{18}$

63. Simplify: $4\sqrt{50} - 5\sqrt{27} + 2\sqrt{75}$

64. Simplify: $\sqrt{20} - 2\sqrt{18} + \sqrt{8}$

65. Simplify: $\sqrt[3]{250x^2} + 3\sqrt[3]{16x^5} - 3\sqrt[3]{432x^2}$

66. Simplify: $5\sqrt[4]{32y} + \sqrt[4]{162y^5} - \sqrt[4]{1250y}$

67. Simplify: $\sqrt[3]{128x} + 2\sqrt[3]{16x^4} - \sqrt[3]{54x}$

68. Simplify: $5\sqrt{6}\left(3\sqrt{8} - 9\sqrt{21}\right)$

69. Simplify: $2\sqrt[3]{9}\left(5\sqrt[3]{3} - 7\sqrt[3]{5}\right)$

70. Simplify: $3\sqrt[4]{8}\left(4\sqrt[4]{2} + 6\sqrt[4]{3}\right)$

71. Simplify: $3\sqrt{2y}\left(7\sqrt{10y} + 4\sqrt{3}\right)$

72. Simplify: $6\sqrt{3z}\left(2\sqrt{6z} - 3\sqrt{5}\right)$

73. Simplify: $2\sqrt[3]{4z}\left(5\sqrt[3]{2z^2} - 7\sqrt[3]{11z}\right)$

74. Simplify: $\left(\sqrt{5} + \sqrt{3}\right)\left(\sqrt{6} + \sqrt{11}\right)$

75. Simplify: $\left(\sqrt{5} - \sqrt{10}\right)\left(\sqrt{2} - \sqrt{15}\right)$

76. Simplify: $\left(\sqrt{6} + \sqrt{5}\right)\left(\sqrt{3} - \sqrt{10}\right)$

77. Simplify: $\left(3\sqrt{5z} + \sqrt{6}\right)\left(3\sqrt{5z} - \sqrt{6}\right)$

78. Simplify: $\left(2\sqrt{3y} + \sqrt{7}\right)\left(2\sqrt{3y} - \sqrt{7}\right)$

79. Simplify: $\left(5\sqrt{2y} - \sqrt{3x}\right)\left(5\sqrt{2y} + \sqrt{3x}\right)$

80. Simplify: $\dfrac{3\sqrt{y}}{y\sqrt{6}}$

81. Simplify: $\dfrac{2\sqrt{x}}{x\sqrt{2}}$

82. Simplify: $\dfrac{3\sqrt{5}}{x + \sqrt{5}}$

83. Simplify: $\dfrac{5\sqrt{2}}{x - \sqrt{2}}$

84. Simplify: $\dfrac{x - \sqrt{3}}{x + \sqrt{3}}$

Practice Test

Take this practice test to be sure that you are prepared for the final quiz in Evaluate.

Assume that x, y, and z are positive numbers.

1. Simplify: $\sqrt[5]{x} \cdot \sqrt{x}$

2. Rewrite the expression using rational exponents.

   $\sqrt[5]{243^3}$

3. Circle the real number(s) in the list below:

   $\sqrt{-100}$

   $\sqrt[3]{-125}$

   $\sqrt[4]{-16}$

   $\sqrt[6]{-729}$

4. Simplify: $\left(\dfrac{8y^{-\frac{1}{2}}}{7^{\frac{3}{2}}x}\right)^2$

5. Simplify: $\sqrt{\dfrac{169}{225}}$

6. Calculate: $\sqrt{(-29)^2}$

7. Which of the radical expressions below is simplified?

   $\sqrt{\dfrac{3}{16}}$

   $\dfrac{xy}{\sqrt{8}}$

   $\dfrac{\sqrt{25}}{y}$

   $\dfrac{\sqrt[3]{3}}{2}$

8. Simplify: $\sqrt{\dfrac{81x^2y^2}{121z}}$

9. Simplify: $6\sqrt{5x} + 3\sqrt{125x} - 3$

10. Find: $\left(3\sqrt{5} - 8\right)\left(3\sqrt{5} + 8\right)$

11. Find: $\left(3\sqrt{2} + 3\right)\left(2\sqrt{2} - 6\right)$

12. Find: $\dfrac{\sqrt{y}}{\sqrt[3]{y}}$

Cumulative Review Problems

These problems combine all of the material you have covered so far in this course. You may want to test your understanding of this material before you move on to the next topic, or you may wish to do these problems to review for a test.

1. Find: $(x^2 + 12x)(x + 3y^2 + 1)$

2. Solve for x: $\dfrac{2x + 5}{2 - x} = 3$

3. Solve for y: $\dfrac{1}{y} - \dfrac{2}{3} = \dfrac{y}{3}$

4. Find:

   a. $(125)^{\frac{1}{3}}(16)^{\frac{3}{4}}$

   b. $(x^3y)^{\frac{1}{3}}$

   c. $\dfrac{a^{\frac{1}{2}}b^2a^{\frac{1}{3}}}{b^{-2}}$

5. Last year Scott earned 5% in interest on his savings account and 13% in interest on his money market account. If he had $14,125 in the bank and earned a total of $1706.25 in interest, how much did he have in each account?

6. Graph the line that passes through the point $(0, -3)$ with slope 2.

7. For what values is the rational expression $\dfrac{x^3 - 3x + 29}{x^2 + 13x + 36}$ undefined?

8. Solve $-10 < 9x - 7 < 11$ for x.

9. Solve this system of equations:

   $$y = -\dfrac{2}{7}x + 3$$

   $$14y + 4x = 14$$

10. Factor: $2ab + 14a + 5b + 35$

11. Angela and Casey were asked to clean their classroom. Working alone, Angela could clean the room in 20 minutes. It would take Casey 25 minutes to clean the room by herself. How long would it take them to clean the room together?

12. Simplify: $\left(\dfrac{27}{x}\right)^{-\frac{1}{3}}\left(\sqrt{x}\right)^{\frac{4}{3}}$

13. Find the equation of the line that passes through the point $(-7, 3)$ and has slope $\dfrac{5}{3}$. Write your answer in point-slope form, in slope-intercept form, and in standard form.

14. Simplify this expression:
    $2r^2s + 3t + 4s^2 - 5r^2s - 6s^2 + 7t$

15. Find:
    $(3a^2b^2 + 2a^2b - 7ab + a) - (a^2b^2 - 12ab + 2a^2b + b)$

16. Simplify: $\dfrac{2 + \sqrt{2}}{\sqrt{2} + \sqrt{6}}$

17. Find:

    a. $\dfrac{3^0 \cdot 10^2}{2^3}$

    b. $(-3a^2)^3$

    c. $[(x^3y^2)^2z]^4$

18. Graph the inequality $2y - 10x \le 32$.

19. Solve for x: $3(x + 2) - x = 3x - 8$

20. Graph the line $y - \dfrac{1}{2} = \dfrac{1}{6}(x + 2)$.

21. Factor: $-16y^2 + 24y - 9$

22. Rewrite using radicals, then simplify:
    $$\dfrac{\left(24^{\frac{1}{3}} + 100^{\frac{1}{2}}\right)}{16^{\frac{1}{4}}}$$

23. Circle the true statements.

    $22 + 32 = 52$

    $|3 - 4| = |3| - |4|$

    The GCF of 52 and 100 is 4.

    $\dfrac{9}{25} = \dfrac{3}{5}$

    The LCM of 30 and 36 is 180.

24. Find the slope of the line that is perpendicular to the line that passes through the points $(8, 2)$ and $(-4, 9)$.

25. Factor: $x^2 + 3x - 130$

26. In a bin, the ratio of red apples to green apples is 10 to 3. If there is a total of 15 green apples, how many red ones are there?

27. Find the slope and y-intercept of this line: $4y + 3x = -18$

28. Graph the system of linear inequalities below to find its solution.

    $3y - 5x < 3$

    $5y + 3x > -10$

29. Simplify: $\dfrac{72x^3y^2}{(2y^2)^2}$

30. Find the slope of the line through the points $\left(\dfrac{3}{4}, 7\right)$ and $\left(\dfrac{1}{4}, -\dfrac{1}{2}\right)$.

31. Simplify: $\dfrac{8}{3 + \sqrt{11}}$

32. Graph the line $2y + 1 = 1 - 3x$.

33. Find: $(2x^3 + 21x^2 - 27x + 8) \div (2x - 1)$

34. Evaluate the expression $3a^2 + ab - b^2$ when $a = 2$ and $b = 8$.

35. Factor: $7x^2y^2 + 14xy^2 + 7y^2$

36. Factor: $5x^2 - 80$

37. Solve for y: $-10 < 5 - 3y \le 2$

38. Rewrite using only positive exponents: $\dfrac{a^3b^{-2}}{(c^{-1})^{-2}}$

39. Find:

    a. $\sqrt{20} + \sqrt{80}$

    b. $\sqrt{6}(\sqrt{6x^2} + \sqrt{3x^2})$

    c. $(a + \sqrt{b})(a - \sqrt{b})$

40. Factor: $a^2 + 6a + 6b + ab$

41. A juggler has 10 more balls than juggling pins. If the number of balls is 1 more than twice the number of pins, how many pins and balls are there?

42. Find: $\dfrac{x^2 - 9}{x^2 + 3x} \cdot \dfrac{x^2 - 7x}{x^2 - 10x + 21}$

43. Simplify: $\dfrac{x - y}{\sqrt{x} - \sqrt{y}}$

44. Solve for y: $3[7y + 5(1 - 2y)] = -27$

45. Factor: $8x^3 - 1$

46. Solve for x: $\dfrac{1}{2}(x + 7) = 12$

47. Solve for a: $\dfrac{a}{a - 5} + 1 = \dfrac{a - 3}{a - 5}$

48. Evaluate the expression $a^3b + 3 - ab^3 + 2ab$ when $a = -2$ and $b = 4$.

49. Simplify: $\left(\dfrac{2y^3}{3x^4}\right)^2$

50. Factor: $2x^2 - 40x + 198$

TOPIC 10
QUADRATIC EQUATIONS

You have already learned how to solve linear equations. Such equations can be written in the form $ax + b = 0$, where $a \neq 0$. Now we will learn how to solve equations that can be written in the form $ax^2 + bx + c = 0$, where $a \neq 0$. Such equations are called quadratic equations.

In this topic, we will learn different methods for solving a quadratic equation. We will also learn strategies for selecting a method of solution. Finally, our work with quadratic equations will lead us to study complex numbers.

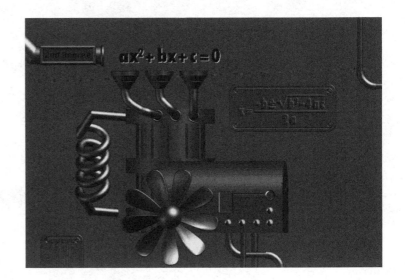

LESSON 10.1
QUADRATIC EQUATIONS I

 Overview

In this topic, you will study quadratic equations in one variable. You will learn four methods for solving such quadratic equations. Depending on the particular quadratic equation, some methods may be easier to use than others.

In this lesson, you will learn how to solve quadratic equations by factoring and by using the square root property.

 Explain

Concept 1 has sections on

- **The Standard Form of a Quadratic Equation**

- **Solving Quadratic Equations by Factoring**

A quadratic equation must have a term of degree 2, such as x^2.

It cannot have a term of higher degree.

We can also write a quadratic equation with 0 on the left side, like this:

$$0 = ax^2 + bx + c$$

CONCEPT 1:
SOLVING BY FACTORING

The Standard Form of a Quadratic Equation

When we use mathematics to model real world situations, we sometimes use quadratic equations. Such equations are also called second degree equations, or equations of degree 2.

— Definition —
Quadratic Equation

A quadratic equation in one variable is an equation that can be written in the form

$$ax^2 + bx + c = 0.$$

where a, b, and c are real numbers and $a \neq 0$.

This is called the **standard form of a quadratic equation**.

In the definition, notice that the terms on the left side of the equation are arranged in descending order by degree. The right side of the equation is zero.

Here are some examples of quadratic equations. To determine the values of a, b, and c, we first write the equation in standard form, $ax^2 + bx + c = 0$.

Non-standard form	Standard form	
$x^2 - 3x = 28$	$\mathbf{1}x^2 - 3x - 28 = 0$	$a = 1, b = -3, c = -28$
$5x^2 = -45$	$5x^2 + \mathbf{0}x + 45 = 0$	$a = 5, b = 0, c = 45$
$-3x^2 = -12x$	$-3x^2 + 12x + 0 = 0$	$a = -3, b = 12, c = 0$

The variable in a quadratic equation can be any letter, not just x. For example:

$$3y^2 + 5y - 9 = 0$$

is a quadratic equation.

Example 10.1.1

For each of the following, if the equation is quadratic, write it in standard form and identify the values of a, b, and c.

a. $3x(x + 4) = 18$ b. $-6x^2 = 8 - 3x(2x + 1)$ c. $0 = 7x^2$

Solution

a.

	$3x(x + 4) = 18$
Distribute $3x$.	$3x^2 + 12x = 18$
Subtract 18 from both sides.	$3x^2 + 12x - 18 = 0$

This is a quadratic equation in standard form. Here $a = 3$, $b = 12$, and $c = -18$.

$ax^2 + bx + c = 0$

When you identify a, b, and c, be careful with signs. In this example, c is negative. In particular, c = −18.

b.

	$-6x^2 = 8 - 3x(2x + 1)$
Distribute $-3x$.	$-6x^2 = 8 - 6x^2 - 3x$
Add $6x^2$ to both sides and rearrange terms.	$0 = \mathbf{0}x^2 - 3x + 8$
Because the coefficient of the x^2-term is 0, the equation is *not* a quadratic equation.	$0 = -3x + 8$

c.

	$0 = 7x^2$
Fill in the missing x-term and the missing constant term.	$0 = 7x^2 + 0x + 0$

This is a quadratic equation, $ax^2 + bx + c = 0$, where $a = 7$, $b = 0$, and $c = 0$.

Solving Quadratic Equations by Factoring

To solve certain quadratic equations, we will use the Zero Product Property. This property states that if the product of two numbers (or polynomials) is 0, then one (or both) factors is 0.

If $P \cdot Q = 0$, then $P = 0$ or $Q = 0$ (or both P and $Q = 0$).

Here, P and Q are polynomials.

In the next two examples, we use the Zero Product Property.

If $w(w - 7) = 0$, then $w = 0$ or $w - 7 = 0$.

If $(y - 4)(y + 6) = 0$, then $y - 4 = 0$ or $y + 6 = 0$.

The following procedure can be used to solve a quadratic equation in standard form where the second-degree polynomial is factorable over the integers.

— Procedure —
To Solve a Quadratic Equation by Factoring

Step 1 Write the equation in the form $ax^2 + bx + c = 0$.

Step 2 Factor the polynomial.

Step 3 Use the Zero Product Property.

Step 4 Solve the resulting equations.

Step 5 Check each answer.

Because the degree of a quadratic equation is 2, each quadratic equation has two solutions.

Example 10.1.2

Solve by factoring: $6x^2 = 8x$

Solution

Step 1 Write the equation in the form $ax^2 + bx + c = 0$.

Subtract $8x$ from both sides. $\qquad\qquad 6x^2 - 8x = 0$

$6x^2 - 8x + 0 = 0$
Here, $a = 6$, $b = -8$, and $c = 0$.

Step 2 Factor the polynomial.

Factor out $2x$. $\qquad\qquad 2x(3x - 4) = 0$

Step 3 Use the Zero Product Property.

Set each linear factor equal to 0. $\qquad 2x = 0 \quad$ or $\quad 3x - 4 = 0$

Step 4 Solve the resulting equations.

Divide both sides of the first equation by 2. $\quad x = 0 \quad$ or $\quad 3x = 4$

Add 4 to both sides of the second equation.
Divide both sides of the second equation by 3. $\quad x = 0 \quad$ or $\quad x = \dfrac{4}{3}$

Step 5 Check each answer.

Check x = 0.   **Check x = $\frac{4}{3}$.**

$$6x^2 = 8x$$ $$6x^2 = 8x$$

Is $6(\mathbf{0})^2 = 8(\mathbf{0})$?   Is $6\left(\frac{4}{3}\right)^2 = 8\left(\frac{4}{3}\right)$?

Is $0 = 0$? **Yes**   Is $6\left(\frac{16}{9}\right) = 8\left(\frac{4}{3}\right)$?

                                          Is $\left(\frac{32}{3}\right) = \left(\frac{32}{3}\right)$? **Yes**

So, the quadratic equation $6x^2 = 8x$ has two solutions, 0 and $\frac{4}{3}$.

Example 10.1.3

Solve by factoring: $x^2 - 14 = -5x$

Solution

Step 1 Write the equation in the form $ax^2 + bx + c = 0$.

Add $5x$ to both sides. $x^2 + 5x - 14 = 0$

Step 2 Factor the polynomial.

The coefficient of x^2 is 1, so find two numbers whose product is -14 and whose sum is 5.
These numbers are -2 and 7. $(x - 2)(x + 7) = 0$

Step 3 Use the Zero Product Property. $x - 2 = 0$ or $x + 7 = 0$

Step 4 Solve the resulting equations. $x = 2$ or $x = -7$

Step 5 Check each answer.

We leave the check to you.

So, the two solutions of $x^2 - 14 = -5x$ are $x = 2$ and $x = -7$.

Example 10.1.4

Solve by factoring: $7x + 6x^2 = 20$

Solution

Step 1 Write the equation in the form $ax^2 + bx + c = 0$.

Subtact 20 from both sides. $6x^2 + 7x - 20 = 0$

You may be able to factor $6x^2 + 7x - 20$ by inspection:
$6x^2 + 7x - 20 = (3x - 4)(2x + 5)$

Step 2 Factor the polynomial.

The coefficient of x^2 is not 1, so find two numbers whose product is ac and whose sum is b.

$$ac = 6(-20) = -120$$
$$b = 7$$

The two numbers are -8 and 15.

Rewrite the middle term, $7x$, as $-8x + 15x$.

$$6x^2 - 8x + 15x - 20 = 0$$

Factor $2x$ from the first pair of terms.

Factor 5 from the second pair of terms.

$$2x(3x - 4) + 5(3x - 4) = 0$$

Factor out the common binomial factor, $3x - 4$.

$$(3x - 4)(2x + 5) = 0$$

Step 3 Use the Zero Product Property. $3x - 4 = 0$ or $2x + 5 = 0$

Step 4 Solve the resulting equations. $x = \dfrac{4}{3}$ or $x = -\dfrac{5}{2}$

Step 5 Check each answer.

We leave the check to you.

So, the two solutions of $7x + 6x^2 = 20$ are $\dfrac{4}{3}$ and $-\dfrac{5}{2}$.

Example 10.1.5

Solve by factoring: $25 + 30x = -9x^2$

Solution

Step 1 Write the equation in the form $ax^2 + bx + c = 0$.

Add $9x^2$ to both sides. $9x^2 + 30x + 25 = 0$

Step 2 Factor the polynomial.

The first and last terms of the trinomial are perfect squares.

$$(3x)^2 + 30x + (5)^2 = 0$$

The middle term, $30x$, is $2(3x)(5)$. $(3x)^2 + 2(3x)(5) + (5)^2 = 0$

Since the trinomial has the form $a^2 + 2ab + b^2$, it is a perfect square trinomial.

A perfect square trinomial can be written as the product of two identical binomials.

$$(3x + 5)(3x + 5) = 0$$

A perfect square trinomial has the form:
$a^2 + 2ab + b^2 = (a + b)^2 = (a + b)(a + b)$
or
$a^2 - 2ab + b^2 = (a - b)^2 = (a - b)(a - b)$

Step 3 Use the Zero Product Property. $3x + 5 = 0$ or $3x + 5 = 0$

Step 4 Solve the resulting equations. $x = -\dfrac{5}{3}$ or $x = -\dfrac{5}{3}$

Step 5 Check each answer.

We leave the check to you.

So, $25 + 30x = -9x^2$ has two equal solutions, $-\dfrac{5}{3}$ and $-\dfrac{5}{3}$.

Every quadratic equation has two solutions.

In the previous example, the two solutions are the same, $-\dfrac{5}{3}$.

We call $-\dfrac{5}{3}$ a solution of **multiplicity two**.

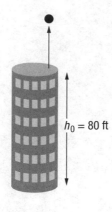

$h_0 = 80$ ft

Example **10.1.6**

The height of a ball thrown straight up is given by

$$h = h_0 + v_0 t + \frac{1}{2}gt^2.$$

Here, h is the height in feet after t seconds, h_0 is the initial height, v_0 is the initial velocity, and g is -32 ft/sec², the acceleration due to gravity.

From the top of an 80-foot tower, a ball is thrown straight up with an initial velocity of 64 feet per second. How long will it take the ball to hit the ground?

Solution

The initial height is 80 feet, the initial velocity is 64 feet per second, and g is -32 ft/sec².

$$h = h_0 + v_0 t + \frac{1}{2}gt^2$$

So, $h_0 = 80$, $v_0 = 64$, and $g = -32$.

$$h = \mathbf{80} + \mathbf{64}t + \frac{1}{2}(\mathbf{-32})t^2$$

The ball will hit the ground when the height, h, is 0.

$$\mathbf{0} = 80 + 64t + \frac{1}{2}(-32)t^2$$

In this quadratic equation, the variable is t. We write the equation in the form

$$0 = at^2 + bt + c.$$

To find the time it takes to hit the ground, solve for t.

Step 1 Write the equation in the form
$$ax^2 + bx + c = 0.$$
$$0 = -16t^2 + 64t + 80$$

Step 2 Factor the polynomial.

Factor out -16.
$$0 = -16(t^2 - 4t - 5)$$

Find two integers whose product is -5 and whose sum is -4.
These integers are -5 and 1.
$$0 = -16(t - 5)(t + 1)$$

Step 3 Use the Zero Product Property.
$$t - 5 \quad \text{or} \quad t + 1 = 0$$

Step 4 Solve the resulting equations.
$$t = 5 \quad \text{or} \quad t = -1$$

Step 5 Check each answer.

We leave the check to you.

Since the ball is thrown at a time $t = 0$ seconds, and the ball hits the ground *after* it is thrown, the time must be positive. Therefore, we disregard the solution $t = -1$ and use only the solution $t = 5$.

The ball will hit the ground 5 seconds after it is thrown.

Here is a summary of this concept from *Academic Systems Algebra*.

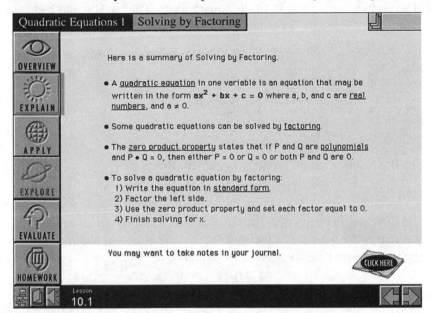

Quadratic Equations I	Solving by Factoring

OVERVIEW

EXPLAIN

APPLY

EXPLORE

EVALUATE

HOMEWORK

Here is a summary of Solving by Factoring.

- A <u>quadratic equation</u> in one variable is an equation that may be written in the form $ax^2 + bx + c = 0$ where a, b, and c are <u>real numbers</u>, and a ≠ 0.

- Some quadratic equations can be solved by <u>factoring</u>.

- The <u>zero product property</u> states that if P and Q are <u>polynomials</u> and P • Q = 0, then either P = 0 or Q = 0 or both P and Q are 0.

- To solve a quadratic equation by factoring:
  1) Write the equation in <u>standard form</u>.
  2) Factor the left side.
  3) Use the zero product property and set each factor equal to 0.
  4) Finish solving for x.

You may want to take notes in your journal.

CLICK HERE

Lesson 10.1

CONCEPT 2: SOLVING BY SQUARE ROOTS

Concept 2 has sections on

- **Square Roots**

- **Solving Quadratic Equations Using the Square Root Property**

Square Roots

Some quadratic equations can be readily solved using square roots. Before we look at some examples, it will be helpful to review what we have learned about square roots.

- Recall that every positive number has two square roots.

  For example:

  The positive square root of 25, written $\sqrt{25}$, is +5 since $(+5)^2 = 25$.

  The negative square root of 25, written $-\sqrt{25}$, is −5 since $(-5)^2 = 25$.

- A square root is in simplified form when there are:

  - No perfect square factors under a square root symbol.

  - No fractions under a square root symbol.

  - No square roots in the denominator of a fraction.

- The Multiplication Property of Square Roots states that the square root of a product is the product of the square roots. That is, if a and b are nonnegative real numbers, then

$$\sqrt{ab} = \sqrt{a}\sqrt{b}.$$

We can use this property to simplify a square root.

For example, let's simplify $\sqrt{24}$.	$\sqrt{24}$
Write 24 as a product.	$= \sqrt{4 \cdot 6}$
Use the Multiplication Property of Square Roots.	$= \sqrt{4}\sqrt{6}$
Simplify $\sqrt{4}$.	$= 2\sqrt{6}$

- The Division Property of Square Roots states that the square root of a quotient is the quotient of the square roots. That is, if a and b are nonnegative real numbers and $b \neq 0$, then

$$\sqrt{\frac{a}{b}} = \frac{\sqrt{a}}{\sqrt{b}}.$$

For example, let's simplify $\sqrt{\dfrac{13}{4}}$.	$\sqrt{\dfrac{13}{4}}$
Use the Division Property of Square Roots.	$= \dfrac{\sqrt{13}}{\sqrt{4}}$
Simplify $\sqrt{4}$.	$= \dfrac{\sqrt{13}}{2}$

Solving Quadratic Equations Using the Square Root Property

The **Square Root Property** can be used to solve a quadratic equation written in the form $x^2 = a$.

— Property —
Square Root Property
If $x^2 = a$, then $x = \sqrt{a}$ or $x = -\sqrt{a}$.
Here, a is a nonnegative real number.
Examples
If $x^2 = 7$, then $x = \sqrt{7}$ or $x = -\sqrt{7}$.
If $(w + 6)^2 = 3$, then $w + 6 = \sqrt{3}$ or $w + 6 = -\sqrt{3}$.

Here's how to use the Square Root Property to solve a quadratic equation.

```
┌─────────────────────────────────────────────────────────────┐
│                      — Procedure —                            │
│   To Solve a Quadratic Equation Using the Square Root Property│
├─────────────────────────────────────────────────────────────┤
│  Step 1  Write the equation in the form $x^2 = a$.            │
│  Step 2  Use the Square Root Property.                        │
│  Step 3  Write each answer in simplified form.                │
│  Step 4  Check each answer.                                   │
└─────────────────────────────────────────────────────────────┘
```

Example 10.1.7

Solve using the Square Root Property: $x^2 - 72 = 0$

Solution

Step 1 Write the equation in the form $x^2 = a$. $x^2 - 72 = 0$

   Add 72 to both sides. $x^2 = 72$

Step 2 Use the Square Root Property. $x = \sqrt{72}$ or $x = -\sqrt{72}$

Step 3 Write each answer in simplified form.

   Simplify each square root. $x = \sqrt{36}\sqrt{2}$ or $x = -\sqrt{36}\sqrt{2}$

                                     $x = 6\sqrt{2}$ or $x = -6\sqrt{2}$

Step 4 Check each answer.

Check $x = 6\sqrt{2}$.	Check $x = -6\sqrt{2}$.
$x^2 - 72 = 0$	$x^2 - 72 = 0$
Is $(6\sqrt{2})^2 - 72 = 0$?	Is $(-6\sqrt{2})^2 - 72 = 0$?
Is $36 \cdot 2 - 72 = 0$?	Is $36 \cdot 2 - 72 = 0$?
Is $0 = 0$? **Yes**	Is $0 = 0$? **Yes**

So, the equation $x^2 - 72 = 0$ has two solutions, $6\sqrt{2}$ and $-6\sqrt{2}$.

Example 10.1.8

Solve using the Square Root Property: $-4x^2 + 64 = 0$

Solution

Step 1 Write the equation in the form $x^2 = a$. $-4x^2 + 64 = 0$

   Subtract 64 from both sides. $-4x^2 = -64$

   Divide both sides by -4. $x^2 = 16$

Step 2 Use the Square Root Property. $x = \sqrt{16}$ or $x = -\sqrt{16}$

Step 3 Write each answer in simplified form. $x = 4$ or $x = -4$

Step 4 Check each answer.

   We leave the check to you.

So, the two solutions of $-4x^2 + 64 = 0$ are 4 and -4.

Another way to write the solution is:
$$x^2 = 16$$
$$x = \pm\sqrt{16}$$
$$x = \pm 4$$

Example 10.1.9

Solve using the Square Root Property: $5(w + 6)^2 - 100 = 0$

Solution

Step 1 Write the equation in the form $x^2 = a$.

Add 100 to both sides.	$5(w + 6)^2 = 100$
Divide both sides by 5.	$(w + 6)^2 = 20$

The equation $(w + 6)^2 = 20$ has the form

$$\underset{x^2}{(w + 6)^2} = \underset{a}{20}$$

where x is $w + 6$ and a is 20.

Step 2 Use the Square Root Property. $w + 6 = \sqrt{20}$ or $w + 6 = -\sqrt{20}$

Step 3 Write each answer in simplified form.

To solve for w, subtract 6 from both sides.	$w = -6 + \sqrt{20}$ or $w = -6 - \sqrt{20}$
Simplify $\sqrt{20}$.	$w = -6 + 2\sqrt{5}$ or $w = -6 - 2\sqrt{5}$

Step 4 Check each answer.

We leave the check to you.

Another way to write the solution is $w = -6 \pm 2\sqrt{5}$.

So, the two solutions of $5(w + 6)^2 - 100 = 0$ are $-6 + 2\sqrt{5}$ and $-6 - 2\sqrt{5}$.

Example 10.1.10

Solve using the Square Root Property: $16x^2 - 24x + 9 = 81$

Solution

Step 1 Write the equation in the form $x^2 = a$.

The first and last terms of the trinomial are perfect squares.	$(4x)^2 - 24x + (3)^2 = 81$
The middle term, $-24x$, is $-2(4x)(3)$.	$(4x)^2 - 2(4x)(3) + (3)^2 = 81$
Since the trinomial has the form $a^2 - 2ab + b^2$, it is a perfect square trinomial.	
A perfect square trinomial can be written as the product of two identical binomials.	$(4x - 3)(4x - 3) = 81$
	$(4x - 3)^2 = 81$

Step 2 Use the Square Root $4x - 3 = \sqrt{81}$ or $4x - 3 = -\sqrt{81}$
Property.

Step 3 Write each answer in simplified form.

Simplify 81. $4x - 3 = 9$ or $4x - 3 = -9$

To solve for x, add 3 to both sides. $4x = 12$ or $4x = -6$

Divide both sides by 4. $x = 3$ or $x = -\dfrac{3}{2}$

Step 4 Check each answer.

We leave the check to you.

So, the two solutions of $16x^2 - 24x + 9 = 81$ are 3 and $-\dfrac{3}{2}$.

Here is a summary of this concept from *Academic Systems Algebra*.

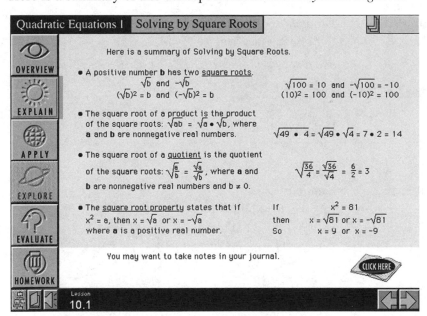

This equation can also be solved by factoring. We first write the equation in the form $ax^2 + bx + c = 0$.

$$16x^2 - 24x + 9 = 81$$

$$16x^2 - 24x - 72 = 0$$

$$8(2x^2 - 3x - 9) = 0$$

$$8(2x + 3)(x - 3) = 0$$

$$2x + 3 = 0 \quad or \quad x - 3 = 0$$

$$x = -\frac{3}{2} \quad or \quad x = 3$$

Checklist Lesson 10.1

Here is what you should know after completing this lesson.

Words and Phrases

standard form of a quadratic equation
multiplicity two

Square Root Property

Ideas and Procedures

❶ **Standard Form of a Quadratic Equation**
Write a quadratic equation in standard form.

Example 10.1.1
    Write $3x(x + 4) = 18$ in standard form and identify
    the values of a, b, and c.

❷ **Solving a Quadratic Equation by Factoring**
Use factoring to solve a quadratic equation.

Example 10.1.3
    Solve by factoring: $x^2 - 14 = -5x$

See also: Examples 10.1.2, 10.1.4, 10.1.5, 10.1.6
    Apply1-28

❸ **Square Root Property**
Write the Square Root Property.

If $x^2 = a$, then $x = \sqrt{a}$ or $x = -\sqrt{a}$.

❹ **Solving a Quadratic Equation by
the Square Root Property**
Use the Square Root Property to solve a
quadratic equation.

Example 10.1.9
    Solve using the Square Root Property:
    $5(w + 6)^2 - 100 = 0$

See also: Example 10.1.7, 10.1.8, 10.1.10
    Apply 29-56

Homework

Homework Problems

Circle the homework problems assigned to you by the computer, then complete them below.

Explain

Solving by Factoring

1. Write $x(2x - 3) = 5$ in standard form.

2. Solve $x^2 - 5x = 0$ by factoring.

3. Solve $2y^2 + 8y = 0$ by factoring.

4. Write $2x - 3x(x - 5) + 1 = 7x - 10$ in standard form.

5. Circle the equations below that are quadratic.

   $-11x^2 = 0$

   $2a(a + 5) = 4$

   $x(7x^2 - 2x + 1) = 0$

   $10x^2 + 3x - 6 = 5x(2x + 7)$

   $6x - 9x^2 = 8$

6. Solve $x^2 + x = 12$ by factoring.

7. Solve $z^2 - 25 = 0$ by factoring.

8. Solve $4b^2 - 12h + 9 = 0$ by factoring.

9. The average depth of the Huang's rectangular swimming pool is 2 meters. If the pool holds 520 m³ of water, and the length of one side is 6 meters less than 2 times the length of the other side, what are the dimensions of the swimming pool?

   Hint: Volume = depth · length · width

   $$520 = 2 \cdot x \cdot (2x - 6)$$

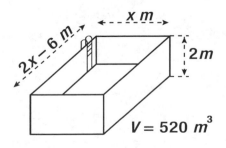

10. Lucy just put a mat around her new Elvis poster. If the matted poster is 19-by-26 inches, and there is 408 in² of the poster showing, how wide is the mat?

    Hint: Find x in this equation:
    $(19 - 2x)(26 - 2x) = 408$

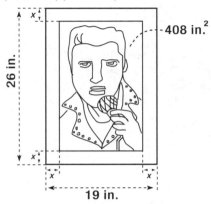

11. Solve $3x^2 + 4x = 5 + 2x$ by factoring.

12. Solve $3r(4r - 7) - 2 = 4$ by factoring.

Solving by Square Roots

13. Solve $a^2 = 100$ using the square root property.

14. Simplify:

    a. $\sqrt{\dfrac{108}{16}}$

    b. $\sqrt{675}$

    c. $\sqrt{49 + 16}$

15. Solve $3x^2 = 108$ using the square root property.

16. Solve $c^2 - 112 = 0$ using the square root property.

17. Solve $2x^2 - 162 = 0$ using the square root property.

18. Solve $(x - 6)^2 = 36$ using the square root property.

19. Solve $x^2 - 2x + 1 = 75$ using the square root property.

20. Solve $9y^2 = 7$ using the square root property.

21. A tree is hit by lightning. The trunk of the tree breaks and the top of the tree touches the ground 20 ft. from the base of the tree. If the top part of the tree is twice as long as the bottom part, approximately how tall was the tree before it was hit by lightning?

(Hint: In a right triangle, $a^2 + b^2 = c^2$, where a and b are the legs of the triangle, and c is the hypotenuse. So $20^2 + x^2 = (2x)^2$.)

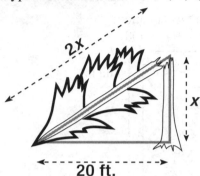

20 ft.

22. Malia is making a cake and she is supposed to pour the batter into a circular pan whose diameter is 10 inches. She doesn't have a circular pan, but she knows that one of her square pans has the same base area as a 10-inch circular pan. What is the length of a side of the square pan?

Area is 25π Area is x^2
square inches   square inches

23. Solve $4x^2 - 36x + 81 = 5$ using the square root property.

24. Solve $4(z + 13)^2 = 17$ using the square root property.

 **Apply**

Practice Problems

Here are some additional practice problems for you to try.

Solving by Factoring

1. Solve $x^2 + 7x = 0$ by factoring.

2. Solve $x^2 + 13x = 0$ by factoring.

3. Solve $6x^2 - 24x = 0$ by factoring.

4. Solve $5x^2 + 35x = 0$ by factoring.

5. Solve $8x^2 + 40x = 0$ by factoring.

6. Solve $10x^2 - 70x = 0$ by factoring.

7. Solve $7x^2 - 42x = 0$ by factoring.

8. Solve $x^2 + 8x + 7 = 0$ by factoring.

9. Solve $x^2 - 7x + 6 = 0$ by factoring

10. Solve $x^2 + 12x + 11 = 0$ by factoring.

11. Solve $x^2 + 12x + 35 = 0$ by factoring.

12. Solve $x^2 - 17x + 66 = 0$ by factoring.

13. Solve $x^2 + 9x + 18 = 0$ by factoring.

14. Solve $x^2 - 3x - 40 = 0$ by factoring.

15. Solve $x^2 - 7x - 18 = 0$ by factoring.

16. Solve $x^2 - 4x - 21 = 0$ by factoring.

17. Solve $x^2 - 5x = 150$ by factoring.

18. Solve $x^2 - 8x = 33$ by factoring.

19. Solve $x^2 - 3x = 10$ by factoring.

20. Solve $x^2 + 7x = 44$ by factoring.

21. Solve $x^2 + 2x = 120$ by factoring.

22. Solve $x^2 + 2x = 24$ by factoring.

23. Solve $x^2 - 3x = 54$ by factoring.

24. Solve $x^2 + 2x = 99$ by factoring.

25. Solve $x^2 - x = 30$ by factoring.

26. Solve $x^2 = 5x + 66$ by factoring.

27. Solve $x^2 = 3x + 180$ by factoring.

28. Solve $x^2 = 4x + 32$ by factoring.

Solving by Square Roots

29. Solve $x^2 = 100$ using the square root property.

30. Solve $x^2 = 81$ using the square root property.

31. Solve $x^2 = 256$ using the square root property.

32. Solve $x^2 = 144$ using the square root property.

33. Solve $x^2 = 48$ using the square root property.

34. Solve $x^2 = 50$ using the square root property.

35. Solve $x^2 = 32$ using the square root property.

36. Solve $5x^2 = 245$ using the square root property.

37. Solve $4x^2 = 324$ using the square root property.

38. Solve $3x^2 = 108$ using the square root property.

39. Solve $7x^2 = 126$ using the square root property.

40. Solve $2x^2 = 90$ using the square root property.

41. Solve $5x^2 = 60$ using the square root property.

42. Solve $5x^2 - 180 = 0$ using the square root property.

43. Solve $2x^2 - 162 = 0$ using the square root property.

44. Solve $3x^2 - 147 = 0$ using the square root property.

45. Solve $(x + 5)^2 = 49$ using the square root property.

46. Solve $(x - 4)^2 = 225$ using the square root property.

47. Solve $(x + 9)^2 = 81$ using the square root property.

48. Solve $(x + 8)^2 = 10$ using the square root property.

49. Solve $(x - 3)^2 = 13$ using the square root property.

50. Solve $(x - 2)^2 = 7$ using the square root property.

51. Solve $x^2 + 6x + 9 = 64$ using the square root property.

52. Solve $x^2 - 10x + 25 = 121$ using the square root property.

53. Solve $x^2 + 4x + 4 = 49$ using the square root property.

54. Solve $4x^2 + 28x + 49 = 32$ using the square root property.

55. Solve $25x^2 - 40x + 16 = 75$ using the square root property.

56. Solve $9x^2 - 30x + 25 = 18$ using the square root property.

Evaluate

Practice Test

Take this practice test to be sure that you are prepared for the final quiz in Evaluate.

1. Write this quadratic equation in standard form and identify a, b, and c.

   $$1 + 2x(x - 8) = x + 3$$

2. Solve the equation $6x^2 - 24x = 0$ by factoring.

3. Circle the quadratic equations.

   $x = 2^2 + 1$

   $2 = (x - 3)^2$

   $x^2 = x^2 + \dfrac{3}{x^2} + 8x$

   $x(x + 9) = 4$

   $x^2 - 9 = 7x + 2$

4. Solve $2x^2 - x - 15 = 0$.

5. Circle the expressions below that are equal to 8.

   $-\sqrt{64}$ $\dfrac{\sqrt{256}}{\sqrt{4}}$

   $\sqrt{(-8)^2}$ $\dfrac{\sqrt{192}}{3}$

   $\sqrt{9 + 16}$ $\sqrt{\dfrac{64}{5}} \cdot \sqrt{5}$

6. Solve $x^2 = 343$ using the square root property.

7. Solve this equation for x:

   $$x = \dfrac{\dfrac{\sqrt{20}}{\sqrt{3}}}{\dfrac{\sqrt{8}}{\sqrt{3}}}$$

8. Solve $(x - 5)^2 = 164$ using the square root property.

LESSON 10.2
QUADRATIC EQUATIONS II

 Overview

You have learned how to solve certain types of quadratic equations by factoring and by the square root method. However, some quadratic equations cannot be solved using these methods.

In this lesson, you will learn how to solve a quadratic equation by completing the square and by using the quadratic formula. Each of these methods can be used to solve *any* quadratic equation.

 Explain

Concept 1 has sections on

- **Completing the Square**

- **Solving Quadratic Equations by Completing the Square**

CONCEPT 1:
COMPLETING THE SQUARE

Completing the Square

Any quadratic equation can be solved using a technique called **completing the square**.

To use this method, we will rewrite the quadratic equation so that one side is a perfect square. Then we solve using the square root property.

Before we solve a quadratic equation in this way, let's learn how to complete the square.

To "complete the square" means to transform a binomial of the form $x^2 + bx$ into a perfect square trinomial by adding a constant term.

For example, let's complete the square for $x^2 + 6x$.

We will use rectangles, called **algebra tiles**, to visualize the process.

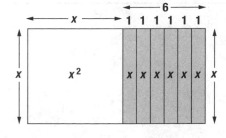

- A square tile measuring x units on a side has area x^2. We will use this tile to represent x^2, the first term of $x^2 + 6x$.

- A rectangular tile that is x units tall and 1 unit wide has an area of $1x$. Since $6 \cdot 1x$ is $6x$, we will use six of these tiles to represent the second term of $x^2 + 6x$.

Placed side by side, the tiles form a rectangle that represents $x^2 + 6x$.

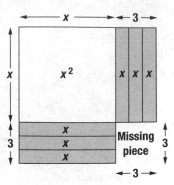

Area = $x^2 + 6x + ?$

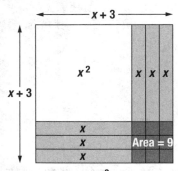

Area = $x^2 + 6x + 9$

Now, we try to rearrange the tiles to form a square.
To do this, we move one-half of the tall thin tiles.
However, the result is not a complete square because the lower right portion is missing.

The missing piece is a 3-by-3 square.
Thus, to "complete the square," we must add $3 \cdot 3 = 9$ unit tiles.

With the 9 new tiles, the area of the entire square is

$$(x + 3)(x + 3) = (x + 3)^2 = x^2 + 6x + 9.$$

By adding 9 to $x^2 + 6x$, we have created the perfect square $(x + 3)^2$.

Let's review the process we used to complete the square.

$x^2 + 6x + ?$

We moved one-half of the x-tiles.

Multiply the coefficient of x by $\frac{1}{2}$.

$$6 \cdot \frac{1}{2} = 3$$

Then we filled in the remaining space with a square of unit tiles.

Square the result.
$$3^2 = 9$$

We added nine tiles to complete the square.

$$x^2 + 6x + 9$$
$$= (x + 3)(x + 3)$$
$$= (x + 3)^2$$

This process holds in general:
To find the number needed to complete the square, multiply the coefficient of the x-term by $\frac{1}{2}$, and then square the result.

— Procedure —
To Complete the Square

To complete the square for a binomial of the form $x^2 + bx$:

Step 1 Calculate $\frac{1}{2} \cdot b$.
(That is, divide b by 2.)

Step 2 Square the result from Step 1.
$\left[\text{That is, calculate } \left(\frac{1}{2} \cdot b\right)^2.\right]$

Step 3 Add the result from Step 2 to $x^2 + bx$.

The new expression, $x^2 + bx + \left(\frac{1}{2} \cdot b\right)^2$, is a perfect square trinomial.

Example 10.2.1

Complete the square for each binomial. Then write each new expression as the square of a binomial.

a. $x^2 + 12x$ b. $x^2 - 5x$

Solution

a. $x^2 + 12x$ has the form $x^2 + bx$, where $b = 12$.

> ***Step 1 Calculate $\frac{1}{2} \cdot b$.*** $\frac{1}{2} \cdot b = \frac{1}{2} \cdot 12 = 6$
>
> ***Step 2 Square the result from Step 1.*** $6^2 = 36$
>
> ***Step 3 Add the result from Step 2 to $x^2 + bx$.*** $x^2 + 12x + 36$

The expression $x^2 + 12x + 36$ is a perfect square trinomial.

Write the expression $x^2 + 12x + 36$ as the square of a binomial. $= (x + 6)^2$

b. $x^2 - 5x$ has the form $x^2 + bx$, where $b = -5$.

> ***Step 1 Calculate $\frac{1}{2} \cdot b$.*** $\frac{1}{2} \cdot b = \frac{1}{2} \cdot (-5) = -\frac{5}{2}$
>
> ***Step 2 Square the result from Step 1.*** $\left(-\frac{5}{2}\right)^2 = \frac{25}{4}$
>
> ***Step 3 Add the result from Step 2 to $x^2 + bx$.*** $x^2 - 5x + \frac{25}{4}$

The expression $x^2 + 5x + \frac{25}{4}$ is a perfect square trinomial.

We have completed the square.
Write the expression as the square of a binomial. $= (x - \frac{5}{2})^2$

Solving Quadratic Equations by Completing the Square

Now, we will complete the square to solve a quadratic equation.

For example, let's solve: $x^2 + 2x = 4$

We begin on the left-side of the equation by completing the square.

To find the number needed to complete the square for $x^2 + 2x$, calculate $\left(\frac{1}{2} \cdot b\right)^2$, $\left(\frac{1}{2} \cdot b\right)^2 = \left(\frac{1}{2} \cdot 2\right)^2 = 1^2 = 1$ where $b = 2$.

Thus, to complete the square for $x^2 + 2x$, we add 1.

However, we are working with an *equation*, so we must add 1 to *both* *sides* of the equation. $x^2 + 2x + 1 = 4 + 1$

The left side can be written as the square of a binomial. $(x + 1)^2 = 5$

To solve this equation, use the Square Root Property:

$$x + 1 = \sqrt{5} \quad \text{or} \quad x + 1 = -\sqrt{5}$$

For each equation, subtract 1 from both sides.

$$x = -1 + \sqrt{5} \quad \text{or} \quad x = -1 - \sqrt{5}$$

So, the two solutions of $x^2 + 2x = 4$ are $-1 + \sqrt{5}$ and $-1 - \sqrt{5}$.

The symbol ± is read "plus or minus."

We can write the solutions using shorthand notation: $x = -1 \pm \sqrt{5}$.

Here is a procedure we can use to solve any quadratic equation.

— Procedure —
To Solve a Quadratic Equation by Completing the Square

Step 1 Isolate the x^2-term and the x-term on one side of the equation.

Step 2 If the coefficient of x^2 is not 1, divide both sides of the equation by the coefficient of x^2.

Step 3 Find the number that completes the square:
- Multiply the coefficient of x by $\frac{1}{2}$.
- Square the result.

Step 4 Add the result of Step 3 to both sides of the equation.

Step 5 Write the trinomial as the square of a binomial.

Step 6 Finish solving using the Square Root Property.

Step 7 Check each solution.

Example 10.2.2

Solve by completing the square: $x^2 - 8x - 48 = 0$

Solution

Step 1 Isolate the x^2-term and the x-term on one side of the equation.

$$x^2 - 8x - 48 = 0$$

Add 48 to both sides of the equation.

$$x^2 - 8x = 48$$

Step 2 If the coefficient of x^2 is not 1, divide both sides of the equation by the coefficient of x^2.

The coefficient of x^2 is 1, so we do not need to divide.

Step 3 Find the number that completes the square: Multiply the coefficient of x by $\frac{1}{2}$. Square the result.

The coefficient of the x-term is -8.

$$\frac{1}{2} \cdot (-8) = -4$$

$$(-4)^2 = \mathbf{16}$$

Step 4 *Add the result of Step 3 to both sides of the equation.*

Add 16 to both sides of the equation. $x^2 - 8x + \mathbf{16} = 48 + \mathbf{16}$

Step 5 *Write the trinomial as the square of a binomial.* $(x - 4)^2 = 64$

Notice that **−4**, *the number you squared in Step 3, is the constant term in the binomial* $(x - 4)$.

Step 6 *Finish solving using the Square Root Property.*

Use the Square Root Property. $x - 4 = \sqrt{64}$ or $x - 4 = -\sqrt{64}$

For each equation, add 4 to both sides and simplify $\sqrt{64}$. $x = 4 + 8$ or $x = 4 - 8$

$x = 12$ or $x = 24$

Step 7 *Check each solution.*

Check x = 12.	**Check x = −4.**
$x^2 - 8x - 48 = 0$	$x^2 - 8x - 48 = 0$
Is $(\mathbf{12})^2 - 8(\mathbf{12}) - 48 = 0$?	Is $(\mathbf{-4})^2 - 8(\mathbf{-4}) - 48 = 0$?
Is $\quad 144 - 96 - 48 = 0$?	Is $\quad 16 + 32 - 48 = 0$?
Is $\quad\quad\quad\quad 0 = 0$? **Yes**	Is $\quad\quad\quad\quad 0 = 0$? **Yes**

The solutions of $x^2 - 8x - 48 = 0$ are 12 and −4.

Example 10.2.3

Solve by completing the square: $5x^2 + 70x - 30 = 0$

Solution

Step 1 *Isolate the x^2-term and the x-term on one side of the equation.* $5x^2 + 70x - 30 = 0$

Add 30 to both sides of the equation. $5x^2 + 70x = 30$

Step 2 *If the coefficient of x^2 is not 1, divide both sides of the equation by the coefficient of x^2.*

The coefficient of x^2 is 5.
Divide both sides of the equation by 5. $x^2 + 14x = 6$

To divide both sides of an equation by 5, we divide each term by 5, like this:

$$\frac{5x^2}{5} + \frac{70x}{5} = \frac{30}{5}$$

$$x^2 + 14x = 6$$

Step 3 *Find the number that completes the square: Multiply the coefficient of x by $\frac{1}{2}$. Square the result.*

The coefficient of the x-term is 14.

$$\frac{1}{2} \cdot 14 = 7$$

$$7^2 = \mathbf{49}$$

Step 4 Add the result of Step 3 to both sides of the equation.

Add 49 to both sides of the equation. $x^2 + 14x + 49 = 6 + 49$

Notice that 7, the number you squared in Step 3, is the constant term in the binomial $(x + 7)$.

Step 5 Write the trinomial as the square of a binomial. $(x + 7)^2 = 55$

Step 6 Finish solving using the Square Root Property.

Use the Square Root Property to write two linear equations. $x + 7 = \sqrt{55}$ or $x + 7 = -\sqrt{55}$

For each equation, subtract 7 from both sides. $x = -7 + \sqrt{55}$ or $x = -7 - \sqrt{55}$

Step 7 Check each solution.

We leave the check for you.

The solutions of $5x^2 + 70x - 30 = 0$ are $-7 + \sqrt{55}$ and $-7 - \sqrt{55}$.

The solutions can also be written as follows: $x = -7 \pm \sqrt{55}$.

Example 10.2.4

Solve by completing the square: $3x^2 - 30 = -21x$

Solution

Step 1 Isolate the x^2-term and the x-term on one side of the equation. $3x^2 - 30 = -21x$

Add $21x$ to both sides. $3x^2 + 21x - 30 = 0$
Add 30 to both sides. $3x^2 + 21x = 30$

Step 2 If the coefficient of x^2 is not 1, divide both sides of the equation by the coefficient of x^2.

Divide both sides by 3. $x^2 + 7x = 10$

To divide both sides of an equation by 3, we divide each term by 3, like this:

$$\frac{3x^2}{3} + \frac{21x}{3} = \frac{30}{3}$$
$$x^2 + 7x = 10$$

Step 3 Find the number that completes the square: Multiply the coefficient of x by $\frac{1}{2}$. Square the result.

The coefficient of the x-term is 7.

$$\frac{1}{2} \cdot 7 = \frac{7}{2}$$
$$\left(\frac{7}{2}\right)^2 = \frac{49}{4}$$

Step 4 **Add the result of Step 3 to both sides of the equation.**

Add $\frac{49}{4}$ to both sides.

$$x^2 + 7x + \frac{49}{4} = 10 + \frac{49}{4}$$

Simplify the right side.
The result is $\frac{89}{4}$.

$$x^2 + 7x + \frac{49}{4} = \frac{89}{4}$$

Step 5 **Write the trinomial as the square of a binomial.**

$$\left(x + \frac{7}{2}\right)^2 = \frac{89}{4}$$

Step 6 **Finish solving using the Square Root Property.**

Use the Square Root Property. $x + \frac{7}{2} = +\sqrt{\frac{89}{4}}$ or $x + \frac{7}{2} = -\sqrt{\frac{89}{4}}$

For each equation, subtract $\frac{7}{2}$ from both sides and simplify the radical.

$$x = -\frac{7}{2} + \frac{\sqrt{89}}{2} \quad \text{or} \quad x = -\frac{7}{2} - \frac{\sqrt{89}}{2}$$

Step 7 **Check each solution.**

We leave the check for you.

The solutions of $3x^2 - 30 = -21x$ are $-\frac{7}{2} + \frac{\sqrt{89}}{2}$ and $-\frac{7}{2} - \frac{\sqrt{89}}{2}$.

To simplify the right side of the equation, first write 10 as a fraction with denominator 4.

$$10 = \frac{10}{1} \cdot \frac{4}{4} = \frac{40}{4}$$

Then add.

$$\frac{40}{4} + \frac{49}{4} = \frac{89}{4}$$

Notice that $\frac{7}{2}$, the number you squared in Step 3, is the constant term in the binomial $(x + \frac{7}{2})$.

We can use the "plus or minus" symbol to write the solutions like this

$$x = -\frac{7}{2} \pm \frac{\sqrt{89}}{2}$$

or like this

$$x = \frac{-7 \pm \sqrt{89}}{2}.$$

Example 10.2.5

Kurt has a rectangular patio that is 12 feet long and 10 feet wide. He wants to increase the length and the width so the area of the new patio will be twice that of the original patio. The length will be increased by twice the amount that the width is increased. By how much should he increase each dimension?

Solution

Calculate the area of the original patio.

original area = (12 feet)(10 feet)

= 120 ft²

The area of the new patio will be twice that of the original patio.

new area = 2 · 120 ft²

= 240 ft²

Let x = the number of feet the width should be increased.

To represent the new width, add x to the original width.

new width = 10 + x ft

Since the length will be increased by twice as much as the width, to represent the new length, add $2x$ to the original length.

new length = 12 + 2x ft

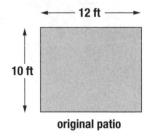

original patio

The area of the rectangle is:
Area = (length)(width)

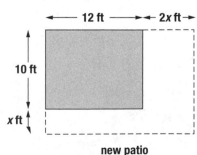

new patio

Now, write an equation for the area of the new patio.

$$\text{new area} = (\text{new length})(\text{new width})$$

Substitute the expressions. $\qquad 240 = (12 + 2x)(10 + x)$

Multiply the binomials. $\qquad 240 = 120 + 12x + 20x + 2x^2$

Simplify. $\qquad 240 = 120 + 32x + 2x^2$

This quadratic equation can be solved by completing the square.

Step 1 Isolate the x^2-term and the x-term on one side of the equation.

Subtract 120 from both sides. $\qquad 120 = 32x + 2x^2$

Write the equation with decreasing powers of x on the left. $\qquad 2x^2 + 32x = 120$

Step 2 If the coefficient of x^2 is not 1, divide both sides of the equation by the coefficient of x^2.

The coefficient of x^2 is 2.
Divide both sides of the equation by 2. $\qquad x^2 + 16x = 60$

Step 3 Find the number that completes the square: Multiply the coefficient of x by $\frac{1}{2}$. Square the result.

The coefficient of the x-term is 16.
$$\frac{1}{2} \cdot 16 = 8$$
$$8^2 = \mathbf{64}$$

Step 4 Add the result of Step 3 to both sides of the equation.

Add 64 to both sides of the equation. $\qquad x^2 + 16x \mathbf{+ 64} = 60 \mathbf{+ 64}$

Step 5 Write the trinomial as the square of a binomial.

Write $x^2 + 16x \mathbf{+ 64}$ as the square of a binomial.
Also, simplify the right side of the equation. $\qquad (x + 8)^2 = 124$

Step 6 Finish solving using the Square Root Property.

Use the Square Root Property. $\qquad x + 8 = \sqrt{124} \text{ or } x + 8 = -\sqrt{124}$

For each equation, subtract 8 from both sides. $\qquad x = -8 + \sqrt{124} \text{ or } x = -8 - \sqrt{124}$

You may want to simplify the radical:

$$\sqrt{124} = \sqrt{4 \cdot 31} = \sqrt{4} \cdot \sqrt{31} = 2\sqrt{31}$$

So the solutions are:

$$-8 \pm 2\sqrt{31}$$

Step 7 Check each solution.

We leave the check for you.

Because this is an applied problem, we use a calculator to approximate $\sqrt{124}$ to two decimal places: $\sqrt{124} \approx 11.14$.

$x \approx -8 + 11.14$ or $x \approx -8 - 11.14$

$x \approx 3.14$ feet or $x \approx -19.14$ feet

Since x is the number of feet the patio width will increase, the only solution that applies is the *positive* solution, 3.14 feet.

Therefore, the width of the patio should be increased by approximately 3.14 feet. The length of the patio should be increased by approximately $2 \cdot (3.14 \text{ feet}) = 6.28$ feet.

We can check the solution of the original problem as follows:

Condition	*Check*
• The length will increase by twice as much as the width.	• The width is increased by 3.14 feet. Twice this is 6.28 feet, the amount the length is increased. ✓
• The new area will be twice the old area.	• The new width of the patio is 10 ft + 3.14 ft = 13.14 ft
	The new length of the patio is 12 ft + 6.28 ft = 18.28 ft.
	The new area of the patio is (13.14 ft)(18.28 ft) $\approx 240 \text{ ft}^2$.
	This is twice 120 ft^2, the area of the original patio. ✓

Here is a summary of this concept from *Academic Systems Algebra.*

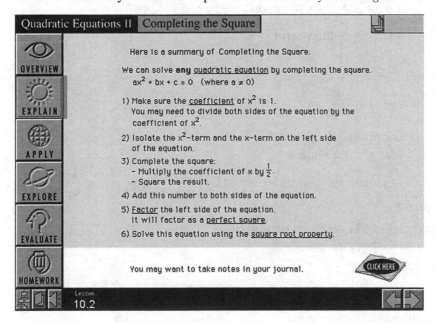

CONCEPT 2: THE QUADRATIC FORMULA

The Quadratic Formula

You can solve any quadratic equation by completing the square.

Now we will complete the square to solve $ax^2 + bx + c = 0$. The solutions will be expressed in terms of a, b, and c. These solutions will give us a formula we can use to solve any quadratic equation.

Step 1 Isolate the x^2-term and the x-term on one side of the equation. $ax^2 + bx + c = 0$

Subtract c from both sides of the equation. $ax^2 + bx = -c$

Step 2 If the coefficient of x^2 is not 1, divide both sides of the equation by the coefficient of x^2.

The coefficient of x^2 is a.
Divide both sides of the equation by a. $\dfrac{ax^2}{a} + \dfrac{bx}{a} = \dfrac{-c}{a}$

$$x^2 + \dfrac{b}{a}x = \dfrac{-c}{a}$$

Step 3 Find the number that completes the square: Multiply the coefficient of x by $\dfrac{1}{2}$. Square the result.

The coefficient of the x-term is $\dfrac{b}{a}$.

$$\dfrac{1}{2} \cdot \dfrac{b}{a} = \dfrac{b}{2a}$$

$$\left(\dfrac{b}{2a}\right)^2 = \dfrac{b^2}{4a^2}$$

Step 4 Add the result of Step 3 to both sides of the equation.

Add $\dfrac{b^2}{4a^2}$ to both sides of the equation. $x^2 + \dfrac{bx}{a} + \dfrac{b^2}{4a^2} = \dfrac{-c}{a} + \dfrac{b^2}{4a^2}$

To combine like terms on the right side, write both fractions with denominator $4a^2$.

$\dfrac{-c}{a} = \dfrac{-c}{a} \cdot \dfrac{4a}{4a} = \dfrac{-4ac}{4a^2}$ $x^2 + \dfrac{bx}{a} + \dfrac{b^2}{4a^2} = \dfrac{-4ac}{4a^2} + \dfrac{b^2}{4a^2}$

Combine like terms on the right side. In the numerator, write the b^2-term first. $x^2 + \dfrac{bx}{a} + \dfrac{b^2}{4a^2} = \dfrac{b^2 - 4ac}{4a^2}$

Step 5 **Write the trinomial as the**
square of a binomial.

$$\left(x + \frac{b}{2a}\right)^2 = \frac{b^2 - 4ac}{4a^2}$$

Step 6 **Finish solving using the**
Square Root Property.

Use the Square Root Property. Rather than writing two separate equations, we write a single equation using the ± sign.

$$x + \frac{b}{2a} = \pm\sqrt{\frac{b^2 - 4ac}{4a^2}}$$

Subtract $\frac{b}{2a}$ from both sides and simplify the radical.

$$x = \frac{-b}{2a} \pm \frac{\sqrt{b^2 - 4ac}}{2a}$$

If $a > 0$, then $4a^2 = 2a$.

If $a < 0$, then $4a^2 = -2a$.

Combine the fractions into a single fraction.

$$x = \frac{-b \pm \sqrt{b^2 - 4ac}}{2a}$$

So,

$$\sqrt{4a^2} = \pm 2a.$$

The result is called the **quadratic formula**.

$$x = \frac{-b \pm \sqrt{b^2 - 4ac}}{2a}$$

— Formula —
The Quadratic Formula

The solutions of the quadratic equation $ax^2 + bx + c = 0$ are given by the quadratic formula:

$$x = \frac{-b \pm \sqrt{b^2 - 4ac}}{2a}$$

Here, a, b, and c are real numbers and $a \neq 0$.

Solving Quadratic Equations Using the Quadratic Formula

To use the **quadratic formula** to solve a quadratic equation, we replace a, b, and c with specific numbers. Then we simplify the resulting expression.

— Procedure —
To Solve a Quadratic Equation Using the Quadratic Formula

Step 1 Write the quadratic equation in standard form,
$ax^2 + bx + c = 0$.

Step 2 Identify the values of a, b, and c.

Step 3 Substitute the values of a, b, and c into the quadratic formula.

Step 4 Simplify.

Step 5 Check each solution.

Example 10.2.6

Solve using the quadratic formula: $3x^2 - 16x = -5$

Solution

Step 1 Write the quadratic equation in standard form, $ax^2 + bx + c = 0$.

$$3x^2 - 16x = -5$$

Add 5 to both sides of the equation. $\qquad 3x^2 - 16x + 5 = 0$

Step 2 Identify the values of a, b, and c.

$$a = 3, b = -16, \ c = 5$$

Step 3 Substitute the values of a, b, and c into the quadratic formula.

$$x = \frac{-b \pm \sqrt{b^2 - 4ac}}{2a}$$

$$x = \frac{-(-16) \pm \sqrt{(-16)^2 - 4(3)(5)}}{2(3)}$$

Step 4 Simplify.

$$x = \frac{16 \pm \sqrt{256 - 60}}{6}$$

$$x = \frac{16 \pm \sqrt{196}}{6}$$

$$x = \frac{16 + 14}{6} \quad \text{or} \quad \frac{16 - 14}{6}$$

$$x = 5 \quad \text{or} \quad x = \frac{1}{3}$$

Step 5 Check each solution.

We leave the check to you.

The two solutions of $3x^2 - 16x = -5$ are $\frac{1}{3}$ and 5.

$3x^2 - 16x + 5 = 0$

When you identify a, b, and c, be careful with the signs. Here,
$b = -16$.

Example 10.2.7

Solve using the quadratic formula: $10 - 5x^2 = 6x$

Solution

Step 1 Write the quadratic equation in standard form, $ax^2 + bx + c = 0$.

Subtract $6x$ from both sides of the equation. On the left side, write the terms in decreasing powers of x.

$$10 - 5x^2 = 6x$$

$$-5x^2 - 6x + 10 = 0$$

Step 2 Identify the values of a, b, and c.

$$a = -5, \ b = -6, \ c = 10$$

Step 3 Substitute the values of a, b, and c into the quadratic formula.

$$x = \frac{-b \pm \sqrt{b^2 - 4ac}}{2a}$$

$$x = \frac{-(-6) \pm \sqrt{(-6)^2 - 4(-5)(10)}}{2(-5)}$$

Step 4 Simplify.

$$x = \frac{6 \pm \sqrt{36 + 200}}{-10}$$

$$x = \frac{6 \pm \sqrt{236}}{-10}$$

Simplify the radical.
$\sqrt{236} = \sqrt{4 \cdot 59} = 2\sqrt{59}$

$$x = \frac{6 \pm 2\sqrt{59}}{-10}$$

Factor -2 from the numerator and denominator.

$$x = \frac{-2(-3 \pm \sqrt{59})}{-2(5)}$$

Reduce by canceling the common factor, -2

$$x = \frac{-3 \pm \sqrt{59}}{5}$$

Step 5 Check each solution.

We leave the check to you.

The two solutions of $10 - 5x^2 = 6x$ are $\dfrac{-3 + \sqrt{59}}{5}$ and $\dfrac{-3 - \sqrt{59}}{5}$.

Here's another way to simplify:

$$x = \frac{6 \pm 2\sqrt{59}}{-10}$$

$$x = \frac{2(3 \pm \sqrt{59})}{2(-5)} \qquad \text{Factor out 2.}$$

$$x = \frac{3 \pm \sqrt{59}}{-5}$$

$$x = \frac{-1}{-1} \cdot \frac{3 \pm \sqrt{59}}{25} \qquad \text{Multiply by } \frac{-1}{-1}.$$

$$x = \frac{-3 \pm \sqrt{59}}{5}$$

*(We multiplied by $\frac{-1}{-1}$ because we do **not** want a negative sign in the denominator.)*

Example 10.2.8

Solve using the quadratic formula: $36x^2 + 16 + 48x = 0$

Solution

Step 1 Write the quadratic equation in standard form,
$ax^2 + bx + c = 0.$

$$36x^2 + 16 + 48x = 0$$

On the left side, write the terms in decreasing powers of x.

$$36x^2 + 48x + 16 = 0$$

Each term is divisible by 4. To simplify the calculations, divide both sides of the equation by 4.

$$9x^2 + 12x + 4 = 0$$

$$9x^2 + 12x + 4 = 0$$

Step 2 Identify the values of a, b, and c.

$$a = 9, \quad b = 12, \quad c = 4$$

The left side of the equation is factorable. Therefore, we could also solve this equation by factoring.

Step 3 Substitute the values of a, b, and c into the quadratic formula.

$$x = \frac{-b \pm \sqrt{b^2 - 4ac}}{2a}$$

$$x = \frac{-(12) \pm \sqrt{(12)^2 - 4(9)(4)}}{2(9)}$$

Step 4 Simplify.

$$x = \frac{-12 \pm \sqrt{144 - 144}}{18}$$

$$x = \frac{-12 \pm \sqrt{0}}{18}$$

$$x = \frac{-12 + \sqrt{0}}{18} \quad \text{or} \quad x = \frac{-12 - \sqrt{0}}{18}$$

$$x = -\frac{2}{3} \quad \text{or} \quad x = -\frac{2}{3}$$

Step 5 Check each solution.

We leave the check to you.

We say that $-\dfrac{2}{3}$ is a solution of multiplicity two.

Example 10.2.9

Solve using the quadratic formula: $x^2 + 5 = 3x$

Solution

Step 1 Write the quadratic equation in standard form,
$ax^2 + bx + c = 0$. $\qquad\qquad\qquad\qquad\qquad x^2 + 5 = 3x$

Subtract $3x$ from both sides of the equation. $\quad x^2 - 3x + 5 = 0$

Step 2 Identify the values of a, b, and c.

$$a = 1,\ b = -3,\ c = 5$$

Step 3 Substitute the values of a,
b, and c into the quadratic $\qquad x = \dfrac{-b \pm \sqrt{b^2 - 4ac}}{2a}$
formula.

$$x = \dfrac{-(-3) \pm \sqrt{(-3)^2 - 4(1)(5)}}{2(1)}$$

Step 4 Simplify. $\qquad\qquad\qquad\qquad x = \dfrac{3 \pm \sqrt{9 - 20}}{2}$

$$x = \dfrac{3 \pm \sqrt{-11}}{2}$$

Notice the negative number under the square root symbol.

The radical $\sqrt{-11}$ does not represent a real number.

Therefore, the equation $x^2 + 5 = 3x$ has no real number solutions.

When you solve an equation of the form $ax^2 + bx + c = 0$,
consider the following:

Here's an example when $a = 0$:
$3x + 5 = 0$
$a = 0, b = 3, c = 5$
*This is a **linear** equation.*

- If $a = 0$, then the equation can be written $bx + c = 0$.
  This is a linear equation, not a quadratic equation.
  So we cannot use the quadratic formula to solve it.

Here's an example when $b = 0$:
$2x^2 + 5 = 0$
$a = 2, b = 0, c = 5$

- If $b = 0$, then the equation can be written $ax^2 + c = 0$.
  We can solve using the quadratic formula with $b = 0$.
  However, it takes fewer steps to solve this equation using
  the Square Root Property.

Here's an example when $c = 0$:
$2x^2 + 3x = 0$
$a = 2, b = 3 , c = 5$

- If $c = 0$, then the equation can be written $ax^2 + bx = 0$.
  We can solve using the quadratic formula with $c = 0$.
  However, it takes fewer steps to solve this equation by factoring.

The Discriminant

In the quadratic formula, the radicand, $b^2 - 4ac$, is called the **discriminant** of the quadratic equation $ax^2 + bx + c = 0$.

We can use the discriminant to determine the nature of the solutions of a quadratic equation without having to solve the equation.

Discriminant   **Solutions**

$b^2 - 4ac > 0$ two different real numbers $x = \dfrac{-b \pm \sqrt{\textbf{positive number}}}{2a}$

$b^2 - 4ac = 0$ two identical real numbers $x = \dfrac{-b \pm \sqrt{0}}{2a} = \dfrac{-b}{2a}$

$b^2 - 4ac < 0$ no real number solutions $x = \dfrac{-b \pm \sqrt{\textbf{negative number}}}{2a}$

If the discriminant is a perfect square, the solutions will not only be real numbers, they will also be rational numbers.

Example 10.2.10

Use the discriminant to determine the nature of the solutions of this quadratic equation: $-2x^2 - x + 7 = 0$

Solution

The equation has the form $ax^2 + bx + c = 0$ where $a = -2$, $b = -1$, and $c = 7$.

Substitute the values of a, b, and c into the discriminant and simplify.

$$b^2 - 4ac = (-1)^2 - 4(-2)(7)$$
$$= 1 + 56$$
$$= 57$$

The discriminant is 57, a positive number.
So the equation $-2x^2 - x + 7 = 0$ has two unequal real number solutions.

Example 10.2.11

Use the discriminant to determine the nature of the solutions of this quadratic equation: $5x^2 - 3x + 8 = 0$

Solution

The equation has the form $ax^2 + bx + c = 0$ where $a = 5$, $b = -3$, and $c = 8$.

Substitute the values of a, b, and c into the discriminant and simplify.

$$b^2 - 4ac = (-3)^2 - 4(5)(8)$$
$$= 9 - 160$$
$$= -151$$

The discriminant is -151, a negative number.
So the equation $5x^2 - 3x + 8 = 0$ has no real number solutions.

Example 10.2.12

Use the discriminant to determine the nature of the solutions of this quadratic equation: $9x^2 - 6x = -1$

Solution

$$9x^2 - 6x = -1$$

To put the equation in standard form, add 1 to both sides of the equation.

$$9x^2 - 6x + 1 = 0$$

Now the equation has the form $ax^2 + bx + c = 0$ where $a = 9$, $b = -6$, and $c = 1$.

Substitute the values of a, b, and c into the discriminant and simplify.

$$b^2 - 4ac = (-6)^2 - 4(9)(1)$$
$$= 36 - 36$$
$$= 0$$

The discriminant is 0.
So the equation $9x^2 - 6x = -1$ has two identical real number solutions.

Strategies for Solving Quadratic Equations.

You have learned four ways to solve a quadratic equation:

- The Square Root Property

- Factoring

- Completing the square

- The quadratic formula

You can solve any quadratic equation by completing the square or by using the quadratic formula. However, for some quadratic equations, it is quicker to solve by factoring or by using the Square Root Property.

When you want to solve a quadratic equation, try the following strategies:

1. Use the **Square Root Property** when the equation can be easily written in the form $x^2 = a$ or $(x + k)^2 = a$.

   For example, the Square Root Property is useful for solving this equation:

   $$(x + 3)^2 - 16 = 0$$

   Add 16 to both sides.

   $$(x + 3)^2 = 16$$

   Use the Square Root Property to write two linear equations.

   $$x + 3 = \sqrt{16} \quad \text{or} \quad x + 3 = -\sqrt{16}$$

   Simplify each square root.

   $$x + 3 = 4 \quad \text{or} \quad x + 3 = -4$$

   Subtract 3 from both sides of each equation.

   $$x = 1 \quad \text{or} \quad x = -7$$

2. If the Square Root Property cannot be easily applied, write the equation in standard form, $ax^2 + bx + c = 0$.

   If the trinomial can be easily factored, solve the equation by **factoring**.

   For example, this strategy is useful for solving this equation: $x^2 - 5x = -6$

   Add 6 to both sides of the equation. $x^2 - 5x + 6 = 0$

   Factor the trinomial. $(x - 2)(x - 3) = 0$

   Set each factor equal to 0. $x - 2 = 0 \quad \text{or} \quad x - 3 = 0$

   Solve each equation. $x = 2 \quad \text{or} \quad x = 3$

3. The **quadratic formula** can be used to solve any quadratic equation, including the equations in the two previous examples.

   You can solve any quadratic equation by completing the square.

   Recall that to obtain the quadratic formula we solved
   $$ax^2 + bx + c = 0$$
   by completing the square.

   For example, the quadratic formula is useful for solving this equation: $x^2 + 1 = -5x$

   To write the equation in standard form, add $5x$ to both sides of the equation. $x^2 + 5x + 1 = 0$

   Use the quadratic formula with $a = 1$, $b = 5$, and $c = 1$. $x = \dfrac{-b \pm \sqrt{b^2 - 4ac}}{2a}$

   Substitute the values for a, b, and c into the quadratic formula. $x = \dfrac{-5 \pm \sqrt{5^2 - 4(1)(1)}}{2(1)}$

   Simplify. $x = \dfrac{-5 \pm \sqrt{21}}{2}$

Here is a summary of this concept from *Academic Systems Algebra*.

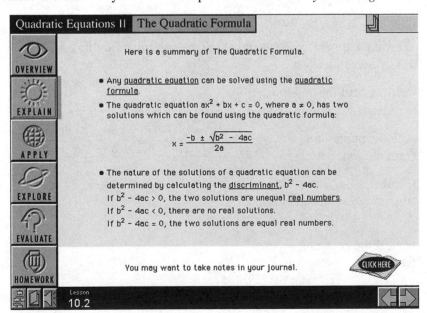

On the computer you examined the solutions of quadratic equations and also explored their discriminants. Here are some additional exploration problems.

Example 10.2.13

The solutions of a quadratic equation are 5 and $-\dfrac{2}{3}$.

Work backwards to find a quadratic equation with these solutions.

Solution

Begin by writing the two solutions. $x = 5$ or $x = -\dfrac{2}{3}$

To clear the fraction in the second solution, multiply both sides of the second equation by 3. $x = 5$ or $3x = -2$

Move the constant to the left side of each equation. $x - 5 = 0$ or $3x + 2 = 0$

Since each binomial is equal to 0, their product is 0. $(x - 5)(3x + 2) = 0$

Multiply the binomials. $3x^2 + 2x - 15x - 10 = 0$

Combine like terms. $3x^2 - 13x - 10 = 0$

The quadratic equation $3x^2 - 13x - 10 = 0$ has the given solutions, 5 and $-\dfrac{2}{3}$.

$$3x^2 - 13x - 10 = 0$$

Any nonzero multiple of this equation also has solutions 5 and $-\dfrac{2}{3}$.
Here are some examples:

$$6x^2 - 26x - 20 = 0$$
$$15x^2 - 65x - 50 = 0$$

The quadratic formula states that the solutions of a quadratic equation, $ax^2 + bx + c = 0$, are

$$x = \frac{-b + \sqrt{b^2 - 4ac}}{2a} \text{ or } x = \frac{-b - \sqrt{b^2 - 4ac}}{2a}.$$

Let's see what happens when we combine the solutions first by addition and then by multiplication:

- When we **add** the solutions, the radicals are eliminated. $\dfrac{-b + \sqrt{b^2 - 4ac}}{2a} + \dfrac{-b - \sqrt{b^2 - 4ac}}{2a}$

  Add the numerators to form one fraction. $= \dfrac{-b + \sqrt{b^2 - 4ac} - b - \sqrt{b^2 - 4ac}}{2a}$

  Combine like terms. The square root terms add to zero. $= \dfrac{-2b}{2a}$

  Cancel the common factor, 2. $= -\dfrac{b}{a}$

Thus, for a quadratic equation, $ax^2 + bx + c = 0$,

the **sum of the solutions** is $-\dfrac{b}{a}$.

- When we multiply the solutions, the radicals are eliminated.

$$\frac{-b + \sqrt{b^2 - 4ac}}{2a} \cdot \frac{-b - \sqrt{b^2 - 4ac}}{2a}$$

Multiply the numerators and multiply the denominators.

$$= \frac{(-b)^2 + b\sqrt{b^2 - 4ac} - b\sqrt{b^2 - 4ac} - (\sqrt{b^2 - 4ac})^2}{4a^2}$$

$$= \frac{b^2 - (b^2 - 4ac)}{4a^2}$$

Combine like terms.

$$= \frac{4ac}{4a^2}$$

Cancel the common factor, $4a$.

$$= \frac{c}{a}$$

Thus, for a quadratic equation, $ax^2 + bx + c = 0$,

the **product of the solutions** is $\dfrac{c}{a}$.

Example **10.2.14**

The solutions of a quadratic equation are 4 and -1. Use their sum and product to find a quadratic equation with those solutions.

Solution

For a quadratic equation, $ax^2 + bx + c = 0$,

the sum of the solutions is $-\dfrac{b}{a}$.

The sum of the given solutions is $4 + (-1) = 3 = \dfrac{3}{1}$.

We have

$$-\frac{b}{a} = \frac{3}{1}$$

So, if $a = 1$, then b -3.

The product of the solutions is $\dfrac{c}{a}$.

The product of the given solutions is $4 \cdot (-1) = -4 = \dfrac{-4}{1}$.

We have

$$\frac{c}{a} = \frac{-4}{1}$$

So, if $a = 1$, then $c = -4$.

For the quadratic equation, $ax^2 + bx + c = 0$, let $a = 1$, $b = -3$, and $c = -4$.

$$ax^2 + bx + c = 0$$

Substitute these values in the equation.

$$1x^2 + (-3)x - 4 = 0$$

Simplify.

$$x^2 - 3x - 4 = 0$$

The equation, $x^2 - 3x - 4 = 0$ is a quadratic equation with solutions 4 and -1.

$x^2 - 3x - 4 = 0$

Any nonzero multiple of this equation also has solutions 4 and -1.
Here are some examples:

$$2x^2 - 6x - 8 = 0$$
$$3x^2 - 9x - 12 = 0$$

Example 10.2.15

The quadratic equation $2x^2 - 7x + c = 0$ has discriminant 9. What are the solutions of the equation?

Solution

First, we'll find the value of c. Then we'll solve the equation.

To find c, we use the discriminant, $b^2 - 4ac$.
For the given equation, $a = 2$ and $b = -7$.
We also know the discriminant is 9.

$$b^2 - 4ac = 9$$

Substitute $a = 2$ and $b = -7$.

$$(-7)^2 - 4(2)c = 9$$

Simplify.

$$49 - 8c = 9$$

Subtract 49 from both sides.

$$-8c = -40$$

Divide both sides by -8.

$$c = 5$$

Now we know that $c = 5$.

We use the quadratic formula to solve the equation $2x^2 - 7x + c = 0$.

$$x = \frac{-b \pm \sqrt{b^2 - 4ac}}{2a}$$

Substitute $a = 2$, $b = -7$, and $c = 5$.

$$x = \frac{-(-7) \pm \sqrt{(-7)^2 - 4(2)(5)}}{2(2)}$$

Simplify.

$$x = \frac{7 \pm \sqrt{49 - 40}}{4}$$

Simplify the radicand.

$$x = \frac{7 \pm \sqrt{9}}{4}$$

Simplify the square root.

$$x = \frac{7 + 3}{4} \quad \text{or} \quad x = \frac{7 - 3}{4}$$

Simplify.

$$x = \frac{5}{2} \quad \text{or} \quad x = 1$$

Thus, if the discriminant of $2x^2 - 7x + c = 0$ is 9, the solutions of the equation are $\frac{5}{2}$ and 1.

Here is a summary of this Exploration from *Academic Systems Algebra*.

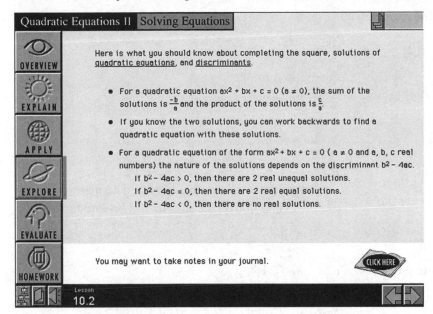

Quadratic Equations II | Solving Equations

OVERVIEW
EXPLAIN
APPLY
EXPLORE
EVALUATE
HOMEWORK

Here is what you should know about completing the square, solutions of quadratic equations, and discriminants.

- For a quadratic equation $ax^2 + bx + c = 0$ ($a \neq 0$), the sum of the solutions is $\frac{-b}{a}$ and the product of the solutions is $\frac{c}{a}$.

- If you know the two solutions, you can work backwards to find a quadratic equation with these solutions.

- For a quadratic equation of the form $ax^2 + bx + c = 0$ ($a \neq 0$ and a, b, c real numbers) the nature of the solutions depends on the discriminant $b^2 - 4ac$.
    If $b^2 - 4ac > 0$, then there are 2 real unequal solutions.
    If $b^2 - 4ac = 0$, then there are 2 real equal solutions.
    If $b^2 - 4ac < 0$, then there are no real solutions.

You may want to take notes in your journal.   CLICK HERE

Lesson
10.2

Checklist Lesson 10.2

Here is what you should know after completing this lesson.

Words and Phrases

completing the square
algebra tiles

quadratic formula
discriminant

Ideas and Procedures

❶ **Complete the Square**
Complete the square for a given binomial.

Example 10.2.1
   Complete the square for $x^2 - 5x$, and then write the new expression as the square of a binomial.

❷ **Solve a Quadratic Equation by Completing the Square**
Solve a quadratic equation by completing the square.

Example 10.2.4
   Solve by completing the square: $3x^2 - 30 = -21x$

See also: Example 10.2.2, 10.2.3, 10.2.5
         Apply 1-28

❸ **Quadratic Formula**
State the quadratic formula.

The solutions of $ax^2 + bx + c = 0$, where $a \neq 0$, are given by
$$x = \frac{-b \pm \sqrt{b^2 - 4ac}}{2a}$$

❹ **Solve a Quadratic Equation Using the Quadratic Formula**
Use the quadratic formula to solve a quadratic equation.

Example 10.2.6
   Solve using the quadratic formula: $3x^2 - 16x = -5$

See also: Example 10.2.7, 10.2.8, 10.2.9
         Apply 29-48

❺ **Discriminant**
State the formula for the discriminant of a quadratic equation

The discriminant of $ax^2 + bx + c = 0$, where $a \neq 0$, is $b^2 - 4ac$.

❻ **Determine the Nature of Solutions Using the Discriminant**
Use the discriminant to determine the nature of the solutions of a quadratic equation.

Example 10.2.10
   Use the discriminant of $-2x^2 - x + 7 = 0$ to determine the nature of its solutions.

See also: Example 10.2.11, 10.2.12
         Apply 49-56

Homework

Homework Problems

Circle the homework problems assigned to you by the computer, then complete them below.

Explain

Completing the Square

1. Complete the square: $x^2 + 13x$.
   What is the area of the completed square?

2. Solve $x^2 + 2x = 8$ by completing the square.

3. Solve $x^2 - 4x = 1$ by completing the square.

4. Solve $x^2 + 9x = -2$ by completing the square.

5. Solve $x^2 - 36x = 40$ by completing the square.

6. Solve $x^2 + 3x - 7 = 0$ by completing the square.

7. Solve $2x^2 + 6x = 2$ by completing the square.

8. Solve $3x^2 - 5x - 9 = 0$ by completing the square.

9. Seana is competing in the bicycle Race Across America. She rode 62 miles before lunch and 69 miles after lunch. She rode for one hour more after lunch than before lunch, but her speed after lunch was 2 mph slower. What were her speeds before and after lunch?

   Hint: Let t be her time spent riding before lunch. Then $t + 1$ is her time spent riding after lunch.

   Since speed $= \dfrac{\text{distance}}{\text{time}}$, we have $\dfrac{62}{t} = \dfrac{69}{t+1} + 2$.
   Now, solve for t.

10. Clair takes 1 hour longer than Jenna to mow the lawn. If they can mow the lawn together in 5 hours, how long would it take each of them to mow the lawn alone?

    (Hint: Let t be the time in hours it takes Jenna to mow the lawn. Then Clair can mow the lawn in $t + 1$ hours.

    To find t, solve $\dfrac{5}{t} + \dfrac{5}{t+1} = 1$.)

11. Solve $9x^2 - 15x = 32$ by completing the square.

12. Solve $5x^2 + 7x + 13 = 0$ by completing the square.

The Quadratic Formula

13. Solve $x^2 + 10x + 25 = 0$ using the quadratic formula.

14. Solve $x^2 - 6x - 16 = 0$ using the quadratic formula.

15. Solve $2x^2 + 3x + 1 = 0$ using the quadratic formula.

16. Solve $20x^2 - 42x - 26 = 0$ using the quadratic formula.

17. Solve $x^2 + 8x + 3 = 0$ using the quadratic formula.

18. Solve $x^2 - 5x = 9$ using the quadratic formula.

19. Solve $3x^2 - 15x = 20$ using the quadratic formula.

20. For each quadratic equation in the list below, calculate the discriminant, then write the letter of the statement that best describes its solutions.

    a. Two unequal real solutions

    b. Two equal real solutions

    c. No real solutions

Equation	Discriminant	Solutions
$x^2 - 2x + 8 = 0$	_____	_____
$x^2 - 5x - 16 = 0$	_____	_____
$49x^2 + 70x + 25 = 0$	_____	_____
$4x^2 - 6x - 9 = 0$	_____	_____
$-2x^2 - 7x + 10 = 0$	_____	_____

21. Pediatricians use formulas to convert adult dosages for medication to child dosages. Most pediatricians use formulas based on the child's weight. However, some use one of the formulas below, where a is the age of the child and d is the adult dosage.

child's dosage $= \dfrac{a}{a + 12}d$

child's dosage $= \dfrac{a + 1}{24}d$

At approximately what age(s) do these two formulas yield the same child dosage?

(Hint: Begin by setting the expressions equal to each other:

$$\dfrac{a}{a + 12}d = \dfrac{a + 1}{24}d$$

Then divide by d: $\dfrac{a}{a + 12} = \dfrac{a + 1}{24}$

Now find the LCD of the denominators, multiply by the LCD, and solve for a.)

22. Joe has a rectangular deck in his backyard. Its length measures 1 foot more than its width. He is planning to extend the length of the deck by 3 additional feet. If the new deck would have an area of 165 square feet, what is the width of the deck?

23. Solve $4x(x + 1) - 9 = 6x^2 - x - 18$ using the quadratic formula.

24. Solve $x^2 + 5 = 0$ using the quadratic formula.

Explore

25. The solutions of a quadratic equation are $-\dfrac{4}{3}$ and 5. What is an equation with these solutions?

26. The solutions of a quadratic equation are 3 and -2. Use their sum and product to find the equation.

27. The quadratic equation $3x^2 + 4x + c = 0$ has a discriminant of 196. What is the value of c? What are the solutions of the equation?

28. The solutions of a quadratic equation are $\dfrac{5 \pm 3\sqrt{13}}{2}$.
What is an equation with these solutions?

29. The solutions of a quadratic equation are $\dfrac{5}{6}$ and $-\dfrac{2}{3}$. Use their sum and product to find an equation with these solutions.

30. The quadratic equation $ax^2 - 5x + 2 = 0$ has a discriminant of 17. What is the value of a? What are the solutions of the equation?

 **Apply**

Practice Problems

Here are some additional practice problems for you to try.

Completing the Square

1. Solve $x^2 - 6x = 27$ by completing the square.

2. Solve $x^2 + 2x = 15$ by completing the square.

3. Solve $x^2 - 4x = 45$ by completing the square.

4. Solve $x^2 + 10x = 56$ by completing the square.

5. Solve $x^2 + 8x = 20$ by completing the square.

6. Solve $x^2 + 12x = -11$ by completing the square.

7. Solve $x^2 - 8x = -7$ by completing the square.

8. Solve $x^2 + 6x = -5$ by completing the square.

9. Solve $x^2 + 6x = 12$ by completing the square.

10. Solve $x^2 - 16x = 13$ by completing the square.

11. Solve $x^2 + 4x = 21$ by completing the square.

12. Solve $x^2 + 12x = -14$ by completing the square.

13. Solve $x^2 - 18x = -57$ by completing the square.

14. Solve $x^2 - 8x = -5$ by completing the square.

15. Solve $x^2 + 3x = 16$ by completing the square.

16. Solve $x^2 + 9x = 15$ by completing the square.

17. Solve $x^2 + 7x = 9$ by completing the square.

18. Practice $x^2 - 7x = 3$ by completing the square.

19. Solve $x^2 - x = 14$ by completing the square.

20. Solve $x^2 - 5x = 2$ by completing the square.

21. Solve $4x^2 + 16x = 84$ by completing the square.

22. Solve $2x^2 + 16x = 40$ by completing the square.

23. Solve $3x^2 + 12x = 36$ by completing the square.

24. Solve $5x^2 - 30x = 200$ by completing the square.

25. Solve $3x^2 - 30x = 432$ by completing the square.

26. Solve $2x^2 - 2x = 112$ by completing the square.

27. Solve $3x^2 - 5x = 7$ by completing the square.

28. Solve $4x^2 + 3x = 6$ by completing the square.

The Quadratic Formula

29. Solve $4x^2 - 5x + 1 = 0$ using the quadratic formula.

30. Solve $3x^2 - 5x - 2 = 0$ using the quadratic formula.

31. Solve $x^2 - 4x + 1 = 0$ using the quadratic formula.

32. Solve $x^2 + 8x - 5 = 0$ using the quadratic formula.

33. Solve $x^2 - 6x + 4 = 0$ using the quadratic formula.

34. Solve $2x^2 - 7x + 2 = 0$ using the quadratic formula.

35. Solve $5x^2 + 3x - 4 = 0$ using the quadratic formula.

36. Solve $3x^2 + 7x - 7 = 0$ using the quadratic formula.

37. Solve $x^2 - 2x = 7$ using the quadratic formula.

38. Solve $x^2 + 8x = 5$ using the quadratic formula.

39. Solve $x^2 + 3x = 8$ using the quadratic formula.

40. Solve $4x^2 + 19x = -17$ using the quadratic formula.

41. Solve $5x^2 - 46x = -48$ using the quadratic formula.

42. Solve $3x^2 - 25x = -28$ using the quadratic formula.

43. Solve $x^2 = 3x + 7$ using the quadratic formula.

44. Solve $x^2 = -3x + 5$ using the quadratic formula.

45. Solve $x^2 = x + 1$ using the quadratic formula.

46. Solve $2x^2 = 5x - 3$ using the quadratic formula.

47. Solve $4x^2 = 9x - 3$ using the quadratic formula.

48. Solve $3x^2 = -2x + 7$ using the quadratic formula.

49. Calculate the discriminant of the quadratic equation $5x^2 + 8x - 9 = 0$ and determine the nature of the solutions of the equation.

50. Calculate the discriminant of the quadratic equation $3x^2 + 2x + 5 = 0$ and determine the nature of the solutions of the equation.

51. Calculate the discriminant of the quadratic equation $4x^2 - 12x + 9 = 0$ and determine the nature of the solutions of the equation.

52. Calculate the discriminant of the quadratic equation $x^2 + 7x - 6 = 0$ and determine the nature of the solutions of the equation.

53. Calculate the discriminant of the quadratic equation $9x^2 + 30x + 25 = 0$ and determine the nature of the solutions of the equation.

54. Calculate the discriminant of the quadratic equation $x^2 + 3x + 4 = 0$ and determine the nature of the solutions of the equation.

55. Calculate the discriminant of the quadratic equation $7x^2 - 6x + 5 = 0$ and determine the nature of the solutions of the equation.

56. Calculate the discriminant of the quadratic equation $4x^2 + 8x - 5 = 0$ and determine the nature of the solutions of the equation.

Evaluate

Practice Test

Take this practice test to be sure that you are prepared for the final quiz in Evaluate.

1. Complete the square for this expression.

   $$x^2 + 9x + \text{ ?}$$

   What is the perfect square?

2. Solve $4x^2 + 8x = 152$ by completing the square.

3. After completing the square by adding 16 to both sides, the result is $(x + 4)^2 = 2$. What was the original equation?

4. Solve $4x^2 - 5x + 1 = 0$ by completing the square.

5. Circle the equation below that has the solution
   $x = \dfrac{-2 \pm 3\sqrt{2}}{2}$.

   $x^2 + 4x - 7 = 0$

   $2x^2 + 4x - 7 = 0$

   $2x^2 + 4x + 7 = 0$

   $x^2 - 4x - 7 = 0$

6. Use the quadratic formula to solve this quadratic equation:
   $6x = 1 - 5x^2$

7. Circle the quadratic equations below that have no real solutions.

   $x^2 + 5x - 9 = 0$

   $x^2 + 4x + 11 = 0$

   $x^2 - x + 1 = 0$

   $4x^2 + 5x + 1 = 0$

   $2x^2 - 10x - 3 = 0$

   $x^2 + 2x + 5 = 0$

8. Find the two values for b for which the quadratic equation $9x^2 + bx + 36 = 0$ has two equal real solutions.

9. The quadratic equation $x^2 - 7x + c = 0$ has a discriminant of 45. What is the value of c? What are the solutions of the equation?

10. The sum of the solutions of a quadratic equation is $\dfrac{3}{2}$. The product of its solutions is 3. What is the equation?

11. Find a quadratic equation whose two solutions are -3 and $\dfrac{1}{5}$.

12. Find the greatest possible value of c in the quadratic equation $2x^2 - 7x + c = 0$ for which there are two real solutions.

LESSON 10.3
COMPLEX NUMBERS

 ## Overview

Prior to the 19th century, mathematicians dismissed the idea that the square root of a negative number had meaning. In fact, such numbers were labeled "imaginary." Eventually, however, people began to develop the mathematics of these numbers and found ways to use them in applications. Today, for example, engineers use such numbers to describe certain properties of electrical circuits.

In this lesson, you will study the complex number system, which includes real numbers as well as "imaginary" numbers.

 ## Explain

Concept 1 has sections on

- **Imaginary Numbers**

- **Complex Numbers**

- **Adding and Subtracting Complex Numbers**

- **Multiplying Complex Numbers**

- **Complex Conjugates**

- **Dividing Complex Numbers**

- **Powers of i**

- **Quadratic Equations with Imaginary Solutions**

When we square a real number, the result is never negative:

> *positive · positive = positive*

> *negative · negative = positive.*

CONCEPT 1:
COMPLEX NUMBER SYSTEM

Imaginary Numbers

You have seen that some quadratic equations have no real number solutions.

For example, let's solve this quadratic equation: $x^2 + 1 = 0$

First, we write the equation in the form $x^2 = a$. $x^2 = -1$

Next, we use the Square Root Property $x = \sqrt{-1}$ or $x = -\sqrt{-1}$
to write two equations:

The solutions, $\sqrt{-1}$ and $-\sqrt{-1}$, are not real numbers because there is no real number whose square is -1.

In order to solve an equation such as $x^2 + 1 = 0$, mathematicians defined a new number, which they represented with the letter i.

The number i is defined as follows:
$$i = \sqrt{-1}.$$
That is,
$$i^2 = -1.$$

The number i is *not* a real number. Instead, i is an example of an **imaginary number**.

Given the definition of i, we can write the solutions of $x^2 + 1 = 0$ as follows:
$$x = \pm\sqrt{-1} = \pm i.$$

We check the solutions by replacing x with i or with $-i$ in the original equation:

Check x = i.	*Check x = −i.*
$x^2 + 1 = 0$?	$x^2 + 1 = 0$?
Is $(i)^2 + 1 = 0$?	Is $(-i)^2 + 1 = 0$?
Is $-1 + 1 = 0$?	Is $i^2 + 1 = 0$?
Is $0 = 0$? **Yes**	Is $-1 + 1 = 0$?
	Is $0 = 0$? **Yes**

We can use an imaginary number to rewrite the square root of a negative number.

— Definition —
Square Root of a Negative Number

If k is a positive real number, then
$$\sqrt{-k} = \sqrt{k} \cdot \sqrt{-1} = \sqrt{k}i.$$
We can also write the i in front of the radical, like this:
$$\sqrt{-k} = i\sqrt{k}.$$

Examples

$\sqrt{-9} = \sqrt{9}i = 3i$

$\sqrt{-5} = \sqrt{5}i.$

*In an expression such as $\sqrt{5}i$ be sure to write the i **outside** the radical symbol.*

Example 10.3.1

Simplify: $\sqrt{-20}$

Solution

Rewrite $\sqrt{-20}$ using $\sqrt{-k} = \sqrt{k}i$.

Simplify $\sqrt{20}$.

$$\sqrt{-20}$$
$$= \sqrt{20}i$$
$$= \sqrt{4 \cdot 5}i$$
$$= \sqrt{4} \cdot \sqrt{5}i$$
$$= 2\sqrt{5}i$$

So, $-20 = 2\sqrt{5}i$.

To find a product such as $\sqrt{-9} \cdot \sqrt{-16}$, begin by rewriting each square root in terms of i.

Example 10.3.2

Simplify: $\sqrt{-9} \cdot \sqrt{-16}$

Solution

Rewrite each square root using $\sqrt{-k} = \sqrt{k}i$.

Simplify each square root.

Multiply.

Use $i^2 = -1$.

Multiply.

$$\sqrt{-9} \cdot \sqrt{-16}$$
$$= \sqrt{9}i \cdot \sqrt{16}i$$
$$= 3 \cdot i \cdot 4 \cdot i$$
$$= 12 \cdot i^2$$
$$= 12 \cdot (-1)$$
$$= -12$$

Thus, $\sqrt{-9} \cdot \sqrt{-16} = -12$.

Be careful! The Multiplication Property of Square Roots,

$$\sqrt{a} \cdot \sqrt{b} = \sqrt{ab}$$

does not apply if a or b is negative.

$$\sqrt{-9} \cdot \sqrt{-16} \neq \sqrt{(-9) \cdot (-16)}$$
$$3i \cdot 4i \neq \sqrt{144}$$
$$-12 \neq 12$$

If the radicand of a square root contains a negative number, be sure to write the square root in terms of i before you simplify.

Complex Numbers

Real numbers and imaginary numbers are each examples of **complex numbers**.

For example, we can combine the real number 5 and the imaginary number $4i$ to form the complex number, $5 + 4i$.

— Definition —
Complex Number

A complex number is a number that can be written in the form $a + bi$, where a and b are real numbers and $i = \sqrt{-1}$.

- The real number a is called the **real part** of the complex number.

- The real number b is called the **imaginary part** of the complex number.

In the complex number a + bi, the imaginary part is b, not bi.

Here are some examples of complex numbers:

Complex Number	Real Part	Imaginary Part
$a + bi$	a	b
$-8 + 12i$	-8	12
$15 - 7i$	15	-7
$6 + 0i$	6	0
$0 - 2i$	0	-2

A complex number whose imaginary part, b, is 0, is called a real number.

For example, the complex number $6 + 0i$ can be written as 6.
The number 6 is a real number.

This means that the real numbers are a subset of the complex numbers.

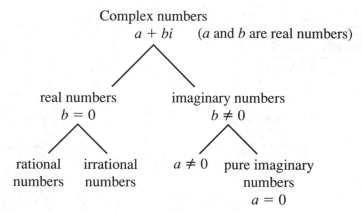

All real numbers are complex numbers of the form $a + 0i$.

A complex number whose imaginary part, b, is *not* 0, is called an **imaginary number**.

For example, the complex number $6 + 4i$ is an imaginary number.

The imaginary numbers are a subset of the complex numbers.

A complex number whose real part, a, is 0, is called a **pure imaginary number**.

For example, the complex number $0 - 2i$ can be written as $-2i$.
The number $-2i$ is a pure imaginary number.

Next we will study the arithmetic of complex numbers. That is, we will learn how to add, subtract, multiply, and divide them.

Before we do so, it will be helpful to define what it means for one complex number to be equal to another complex number.

Two complex numbers are equal if their real parts are equal and their imaginary parts are equal.

That is,

$$a + bi = c + di$$

if $a = c$ and $b = d$.

Here, a, b, c, and d are real numbers.

Here are some examples:

3 + 5i = (7 − 4) + 5i since $3 = 7 - 4$

8 + 2i = 8 + (1 + 1)i since $2 = 1 + 1$

8 + 7i = 7i + 8

since the real part of each complex number is 8 and the imaginary part of each is 7.

Adding and Subtracting Complex Numbers

Adding or subtracting complex numbers is like adding or subtracting polynomials.

Adding Polynomials	*Adding Complex Numbers*
$(5 + 3x) + (6 - 7x)$	$(5 + 3i) + (6 - 7i)$

Remove parentheses. $= 5 + 3x + 6 - 7x$ $= 5 + 3i + 6 - 7i$

Combine like terms. $= 11 - 4x$ $= 11 - 4i$

— Procedure —
To Add or Subtract Complex Numbers

To add two complex numbers, add their real parts and add their imaginary parts.

$$(a + bi) + (c + di) = (a + c) + (b + d)i$$

To subtract one complex number from another, subtract their real parts and subtract their imaginary parts.

$$(a + bi) - (c + di) = (a - c) + (b - d)i$$

When we add or subtract complex numbers, we usually write the result in the form a + bi.

Example 10.3.3

Find: $(10 - 7i) + (-2 + 5i)$

Solution $(10 - 7i) + (-2 + 5i)$

Remove the parentheses. $= 10 - 7i - 2 + 5i$

Combine like terms. $= 8 - 2i$

We write 8 − 2i in the form a + bi like this:

$$8 + (-2)i$$

So, $(10 - 7i) + (-2 + 5i) = 8 - 2i$.

Example 10.3.4

Find: $(6 + 12i) - (15 - 3i)$

Solution

Remove the parentheses. Be sure to subtract each term of $(15 - 3i)$.	$(6 + 12i) - (15 - 3i)$ $= 6 + 12i - 15 + 3i$
Combine like terms.	$= -9 + 15i$

So, $(6 + 12i) - (15 - 3i) = -9 + 15i$.

Example 10.3.5

Find: $(6 + \sqrt{-64}) - (-15 + \sqrt{-144})$

Solution

Rewrite each square root using $\sqrt{-k} = \sqrt{k}\,i$.	$(6 + \sqrt{-64}) - (-15 + \sqrt{-144})$ $= (6 + \sqrt{64}\,i) - (-15 + \sqrt{144}\,i)$
Simplify each square root.	$= (6 + 8i) - (-15 + 12i)$
Remove the parentheses. Be sure to subtract each term of $(-15 + 12i)$.	$= 6 + 8i + 15 - 12i$
Combine like terms.	$= 21 - 4i$

So, $(6 + \sqrt{-64}) - (-15 + \sqrt{-144}) = 21 - 4i$.

We write $21 - 4i$ in the form $a + bi$ like this:

$$21 + (-4)i$$

Multiplying Complex Numbers

Multiplying complex numbers is very much like multiplying polynomials. When we simplify the result, we replace each occurrence of i^2 with -1. We often write the final result in the form $a + bi$.

Example 10.3.6

Find: $5i \cdot 7i$

Solution

	$5i \cdot 7i$
Multiply $5 \cdot 7$ and multiply $i \cdot i$.	$= 35 \cdot i^2$
Replace i^2 with -1.	$= 35 \cdot (-1)$
Multiply.	$= -35$

So, $5i \cdot 7i = -35$.

We write -35 in the form $a + bi$ like this:
$$0 + (-35)i$$

Example 10.3.7

Find: $4i(9 - 6i)$

Solution

Distribute $4i$.

Multiply the factors in each term.

Replace i^2 with -1.

Simplify.

Write the result in the form $a + bi$.

$$4i(9 - 6i)$$
$$= 4i \cdot 9 - 4i \cdot 6i$$
$$= 36i - 24i^2$$
$$= 36i - 24(-1)$$
$$= 36i + 24$$
$$= 24 + 36i$$

So, $4i(9 - 6i) = 24 + 36i$.

Example 10.3.8

Find: $(7 - 4i)(10 + 5i)$

Solution

Multiply using the FOIL method.

Multiply the factors in each term.

Replace i^2 with -1.

Combine like terms.

$$(7 - 4i)(10 + 5i)$$
$$= 7 \cdot 10 + 7 \cdot 5i - 4i \cdot 10 - 4i \cdot 5i$$
$$= 70 + 35i - 40i - 20i^2$$
$$= 70 + 35i - 40i - 20(-1)$$
$$= 70 + 35i - 40i + 20$$
$$= 90 - 5i$$

So, $(7 - 4i)(10 + 5i) = 90 - 5i$.

Complex Conjugates

Two complex numbers of the form $a + bi$ and $a - bi$ are called **complex conjugates**. Notice that complex conjugates have the same real part. Their imaginary parts are the same, except they have opposite signs.

Here are several pairs of complex conjugates:

$7 + 2i$	and	$7 - 2i$
$-3 + 6i$	and	$-3 - 6i$
$12 - 8i$	and	$12 + 8i$

Here are several pairs of complex numbers that are NOT complex conjugates:

$4 - 7i$	*and*	$7 - 4i$
$3 + 5i$	*and*	$-3 - 5i$
$7 + 2i$	*and*	$-7 + 2i$

Example 10.3.9

Find: $(6 + 4i)(6 - 4i)$

Solution

$(6 + 4i)(6 - 4i)$

Multiply using FOIL.

$= 6 \cdot 6 - 6 \cdot 4i + 4i \cdot 6 - 4i \cdot 4i$

Multiply the factors in each term.

$= 36 - 24i + 24i - 16i^2$

Replace i^2 with -1.

$= 36 - 24i + 24i - 16(-1)$

Combine like terms. Note that the i terms cancel.

$= 52$

So, $(6 + 4i)(6 - 4i) = 52$.

Notice that $(6 + 4i)$ and $(6 - 4i)$ are complex conjugates. Their product is 52, a real number.

The next example demonstrates that the product of two complex conjugates is always a real number.

Example 10.3.10

Find: $(a + bi)(a - bi)$

Solution

$(a + bi)(a - bi)$

Multiply using the FOIL method.

$= a \cdot a - a \cdot bi + bi \cdot a - bi \cdot bi$

Multiply the factors in each term.

$= a^2 - abi + abi - b^2i^2$

Replace i^2 with -1.

$= a^2 - abi + abi - b^2(-1)$

$= a^2 - abi + abi + b^2$

Combine like terms. Note that the i terms add to zero.

$= a^2 + b^2$

Thus,

$$(a + bi)(a - bi) = a^2 + b^2$$

Dividing Complex Numbers

Next we will use complex conjugates to simplify the quotient of two complex numbers.

For example, we will write a fraction like $\dfrac{6-4i}{5+3i}$ in the form $a + bi$.

To do this, we will multiply the numerator and denominator by the complex conjugate of the denominator.

The result is an expression whose denominator is a real number.

The following example illustrates the process.

Example | **10.3.11**

Find: $(6 - 4i) \div (5 + 3i)$

Solution

$$(6 - 4i) \div (5 + 3i)$$

Rewrite the division problem as a fraction.

$$= \frac{6-4i}{5+3i}$$

The denominator is $5 + 3i$.
Its conjugate is $5 - 3i$.

Multiply the numerator and the denominator by $5 - 3i$. That is, multiply the fraction by $\dfrac{5-3i}{5-3i}$.

$$= \frac{6-4i}{5+3i} \cdot \frac{\mathbf{5-3i}}{\mathbf{5-3i}}$$

Multiply the numerators.
Multiply the denominators.

$$= \frac{30 - 18i - 20i + 12i^2}{25 - 15i + 15i - 9i^2}$$

Replace i^2 with -1.

$$= \frac{30 - 18i - 20i + 12(\mathbf{-1})}{25 - 15i + 15i - 9(\mathbf{-1})}$$

Combine like terms.

$$= \frac{18 - 38i}{34}$$

Write as two terms.

$$= \frac{18}{34} - \frac{38}{34}i$$

Reduce.

$$= \frac{9}{17} - \frac{19}{17}i$$

So,

$$(6 - 4i) \div (5 + 3i) = \frac{9}{17} - \frac{19}{17}i.$$

Multiplying by $\dfrac{5-3i}{5-3i}$ does not change the value of $\dfrac{6-4i}{5+3i}$ because $\dfrac{5-3i}{5-3i} = 1$.

$$\frac{6-4i}{5+3i} \cdot \frac{5-3i}{5-3i}$$

The product of the denominators can be found using $(a+bi)(a-bi) = a^2 + b^2$.

$$(5+3i)(5-3i) = 5^2 + 3^2$$
$$= 25 + 9$$
$$= 34$$

We write $\dfrac{9}{17} - \dfrac{19}{17}i$ in the form $a + bi$ like this:

$$\frac{9}{17} + \left(-\frac{19}{17}\right)i$$

When the denominator of a fraction is a pure imaginary number, we can shorten the process. We simply multiply the numerator and the denominator each by i.

Example 10.3.12

Find: $\dfrac{8 + 9i}{2i}$

Solution

The denominator is a pure imaginary number, $2i$.

$\dfrac{8 + 9i}{2i}$

To eliminate i from the denominator, multiply the expression by $\dfrac{i}{i}$.

$= \dfrac{8 + 9i}{2i} \cdot \dfrac{i}{i}$

Multiply the numerators. Multiply the denominators.

$= \dfrac{8i + 9i^2}{2i^2}$

Replace i^2 with -1.

$= \dfrac{8i + 9(-1)}{2(-1)}$

Simplify.

$= \dfrac{8i - 9}{-2}$

Write as two terms and reduce.

$= \dfrac{8i}{-2} - \dfrac{9}{-2}$

$= -4i + \dfrac{9}{2}$

We can also write the result like this:

$\dfrac{9}{2} - 4i$

Write in the form $a + bi$.

$= \dfrac{9}{2} + (-4)i$

So, $(8 + 9i) \div (2i) = \dfrac{9}{2} + (-4)i$.

Powers of i

Now we will examine an interesting property of i. When we raise it to any positive integer power and simplify, the result is one of only four possibilities: i, -1, $-i$, or 1.

$i^1 = i$

$i^2 = -1$

$i^3 = i^2 \cdot i = (-1) \cdot i = -i$

$i^4 = i^2 \cdot i^2 = (-1)(-1) = 1$

$i^5 = i^4 \cdot i^1 = 1 \cdot i = i$

$i^6 = i^4 \cdot i^2 = 1 \cdot (-1) = -1$

$i^7 = i^4 \cdot i^3 = 1 \cdot -i = -i$

$i^8 = i^4 \cdot i^4 = 1 \cdot 1 = 1$

$i^9 = i^4 \cdot i^4 \cdot i = 1 \cdot 1 \cdot i = i$

The pattern repeats:
$i, -1, -i, 1, i, -1, -i, 1, \ldots$

Look at the powers of i listed in the table.

To simplify a higher power of i, we use this fact: $i^4 = 1$.

For example, let's simplify i^{10}.

i^{10}

Use the Multiplication Property of Exponents to write i^{10} as a product where one factor is a power of i that is a multiple of 4.

$= i^8 \cdot i^2$

Rewrite i^8 in terms of i^4.

$= (i^4)^2 \cdot i^2$

Replace i^4 with 1. Replace i^2 with -1.

$= (1)^2 \cdot (-1)$

Multiply.

$= -1$

So, $i^{10} = -1$.

We can follow the same process to simplify i^{27}.

Write i^{27} using a multiple of 4.	$i^{27} = i^{24} \cdot i^3$	
Rewrite i^{24} in terms of i^4.	$= (i^4)^6 \cdot i^3$	$i^1 = i$
Replace i^4 with 1.	$= 1^6 \cdot i^3$	$i^2 = -1$
Replace i^3 with $-i$.	$= 1 \cdot (-i)$	$i^3 = -i$
Multiply.	$= -i$	$i^4 = 1$

So, $i^{27} = -i$.

Example 10.3.13

Simplify.

a. i^{35}　　　　b. i^{82}　　　　c. i^{20}

Solution

a. To simplify i^{35}, divide 35 by 4.
    The result is 8 with remainder 3.

$$i^{35} = (i^4)^8 \cdot i^3$$
$$= 1^8 \cdot i^3$$
$$= 1 \cdot (-i)$$
$$= -i$$

$$\begin{array}{r} 8 \\ 4\overline{)35} \\ \underline{32} \\ 3 \end{array}$$ ◀—— Remainder

b. To simplify i^{82}, divide 82 by 4.
    The result is 20 with remainder 2.

$$i^{82} = (i^4)^{20} \cdot i^2$$
$$= 1^{20} \cdot i^2$$
$$= 1 \cdot (-1)$$
$$= -1$$

$$\begin{array}{r} 20 \\ 4\overline{)82} \\ \underline{80} \\ 2 \end{array}$$ ◀—— Remainder

c. To simplify i^{20}, divide 20 by 4.
    The result is 5 with remainder 0.

$$i^{20} = (i^4)^5 \cdot i^0$$
$$= 1^5 \cdot 1$$
$$= 1 \cdot 1$$
$$= 1$$

$$\begin{array}{r} 5 \\ 4\overline{)20} \\ \underline{20} \\ 0 \end{array}$$ ◀—— Remainder

Quadratic Equations with Imaginary Solutions

Recall that a quadratic equation is an equation that can be written in the form $ax^2 + bx + c = 0$, where $a \neq 0$.

Any quadratic equation can be solved using the quadratic formula:

$$x = \frac{-b \pm \sqrt{b^2 - 4ac}}{2a}.$$

In Lesson 10.2 we noted that if the discriminant, $b^2 - 4ac$, is negative then the equation has no real number solutions.

Now we know that the square root of a negative number is an imaginary number. In particular, if the discriminant $b^2 - 4ac < 0$ then the quadratic equation has two imaginary solutions. In fact, the solutions are complex conjugates.

Example 10.3.14

Solve using the quadratic formula: $x^2 + 2x = -5$

Solution

Step 1 Write the quadratic equation in standard form.

Add 5 to both sides of the equation. $\qquad\qquad x^2 + 2x + 5 = 0$

Step 2 Identify the values of a, b, and c.

$\qquad a = 1, b = 2, c = 5$

Step 3 Substitute the values of a, b, and c into the quadratic formula. $\qquad x = \dfrac{-b \pm \sqrt{b^2 - 4ac}}{2a}$

Substitute 1 for a, 2 for b, and 5 for c. $\qquad x = \dfrac{-(2) \pm \sqrt{(2)^2 - 4(1)(5)}}{2(1)}$

Step 4 Simplify.

Simplify the radicand and the denominator. $\qquad x = \dfrac{-2 \pm \sqrt{-16}}{2}$

Use $\sqrt{-k} = \sqrt{k}i$ to simplify the square root. $\qquad x = \dfrac{-2 \pm 4i}{2}$

Cancel the common factor, 2, in the numerator and denominator. $\qquad x = -1 \pm 2i$

Step 5 Check each solution.

We leave the check to you.

So, the solutions of $x^2 + 2x = -5$ are $-1 + 2i$ and $-1 - 2i$.

Notice that $-1 + 2i$ and $-1 - 2i$ are complex conjugates.

(margin notes:)

$x^2 + 2x + 5 = 0$

The discriminant of the equation is
$b^2 - 4ac = 2^2 - 4(1)(5) = -16.$

Since the discriminant is negative, we know that the two solutions will be complex conjugates.

$\sqrt{-16} = \sqrt{16}i = 4i$

Be careful when you cancel. Be sure to divide each term of the numerator by 2.

$\dfrac{-2 \pm 4i}{2} = \dfrac{-2}{2} \pm \dfrac{4i}{2} = -1 \pm 2i$

Example 10.3.15

Solve using the quadratic formula: $2x^2 + 7 = 3x$

Solution

Step 1 Write the quadratic equation in standard form.

Subtract $3x$ from both sides of the equation. $\qquad 2x^2 - 3x + 7 = 0$

Step 2 Identify the values of a, b, and c.

$\qquad a = 2, b = -3, c = 7$

Step 3 Substitute the values of a, b, and c into the quadratic formula.

$$x = \frac{-b \pm \sqrt{b^2 - 4ac}}{2a}$$

Substitute 2 for a, -3 for b, and 7 for c.

$$x = \frac{-(-3) \pm \sqrt{(-3)^2 - 4(2)(7)}}{2(2)}$$

Step 4 Simplify.

Simplify the radicand and the denominator.

$$x = \frac{3 \pm \sqrt{-47}}{4}$$

Use $\sqrt{-k} = \sqrt{k}\,i$ to simplify the square root.

$$x = \frac{3 \pm \sqrt{47}\,i}{4}$$

Write the final answer in the form $a + bi$.

$$x = \frac{3}{4} \pm \frac{\sqrt{47}}{4}\,i$$

Step 5 Check each solution.

We leave the check to you.

So, the solutions of $2x^2 + 7 = 3x$ are $\frac{3}{4} + \frac{\sqrt{47}}{4}\,i$ and $\frac{3}{4} - \frac{\sqrt{47}}{4}\,i$.

Notice that the solutions are complex conjugates.

Here is a summary of this concept from *Academic Systems Algebra*.

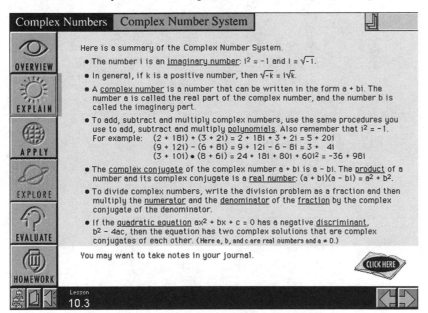

Complex Numbers | Complex Number System

OVERVIEW
EXPLAIN
APPLY
EXPLORE
EVALUATE
HOMEWORK

Here is a summary of the Complex Number System.

- The number i is an <u>imaginary number</u>: $i^2 = -1$ and $i = \sqrt{-1}$.

- In general, if k is a positive number, then $\sqrt{-k} = i\sqrt{k}$.

- A <u>complex number</u> is a number that can be written in the form a + bi. The number a is called the real part of the complex number, and the number b is called the imaginary part.

- To add, subtract and multiply complex numbers, use the same procedures you use to add, subtract and multiply <u>polynomials</u>. Also remember that $i^2 = -1$.
  For example: $(2 + 18i) + (3 + 2i) = 2 + 18i + 3 + 2i = 5 + 20i$
  $\qquad (9 + 12i) - (6 + 8i) = 9 + 12i - 6 - 8i = 3 + \quad 4i$
  $\qquad (3 + 10i) \bullet (8 + 6i) = 24 + 18i + 80i + 60i^2 = -36 + 98i$

- The <u>complex conjugate</u> of the complex number a + bi is a - bi. The <u>product</u> of a number and its complex conjugate is a <u>real number</u>: $(a + bi)(a - bi) = a^2 + b^2$.

- To divide complex numbers, write the division problem as a fraction and then multiply the <u>numerator</u> and the <u>denominator</u> of the <u>fraction</u> by the complex conjugate of the denominator.

- If the <u>quadratic equation</u> $ax^2 + bx + c = 0$ has a negative <u>discriminant</u>, $b^2 - 4ac$, then the equation has two complex solutions that are complex conjugates of each other. (Here a, b, and c are real numbers and a ≠ 0.)

You may want to take notes in your journal.

CLICK HERE

Lesson 10.3

Checklist Lesson 10.3

Here is what you should know after completing this lesson.

Words and Phrases

imaginary number
complex number
real part of a complex number

imaginary part of a complex number
pure imaginary number
complex conjugates

Ideas and Procedures

❶ Imaginary Number
Define imaginary number.

An imaginary number is a number that can be written in the form $a + bi$, where a and b are real numbers, $b \neq 0$ and $i = \sqrt{-1}$.

❷ Square Root with a Negative Radicand
Write a square root with a negative radicand as an imaginary number.

Example 10.3.1
Simplify: $\sqrt{-20}$

See also: Apply 1-4

❸ Multiply Imaginary Numbers
Multiply square roots that each contain negative radicands.

Example 10.3.2
Simplify: $\sqrt{-9} \cdot \sqrt{-16}$

See also: Apply 8-10

❹ Complex Number
Define a complex number and identify its real part and its imaginary part.

A complex number is a number that can be written in the form $a + bi$, where a and b are real numbers and $i = \sqrt{-1}$. The real part of the complex number is a. The imaginary part is b.

❺ Add and Subtract Complex Numbers
Add and subtract complex numbers.

Example 10.3.3
Find: $(10 - 7i) - (-2 + 5i)$

See also: Example 10.3.4, 10.3.5
Apply 11-16

❻ Multiply Complex Numbers
Find the product of two complex numbers.

Example 10.3.8
Find: $(7 - 4i)(10 + 5i)$

See also: Example 10.3.6, 10.3.7, 10.3.9, 10.3.10
Apply 17-22

❼ Complex Conjugates
Define complex conjugates.

Two complex numbers of the form $a + bi$ and $a - bi$ are called complex conjugates.

⑧ Divide Complex Numbers
Find the quotient of two complex numbers.

Example 10.3.11
   Find: $(6 - 4i) \div (5 + 3i)$

See also: Example 10.3.12
          Apply 23-25

⑨ Powers of i
Simplify a given power of i.

Example 10.3.13
   Simplify: i^{82}

See also: Apply 5-7

⑩ Quadratic Equations with Imaginary Solutions
Use the quadratic formula to solve a quadratic
equation with imaginary solutions.

Example 10.3.15
   Solve using the quadratic formula: $2x^2 + 7 = 3x$

See also: Example 10.3.14
          Apply 26-28

Homework Problems

Circle the homework problems assigned to you by the computer, then complete them below.

☀ Explain

Complex Number System

1. Circle the complex numbers below that are equal to $7 - 4i$.

   $4i - 7$ $7 - (2 - 6)i$

   $-4i + 7$ $7 - 3i - i$

   $6 + 1 - 4i$

2. Circle the pairs below that are complex conjugates of each other.

   $2 + 3i$ and $2 - 3i$ $9 + 7i$ and $7 + 9i$

   $5 + 3i$ and $3 - 5i$ $4 + 6i$ and $4 - 6i$

   $8 + i$ and $-8 - i$

3. Simplify each expression below.

   a. $\sqrt{-16}$

   b. $\sqrt{-25}$

   c. $\sqrt{-16} + \sqrt{-25}$

   d. $\sqrt{-16} \cdot \sqrt{-25}$

   e. i^{20}

   f. i^{47}

In questions 4–12, perform the indicated operation.

4. a. $(5 + 7i) + (2 + 4i)$

   b. $(6 + i) + (8 + 3i)$

5. a. $(10 + 6i) + (7 - 4i)$

   b. $(8 + 9i) - (5 + 2i)$

   c. $3i(11 - 4i)$

6. a. $(2 + 7i)(14 - i)$

   b. $(4 - 12i)(5 - 3i)$

   c. $(5 + 6i) \div (2 + 7i)$

7. a. $(6 + 11i)(6 - 11i)$

   b. $(7 + 12i) \div (9 - 4i)$

   c. Solve for x: $x^2 + 4x + 8 = 0$

8. a. $(3 + 10i) \div (8 - 5i)$

   b. $(9 + 5i) \div (7 - 2i)$

   c. Solve for x: $x^2 + 6x + 15 = 0$

9. a. $(2 + 4i)(5 - 6i)$

   b. $(1 + 2i) \div (1 - 2i)$

10. a. Solve for x: $x^2 - 4 = 0$

    b. Solve for x: $x^2 + 4 = 0$

    c. $(1 - 2i) \div (1 + 2i)$

11. a. $(2i + 7)(3 - 8i)$

    b. $(6 + 5i) \div (1 - 4i)$

    c. Solve for x: $x^2 + 2x + 9 = 0$

12. a. $(4 + 7i) \div (3 + 5i)$

    b. Solve for x: $x^2 - 4x + 11 = 0$

Apply

Practice Problems

Here are some additional practice problems for you to try.

Complex Number System

1. Simplify: $\sqrt{-169}$

2. Simplify: $-\sqrt{-144}$

3. Simplify: $\sqrt{16} - \sqrt{-25}$

4. Simplify: $-\sqrt{9} + \sqrt{-16}$

5. Simplify: i^{125}

6. Simplify: i^{234}

7. Simplify: i^{100}

8. Simplify: $\sqrt{-7} \cdot \sqrt{-16}$

9. Simplify: $\sqrt{-5} \cdot \sqrt{-10}$

10. Simplify: $\sqrt{-6} \cdot \sqrt{-4}$

11. Find: $(7 + \sqrt{-9}) + (12 - \sqrt{-36})$

12. Find: $(10 - \sqrt{-121}) - (3 + \sqrt{-25})$

13. Find: $(5 + \sqrt{-4}) + (8 - \sqrt{-49})$

14. Find: $5(3 - 6i) + 3(7 + 2i)$

15. Find: $4(8 + 3i) - 2(7 + 9i)$

16. Find: $3(4 + 3i) - 6(1 + 2i)$

17. Find: $(3 + 7i)(2 + 3i)$

18. Find: $(4 - 7i)(6 - 9i)$

19. Find: $(2 - 5i)(6 + 4i)$

20. Find: $(4 - 7i)(4 + 7i)$

21. Find: $(8 + 3i)(8 - 3i)$

22. Find: $(5 - 3i)(5 + 3i)$

23. Find: $(4 + 5i) \div (2 + 7i)$

24. Find: $(3 - 2i) \div (4 + i)$

25. Find: $(5 - 2i) \div (3 + 4i)$

26. Solve for x: $x^2 - 5x + 8 = 0$

27. Solve for x: $x^2 + 8x + 18 = 0$

28. Solve for x: $x^2 + 6x + 11 = 0$

Evaluate

Practice Test

Take this practice test to be sure that you are prepared for the final quiz in Evaluate.

1. Find:

    a. $(7 + 2i) + (4 + 6i)$

    b. $(7 + 2i) - (4 + 6i)$

2. Circle the expressions below that are equal to $8 + 4i$.

    $(2i)(4i + 2)$

    $3i + 6i - i$

    $-8i^2 - 4i^3$

    $\sqrt{-64}$

3. Find: $(3 + \sqrt{-16}) + (2 + \sqrt{-9})$

4. Find: $(4 + 2i)(3 + 5i)$

5. Find: $(5 + 3i)(5 - 3i)$

6. Find: $2 \div (4 + 7i)$

7. Circle the expressions below that are equal to i.

    i^4

    i^{37}

    $(i^5)^{10}$

    $-i^3$

8. Use the quadratic formula to find the solutions of each equation below.

    a. $x^2 + 3x + 7 = 0$

    b. $x^2 - 5x + 9 = 0$

    c. $3x^2 + 2x + 1 = 0$

Cumulative Review Problems

These problems combine all of the material you have covered so far in this course. You may want to test your understanding of this material before you move on to the next topic, or you may wish to do these problems to review for a test.

1. Factor: $3b + 6bx + 10x + 5$

2. Solve for x: $|3x + 4| = 10$

3. Find:
    $(xy^3 - 5x^2y + 11xy - 1) + (4xy^3 - 7 - x^2y + 3xy)$

4. Solve $x^2 - 11x + 30 = 0$ for x.

5. Graph the line that passes through the point $(-2, -4)$ with slope 1.

6. Factor: $5x^2 + 9xy - 2y^2$

7. Solve $\dfrac{1}{x-3} = \dfrac{x}{4}$ for x.

8. Simplify the expressions below.
    a. $\sqrt{\dfrac{81x^4}{16}}$

    b. $\left(9^{\frac{5}{2}}\right)(3^{-2})$

    c. $\dfrac{\sqrt[3]{x^6}}{5}$

9. Solve $y^2 + 1 = -3$ for y.

10. Find:
    a. $\dfrac{a^2 \cdot c}{a^5 \cdot b^6 \cdot c^4}$

    b. $6x^0 \cdot y^4$

    c. $(7a^0)^2$

11. Solve for x: $|x + 5| \le 7$

12. Factor: $x^2 - 14x + 13$

13. Find:
    a. $(7 + 4i)(1 - 5i)$

    b. $(6 - 2i)(6 + 2i)$

14. Solve $-1 < 2x - 3 \le 4$ for x, then graph its solution on the number line below.

15. Find the equation of the line that passes through the point $(11, -4)$ that has slope $-\dfrac{6}{5}$:
    a. in point-slope form.
    b. in slope-intercept form.
    c. in standard form.

16. Solve for x: $2(5 + x) = 2x - 4$

17. Evaluate the expression $5xy + 1 - 4xy^3 - x^2$ when $x = 3$ and $y = -2$.

18. Find:
    a. $3 \div (2 + 5i)$
    b. $(8 + 4i) \div (6 - 3i)$

19. Solve $2y^2 - 17y + 21 = 0$ for y.

20. Graph the line $x - \dfrac{4}{3}y = 6$.

21. Find: $\dfrac{1}{2^{-3} + 4^{-2}}$

22. Factor: $3x^2y + 36xy + 108y$

23. Simplify this expression:
    $w^2xy - w^2x + 4w^2xy + y - 5w^2x$

24. a. Find the slope of the line through the points $(-14, 8)$ and $(-2, 5)$.

    b. Write the equation of the line passing through the point $(-4, 6)$ that is parallel to the line in (a).

25. Find the slope of the line through the points $(28, 4)$ and $(-19, -12)$.

26. Rewrite the expressions below using only positive exponents. Then simplify.

   a. $\dfrac{3^{\frac{4}{3}}x^{\frac{3}{2}}}{3^{-\frac{2}{3}}x^{-\frac{5}{2}}}$

   b. $\dfrac{2^{\frac{1}{3}}x^{-\frac{4}{3}}}{2^{-\frac{1}{9}}x^{\frac{2}{3}}}$

27. Solve $\dfrac{5}{x} + \dfrac{7}{6} = \dfrac{4}{x-4}$ for x.

28. Solve $5y^2 - 16y + 4 = 0$ for y.

29. Solve for x: $|2x + 7| - 4 = 8$

30. Factor: $12xy + 18y - 2x - 3$

31. Find: $\left(\dfrac{2}{5}x^2 - 3x\right)\left(5x - \dfrac{7}{3}\right)$

32. For what values of x is the expression $\dfrac{2}{x^2 - 25}$ undefined?

33. Solve $3x^2 + 7x + 4 = 0$ for x.

34. Solve $\dfrac{3}{2x} + \dfrac{1}{6x} = \dfrac{4}{5}$ for x.

35. Factor: $25y^2 - 30y + 9$

36. Solve for x: $|2x - 3| > 6$

37. Circle the true statements.

   $2\dfrac{6}{7} + 5\dfrac{1}{4} = 7\dfrac{7}{11}$

   $|11 - 5| = 6$

   $\dfrac{5}{3} \div \dfrac{2}{3} = \dfrac{10}{9}$

   $8 + 4(3 + 6) = 12(3 + 6)$

   The GCF of 64 and 81 is 1.

   If $S = \{1, 2, 3, 4, 5, 6, 7, 8, 9, 10\}$, then $16 \notin S$.

38. Evaluate the expression $5a^3 + 4a^2b - b^2$ when $a = -3$ and $b = -2$.

39. Find: $(2a^4 + 5b^2)(2a^4 - 5b^2)$

40. Rewrite the expressions below without using radicals or exponents.

   a. $\sqrt{-81}$

   b. $\sqrt[3]{-64}$

   c. $\sqrt{0.09}$

   d. $4^{\frac{3}{2}}$

41. Solve $16x^2 - 16x + 1 = 0$ for x.

42. Factor: $5x^2 + 9xy - 2y^2$

43. Solve $-17 \le 6y + 7 < 17$ for y.

44. Find:

   a. $(3 + 5i) + (4 - 7i)$

   b. $(8 - 2i) - (3 - 6i)$

45. Find the x- and y-intercepts of the line $4x - 3y = 5$.

46. Solve for a: $\dfrac{6}{a-2} + 1 = \dfrac{1}{a}$

47. Factor: $x^4 - y^2$

48. Find: $(6x + y)^2$

49. Solve $3x^2 - 5x - 22 = 0$ for x.

50. Find:

   a. $7^3 \cdot 7^5$

   b. $(5x^4)^3$

   c. $\dfrac{b^{21}}{b^{24}}$

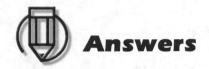 **Answers**

Lesson EI.A Fractions
Homework

1a. $\frac{27}{45}$ **b.** $\frac{105}{120}$ **2.** $2 \cdot 2 \cdot 3 \cdot 7$ **3.** 18 **4.** $\frac{5}{18}$ **5.** 36

6. $\frac{4}{5}$ **7a.** $\frac{10}{21}$ **b.** $\frac{2}{15}$ **8a.** $\frac{14}{15}$ **b.** $\frac{1}{14}$ **9.** $\frac{1}{47}$

10a. $\frac{5}{6}$ **b.** $\frac{20}{9}$ **11.** $\frac{5}{66}$ **12.** $\frac{5}{24}$ **13.** $\frac{20}{29}$ **14.** 12 **15.** 12

16. $\frac{11}{12}$ **17.** $\frac{3}{7}$ **18.** 180 **19.** 96 **20.** $\frac{5}{21}$ **21.** $\frac{5}{7}$

22. 210 **23.** 120 **24.** $\frac{14}{15}$

Apply - Practice Problems

1. 10 **2.** 12 **3.** 30 **4.** $2 \cdot 2 \cdot 2 \cdot 3 \cdot 3$ **5.** $3 \cdot 3 \cdot 5$

6. $2 \cdot 3 \cdot 3 \cdot 5$ **7.** 6 **8.** 6 **9.** 3 **10.** $\frac{5}{8}$ **11.** $\frac{3}{4}$ **12.** $\frac{7}{13}$

13. $\frac{1}{23}$ **14.** $\frac{1}{35}$ **15.** $\frac{3}{2}$ **16.** $\frac{3}{5}$ **17.** $\frac{2}{7}$ **18.** $\frac{2}{7}$ **19.** $\frac{1}{5}$

20. $\frac{3}{5}$ **21.** $\frac{1}{3}$ **22.** $\frac{2}{5}$ **23.** $\frac{2}{25}$ **24.** 10 **25.** $\frac{4}{21}$ **26.** $\frac{12}{77}$

27. 7 **28.** 6 **29.** $\frac{5}{17}$ **30.** $\frac{9}{23}$ **31.** 70 **32.** 72 **33.** 126

34. 180 **35.** 42 **36.** 72 **37.** $\frac{1}{4}$ **38.** $\frac{2}{15}$ **39.** $\frac{17}{36}$

40. $\frac{5}{8}$ **41.** $\frac{9}{16}$ **42.** $\frac{137}{120}$ **43.** 42 **44.** 150 **45.** 252

46. 60 **47.** 30 **48.** 120 **49.** $\frac{59}{60}$ **50.** $\frac{43}{60}$ **51.** $\frac{115}{144}$

52. $\frac{13}{48}$ **53.** $\frac{17}{24}$ **54.** $\frac{80}{63}$ or $1\frac{17}{63}$ **55.** $\frac{129}{140}$ **56.** $\frac{37}{42}$

Evaluate - Practice Test

1. 6 **2.** $\frac{4}{15}$ **3.** $\frac{45}{13}$ **4.** $\frac{7}{20}$ **5.** 140 **6.** 60 **7.** $\frac{9}{20}$

8. $\frac{175}{36}$

Lesson EI.B Signed Numbers
Homework

1. 38 **2a.** –3 **b.** 13 **3a.** 35 **b.** 72 **4a.** 28 **b.** –14

5. 21 **6.** 18 **7a.** 8 **b.** 9 **8a.** 13 **b.** 65

9a. –25 **b.** –23 **10.** 20 **11.** 39 **12.** 10 **13a.** –84 **b.** –3

14a. 140 **b.** 12 **15.** The base is 13, and the exponent is 28.

16. –15 **17.** 72 **18.** 128 **19.** –20 **20.** 2 **21.** no **22.** 10

23. 75 **24.** no

Apply - Practice Problems

1. 4 **2.** 5 **3.** –7 **4.** –6 **5.** –10 **6.** –19 **7.** –20

8. –28 **9.** –18 **10.** –44 **11.** –32 **12.** –10 **13.** –112

14. 11 **15.** 1 **16.** 8 **17.** –11 **18.** –19 **19.** –53

20. –75 **21.** –27 **22.** –38 **23.** –48 **24.** 11 **25.** 10

26. 20 **27.** 15 **28.** –22 **29.** –32 **30.** 54 **31.** –42

32. –4 **33.** –3 **34.** 6 **35.** –36 **36.** –15 **37.** 9

38. $3 \cdot 3 \cdot 3 \cdot 3 = 81$ **39.** $4 \cdot 4 \cdot 4 = 64$

40. $5 \cdot 5 \cdot 5 \cdot 5 = 625$ **41.** $2 \cdot 2 \cdot 2 \cdot 2 \cdot 2 \cdot 2 = 64$

42. no **43.** no **44.** no **45.** 18 **46.** –20 **47.** 4 **48.** 24

49. 80 **50.** –80 **51.** 32 **52.** 2 **53.** 5 **54.** 10 **55.** 24

56. –44

Evaluate - Practice Test

1a. 19 **b.** –11 **c.** 15 **2.** –15 **3a.** 24 **b.** –37 **c.** –27

4. 39 **5a.** 102 **b.** 84 **c.** –25 **6.** 11^9 **7.** –28

8a. 4 **b.** 52

Topic EI Cumulative Review Problems

1. $\frac{16}{56}$ **2.** $\frac{1}{18}$ **3.** -2 **4.** $\frac{7}{12}$ **5.** 112 **6.** -8 **7.** 125

8. 4 **9.** $261 \cdot 479$ **10.** 18^4 **11.** $\frac{1}{4}$ **12.** $\frac{1}{1000}$ **13.** 30

14. -3 **15.** 29 **16.** $2 \cdot 3 \cdot 3 \cdot 3$ **17.** 6 **18.** 25

19. $4 \cdot 13 + 4 \cdot 7$ or 80 **20.** $\frac{9}{5}$ **21.** $\frac{34}{35}$ **22.** 72

23. The base is 26 and the exponent is 11. **24.** 18

25. $\frac{17}{14}$ **26.** -9 **27.** $\frac{33}{42}$ **28.** -8 **29.** $\frac{3}{5}$ **30.** 18 **31.** 27

32. $\frac{1}{10}$ **33.** 0 **34.** 4 **35.** 1 **36.** $-\frac{3}{4}$ **37.** -2

38. 70 **39.** 56 **40.** $-\frac{3}{2}$ **41.** $\frac{87}{13}$ **42.** $\frac{8}{129}$ **43.** 80

44. $(-2)^6$ **45.** $\frac{15}{17}$ **46.** $\frac{16}{25}$ **47.** 25 **48.** $\frac{7}{12}$

49. $3 \cdot 11 \cdot 11$ **50.** $\frac{5}{21}$

Lesson 1.1 The Real Numbers
Homework

1. $3 < 12, 5 = \frac{20}{4}, 4 \le 4, 6 \ne 7$ **3.** $5 \cdot 5 \cdot 5 \cdot 5 = 625$

5a. 9 **b.** 17 **c.** 2.3 **d.** 4.8 **e.** 0.485 **7.** 8

9. $12^3 = 1728$ eggs **11.** $2^4 \cdot 7^3$

Apply - Practice Problems

1. $9 = 9, 7 \le 11, 15 \le 15$ **3.** $6 \le 12, 9 \ge 9$

5a. 0 **b.** 100 **c.** 0.001 **d.** 4.33 **e.** 2.497

7. 64 **9.** 343 **11.** 243 **13.** 7^8 **15.** 8^5

17a. true **b.** false **c.** true **d.** true

19. 64 **21.** 1 **23.** 2000

Evaluate - Practice Test

1. $3 > -4$, $-5 > -7$, $-6 \le -6$, $-1 \ge -1$

2a. 8 **b.** 12.18 **c.** 0.23 **d.** 15 **e.** 3.7 **3.** $>, \ge$, or $\ne$

4. $(.91)^2 = 0.8281$ **5.** 2^5 **6.** 43

7. $-(1.4)^2, -\sqrt{2}, \frac{0}{6}, (0.7)^2$, and $\frac{13}{9}$

8a. false **b.** true **c.** true **d.** false

Lesson 1.2 Factoring and Fractions
Homework

1. 12 **3.** 6 **5.** 108 **7.** 15 **9.** 18 **11.** 1 **13.** $\frac{7}{8}$ **15.** $\frac{7}{11}$

17. $\frac{3}{8}$ **19.** $\frac{14}{9}$ **21.** $30\frac{7}{8}$ **23.** $5\frac{23}{36}$ **25.** 21 **27.** 45

29. 56

Apply - Practice Problems

1. GCF: 2; LCM: 72 **3.** GCF: 2; LCM: 42

5. GCF: 1; LCM: 450 **7.** GCF: 16; LCM: 48

9. GCF: 28; LCM: 168 **11.** GCF: 12; LCM: 240

13. GCF: 12; LCM: 432 **15.** GCF: 7; LCM: 490

17. GCF: 21; LCM: 210 **19.** GCF: 9; LCM: 504

21. GCF: 19; LCM: 285 **23.** GCF: 4; LCM: 144

25. GCF: 1; LCM: 70 **27.** GCF: 8; LCM: 12,768

29. $\frac{1}{3}$ **31.** $\frac{6}{35}$ **33.** $\frac{9}{20}$ **35.** $\frac{3}{2}$ **37.** $\frac{3}{4}$ **39.** $\frac{21}{8}$ **41.** $\frac{10}{11}$

43. $\frac{4}{19}$ **45.** $\frac{27}{40}$ **47.** $\frac{35}{36}$ **49.** $\frac{87}{100}$ **51.** $\frac{26}{45}$ **53.** $\frac{33}{56}$

55. $\frac{16}{75}$

Evaluate - Practice Test

1. The prime factorization of 12 is $2 \cdot 2 \cdot 3$.
   The prime factorization of 28 is $2 \cdot 2 \cdot 7$.
   The prime factorization of 40 is $2 \cdot 2 \cdot 2 \cdot 5$.

2. 4 **3.** 840 **4.** $\frac{3}{8}$

5. In the factor trees, the prime factors appear at the bottom branch.

$$42 \qquad 55 \qquad 63$$
$$2 \cdot 21 \quad 5 \cdot 11 \quad 3 \cdot 21$$
$$3 \cdot 7 \qquad\qquad 3 \cdot 7$$

6. $\frac{11}{6}$ **7.** 6 **8.** 150 **9.** 72 **10.** $\frac{4}{15}$

11. 2 and 7 **12.** LCM: 210; GCF: 14

Lesson 1.3 Arithmetic of Numbers Homework

1. −284 **3.** 9 **5.** −4 **7.** −190

9. He gets $1.60 change **11.** −14

13a. 26 **b.** 24 **c.** 30 **d.** $\frac{21}{2}$ or $10\frac{1}{2}$ **e.** −19 **f.** −46

15a. 6 **b.** 10 **c.** 0 **d.** 54 **e.** −6 **f.** $\frac{27}{4}$ or $6\frac{3}{4}$

17. true

Apply - Practice Problems

1. 48 **3.** −34 **5.** −45 **7.** −60 **9.** −65 **11.** 336 **13.** −6

15. −4 **17.** 9 **19.** 7 **21.** −13 **23.** 48 **25.** 19 **27.** −50

Evaluate - Practice Test

1a. 1 **b.** −5 **c.** −6 **d.** −1 **e.** −13 **f.** 10

2a. 32 **b.** −32 **c.** −32 **d.** 2 **e.** −2 **f.** −2

3. 32 **4a.** true **b.** false **c.** true **d.** false

5. Associative Property of Addition;
Commutative Property of Addition;
Associative Property of Addition

6. $7.25

7. Distributive Property

8. −7

Topic 1 Cumulative Review Problems

1. b, c, e **3.** 1 **5.** $\frac{5}{7}$ **7.** a, b, c **9.** $\frac{8}{9}$ **11.** −61

13. 240 **15.** 18 **17.** $\frac{8}{9}$ **19.** $\sqrt{8}$, π, 4, $\sqrt{17}$

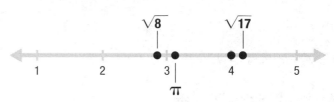

21. a, c **23.** 18 **25.** $\frac{11}{75}$ **27.** $-\frac{22}{75}$ **29.** 11

Lesson 2.1 Algebraic Expressions Homework

1. 11, −6, −1 **3.** −19 **5.** $3x + 2$ (in either order)

7. $11y + 4xy − 7$ (in any order) **9.** $53

11. $6 − x + 2y$ (in any order)

Apply - Practice Problems

1. $6x^3$, $5xy^2$, $−y$, and 25 **3.** $6y + 4$ **5.** $−5x + 38$

7. $5x − 27$ **9.** $7y + 14$ **11.** $−5x − 3xy + 20$

13. $−14x^2 − 30x − 36$ **15.** $3y^2 + 16y + 58$

17. $10x^2 − 15x − 6$ **19.** $3n^2 − 17mn − 32m$

21. 0 **23.** 5 **25.** −86 **27.** 29

Evaluate - Practice Test

1. 2, −1, 7, −4, 12 **2.** $5x + 39$

3. $3y + 4y^2 + 3x + 7xy$ **4.** 8

5. −17 **6.** $6y − 4y^2 + 7$

7. 63 **8.** $5x^2 + 7x^2y − 10x$

Lesson 2.2 Solving Linear Equations Homework

1. $x = 22$ **3.** $t = 12$ **5.** $v = 6$ **7.** $y = -12$ **9.** $1.50

11. $z = -3$ **13.** $y = 3$ **15.** no solution **17.** $z = -3$

19. $r = \dfrac{C}{2\pi}$ **21.** $x = 17$ **23.** $z = 3x - 3$ **25.** $x = 1$

27. $y = -27$ (LCM = 42) **29.** $z = -3$

Apply - Practice Problems

1. no **3.** $a = 18$ **5.** $b = 24$ **7.** $z = 19$ **9.** $x = 8$

11. $r = 5$ **13.** $a = 4$ **15.** $p = 4$ **17.** $b = -4$ **19.** $n = -7$

21. $q = -8$ **23.** $c = -5$ **25.** $x = -2$ **27.** $f = -4$

29. $h = 3$ **31.** $t = -2$ **33.** $c = -1$ **35.** $p = 17$

37. $y = 13$ **39.** $c = -16$ **41.** $a = \dfrac{5}{4}$ **43.** $n = \dfrac{16}{3}$

45. Any r is a solution. **47.** There is no solution.

49. There is no solution. **51.** Any z is a solution.

53. $z = \dfrac{3}{4}y + 2$ **55.** $x = 9y - 12$ **57.** $b = \dfrac{2A}{h}$

59. $w = \dfrac{3V}{lh}$

Evaluate - Practice Test

1. $x = -11$ **2.** -2 **3.** $y = -9$ **4.** $x = 5$

5. The equation is true for all values of x.

6. There is no solution. **7.** $10x - 2 = 6$

8. $z = 1$ **9.** $15x - 10 = 2x + 6$

10. $x = 1$ **11.** $y = 8x - 5$ **12.** $x = \dfrac{1}{8}y + \dfrac{5}{8}$

Lesson 2.3 Problem Solving Homework

1. $-31, -30, -29, -28$ **3.** 26, 27, 28

5. K2 is 8611 meters tall,
and Mount Everest is 8848 meters tall.

7. 8 atoms of carbon, 18 atoms of hydrogen **9.** 11

11. -45 degrees Celsius

13. The legs are 6 inches, 8 inches, and 12 inches.

15. $8'' \times 17''$ **17.** 10 feet **19.** $6' \times 6'$ **21.** $7''$, $7''$, and $4''$

23. $200 + 50\pi$

Apply - Practice Problems

1. 15 and 27 **3.** 18 and 27 **5.** 28 and -12 **7.** 9 and 47

9. 31, 32, and 33 **11.** 27, 28, 29, and 30

13. $-82, -80, -78,$ and -76 **15.** 6 years old

17. 31 years old

19. Miriam is 48 years old. Edward is 58 years old.

21. Mark is 15 years old. Luke is 5 years old.

23. Boris is 20 years old. Svetlana is 80 years old.

25. Masato is 40 years old. Kim is 20 years old.

27. Maria will be 66 years old. Angelica will be 15 years old.

29. Each of the other two angles measures 47.5 degrees.

31. 36 degrees, 44 degrees, and 100 degrees

33. 25 degrees, 75 degrees, and 80 degrees

35. 3 cm, 13 cm, 15 cm **37.** 6 cm, 10 cm, 10 cm

39. 16 inches, 32 inches, 32 inches

41. The length is 11 inches, and the width is 7 inches.

43. The length is 20 cm, and the width is 6 cm.

45. The length is 10 inches, and the width is 4 inches.

47. The length is 11 inches, and the width is 8 inches.

49. The perimeter of the triangle is 120 cm, and the perimeter of the hexagon is 30 cm.

51. 2500 square feet **53.** 1350 square feet

55. 324 square feet

Evaluate - Practice Test

1. 9 and 12 **2.** 18 years old and 15 years old

3. 15 years old **4.** 11, 13, 15

5. width = 3 yards; length = 9 yards

6. 40 degrees, 50 degrees, and 90 degrees

7. width = 50 yards; length = 90 yards

8. Each side of the triangle is 4 inches, and each side of the square is 3 inches.

Lesson 2.4 Linear Inequalities Homework

1. $x < 9$ **3.** $-4 \leq x \leq 4$ **5.** $x < -3$ **7.** $x < ?$

9. $x \leq \$24.50$ **11.** $x < \dfrac{7}{3}$

13.

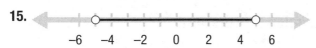

$x = 7$ is not included in the solution of the inequality $x - 2 < 5$. This is indicated by the open circle.

15.

17.

Apply - Practice Problems

1. $x \leq 4$ **3.** $a > 12$ **5.** $b < 6$ **7.** $c \geq -5$ **9.** $d < -\dfrac{5}{4}$

11. $x < 2$ **13.** $z > 3$ **15.** $a < -\dfrac{1}{5}$ **17.** $x > 8$

19. $p \leq -2$ **21.** $z > -8$ **23.** $-11 \leq y < 8$

25. $-1 < z < 39$ **27.** $-4 \leq x \leq -\dfrac{7}{3}$

Evaluate - Practice Test

1. $x < 7$ **2.** $z \leq 4$ **3.** $x < 3$ **4.** $y > -14$

5. $x \leq 7$ **6.** $x \leq 8$ **7.** $0 < z < 5$ **8.** 9 or more hours

Topic 2 Cumulative Review Problems

1. $8x^2y - 8y + 4x$ (in any order) **3.** $-\dfrac{7}{4} < x < 1$

5. 9, 25 **7.** $\dfrac{1}{2} \leq y < \dfrac{8}{3}$ **9.** $-x^2y^2 - 27x + 4xy - 2$

11. $\dfrac{1}{6}$

13. $y \geq 5$

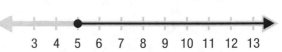

15. $z = 3$ **17.** -12

19. Bjorn is 32 years old, and Ivar is 34 years old.

21. $r = \sqrt{\dfrac{A}{\pi}}$ **23.** 5 meters **25.** Any x is a solution.

27. $\dfrac{17}{12}$ **29.** $-\dfrac{9}{7}$

Lesson 3.1 Introduction to Graphing Homework

1. (3, 4) **3.** Quadrant IV

5.

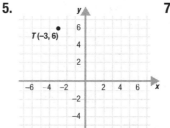

7.

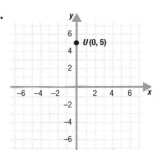

9.

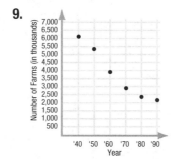

11.

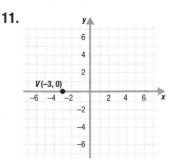

13.

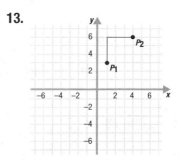

15. rise = 2, run = 3   **17.** rise = −4, run = −4

19. rise = 8, run = 24   **21.** from 1975–1980

23. rise = 126, run = 85   **25.** $c = 13$ **27.** $\sqrt{29}$

29. center: (−5, 7); radius: 2   **31.** $\sqrt{74}$

33. He ran $\sqrt{2000}$ yards;
the distance is approximately 44.7 yards.

35. $(x + 3)^2 + (y − 2)^2 = 5^2$ or $(x + 3)^2 + (y − 2)^2 = 25$

Apply - Practice Problems

1.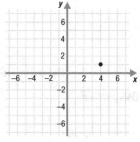

3.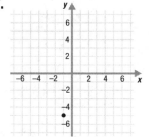

5.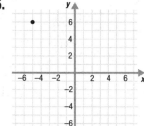

7.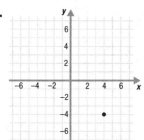

9.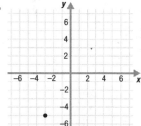

11.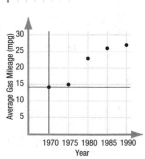

13.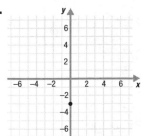

15.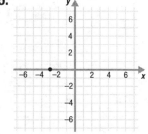

17. (−2, −3)   **19.** (−4, 3)   **21.** (4, −6)   **23.** (0, −5)

25. Quadrant II   **27.** Quadrant IV   **29.** rise = 2, run = 8

31. rise = 4, run = −9   **33.** rise = 11, run = 8

35. rise = 6, run = −3   **37.** rise = 3, run = 6

39. rise = −6, run = −8   **41.** rise = 11, run = 13

43. rise = 7, run = 10   **45.** rise = 47, run = 28

47. rise = 22, run = 13   **49.** rise = 26, run = 27

51. The run from P_1 to P_2 is greater.   **53.** (15, 13)   **55.** (1, 20)

57. $c = 20$ **59.** $c = 39$ **61.** $(x − 2)^2 + (y + 3)^2 = 16$

63. $(x + 3)^2 + (y − 1)^2 = 25$ **65.** $(x + 3)^2 + (y − 7)^2 = 64$

67. $\sqrt{85}$ **69.** $\sqrt{226}$ **71.** $\sqrt{162}$ **73.** 5   **75.** 10   **77.** 13

79. center: (−5, −2); radius: 3   **81.** center: (−9, 12); radius: 6

83. center: (−9, 3); radius: 11

Evaluate - Practice Test

1. $K(3, −4)$ **2.**

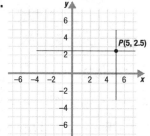

3. S lies in Quadrant III.   **4.**

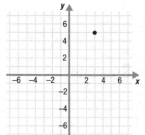

5. rise = 10, run = 6

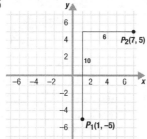

6. rise = 12, run = 7   **7.** rise = 9, run = 36

8. The greatest rise in gas prices was between the years 1975 and 1980.

9. $c = 15$ **10.** The distance from $(-3, 1)$ to $(1, -2)$ is 5.

11. The distance between $(10, 2)$ and $(-2, -7)$ is 15.

12. The radius is 2, and the center is at $(1, -5)$.

13. Quadrant II

14. Several possible answers are shown.

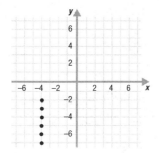

15. $(2, 7)$

16. Several possible answers are shown.

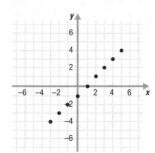

Topic 3 Cumulative Review Problems

1. $\frac{1}{3}$ **3.** $x - 3$

5. rise = 8, run = 3

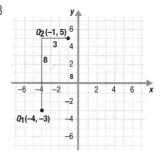

7. Christine is 28 years old, and Raoul is 35 years old.

9. $x < 1$

11. $c = \sqrt{\dfrac{E}{m}}$ **13.** 0

15. Several possible answers are shown.

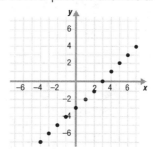

17. $16 \div (-2) = (-16) \div 2$; $2^3 \cdot 5^2 = 5^2 \cdot 2^3$; $\dfrac{6}{9} = \dfrac{2}{3}$

19. $\dfrac{5}{24}$ **21.** $2 < x \le \dfrac{13}{3}$

23. and 25.

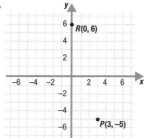

27. $x = 5$

29. $(x - 2)^2 + (y - 3)^2 = 4^2$ or $(x - 2)^2 + (y - 3)^2 = 16$

31. $\frac{3}{5}$ **33.** no solution **35.** center: (–5, 1); radius: 7

Lesson 4.1 Graphing Equations
Homework

1. (1, 4), (–2, 7)

3.
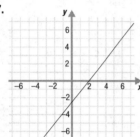

5.

7.
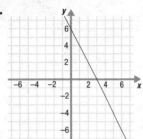

9.
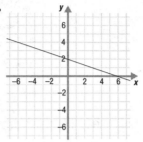

11.
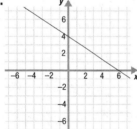

13. (5, 5), (3, 5), (0, 5), (2, 5), (–2, 5), (–4, 5)

15. x-intercept = (4, 0), y-intercept = (0, 1)

17.
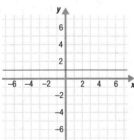

19.
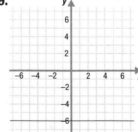

21.
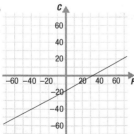

23.
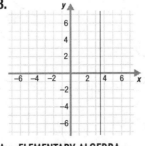

25. slope = 1

27.
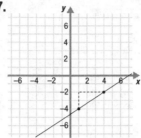

29. undefined **31.** slope $= -\frac{4}{5}$

33. Answers may vary; some include: (1, 12), (2, 24), etc.

35. The line through (2, 5) and (–1, –2).
The line through (4, 5) and (1, –2).

A line with slope 2.
The line through (3, 2) and (5, 6).

The line through (9, –1) and (3, –4).
The line through (–1, 1) and (11, 7).

The line through (1, 2) and (5, –1).
A line with slope $-\frac{3}{4}$.

Apply - Practice Problems

1. (3, 1), (0, –5), and (1, –3) **3.** (0, 3), (6, 0), and (–2, 4)

5. (1, 1), (0, –3), and (2, 5) **7.** (–6, 8), (12, 0), and (21, –4)

9.
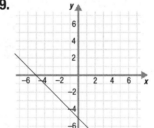

11.
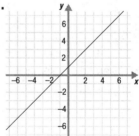

13.
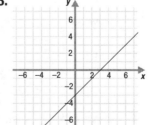

15.
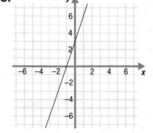

716 ACADEMIC SYSTEMS ALGEBRA – ELEMENTARY ALGEBRA

17.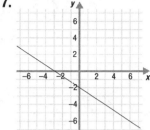

19.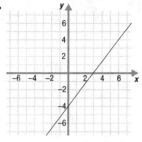

37.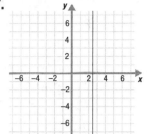

39.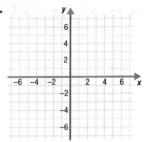

21.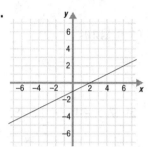

23.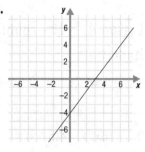

41.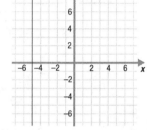

25.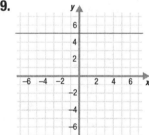

27.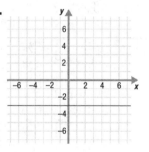

29.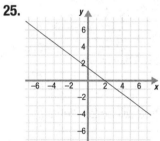

31.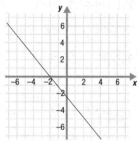

33.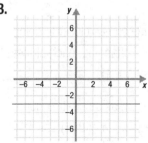

35.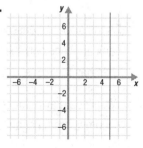

43. x-intercept: $(6, 0)$; y-intercept: $(0, -6)$

45. x-intercept: $(3, 0)$; y-intercept: $(0, 9)$

47. x-intercept: $(3, 0)$; y-intercept: $(0, 6)$

49. x-intercept: $(6, 0)$; y-intercept: $(0, -8)$

51. x-intercept: $(3, 0)$; y-intercept: $\left(0, \frac{9}{4}\right)$

53. x-intercept: $(5, 0)$; y-intercept: $\left(0, -\frac{10}{3}\right)$

55. x-intercept: $(9, 0)$; y-intercept: $(0, 12)$

57. $\frac{3}{2}$ **59.** $\frac{2}{3}$ **61.** -2 **63.** 1 **65.** $\frac{4}{7}$ **67.** $-\frac{7}{4}$ **69.** 0

71. $\frac{5}{4}$ **73.** 1 **75.** $-\frac{8}{9}$ **77.** $-\frac{1}{2}$ **79.** $-\frac{2}{5}$ **81.** -2

83.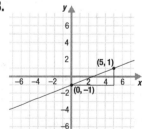

Evaluate - Practice Test

1.

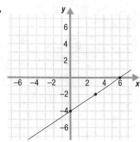

2. (–5, –2), (3, –4), and (4, 11)

3.

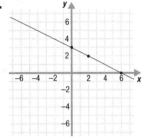

4. The completed table is shown below.

x	y
30	–5
10	5
0	10
–10	15
20	0

5.

x	y
–3	0
–3	5
–3	–4

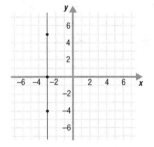

6. The graph of $y = -7$ is a horizontal line.

7. The x-intercept is $\left(\frac{7}{4}, 0\right)$. The y-intercept is (0, –7).

8. The x-intercept is (3, 0). The y-intercept is (0, –5).

9. $-\frac{7}{3}$ **10.** $\frac{5}{4}$

11. The slope of the perpendicular line is 5.

12.

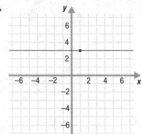

Lesson 4.2 The Equation of a Line
Homework

1. $y - 1 = 2(x - 4)$ **3.** $3x + y = 23$

5. $y - 3 = 3(x - 6)$ or $y = 3(x - 5)$ **7.** $y - 4 = -1(x - 8)$

9. $y = 6x$; $x = 4.5$ hours

11. point-slope form: $y + 7 = -\frac{2}{5}x$

standard form: $2x + 5y = -35$

13. slope = 2; y-intercept = (0, 5) **15.** $x = 4$

17. $y = x - 6$ **19.** slope = $\frac{7}{4}$; y-intercept = $\left(0, -\frac{1}{2}\right)$

21. $y = 4x + 6$; In four years the tree will be 22 feet tall.

23. slope-intercept form: $y = -\frac{7}{4}x - 3$

standard form: $7x + 4y = -12$

25.

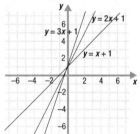

As the slope increases, the line comes closer to being vertical. Since only the slope is changing, each of these lines has the same y-intercept, (0, 1).

27. With lines drawn through (–2, 3), as a negative slope becomes more negative, the y-value of the y-intercept decreases.

29.

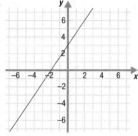

x-intercept: (–2, 0)

It is easy to find the slope using the *x*- and *y*-intercepts.

Apply - Practice Problems

1. $y - 1 = 2(x - 3)$ **3.** $y - 7 = -3(x - 2)$

5. $y - (-2) = \frac{2}{3}(x - 4)$ or $y + 2 = \frac{2}{3}(x - 4)$

7. $y - (-1) = -\frac{1}{2}(x - 3)$ or $y + 1 = -\frac{1}{2}(x - 3)$

9. $y - 3 = \frac{3}{8}[x - (-5)]$ or $y - 3 = \frac{3}{8}(x + 5)$

11. $-3x + y = -13$ **13.** $-5x + y = -23$

15. $5x + y = 3$ **17.** $-\frac{3}{4}x + y = -2$ **19.** $\frac{2}{5}x + y = -10$

21. point-slope form: $y - 2 = -2(x + 6)$ or $y + 4 = -2(x + 3)$;
standard form: $2x + y = -10$

23. point-slope form: $y - 7 = 2(x - 2)$ or $y - 13 = 2(x - 5)$;
standard form: $-2x + y = 3$

25. point-slope form: $y - 7 = 3(x - 6)$ or $y + 2 = 3(x - 3)$;
standard form: $-3x + y = -11$

27. point-slope form: $y - 4 = -\frac{3}{4}(x + 3)$ or $y + 2 = -\frac{3}{4}(x - 5)$;
standard form: $3x + 4y = 7$

29. $y = 4x - 11$ **31.** $y = -2x + 6$ **33.** $y = -x - 1$

35. $y = 2x + 4$ **37.** $y = \frac{1}{3}x - 6$ **39.** $y = 3x - \frac{3}{5}$

41. $y = 4x - \frac{1}{2}$ **43.** $y = -5x - 3$

45. slope = 3, *y*-intercept = (0, 8)

47. slope = 2, *y*-intercept = (0, –4)

49. slope = $\frac{4}{3}$, *y*-intercept = (0, –2)

51. $x = 7$ **53.** $x = 8$ **55.** $y = 9$

Evaluate - Practice Test

1. $y + 5 = -2(x - 2)$

2. The slope of the line is $m = 4$, and a point that lies on the line is (–2, 1).

3. $-\frac{4}{7}x + y = -\frac{1}{7}$ or $-4x + 7y = -1$ or $4x - 7y = 1$

4. $-3x + y = 10$ or $3x - y = -10$ **5.** $3x + y = 2$

6. The slope of the line is $m = 2$, and the *y*-intercept of the line is (0, –7).

7. $y = -6$

8. Several possible choices for Q are shown.

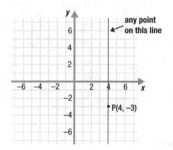

9. $y - 2 = 3(x - 5)$
$y - 2 = \frac{3}{4}(x - 5)$

10. $-3x + y = -9$ or $3x - y = 9$

11. The slope of line A is greater than the slope of line B.

The *y*-coordinate of the *y*-intercept of line A is less than the *y*-coordinate of the *y*-intercept of line B.

The *x*-coordinate of the *x*-intercept of line A is less than the *x*-coordinate of the *x*-intercept of line B.

12. $2x - y = -3$
$2x - y = 4$

Lesson 4.3 Graphing Inequalities
Homework

1.

	(1, 7)	(4, 2)	(2, 5)	(0, 0)	(–6, 3)	(–4, –3)	(3, –6)
$y < 2x + 1$		X		X			X
$y = 2x + 1$			X				
$y > 2x + 1$	X				X	X	

3.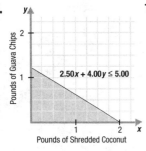

5.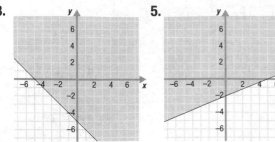

9.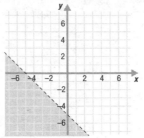

11.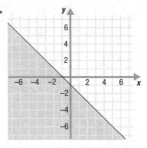

7. The graph of the inequality $x + y \leq 4$ includes the points on the line $x + y = 4$, but the graph of the inequality $x + y < 4$ does not include these points.

9.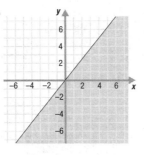

11.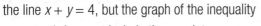

13.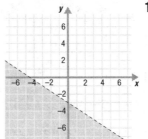

15.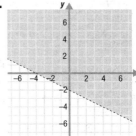

17.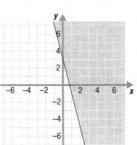

19.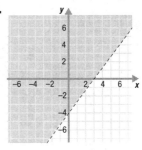

Apply - Practice Problems

1.

	(2, –1)	(4, –2)	(–5, 2)	(3, 8)	(–3, 1)	(4, 3)	(–1, 6)
$x - y < 1$			X	X	X		X
$x - y = 1$						X	
$x - y > 1$	X	X					

3.

	(–3, 4)	(–5, 3)	(–1, 4)	(3, 5)	(3, –8)	(5, –1)	(–4, –5)
$2x - y < 1$	X	X	X				X
$2x - y = 1$				X			
$2x - y > 1$					X	X	

21.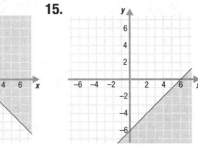

23.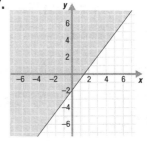

5.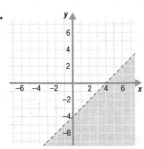

7.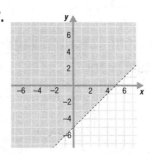

25.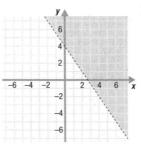

27.

Evaluate - Practice Test

1.

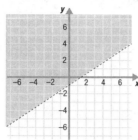

2. (0, 0), (−3, −1), (8, −4)

3.

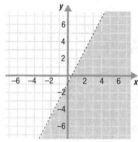

4. The points (8, −14) and (0, 0) satisfy this inequality.

5. $5x + 4y > -20$

6.

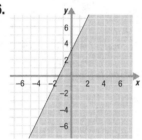

7. (1, 2), (−3, 3), (−5, 6) **8.** $y \geq -x + 2$

Topic 4 Cumulative Review Problems

1.

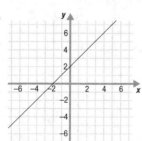

3. $5x - 4y = 29$ **5.** 120

7.

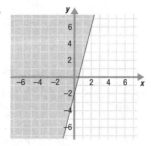

9. $\frac{2}{3}$ **11.** $\frac{1}{18}$

13.

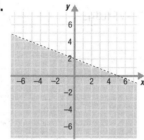

15a. Answers may vary. Some possible answers are (0, 2), (1, 0), (2, 0), and (3, 0).

   b. Answers may vary. Some possible answers are (2, 2), (3, 2), (3, 3), and (3, 4).

   c. Answers may vary. Some possible answers are (1, 2), (5, 0), (3, 1), and (−1, 3).

17. $4\frac{9}{35}$ **19.** $\frac{5}{2}$ **21.** $-\frac{1}{7}x + y = 4$ or $-x + 7y = 28$

23. $y = \frac{71}{47}$ **25.** Paul is 52 years old, and Rita is 31 years old.

27.

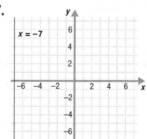

29. $-2 < x \leq \frac{7}{2}$

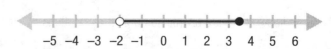

31.

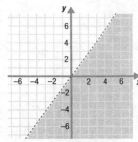

33. $y = -\dfrac{36}{7}$ **35.** slope $= \dfrac{1}{4}$ **37.** $y + 1 = 4(x - 5)$ **39.** $5\dfrac{4}{9}$

Lesson 5.1 Solving Linear Systems Homework

1. $-x + 2y = 4$ and $x + y = -1$

3. $-x + 2y = 4$ and $x + y = 2$

5. $-x + y = 5$ and $3x + y = 9$

7. $-x + y = 5$ and $-x + y = 2$

9. No. It will take him 15 weeks instead of 14 weeks to reach his goal.

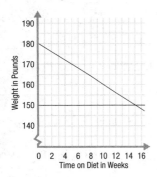

11. One possible solution is shown.

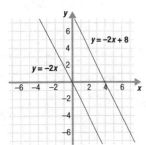

13. (2, 1)   **15.** (−1, 4)

17. Same line—there are an infinite number of solutions.

19. The system has no solution.

21. You can drive up to 50 miles before the cost of paying for mileage is the same as getting unlimited mileage.

23. (−3, 7)   **25.** $y = 6x - 8$ or $y = \dfrac{3}{2}x + 1$

27. (0, 4), (−6, −2) and (6, −8)

29. $y = x + 3$
   $x + y = -1$

Apply - Practice Problems

1. A and C   **3.** C and D   **5.** C and D

7. (2, 0)

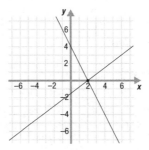

9. (−3, −1)

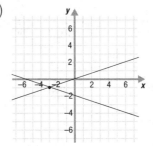

11. There is no solution.

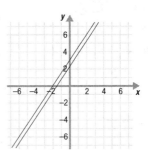

13. There is no solution.

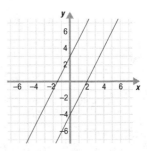

15. $(-1, -4)$

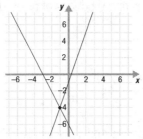

17. There are an infinite number of solutions.

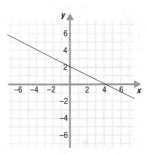

19. There are an infinite number of solutions.

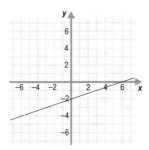

21. $(1, 3)$

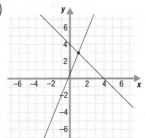

23. There are many possible answers. Any line that is parallel to the given line is a solution. Here is one example.

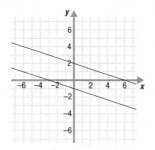

25. There are many possible answers. Any line that is parallel to the given line is a solution. Here is one example.

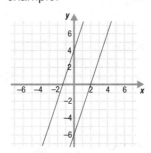

27. There are many possible answers. Any line other than the given line that passes through the point $(-4, 3)$ is a solution. Here is one example.

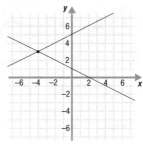

29. $x = 3, y = 2$ **31.** $x = 2, y = -5$ **33.** $x = 2, y = -1$

35. $x = \dfrac{12}{7}, y = \dfrac{1}{7}$ **37.** $x = \dfrac{5}{16}, y = -\dfrac{9}{16}$

39. $x = -\dfrac{16}{5}, y = -\dfrac{18}{5}$

41. All ordered pairs (x, y) that satisfy $3x - y = 5$ are solutions; both equations represent the same line.

43. $x = 4, y = 1$ **45.** $x = 6, y = 4$ **47.** $x = 3, y = 2$

49. $x = 6, y = 7$ **51.** $x = 2, y = 0$

53. $x = -\dfrac{13}{17}, y = \dfrac{6}{17}$

55. The system has no solution; the equations represent parallel lines.

Evaluate - Practice Test

1. (4, 2)   **2.** (–4, 5)

3. The system has a solution at the point (–2, –5).   **4.** (5, 0)

5. The other equation in the system is $3x + 4y = 6$.

6. $x + y = 2$ **7.** (–1, 4)

8. The system has only one solution, the point (–2, –3).

9. (12, 5)   **10.** (9, 4)   **11.** (1, 2)   **12.** (3, –1)

Lesson 5.2 Problem Solving
Homework

1. 12 and 3   **3.** 310 adult tickets and 230 student tickets.

5. $1150 into his savings account and $250 in his checking account

7. 51 quarters   **9.** 26 and 19

11. 2.1 pounds of almonds and 0.9 pound of walnuts.

Apply - Practice Problems

1. 198 and 169   **3.** 120 and 15

5. $1275 in the 3% account and $1200 in the 6.5% account

7. $1788 in the 12% fund and $1712 in the 9.5% fund

9. He owes $3200 on the 9% loan and $4700 on the 7% loan

11. 17 quarters and 23 dimes   **13.** 18 dimes and 47 nickels

15. 23 dimes and 115 quarters

17. 160 ml of 75% sulfuric acid and 240 ml of 25% sulfuric acid

19. 120 ml of 65% boric acid and 180 ml of 15% boric acid

21. 15 ounces

23. 10 pounds of the $6.50 per pound nuts and 15 pounds of the $4.00 per pound nuts

25. 11 pounds of raisins and 9 pounds of peanuts

27. 8 pounds

Evaluate - Practice Test

1. 9 and 16

2. She has 8 five-dollar bills and 11 ten-dollar bills.

3. 560

4. 1.6 pounds of Ethiopian Harrar beans and 1.4 pounds of Arabian Mocha beans should be used for the blend.

5. Deac is now 37 years old and Irina is 15 years old.

6. 60

7. He needs 150 ml of 5% HCl and 50 ml of 9% HCl.

8. She invested $1325 at 4% interest and $1050 at 11% interest.

Lesson 5.3 Systems of Inequalities
Homework

1. (–1, –7), (4, –4), (6, –2), (7, –6)   **3.**

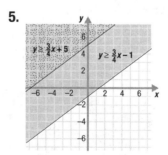

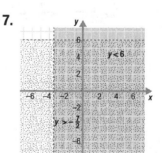

5.

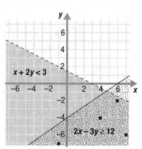

7.

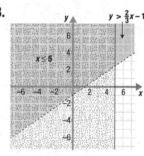

9. $x + y \leq 10$

$x \qquad \leq y$

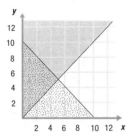

11.

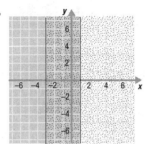

13. (0, 5), (3, 0), and (0, −5)

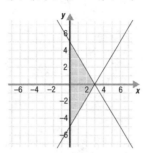

15. (0, 5), (3, 5), (0, 0), (3, 0); Area = 15 square units

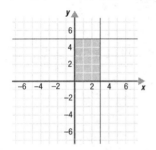

17. Answers may vary; some possible answers are:

(0, 0), (1, 3), (1, 2), (4, 8)

Apply - Practice Problems

1.

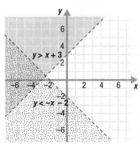

3.

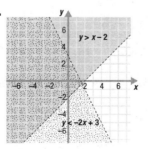

5.

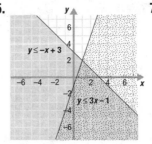

7.

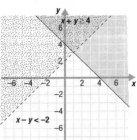

9.

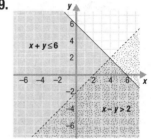

11.

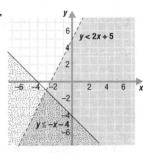

13.

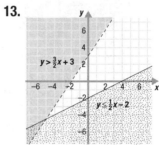

15.

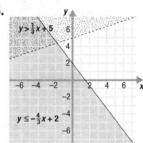

17.

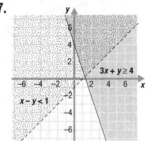

19.

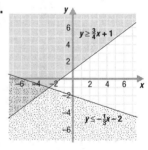

21.

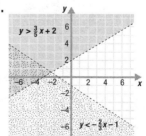

23.

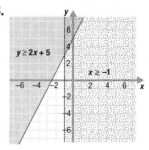

25.

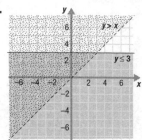

27.

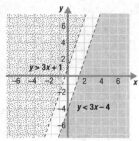

7. If the direction of the first inequality sign is reversed, the graph of the new system is:

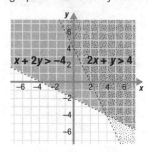

The overlapping region is the solution of the system.

Evaluate - Practice Test

1. $(-3, -3)$, $(2, -4)$, $(4, 1)$, and $(7, -2)$

2.

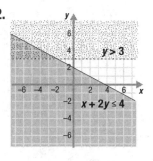

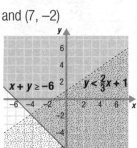

8.

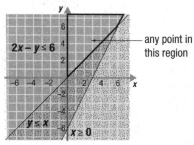

Any point that lies in the region shown satisfies the first two inequalities, but not the third.

3. $(5, -1)$, and $(7, -3)$

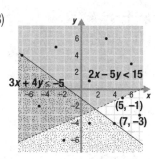

Topic 5 Cumulative Review Problems

1. -7 **3.** 34 and 19   **5.** $x = \dfrac{11}{2}$, $y = -\dfrac{3}{2}$ **7.** -1

9.

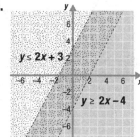

4.

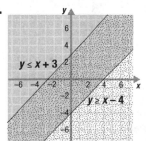

5.

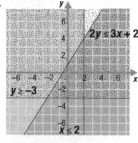

6. $(-1, 0)$, $(-3, 1)$ and $(-4, 4)$

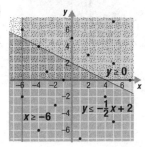

11. $x = 4$, $y = -3$ **13.** slope $= -\dfrac{9}{4}$ **15a.** 21   **b.** 27, 720

17. $y = \dfrac{4}{5}$ **19.** $x = -7$, $y = 8$ **21.** 452   **23.** B and D

25. A and B   **27.** $\dfrac{1}{42}$ **29.** $x = -\dfrac{61}{39}$, $y = \dfrac{10}{39}$

31.

33. 93 dimes   **35.** $y = -\dfrac{6}{11}$ **37.** slope $= \dfrac{6}{5}$

Lesson 6.1 Exponents
Homework

1a. 3^7 **b.** 5^7 **c.** 7^7 **3a.** 7^6 **b.** 7^6

5a. x^8 **b.** a^0 **c.** 1 **d.** $\frac{x^3}{4}$ **7a.** b^{18} **b.** y^{11} **c.** $\frac{b^3}{a^7}$

9. $\frac{1}{x}$ **11a.** 1 **b.** $\frac{1}{y^3}$ **c.** $\frac{1}{b^4}$ **d.** 3

Apply - Practice Problems

1. 7^8 **3.** b^{15} **5.** a^{11} **7.** 9^6 **9.** n^5

11. 5^{12} **13.** 13^{30} **15.** z^{48} **17.** $81a^4$

19. $8y^3$ **21.** $\frac{m^4}{n^6}$ **23.** 1 **25.** 1 **27.** 3

Evaluate - Practice Test

1a. 11^4 **b.** 3^2y^5 **c.** 5^{43} **d.** $x^{21}y^{26}$ **e.** $7^{18}b^{14}$

2a. 2^3 **b.** b^6 **c.** $\frac{3^3}{x^9}$ **d.** $\frac{1}{y^4}$

3. $\frac{x^6y^2}{x^3y^7}$ and $\frac{x^7y}{x^4y^6}$ **4.** $(31x^8)^0 \cdot 5y$, $\frac{5y^2}{y}$, and $\frac{(5y)^2}{5y}$

5a. b^{48} **b.** $3^{10}a^{12}$ **c.** $2^{99}x^{44}y^{66}$

6a. $\frac{5^4y^{40}}{3^4x^{32}}$ **b.** $\frac{7^6a^6b^{24}}{5^6}$

7a. -1 **b.** 1 **c.** -3 **d.** 1

8a. a^{35} **b.** $\frac{1}{a^{35}}$

Lesson 6.2 Polynomial Operations I
Homework

1. $3\frac{1}{4}y^3 + 3y^2 - 5$ **3a.** $-4y^5 - 2y^3 + 3y + 2$

b. $5, 3, 1, 0$ **c.** 5 **5.** $-4v^7 + v^3 + 6v^2 - 5v + 5$

7. $-7s^3t^3 + 7st^2 - s^2t + 2st - 13t + 9$

9. $2x^2y + 10xy^2 + 4y^3 + 3$

11. $4w^2yz + 3w^3 - 4wyz^2 + 6wyz - 4wy^2z + 3$

13. $x^3y^3z^3$ **15.** $-3t^4u^4v^{15}$ **17.** $10p^3r^4 + 5p^4r^5$

19. $\frac{3xw^5}{y}$ **21.** $\frac{3a^3d}{2b^5c^3}$ **23.** $\frac{4xy^2}{3} + \frac{5x^2y^3}{3}$ or $\frac{xy^2}{3}(4 + 5xy)$

Apply - Practice Problems

1. $2xy + 5xz$; $9y^2 + 13yz - 8z^2$

3a. binomial **b.** binomial **c.** trinomial **d.** monomial
  e. trinomial

5. 8 **7.** 9 **9.** 7 **11.** 6 **13.** 84 **15.** $6x^2 + 11x - 8$

17. $15m^2n^3 + 2m^2n^2 - 7mn$ **19.** $15a^3b^2 + 4a^2b - ab^3$

21. $20xy^2z^3 - 30x^2yz^2 + 10x^3y^3z$ **23.** $4x^3 + 7x - 8$

25. $y^2 + 6xy + 4y$ **27.** $11a^5b^3 - 4a^4b - 9b$ **29.** $15y^5$

31. $-45a^9$ **33.** $28x^4y^8$ **35.** $-6w^2x^5y^3z^3$

37. $-6a^7b^7 + 10a^4b^5 - 12a^4b^2$

39. $20a^4b^2 + 10a^4b^3 - 35a^3b^4 - 15a^2b^3$

41. $12x^6y^3 - 28x^4y^5 + 8x^4y^4 - 4x^3y^4$

43. $5a^2b^5$ **45.** $\frac{8a^2b^3}{3c}$ **47.** $\frac{3x^3y^2z^5}{2w}$ **49.** $\frac{3n^5p^3}{2mq}$

51. $4a + 3a^3$ **53.** $\frac{7}{y} + 4x^3y$ **55.** $\frac{2}{x} - \frac{x^2z^3}{2y^2}$

Evaluate - Practice Test

1. $t^2 - s + 5$, $m^5n^4o^3p^2r$, and $\frac{5}{7}c^{15} + \frac{3}{14}c^{11} - 3\pi$

2. w^5x^4 is a monomial.

   $2x^2 - 36$ is a binomial.

   $\frac{1}{3}x^{17} + \frac{2}{3}x^{12} - \frac{1}{3}$ is a trinomial.

   27 is a monomial.

   $27x^3 - 2x^2y^3$ is a binomial.

   $x^2 + 3xy - \frac{2}{3}y^2$ is a trinomial.

3. $8w^8 + 7w^5 + 3w^3 - 13w^2 - 2$

4a. $3x^3y - 8x^2y^2 - 5y^3 + xy + y^2 + 19$

  b. $7x^3y - 8x^2y^2 + 3y^3 + 5xy - y^2 + 7$

5. $x^8y^3w^5$

6. $3n^3p^3 + 2n^5p^5 - 35n^2p^7$

7. $\frac{3x^4yz^6}{2}$

8. $\frac{3t^2u}{2v} - \frac{1}{2}t^4$

Lesson 6.3 Polynomial Operations II Homework

1. First terms: $2p$ and p
Outer terms: $2p$ and $-p^2$
Inner terms: 3 and p
Last terms: 3 and $-p^2$

3. $2s^3, 5$ **5.** $12x^2 + 24x - 6yx - 12y$

7a. $9x^4 - 4$ **b.** $9x^4 - 12x^2 + 4$ **c.** $9x^4 + 12x^2 + 4$

9. $169s^2 - 4h^2$ **11.** $91x^4y^4 - 148x^5y^2 + 60x^6$

13. $3x^2 + 4x^2y + 7x + 8xy + 2$

15. $x^2 + x - y^2 - y$ or $x(x+1) - y(y+1)$ **17.** $4x^2 - 8x$

19. $48x^5 - 48x^4 - \frac{76}{3}x^3 + 24x^2 + \frac{7}{3}x + 7$

21. $3x - 7 + \frac{20}{x+3}$ **23.** $15x^2 - 44x + 132 + \frac{-391}{x+3}$

25. $9a^2 - 1$ **27.** $a^2 - b^2, 4x^2 - 9y^2$

29. $a^2 - 2ab + b^2, 4t^6 - 16u^2t^3 + 16u^4$

Apply - Practice Problems

1. $a^2 + 7a + 10$ **3.** $x^2 - 15x + 44$ **5.** $5y^2 + 7y - 24$

7. $8a^2 + 26ab + 15b^2$ **9.** $18y^2 + 9xy - 5x^2$

11. $x^2 + 6x + 9$ **13.** $25q^2 + 30q + 9$

15. $z^2 - 10z + 25$ **17.** $t^2 - 12t + 36$

19. $16a^2 - 56ac + 49c^2$ **21.** $25m^2 - n^2$

23. $4x^2 - y^2$ **25.** $25x^2 - 9$ **27.** $4a^2 - 49b^2$

29. $8a^2 - 34ab + 21b^2$ **31.** $18m^2 + 9mn - 20n^2$

33. $14xy + 21x - 8y - 12$

35. $3m^3n + 11m^2n - 4mn - 9mn^2 + 3n^2$

37. $21a^3b + 16a^2b + 9ab^2 - 16ab + 12b^2$

39. $10x^3y - 30xy^2 + 19x^2y - 12y^2 + 6xy$

41. $20m^5n - 15m^4n^2 + 40m^3n^3 -$
$15m^2n^3 + 12m^3n - 9m^2n^2 + 24mn^3 - 9n^3$

43. $x^2 + 3x - 7$ **45.** $x^2 + 7x + 2$

47. $x^2 + 5x - 1$ **49.** $2x^2 - 3x + 1$

51. $x^2 + 2x - 3$ remainder 3 or $x^2 + 2x - 3 + \frac{3}{4x-1}$

53. $x^2 + 4x + 1$ remainder -10 or $x^2 + 4x + 1 - \frac{10}{3x+2}$

55. $2x^2 - 6x + 1$

Evaluate - Practice Test

1. $6x^5y - 4x^2 + 9x^4y^2 - 6xy$ **2.** $4x^2 - 12xy + 9y^2$

3. $4x^2 + 12xy + 9y^2$ **4.** $4x^2 - 9y^2$

5. $15x^3 + 14x^2 - 22x + 4$

6. $12r^8 - 15p^2r^4 - 18p^4 - 7r^4 + 36p^2 - 10$

7. $3t + 1$ **8.** $2x^2 - x + 2 + \frac{-6}{4x+2}$

9a. $a^4 + a^5 - a^6 - a^7$

b. The degree of the resulting polynomial is 7.

10. $15y^6 - 5y^5 + 4y^4 + 5y^3 - 5y^2 + 2y$

11.

	$2x^3$	$-3x$	7
$5x^4$	$10x^7$	$-15x^5$	$35x^4$
8	$16x^3$	$-24x$	56

$10x^7 - 15x^5 + 35x^4 + 16x^3 - 24x + 56$

12.

	$5x^4$	$-7x^3$	$7x^2$	$-8x$
x^2	$5x^6$	$-7x^5$	$7x^4$	$-8x^{33}$
1	$5x^4$	$-7x^3$	$7x^2$	$-8x$

$5x^6 - 7x^5 + 12x^4 - 15x^3 + 7x^2 - 8x$

Topic 6 Cumulative Review Problems

1a. 2^{16} **b.** x^7 **c.** $a^{20}b^8$

3a. $y - 7 = -\frac{2}{7}(x-3)$ **b.** $y = -\frac{2}{7}x + \frac{55}{7}$ **c.** $2x + 7y = 55$

5. The numbers are 14 and 46.

7a. $y + 9 = -\frac{8}{5}(x - 20)$ **b.** $y = -\frac{8}{5}x + 23$ **c.** $8x + 5y = 115$

9a. 1 **b.** –1 **c.** 1 **11.** $\frac{3x^2y^4}{2z^6}$

13. slope = 4, y–intercept = (0, –7) **15.** $-5 < x < -3$

17. $\frac{26}{117} = \frac{2}{9}$, The GCF of 72 and 108 is 36.

19.

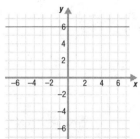

21. $\left(\frac{3}{2}, -3\right)$ **23.** $y = 3x - 4$ **25.** $-\frac{2}{13}$

27. no solution for y **29.** A and B **31.** A and C **33.** –261

35.

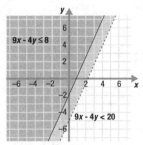

37. Manuel split his money by putting $984 in his checking account and $1581 in his savings account.

39a. binomial **b.** trinomial **c.** monomial **d.** binomial **e.** monomial **f.** trinomial

41. $-4a^2b + 10a - 7b$

Lesson 7.1 Factoring Polynomials I Homework

1. x^3yz^2, x **3.** $6xy$ **5.** $y(x^2 + 6y)$ **7.** $4ab(a - b)$

11. $17x^2y^2z(z + 4x^8y^{30} + 9x^7y^2z^{11})$ **13.** $x^5 + y$

15. $(xy + yz)$ **17.** $(a^2 + b^2)(a - b)$

19. $(x^4y + z)(x + y + z)$ **21.** $(x^2 + y^2)(z + 3)$

23. $(x + y)(3 + z)$

Apply - Practice Problems

1. 23 and $8m^3n$ **3.** $4ab$ **5.** $5xy^2$ **7.** $3ac^2$

9. $8m(2n^4 + 1)$ **11.** $2xy(3x^3y^2 + 7)$ **13.** $2ab(4a^2b - 5)$

15. $9y^3z^5(4y^4z^3 - 5)$ **17.** $2mn(2 + 5n^2 - 9m^3)$

19. $4ab(2a^2b^3 - 3 + 5a^2)$ **21.** $8p^5q^3r(4p^2r^3 - 5q^2)$

23. $3xy^2z^3(3 - 5x^2y^3z + 7x^3z^2)$

25. $4a^2bc^2(5ab^4 + 3a^2bc - 2c)$

27. $3a^2b^2c^2(2ab^3 - 3a^2b^2c + 6b - 7a^4c)$

29. $(x + y)(z + 3)$ **31.** $(a + 9)(3b - 4)$

33. $(8m + 17)(3n^3 - 4)$ **35.** $(7x - 11)(2x^2 + 3)$

37. $(m - 3n)(5m + 2n)$ **39.** $(x + y)(w + z)$

41. $(a - b)(c + d)$ **43.** $(2a - 7)(2a + 1)$

45. $(6a + 5b)(2a + 3)$ **47.** $(5x + 2y)(3x + 7)$

49. $(2z + w)(4z - 1)$ **51.** $(4a - 5b)(3a + 2)$

53. $(6x - 5y)(3x + 2)$ **55.** $(3pr - 4s)(4r + 5)$

Evaluate - Practice Test

1. GCF = x **2.** GCF = xyz **3.** $3xy(x - y)$

4. $3xy^2(y - 2 + x^2y^2)$ **5.** $(x^2 + 4)(13 + 6y)$

6. $(3xyz + 4z)(17x^2 - 3yz)$ **7.** $(3r - 1)(13s + 3)$

8. $2(3w - 11)(2z + 3)$

Lesson 7.2 Factoring Polynomials II Homework

1. $(x + 4)(x + 3)$ **3.** $(x + 5)(x + 7)$ **5.** $(x + 3)(x - 8)$

7. $(x - 3)(x + 2)$ **9.** $(x - 7)(x + 3)$ **11.** $(x + 36)(x - 1)$

13. $(x + 5)(2x + 1)$ **15.** $(2y + 3)(2y - 7)$

17. $15(a - 1)(a - 1)$ **19.** $x = \frac{1}{5}$ or $x = -\frac{2}{5}$

21. $(13x + 11)(x + 2)$ **23.** $(x + y)(x + y)$ **25.** xy

27. $\frac{y}{2}(x^2 - 1)$ or $\frac{1}{2}y(x^2 - 1)$

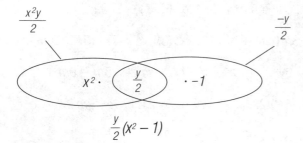

$$\frac{y}{2}(x^2 - 1)$$

29. GCF $= x$

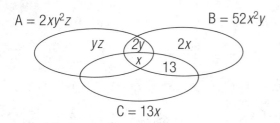

$A = 2xy^2z$ $B = 52x^2y$

yz $2y$ $2x$

x 13

$C = 13x$

Apply - Practice Problems

1. $(x + 1)(x + 4)$ **3.** $(x + 1)(x + 14)$ **5.** $(x + 3)(x + 5)$

7. $(x + 4)(x + 3)$ **9.** $(x - 2)(x - 6)$ **11.** $(x - 11)(x - 4)$

13. $(x - 7)(x - 3)$ **15.** $(x + 3)(x - 10)$ **17.** $(x + 7)(x - 3)$

19. $(x + 9)(x - 4)$ **21.** $(x - 9)(x + 2)$ **23.** $(x - 7)(x + 3)$

25. $(x - 9)(x + 7)$ **27.** $(x - 12)(x + 5)$ **29.** $(2x + 5)(x + 1)$

31. $(3x + 2)(x - 7)$ **33.** $(2x + 7)(x - 4)$

35. $(2x - 3)(x + 4)$ **37.** $(2x + 3)(x + 5)$

39. $(3x + 2)(x + 3)$ **41.** $(5x - 2)(2x - 1)$

43. $(3x + 2)(2x - 5)$ **45.** $(2x + 1)(4x - 3)$

47. $(3x - 5)(3x + 4)$ **49.** $(4x + 1)(9x + 1)$

51. $(5x - y)(x + 3y)$ **53.** $(3x + y)(x - 2y)$

55. $(3x - 2y)(3x + y)$ **57.** $x = 6$ or $x = -2$

59. $x = 5$ or $x = 8$ **61.** $x = -\frac{5}{2}$ or $x = 1$

Evaluate - Practice Test

1. $(x - 4)(x - 6)$

2. $x^2 + 2x - 1$ cannot be factored using integers.

3. $(t + 1)(t - 17)$ **4.** $(r + 5t)(r + 5t)$ **5.** $(x + 2)(5x - 2)$

6. $(9v - 7)(3v - 4)$ **7.** $(x + 12)(4x + 9)$ **8.** $x = \frac{12}{7}$ or $x = -1$

9. The two true statements are:
- Two factors of C are z and 2.
- The GCF of A, B, and C is $4z$.

10. $15u^2 + 20uv$ and $9uv + 12v^2$

11. $7y - 3x$

12.

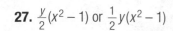

	$3x$	y
$2x$	$6x^2$	$2xy$
$-3y$	$-9xy$	$-3y^2$

Lesson 7.3 Factoring By Patterns Homework

1. $(x + 7)^2$ **3.** $(x + 5)(x^2 - 5x + 25)$ **5.** $x(3y - 1)(3y + 1)$

7. $(x + 4w^2)^2$ **9.** $(7y - 2x)^2$ **11.** $2x(x + 3)^2$

Apply - Practice Problems

1. $(a + 9)(a + 9)$ or $(a + 9)^2$

3. $(3x + 7)(3x + 7)$ or $(3x + 7)^2$

5. $(2a + 5)(2a + 5)$ or $(2a + 5)^2$

7. $(z - 11)(z - 11)$ or $(z - 11)^2$

9. $(4a - 5)(4a - 5)$ or $(4a - 5)^2$

11. $(3x - 2)(3x - 2)$ or $(3x - 2)^2$

13. $(x + 6)(x - 6)$ **15.** $25(a + 5b)(a - 5b)$

17. $(a - 6)(a^2 + 6a + 36)$ **19.** $(x - 5)(x^2 + 5x + 25)$

21. $(3z - 7)(9z^2 + 21z + 49)$

23. $(c + 4)(c^2 - 4c + 16)$ **25.** $(y + 3)(y^2 - 3y + 9)$

27. $2mn(5m + 8n)(5m - 8n)$

Evaluate - Practice Test

1. $9x^2 + 12x + 4$, $0.25x^2 + 8x + 64$, and $x^2 - 2x + 1$

2a. $(x-5)(x-5)$ **b.** $(7y+2)(7y+2)$ **c.** $(4x+1)(4x-1)$

 d. $(3y+6)(3y-6)$

3. $x^2 - 1000$ and $9m^2 - 24mn - 16n^2$

4. $3x(2x-5)(2x-5)$ **5.** $x^2 + 8x + 16$ and $4x^2 - 12x + 9$

6a. $4(x-3)(x-3)$ **b.** $(8z+1)(8z+1)$ **c.** $(2w+7)(2w-7)$

 d. $(3m+n)(3m-n)$

7a. $(x+10)(x^2-10x+100)$ **b.** $(6y-1)(36y^2+6y+1)$

 c. $(7x+2y)(49x^2-14xy+4y^2)$

8. $3w(3w+5)(3w+5)$

Topic 7 Cumulative Review Problems

1. $a^3 - 2a + 5$ **3.** $7x^2 + 5y + 2$

5. Alfredo should use 130 ml of the 15% solution and 120 ml of the 40% solution.

7. $(x-3)^2$ **9.** a, d, e

11.

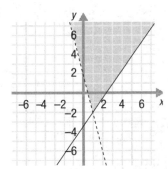

13. $(a^2 + 2)^2$

15. $6 \leq x < 10$

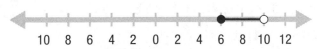

17a. $y - 12 = -2(x+7)$ **b.** $y = -2x - 2$ **c.** $2x + y = -2$

19. $x = 7$ or $x = -2$

21a. $y + 3 = -\frac{8}{5}(x-4)$ **b.** $y = -\frac{8}{5}x + \frac{17}{5}$ **c.** $8x + 5y = 17$

23. $\frac{8}{33}$ **25.** no solutions **27.** $(5x+7)(x-1)$

29. 128 **31.** $a^2 + 2a - 8$

33. Jerome owed $1190 on the credit card that charged 16% interest and $630 on the credit card that charged 14% interest.

35a. $y - 3 = \frac{5}{6}(x-5)$ **b.** $y = \frac{5}{6}x - \frac{7}{6}$

 c. $-5x + 6y = -7$ or $5x - 6y = 7$

37. **39.**

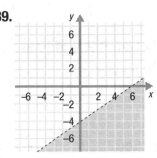

41. $(6b+5)^2$ **43.** $4x^3 + 7xy^2 + 7$ **45.** $(-2, 5)$

47. $5x^2 + x^2y + 2xy + 25x - 15y$

49. The width of the rectangle is 17 feet, and the length is 51 feet.

Lesson 8.1 Rational Expressions I Homework

1. $x = 14$ or $x = -2$ **3.** $\frac{a}{9b^2}$ **5.** $\frac{3y^2}{7}$ **7.** $\frac{3w}{y^2}$ **9.** $\frac{5}{9a}$

11. $\frac{x(x+1)}{x-1}$ or $\frac{x^2+x}{x-1}$ **13.** $\frac{21x}{5y}$ **15.** $\frac{x+4}{x^2-4}$ or $\frac{x+4}{(x+2)(x-2)}$

17. $\frac{5}{x-7}$ **19.** $\frac{7}{15x}$ **21.** $\frac{8\pi r^3}{3}$ **23.** $\frac{1}{3}$

Apply - Practice Problems

1. -5 **3.** $2, -2$ **5.** $\frac{4m^4}{3n^3}$ **7.** $\frac{4b^3}{7a^5}$ **9.** $\frac{x+5}{x-2}$ **11.** $\frac{14}{a^2b^2c^2}$

13. $\frac{14m^7}{9n^4}$ **15.** $\frac{2m^4}{3n^3p}$ **17.** $\frac{3a}{2bc^2}$ **19.** $\frac{yz}{x}$ **21.** $\frac{3m^2np}{2q}$

23. $\frac{2m}{n^2}$ **25.** $\frac{4a}{b^2}$ **27.** $\frac{x^2-3x}{2x+14}$ or $\frac{x(x-3)}{2x+14}$ **29.** $\frac{5a}{7b}$

31. $\frac{3b+5}{2b+1}$ **33.** $\frac{7x+2}{5x-1}$ **35.** $\frac{2b-4}{2b+9}$ **37.** $\frac{11+5n}{7n}$

39. $\frac{3}{x+2}$ **41.** $\frac{2}{x-3}$ **43.** $\frac{4}{x-2}$ **45.** $\frac{x+1}{x+3}$ **47.** $\frac{x+5}{x+6}$

49. $\frac{3}{2}$ **51.** $\frac{1}{x+5}$ **53.** $\frac{1}{x-1}$ **55.** $\frac{3}{5}$

Evaluate - Practice Test

1. $x = -3$ or $x = 2$ **2.** $\dfrac{x-7}{x+6}$ **3a.** $\dfrac{5}{9z}$ **b.** $\dfrac{8x}{z^2}$

4a. $\dfrac{6x}{7}$ **b.** $\dfrac{xw}{15y}$ **5a.** $\dfrac{7x}{13y}$ **b.** $\dfrac{3w+14}{z-8}$

6. $\dfrac{9y-3}{7x}$ **7.** $\dfrac{4}{x-6}$ **8.** $\dfrac{6y+4}{y-7}$

Lesson 8.2 Rational Expressions II
Homework

1. $\dfrac{1}{125}$ or $\dfrac{1}{5^3}$ **3.** 1000 **5.** $\dfrac{2}{m^3 n^3}$ **7.** $\dfrac{2t^{13}}{s^9}$

9. 0.00000001 cm, 0.00000005 cm **11.** $\dfrac{z^{10}}{9x^8 y^2}$

13. -1 **15.** $-x$ **17.** $\dfrac{2x}{x+1}$ **19.** $\dfrac{y+8}{2y-1}$

21. $\dfrac{z+3}{(z-4)(z+5)}$ **23.** $\dfrac{2}{3z}$ **25.** $(x+5)(x+5)(x-8)$

27. $\dfrac{5x+14y}{x^2 y^3}$ **29.** $\dfrac{4z-3y}{xy^2 z^2}$ **31.** $\dfrac{1}{y-2}$

33. $\dfrac{1}{n-1} - \dfrac{1}{n(n-1)}$

$= \dfrac{n}{n(n-1)} - \dfrac{1}{n(n-1)}$

$= \dfrac{n-1}{n(n-1)}$

$= \dfrac{1}{n}$

The two fractions are $\dfrac{1}{4}$ and $\dfrac{1}{20}$.

35. $R = \dfrac{R_1 R_2}{R_1 + R_2}$; $R = \dfrac{12}{7}$ ohms

Apply - Practice Problems

1. $\dfrac{1}{8}$ **3.** $\dfrac{1}{81}$ **5.** 81 **7.** $\dfrac{1}{16}$ or 4^{-2} **9.** $\dfrac{1}{125}$ or 5^{-3} **11.** $\dfrac{4800}{89}$

13. $\dfrac{1}{a^4 b^6}$ **15.** $\dfrac{1}{m^{24} n^{12} p^4}$ **17.** $\dfrac{b^{28}}{a^{12}}$ **19.** $\dfrac{a^4 d^{10}}{c^8}$ **21.** $\dfrac{m^{16}}{n^{20} p^{12}}$

23. $\dfrac{4a^{25} b^5}{c^6}$ **25.** 5.7×10^{-5} **27.** 4,300,000 **29.** -1

31. $\dfrac{x-7}{x-5}$ **33.** $-\dfrac{x-1}{7+x}$ **35.** $-\dfrac{x+1}{9+x}$ **37.** $\dfrac{x-4}{x+3}$

39. $-\dfrac{3x(x-1)}{x+1}$ **41.** $\dfrac{-2x(x+5)}{x-5}$ or $\dfrac{2x(x+5)}{5-x}$ **43.** $\dfrac{x+5}{x-2}$

45. $\dfrac{x-5}{x+3}$ **47.** $\dfrac{x+1}{x-7}$ **49.** $\dfrac{x+11}{3}$ **51.** $\dfrac{3x}{x+7}$ **53.** $\dfrac{5x}{x-3}$

55. $\dfrac{(x-3)(x-3)}{5x(x-7)}$ or $\dfrac{x^2-6x+9}{5x^2-35x}$ **57.** $(x+3)(x+4)(x-7)$

59. $x(x+4)(x-1)(x-1)$ **61.** $\dfrac{4b+6a}{9ab}$ **63.** $\dfrac{2y+x}{3xy}$

65. $\dfrac{2x-5}{(x+10)(x-5)}$ **67.** $\dfrac{2x^2+x+4}{(x+1)(x-4)}$ **69.** $\dfrac{6x^2+8x-3}{(x-3)(x+2)}$

71. $\dfrac{2x^2-x-29}{(x+2)(x+3)(x-5)}$ **73.** $\dfrac{4n-m}{m^2 n^2}$ **75.** $\dfrac{3x-2yz}{x^2 yz}$

77. $\dfrac{3x^2-2x+88}{(x-8)(x+3)}$ **79.** $\dfrac{-3x-5}{(x+5)(x+1)(x-1)}$

81. $\dfrac{4x+10}{(x+2)(x+3)(x-1)}$ **83.** $\dfrac{3x+2}{x+4}$

Evaluate - Practice Test

1. 8 **2.** 7.3901, 10^{-5}, , 208.1, and 0.00009019

3. $\dfrac{b^{15}}{a^6}$ **4.** $\dfrac{x^3}{64y^8}$ **5.** $-x-2$ **6a.** $\dfrac{x+3}{x+2}$ **b.** $\dfrac{2(x-1)^2}{x^2}$

7a. -3 **b.** $\dfrac{y+4}{(y+6)(y+1)}$ **8.** $\dfrac{2(x-1)}{5(x-3)}$

9. LCM $= x(x+5)(x-5)(x+7)$

10. $\dfrac{7b+17}{(b+1)(b+2)(b+3)}$ **11.** $\dfrac{y}{(y+4)(y+5)}$ **12.** $\dfrac{3x}{5(1+3x)}$

Lesson 8.3 Equations With Fractions
Homework

1. $x = 3$ **3.** $x = 6$ or $x = 1$ **5.** $x = 6$ **7.** $y = \dfrac{3}{2}$

9. 60.8 lbs. **11.** $x = 3$ or $x = -1$

12. $x = 2$; The solution is extraneous.

Apply - Practice Problems

1. $x = 7$ **3.** $x = 2$ **5.** $x = -9$ **7.** $x = -8$ **9.** $x = -3$

11. $x = 4$ **13.** $x = 2$ **15.** $x = 1$ or $x = -\dfrac{4}{5}$

17. $x = 2$ or $x = \dfrac{3}{2}$ **19.** $x = 3$ or $x = -6$

21. $x = 5$ or $x = -1$ **23.** $x = 14$ or $x = -5$

25. $x = 4$ or $x = 8$ **27.** no solution

Evaluate - Practice Test

1. $-5 = x$; The solution is not extraneous.

2. $y = 3$; The solution is not extraneous.

3. $\frac{3V}{\pi r^2} = h$ **4.** $x = 4$

5. $4 = y$; The solution is not extraneous.

6. $x = 5$; The solution is not extraneous.

7. $\frac{S}{2\pi r} - r = h$ **8.** $y = 2$

Lesson 8.4 Problem Solving Homework

1. 16.8 hr   **3.** 357 jellybeans

5. $\frac{105}{22}$ hours (approximately 4.8 hours or 4 hours and 46 minutes)

7. 4 inches by 12 inches

9. $\frac{77}{18}$ hours (approximately 4.3 hours or 4 hours and 17 minutes)

11. 5778 fish

Apply - Practice Problems

1. $\frac{20}{9}$ hours or approximately 2 hours 13 minutes

3. 45 minutes   **5.** $\frac{21}{4}$ hours or 5 hours and 15 minutes

7. 30 minutes   **9.** 24 caramels, 18 nougats

11. 35 puppies, 20 adult dogs   **13.** 65 units

15. Jayme: 30 miles; Terry: 45 miles

17. Sasha: 2 miles; Leroy: 3 miles

19. Ranji: 45 miles, Paula: 30 miles

21. 68 miles per hour   **23.** 180 pounds

25. 135 square inches   **27.** $V = \frac{kT}{P}$

Evaluate - Practice Test

1. It will take them $\frac{12}{7}$ hours, or about 1 hour and 43 minutes, to wash the dishes working together.

2. Trish lives 4 miles from the park.

3. There are 252 peanuts in the bag of mix.

4. The area of the kite is 52 inches^2.

5. It will take them 36 minutes working together.

6. The hummingbird can fly at 50 km per hour, and the eagle can fly at 85 km per hour.

7. The florist received 189 roses.

8. The speed of the wave is 8 feet per second.

Topic 8 Cumulative Review Problems

1. $-2 \le x < \frac{7}{5}$ **3.** $(a + b)(a - b)$ **5.** 13 units

7. $y = 3x + 11$ **9.** $x = -1$

11. $m = -\frac{9}{5}$, y-intercept $= \left(0, \frac{11}{5}\right)$

13. $t = \frac{20}{13}$ hours $\approx$ 1 hour and 32 minutes

15. $\frac{4x - 11}{(x - 2)(x - 3)}$ or $\frac{4x - 11}{x^2 - 5x + 6}$ **17.** $(x^2 + y^2)(x + y)(x - y)$

19. no solution   **21.** 61 units

23. $\frac{3a}{c^3} - \frac{4c^2}{a^3}$ or $\frac{3a^4 - 4c^5}{a^3 c^3}$ **25.** A and B

27.

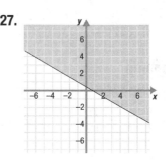

29. $m = \frac{9}{2}$ **31.** $6ab^2(a^2 - 4ab + 4)$ **33.** $\frac{x}{x + 5}$

35. $x = -9$ **37a.** $y - 6 = \frac{4}{3}(x + 2)$ **b.** $y = \frac{4}{3}x + \frac{26}{3}$

c. $-4x + 3y = 26$

39a. 3 **b.** 1 **c.** $\frac{1}{a^3b^6c^3}$ or $a^{-3}b^{-6}c^{-3}$

41. radius: 5; center: (2, –6)

43. $(7x-1)(7x-1)$ or $(7x-1)^2$ **45.** Any x is a solution.

47. $y = -\frac{1}{2}x + 2$ **49.** $(x-3)(x-1)$

Lesson 9.1 Roots and Radicals
Homework

1a. $\sqrt[3]{27}$ **b.** 27 **c.** 3 **d.** 3 **3.** –10 **5.** $\frac{6\sqrt{3}}{5}$ **7.** $5\sqrt[3]{6}$

9. 38π cm² or approximately 119 cm² **11.** $7a^{10}b\sqrt{3b}$

13. $\sqrt{3} + 6\sqrt{13} + 3$ **15.** $3\sqrt{55} + 8\sqrt{5}$ **17.** $7\sqrt[3]{3}$

19. $\frac{9\sqrt{10}}{110}$ **21.** 100π square feet **23.** $x = 81$

Apply - Practice Problems

1. –5 **3.** 10.5 feet **5.** 12 cm **7.** 5 **9.** $x^2y\sqrt{x}$

11. $2\sqrt{3}$ **13.** $-1 + \sqrt{5}$ **15.** 10 **17.** a **19.** 6

Evaluate - Practice Test

1a. –1.1 **b.** 1.21 **2.** –4 and –3. **3.** 7

4. $2u\sqrt{7u}$ **5.** $5\sqrt{11} - 6\sqrt{2}$ **6.** –41

7a. $\frac{5(\sqrt[3]{-6})^2}{-6}$ **b.** $\frac{1-\sqrt{7}}{-2}$ or $\frac{-1+\sqrt{7}}{2}$

8. $x = -11$

Lesson 9.2 Rational Exponents
Homework

1. $\sqrt[3]{8} = 2$ **3.** $2^{\frac{13}{20}}$ **5.** 4 **7.** not a real number

9. 1024 cells **11.** $\frac{x^{\frac{1}{7}}}{y^5}$ **13.** $\frac{3}{5}$ **15.** $\sqrt{x}$ **17.** $-3x^2y$

19. $2x^3y\sqrt[3]{2yz^2}$ **21.** $\sqrt[3]{2}m$ **23.** $2x^2y^3z\sqrt{xy}$

25. $7\sqrt[4]{360}$, $\frac{\sqrt[4]{360}}{72}$, $\frac{-11}{4}\sqrt[4]{360}$

27. –450 **29.** $16\sqrt[3]{3} + \frac{1}{4}\sqrt[3]{2} + 1$

31. $\sqrt[3]{24}$, $2\sqrt[3]{3}$, $\sqrt[3]{8} \cdot \sqrt[3]{3}$, $\frac{\sqrt[3]{3}}{27}$, $3^{\frac{1}{3}}$ **33.** $\sqrt{2}\pi$

35. $\frac{\sqrt[3]{98}}{7}$

Apply - Practice Problems

1. $\sqrt{9^5}$ or $\left(\sqrt{9}\right)^5$; 243 **3.** $\sqrt[3]{27^2}$ or $\left(\sqrt[3]{27}\right)^2$; 9

5. $\sqrt[4]{81^3} = \left(\sqrt[4]{81}\right)^3 = 27$ **7.** 6 **9.** –3 **11.** –6

13. $312^{\frac{4}{5}}$ **15.** $200^{\frac{5}{7}}$ **17.** $y^{\frac{11}{12}}$ **19.** $x^{\frac{11}{30}}$ **21.** x

23. $\frac{16b^8}{81a^3}$ **25.** $\frac{64}{27x^2y^3}$ **27.** $\frac{y^{\frac{12}{11}}}{x^{\frac{8}{9}}}$

29. $\frac{11}{8}$ **31.** $\frac{13}{24}$ **33.** $-\frac{4}{5}$ **35.** $-\frac{2}{3}$ **37.** $\frac{3}{2}$

39. 56 **41.** –47 **43.** $\frac{\sqrt[4]{7}}{x}$ **45.** $6ab^3$ **47.** $8x^2y^3z^5$

49. $6m^2n^4\sqrt{3mn}$ **51.** $4abc^3\sqrt[3]{3b^2}$ **53.** $2np^2\sqrt[5]{5m^2n^2p^2}$

55. $2m^2\sqrt[3]{4n^2}$ **57.** $\sqrt{5}$, $\frac{1}{3}\sqrt{5}$, $\frac{7\sqrt{5}}{8}$ **59.** $-3\sqrt{5}$

61. $-2\sqrt{3}$ **63.** $20\sqrt{2} - 5\sqrt{3}$

65. $6x\sqrt[3]{2x^2} - 13\sqrt[3]{2x^2}$ or $(6x-13)\sqrt[3]{2x^2}$

67. $4x\sqrt[3]{2x} + \sqrt[3]{2x}$ or $(4x+1)\sqrt[3]{2x}$ **69.** $30 - 14\sqrt[3]{45}$

71. $42y\sqrt{5} + 12\sqrt{6y}$ **73.** $20z - 14\sqrt[3]{44z^2}$

75. $\sqrt{10} - 5\sqrt{3} - 2\sqrt{5} + 5\sqrt{6}$ **77.** $45z - 6$

79. $50y - 3x$ **81.** $\frac{\sqrt{2x}}{x}$ **83.** $\frac{5x\sqrt{2} + 10}{x^2 - 2}$

Evaluate - Practice Test

1. $x^{\frac{7}{10}}$ **2.** $243^{\frac{3}{5}}$ **3.** $\sqrt[3]{-125}$ **4.** $\frac{64}{343x^2y}$

5. $\frac{13}{15}$ **6.** 29 **7.** $\frac{\sqrt[3]{3}}{2}$ **8.** $\frac{9xy\sqrt{z}}{11z}$

9. $21\sqrt{5x} - 3$ **10.** –19 **11.** $-6 - 12\sqrt{2}$ **12.** $y^{\frac{1}{6}}$

Topic 9 Cumulative Review Problems

1. $x^3 + 3x^2y^2 + 36xy^2 + 13x^2 + 12x$ **3.** $y = 1$ or $y = -3$

5. Investment at 5% = $1625
Investment at 13% = $12,500

7. $x = -4$ or $x = -9$ **9.** no solution

11. $11\frac{1}{9}$ minutes

13. point-slope form: $y - 3 = \frac{5}{3}(x + 7)$

slope intercept form: $y = \frac{5}{3}x + \frac{44}{3}$

standard form: $3y - 5x = 44$

15. $2a^2b^2 + 5ab + a - b$

17a. $\frac{25}{2}$ **b.** $-27a^6$ **c.** $x^{24}y^{16}z^4$ **19.** $x - 14$

21. $(-4y + 3)(4y - 3)$ or $-(4y - 3)^2$

23. True: The GCF of 52 and 100 is 4.
The LCM of 30 and 36 is 180.

25. $(x + 13)(x - 10)$ **27.** slope $= -\frac{3}{4}$, y-intercept $= \left(0, -\frac{9}{2}\right)$

29. $\frac{18x^3}{y^2}$ **31.** $-12 + 4\sqrt{11}$ **33.** $x^2 + 11x - 8$

35. $7y^2(x + 1)^2$ **37.** $1 \leq y < 5$

39a. $6\sqrt{5}$ **b.** $6x + 3x\sqrt{2}$ **c.** $a^2 - b$

41. 9 pins, 19 balls   **43.** $\sqrt{x} + \sqrt{y}$

45. $(2x - 1)(4x^2 + 2x + 1)$ **47.** $a = 2$ **49.** $\frac{4y^6}{9x^8}$

Lesson 10.1 Quadratic Equations I Homework

1. $2x^2 - 3x - 5 = 0$ **3.** $y = 0, y = -4$

5. $-11x^2 = 0$, $2a(a + 5) = 4$, $6x - 9x^2 = 8$ **7.** $z = \pm 5$

9. The dimensions are 2m by 13m by 20m.

11. $x = 1, x = -\frac{5}{3}$ **13.** $a = \pm 10$ **15.** $x = \pm 6$

17. $x = \pm 9$ **19.** $x = 1 \pm 5\sqrt{3}$

21. The tree was approximately 34.6 feet tall $\left(20\sqrt{3} \text{ feet}\right)$.

23. $x = \frac{9 \pm \sqrt{5}}{2}$

Apply - Practice Problems

1. $x = -7$ or $x = 0$ **3.** $x = 4$ or $x = 0$ **5.** $x = -5$ or $x = 0$

7. $x = 6$ or $x = 0$ **9.** $x = 1$ or $x = 6$ **11.** $x = -5$ or $x = -7$

13. $x = -3$ or $x = -6$ **15.** $x = -2$ or $x = 9$

17. $x = -10$ or $x = 15$ **19.** $x = 5$ or $x = -2$

21. $x = -12$ or $x = 10$ **23.** $x = -6$ or $x = 9$

25. $x = 6$ or $x = -5$ **27.** $x = -12$ or $x = 15$

29. $x = -10$ or $x = 10$ **31.** $x = -16$ or $x = 16$

33. $x = -4\sqrt{3}$ or $x = 4\sqrt{3}$ **35.** $x = -4\sqrt{2}$ or $x = 4\sqrt{2}$

37. $x = -9$ or $x = 9$ **39.** $x = -3\sqrt{2}$ or $x = 3\sqrt{2}$

41. $x = -2\sqrt{3}$ or $x = 2\sqrt{3}$ **43.** $x = -9$ or $x = 9$

45. $x = -12$ or $x = 2$ **47.** $x = -18$ or $x = 0$

49. $x = 3 - \sqrt{13}$ or $x = 3 + \sqrt{13}$ **51.** $x = -11$ or $x = 5$

53. $x = -9$ or $x = 5$ **55.** $x = \frac{4}{5} - \sqrt{3}$ or $x = \frac{4}{5} + \sqrt{3}$

Evaluate - Practice Test

1. $2x^2 - 17x - 2 = 0$
So $a = 2$, $b = -17$, and $c = -2$.

2. $x = 0$ or $x = 4$

3. $2 = (x - 3)^2$, $x(x + 9) = 4$, and $x^2 - 9 = 7x + 2$

4. $x = -\frac{5}{2}$ or $x = 3$ **5.** $\sqrt{(-8)^2}$, $\frac{\sqrt{256}}{\sqrt{4}}$, and $\sqrt{\frac{64}{5}} \cdot \sqrt{5}$

6. $x = 7\sqrt{7}$ and $x = -7\sqrt{7}$ **7.** $\frac{\sqrt{10}}{2}$

8. $x = 5 + 2\sqrt{41}$ and $x = 5 - 2\sqrt{41}$

Lesson 10.2 Quadratic Equations II Homework

1. $x^2 + 13x + \frac{169}{4}$, $\left(x + \frac{13}{2}\right)^2$

3. $x = 2 \pm \sqrt{5}$ **5.** $x = 18 \pm 2\sqrt{91}$

7. $x = \frac{-3}{2} \pm \frac{\sqrt{13}}{2}$

9. Seana's speed before lunch was approximately 16.5 mph and after lunch it was approximately 14.5 mph.

11. $x = \frac{5}{6} \pm \frac{\sqrt{17}}{2}$ **13.** $x = -5$ **15.** $x = -1, x = -\frac{1}{2}$

17. $-4 \pm \sqrt{13}$ **19.** $\frac{15 \pm \sqrt{465}}{6}$

21. The formulas yield the same child's dosage at approximately 1.2 and 9.8 years.

23. $\dfrac{5 \pm \sqrt{97}}{4}$ **25.** $3x^2 - 11x - 20 = 0$

27. $c = -15$, $x = -3$, and $x = \dfrac{5}{3}$ **29.** $18x^2 - 3x - 10 = 0$

Apply - Practice Problems

1. $x = -3$ or $x = 9$ **3.** $x = -5$ or $x = 9$ **5.** $x = -10$ or $x = 2$

7. $x = 1$ or $x = 7$ **9.** $x = -3 - \sqrt{21}$ or $x = -3 + \sqrt{21}$

11. $x = 3$ or $x = -7$ **13.** $x = 9 - 2\sqrt{6}$ or $x = 9 + 2\sqrt{6}$

15. $x = \dfrac{-3 \pm \sqrt{73}}{2}$ **17.** $x = \dfrac{-7 \pm \sqrt{85}}{2}$ **19.** $x = \dfrac{1 \pm \sqrt{57}}{2}$

21. $x = -7$ or $x = 3$ **23.** $x = -6$ or $x = 2$

25. $x = -8$ or $x = 18$ **27.** $x = \dfrac{5 \pm \sqrt{109}}{6}$

29. $x = \dfrac{1}{4}$ or $x = 1$ **31.** $x = 2 \pm \sqrt{3}$ **33.** $x = 3 \pm \sqrt{5}$

35. $x = \dfrac{-3 \pm \sqrt{89}}{10}$ **37.** $x = 1 \pm 2\sqrt{2}$ **39.** $x = \dfrac{-3 \pm \sqrt{41}}{2}$

41. $x = \dfrac{6}{5}$ or $x = 8$ **43.** $x = \dfrac{3 \pm \sqrt{37}}{2}$ **45.** $x = \dfrac{1 \pm \sqrt{5}}{2}$

47. $x = \dfrac{9 \pm \sqrt{33}}{8}$

49. The equation has two unequal real solutions.

51. The equation has one real solution.

53. The equation has one real solution.

55. The equation has no real solutions.

Evaluate - Practice Test

1. $x^2 + 9x + \dfrac{81}{4}$; $\left(x + \dfrac{9}{2}\right)^2$ **2.** $x = -1 \pm \sqrt{39}$

3. $x^2 + 8x = -14$ **4.** $x = 1$ or $x = \dfrac{1}{4}$

5. $2x^2 + 4x - 7 = 0$ **6.** $x = \dfrac{-3 \pm \sqrt{14}}{5}$

7. $x^2 + 4x + 11 = 0$, $x^2 - x + 1 = 0$, and $x^2 + 2x + 5 = 0$

8. $+36$ and -36 **9.** $x = \dfrac{7 \pm 3\sqrt{5}}{2}$ **10.** $2x^2 - 3x + 6 = 0$

11. $5x^2 + 14x - 3 = 0$ **12.** $c = \dfrac{49}{8}$

Lesson 10.3 Complex Numbers
Homework

1. $-4i + 7$; $6 + 1 - 4i$; $7 - 3i - i$

3a. $4i$ **b.** $5i$ **c.** $9i$ **d.** -20 **e.** 1 **f.** $-i$

5a. $17 + 2i$ **b.** $3 + 7i$ **c.** $12 + 33i$

7a. 157 **b.** $\dfrac{15 + 136i}{97}$ or $\dfrac{15}{97} + \dfrac{136}{97}i$ **c.** $x = -2 \pm 2i$

9a. $34 + 8i$ **b.** $\dfrac{-3 + 4i}{5}$ or $-\dfrac{3}{5} + \dfrac{4}{5}i$

11a. $37 - 50i$ **b.** $\dfrac{-14 + 29i}{17}$ or $-\dfrac{14}{17} + \dfrac{29}{17}i$

   c. $x = -1 \pm 2i\sqrt{2}$

Apply - Practice Problems

1. $13i$ **3.** $4 - 5i$ **5.** i **7.** 1 **9.** $-5\sqrt{2}$ **11.** $19 - 3i$

13. $13 - 5i$ **15.** $18 - 6i$ **17.** $-15 + 23i$ **19.** $32 - 22i$

21. 73 **23.** $\dfrac{43}{53} - \dfrac{18}{53}i$ **25.** $\dfrac{7}{25} - \dfrac{26}{25}i$ **27.** $x = -4 \pm \sqrt{2}i$

Evaluate - Practice Test

1a. $11 + 8i$ **b.** $3 - 4i$ **2.** $-8i^2 - 4i^3$ **3.** $5 + 7i$

4. $2 + 26i$ **5.** 34 **6.** $\dfrac{8 - 14i}{65}$ or $\dfrac{8}{65} - \dfrac{14}{65}i$

7. i^{37} and $-i^3$

8a. $x = \dfrac{-3 \pm i\sqrt{19}}{2}$ **b.** $x = \dfrac{5 \pm i\sqrt{11}}{2}$ **c.** $x = \dfrac{-1 \pm i\sqrt{2}}{3}$

Topic 10 Cumulative Review Problems

1. $(3b + 5)(2x + 1)$ **3.** $5xy^3 - 6x^2y + 14xy - 8$

5.

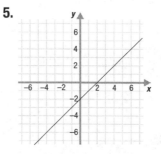

7. $x = 4$ or $x = -1$ **9.** $y = 2i$ or $y = -2i$

11. $-12 \le x \le 2$ **13a.** $27 - 31i$ **b.** 40

15a. $y + 4 = -\frac{6}{5}(x - 11)$ **b.** $y = -\frac{6}{5}x + \frac{46}{5}$

   c. $6x + 5y = 46$

17. 58   **19.** $y = 7$ or $y = \frac{3}{2}$ **21.** $\frac{16}{3}$

23. $5w^2xy - 6w^2x + y$ **25.** $\frac{16}{47}$ **27.** $x = 6$ or $x = -\frac{20}{7}$

29. $x = \frac{5}{2}$ or $x = -\frac{19}{2}$ **31.** $2x^3 - \frac{239}{15}x^2 + 7x$

33. $x = -1$ or $x = -\frac{4}{3}$ **35.** $(5y - 3)(5y - 3)$ or $(5y - 3)^2$

37. $|11 - 5| = 6$

   The GCF of 64 and 81 is 1.

   If $S = \{1, 2, 3, 4, 5, 6, 7, 8, 9, 10\}$, then $16 \notin S$.

39. $4a^8 - 25b^4$

41. $x = \frac{2 \pm \sqrt{3}}{4}$ **43.** $-4 \leq y < \frac{5}{3}$

45. x-intercept: $\left(\frac{5}{4}, 0\right)$, y-intercept: $\left(0, -\frac{5}{3}\right)$

47. $(x^2 + y)(x^2 - y)$ **49.** $x = \frac{11}{3}$ or $x = -2$

Index